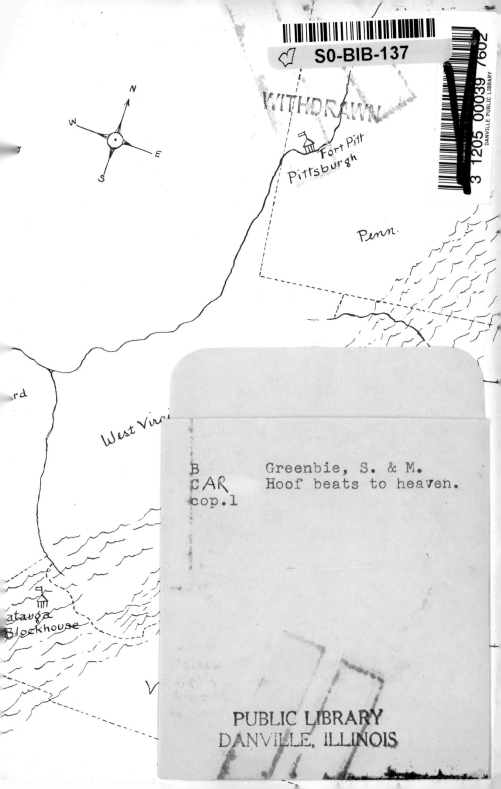

N
W — E
S

Fort Pitt
Pittsburgh

Penn.

West Virginia

rd

atauga
Blockhouse

V

BOOKS BY SYDNEY GREENBIE

ANNA ELLA CARROLL AND ABRAHAM LINCOLN
FRONTIERS AND THE FUR TRADE
FURS TO FURROWS
GOLD OF OPHIR
JAPAN, REAL AND IMAGINARY
THE PACIFIC TRIANGLE
THE ROMANTIC EAST
ASIA UNBOUND
LEISURE FOR LIVING
REPUBLICS OF THE PAMPAS—ARGENTINA, URUGUAY, PARAGUAY
THREE ISLAND NATIONS—CUBA, HAITI, DOMINICAN REPUBLIC
BY CARIBBEAN SHORES—VENEZUELA, COLOMBIA, PANAMA
THE CENTRAL FIVE—CENTRAL AMERICAN REPUBLICS
CHILDREN OF THE SUN—PERU, ECUADOR, BOLIVIA
BETWEEN MOUNTAIN AND SEA—CHILE
NEXT DOOR NEIGHBOR—MEXICO
THE FERTILE LAND—BRAZIL

BOOKS BY MARJORIE BARSTOW GREENBIE

ANNA ELLA CARROLL AND ABRAHAM LINCOLN
MY DEAR LADY
LINCOLN'S DAUGHTERS OF MERCY
AMERICAN SAGA
GOLD OF OPHIR
IN THE EYES OF THE EAST
PERSONALITY
THE ARTS OF LEISURE
IN QUEST OF CONTENTMENT
THE ART OF LIVING IN WAR TIME
BE YOUR AGE
WORDSWORTH'S THEORY OF POETIC DICTION
MEMORIES (YALE PRIZE IN POETRY)

CHILDREN'S BOOKS

THE AUNTY MAR SERIES (SHELLS ARE FUN, ETC.)
YOUNG AMERICA TRAVELS ABROAD
AMERICAN BOY IN THE ORIENT

PLAYS IN COLLABORATION

THIS WE INHERIT
DANCER FROM HEAVEN
COUNT PHILIPPE'S WILD ORANGE TREE (4 Acts)
THE GENERAL WAS A LADY (3 Acts) based on Anna Ella Carroll

Deeply alien to everything American, craving only a library and a little garden, FRANCIS ASBURY threw his frail body and indomitable spirit against the wilderness and won it, mile by mile.

HOOF BEATS TO HEAVEN

A True Chronicle of the
Life and Wild Times of
Peter Cartwright, Circuit Rider

by

Sydney Greenbie
and

Marjorie Barstow Greenbie

TRAVERSITY PRESS
Penobscot, Maine

PREFACE

No such figure as the American circuit rider is to be found this side of the apostles. No bearer of arms ever waged a greater battle with the hordes of Hell. Those rugged, two-fisted, guntoting preachers of the Methodist Church, riding ahead of the settlers, determined to be wherever a child was laid in the cradle or a body laid in the grave, epitomize and dramatize the spirit that civilized our American West.

This book is the first of three volumes, each a complete story in itself, which describe the progress of American civilization through the dramatic and often melodramatic story of Peter Cartwright, the most spectacular of the circuit riders. The hero of this great American saga saw, in his eighty-seven years, the United States reach from the Atlantic to the Pacific. In his younger years, his activities traversed the Mississippi Valley. His older years spanned the continent from Boston to Oregon. His tempestuous story is less the biography of a man than of America.

In assembling the material for this chronicle we have gone to the limit of patience, persistence, and ingenuity in obtaining every detail that can be recovered from county court records, state archives, church records, diaries, memoirs, volumes of local history, and reports of contemporary travelers. Piece by piece we have inserted each fragment of fact in its place in the calendar, covering the years from 1783 on, week by week, month by month. At the same time we have traversed the whole area of which we write, and, with the help of old records, have tried to locate every event accurately in space.

In so doing we have corrected some errors which have persisted through a century of history writing, and have furnished, we hope, the means of eliminating forever such glib generalizations as: "At the beginning of the century, a wave of religious hysteria, originating in the Cumberland region, spread throughout the West," by giving, instead, a blow by blow description of what actually

ix

happened. For the record, when disinterred and properly put together, shows that revivalism was only the reaction of decent young people to crime which had frustrated and rendered their lives abnormal for many years.

But however one recovers and fits together the bare bones of the past, there remains much which must be filled out with inference or imaginative reconstruction. If the historian fails to provide this filler, out of his special knowledge of the past, it will be provided by the reader's own imagination. The result may be not truth, but misunderstanding. As Sydney Greenbie said, in a discussion of "History and Imagination" in the *Springfield Republican* many years ago, "Unless there is the will for truth and the imagination to grasp it, in all its living implications, the most scientific historian may, by a process of elimination, build up an edifice of error."

In the current academic style of writing history, the usual way of introducing this filler is to say something like this: "Grant *probably could* have said," "Such was the report that Lincoln *must have had* in his hands," "But McClellan *probably* did not show Halleck."

Instead of this *probably-perhaps-maybe* filler, we insert between the bits and pieces of written record material which we derive from an almost inexhaustible deposit of oral tradition, letters, old papers, and old possessions of a family of hard riding circuit judges, preachers, and physicians, contemporary with Peter Cartwright and Lincoln, whose activities, in the period between the American Revolution and the Civil War, covered every one of the present states of the Mississippi Valley.

Our immediate contact with this vast family experience is with Doctor Johnston Latta who, in 1823, took up seven square miles of the tract newly opened for settlement across Illinois and Indiana, to which Peter Cartwright moved in that same year. Doctor Latta's grandfather had been a shipbuilder in Belfast, Ireland, and a leader and capitalist in the great Scotch Irish migration which had begun in 1706. Many of his kin were Presbyterian preachers who doubled as schoolmasters, as the Scotch Irish spread west from Philadelphia, south along the valleys of the Alleghenies, and over the mountains into Kentucky and Tennessee. As a young physician, he covered the area we describe in this book in 200 and 300 mile circuits out of Cincinnati, observing, with a shrewd and sympathetic eye, the disproportionate amount of mental illness on the frontier, and the reasons for it. One of his brothers was a circuit judge. Another, Samuel Latta, was converted to Methodism, set up the Methodist Book Concern in Cincinnati, and helped to cover the wilderness with the texts of "Saddlebag College." A nephew, Samuel Latta, Jr., wrote the revival hymn, "Wash Me in the Blood of the Lamb." Another kinsman, Alexander Latta, built the first railroad train west of the Alleghenies and ran it from Cincinnati to Columbus, Ohio. Some of the family co-operated in the founding and early functioning of DePauw University.

Doctor Latta's mother was Isabella Johnston, of that widespread family whose activities and vivid personalities covered the southern side of the western frontier, from North Carolina to Texas. He married the grandniece of Rufus Putnam, the founder of the Yankee veterans' settlement at Marietta, Ohio, and this brought the Yankees within range of his observation and comment.

Doctor Latta's daughter, Mary, married into the Barstow family who began to figure as capitalists and political leaders when the settlers crossed the Mississippi. One of these Barstows was a slave-owner in Mississippi, one a missionary preacher in Iowa, one a governor of Wisconsin, and, for one of them, the town of Barstow, California, is named. Their record supplements the Latta-Johnston record in later volumes of this chronicle.

To distinguish this filler clearly from printed material in primary sources, we have adopted a simple device. For all persons mentioned in this story by their full names—James McGready, Beverly Allen, Micajah Harpe, etc—there is printed documentation for every detail, including personal appearance and such dramatic scenes as the encounter of the doctor with Marguerite Douglas and the capture of Micajah Harpe. These names are indexed. But supplementing what is in available documents we introduce persons for whom we give only first names or nicknames. These are type characters. Some one of the type was there and did or said pretty much what we have indicated. But there is no document. You have to take our word for it. For example, there is the man named Dominie. Every settlement had its Dominie. Without him and his wife, the West could hardly have emerged from the condition of the Indians. Peter Cartwright, in his *Autobiography,* mentions a class leader who was able to guide them in producing an acceptable grade of gunpowder. In that place and at that time, if this person wasn't what we have described, he was an exception who should have a whole Ph.D. dissertation written to explain how come he was different. We have assigned a physical appearance to Dominie. This isn't a fiction writer's license. Nowadays, when the American blood has become so mixed, there are a great variety of human types. But at the time we are talking about, the different groups of people were as distinguishable by their appearance as different breeds of purebred animals. They had lived together for generations in little knots, and were so intermarried within each group that everybody tended to look like everybody else in the group. So, since none of the local recorders make a point of the looks of this gunpowder Methodist, as they tend to do whenever there is a variation in physical type, one may assume that his appearance was what we describe or very much like it.

This filler, which we introduce only after we have exhausted all available written records, we have put in the form of conversation and descriptions of social behavior. This gives our narrative the appearance of fiction. But it is not fiction. It is, on the contrary, an effort to avoid three kinds of fiction generally produced by historians—fiction by evasion, fiction by incantation, and fiction by generalization.

Much of the *probably-perhaps-maybe* style of writing is fiction by evasion. A question is raised, but no adequate attempt is made to answer it. The historian, like the scientist, cannot proceed without hypotheses, but hypothesis, to be of use, must be clear and precise and elaborated in detail. You cannot hope to be clearly and precisely right if you are not ready, in seeking to be right, to be clearly and precisely wrong. As much careful and ingenious research must go into an hypothesis as into the scrutiny of a document. Where the material you are investigating consists of human beings who, in their time, ate and drank, slept and woke, felt heat and cold, talked together and made love, and felt pity, fear, and anger, you cannot understand what they did and what happened to them unless you make an earnest attempt to see them in the full round process of living. This we have tried to do even if we run afoul of the evaders and generalizers who cry, "This is fiction."

A second form of fiction we have tried to avoid is fiction by incantation. This consists of a kind of ritual intonation of the known names of history — "Horace Greeley. Horace Greeley. Horace Greeley."— without taking the trouble to specify what he said and what he did. The name is enough. The magic incantation of names creates a fiction of personalities—vague, ghostlike, but potent. Certain ideas become popular among historians and are employed in the same ritualistic fashion. Such is the idea of the magical relation of the *frontier* to *democracy*. You just have to utter the two words together, and all is explained. While we use the word *frontier* frequently, we try each time to convey a fact about the particular frontier we are talking about—a fact which, in most cases, by no means applies to other frontiers, such as the frontier of New Zealand, Australia, or western China.

A third form of fiction is fiction by generalization. Without generalization there can be no body of knowledge. But no amount of invention in the way of conversation and typical incident can be as deeply and essentially false as some generalizations by historians. For history, by its very nature, is a record in time. And generalizations have a way of combining selected facts, widely separated in time, into something that does not specifically apply to anything that ever happened to anybody anywhere. An example is Arnold Toynbee's absurd references to the state of Maine.

The history of the settling of the West has been particularly falsified by generalization. It is represented as a continual flow of somebody into somewhere, in generalizations about "cheap land" and "pushing west the frontier." The fact is that there were three specific mother-settlements of the West, as distinct in their character as the colonies of Massachusetts Bay, New Amsterdam, and Jamestown, Virginia. These were (1) the settlement of central Kentucky begun by Daniel Boone; (2) the settlement centering Nashville, Tennessee, but including the Military Tract in Kentucky, and the Cumberland region generally; and (3) the settlement of the Yankee veterans at Marietta, Ohio. The settlement of other parts of the West radiated out from these.

In the present book we try to describe one of these settlements with the kind of specific detail which has long since established the character of the Plymouth colony of Massachusetts in the American mind. And we do this in the belief that it was here, on the Military Tract of Kentucky, rather than at Plymouth or Jamestown, that American democracy began, and that the G.I.'s of the American Revolution, toting their wives and their children and their household gear over the Alleghenies, deserve their specific place in American history even more than the brave little band on the Mayflower.

As for the dramatization of the material by the use of conversation, there is precedent for this in the writing of one who is universally conceded to have been the father of scientific history—Thucydides. On occasion, he presents you with scenes as definitely in the style of the drama of his day, which was rather formal and stilted, as our narrative is in the informal style of the current novel. But that does not obscure the fact that he used every resource at his command to recover the facts and the underlying truth of what was to him a not-too-long distant past. This is what we, on our part, have also tried to do.

This is therefore a patient chronicle, designed to tell as truthfully as possible, what actually happened, vivified by conversation and descriptions of behavior, but based upon an immense documentation and a special family tradition. What distinguishes it from fiction is not its style but its motive. An historical novel is written to entertain or to move the feelings. Actually, many an historical novel represents more and better research than many an academic history of the same period, and is truer to fact. But the writer is nevertheless bound to select and heighten his material to make a gripping story. Similarly our chronicle may entertain and may move the feelings. We hope it does. But our aim is to inform and to interpret, and we have kept ourselves rigorously to that purpose, selecting details for that purpose only, and keeping strictly to that sequence in time which is the essence of history.

The amalgamation of bits and pieces of ascertained fact to form a filler between the materials that can be recovered from documents we have called *synthetic*. Practiced with humility and sensitive awareness, the synthetic method creates a proper climate for further research. It is the method by which a British biologist, a century ago, recreated a complete image of the extinct New Zealand bird, the giant Moa, out of the study of a single thigh bone. Later, when a complete skeleton of the bird was assembled, his picture of the creature was found to be correct. Feeling as we do, that fiction by evasion, fiction by incantation, and fiction by generalization too often build up a fiction of scholarship, we have striven to approximate to the method of Darwin which he described as "patiently collecting and meditating on facts." When *we* reform the shards of ancient pottery, you may see the iron glue and the cracks, but the shape and purpose are as functional as a synthetic tire.

The notes and bibliography for this work will be published when we have completed the third volume. We are not publishing them now because of our unhappy experience with the documentation of our biography of *Anna Ella Carroll and Abraham Lincoln* which we made freely available, with three dire results:

1. We laid ourselves open to the piracy rampant in this age of motion pictures, radio, and television, in which a vast commercial enterprise is incapable of functioning except by the use of the research that goes into this kind of book. A lot of people who have done no research whatever on their own part but who see the possibility of supplying the voracious appetite of the industry for dramatic material think that any non-fiction work, using materials in the "public domain," is theirs for the taking. They may distort it, doll it up sleekly, and put stars in the eyes of hero and heroine, without once considering the labor and expense that have gone into the original work.

By placing in a book detailed directions for notes and sources, you enable them to pretend that they have taken material from the original documents, when they have never touched them. They use your charts and claim that they have traversed the same seas when they have never left the shore. Taking material out of your book, but armed with your list of sources, they change a *perhaps* to a *maybe* and a *maybe* to a *perhaps*, and go out and sell your writing as their own. By this method they add nothing to scholarship. They even repeat your errors.

For six years we suffered this kind of piracy with regard to our material on Anna Ella Carroll till finally forced to take it to law.

2. We ran afoul of a certain type of academician who, to defend his own vested interests in the "truth" as he had published it, took our published notes and sources, lifted whatever he wished out of the original sources, and belied what we had written in any way that pleased him, and by references to our sources pretended to research he had not done.

For six years we have buffeted our way between the Scylla of the story pirate and the Charybdis of the probably-perhaps-may-be historian, and have found the historian the worse of the two. Standing on his academic authority, he has abused and distorted our sources, and no amount of correction has afforded redress or clarified public understanding.

3. We provided material for apparently learned references to nonexistent tomes. Seeing our extensive bibliography which actually consisted only of primary sources, both newspaper reviewers and professors have jumped to the conclusion that there were many available books on the same subject, and have referred loftily though vaguely, to other books on Anna Ella Carroll, or other authorities on the subject, when actually there was no available book whatsoever except our own earlier book, and the novel against whose publisher we were forced to institute suit for infringement of copyright. These sweeping bibliographical references were made by a reviewer for a Milwaukee newspaper, a professor of the University of Chicago, reviewing for the *New York Herald Tribune,* and a reviewer in *The Lincoln Herald.* Neither academic position nor the standing of a publication has been a warrant against these fake bibliographical references.

We are therefore reserving our notes and sources and our bibliography until we have completed our third volume. But they are on file, and we shall be glad to share them with any scholar sincerely seeking to check on our research and to aid in the uncovering of truth.

It remains only to thank those who have given us invaluable aid in preparing this first instalment of the chronicle of Peter Cartwright and his wild times. Primarily we are grateful to Doctor James Joy of the Methodist Historical Library in New York City for his genial and helpful interest and his many suggestions. We also owe much to the library at the Methodist headquarters at 810 Broadway in Nashville, Tennessee, and the kindly and interested persons there, and especially to Curtis Brabson Haley, formerly a book editor of the Methodist Church, for his generous help at many points. We thank Doctor James A. James, of the Northwestern University Committee on Archives and History, for referring us to Helen Hardie Grant, wife of Doctor Frederick Grant, professor in the Union School of Theology, and for Mrs. Grant's cordial interest. Others who gave invaluable aid were Miss Elizabeth Royer of the Theology Library at Emory University, Georgia; William J. Van Schreevan, head archivist of the Commonwealth of Virginia; Mr. Milton C. Russell of the State Library at Richmond, Virginia; and Mr. Russell Dyche of the Commonwealth of Kentucky Division of Parks. Above all, we thank the Library of Congress for our cozy study room there, and the many strange and wonderful discoveries we made in their Local History Division.

MARJORIE BARSTOW GREENBIE
SYDNEY GREENBIE

CONTENTS

BOOK III

JOHN ADAMS, PRESIDENT

1796-1800

BOOK IV

THOMAS JEFFERSON, PRESIDENT

1800-1802

LIST OF ILLUSTRATIONS

BOOK I

1783 - 1790

under

The Articles of Confederation

Strange that a man can go through eight years of war without a scratch, and then sprain his ankle the first time he steps out as a civilian! So thought Justurian Cartwright, ex-sergeant of artillery under George Washington, as he sat on a rock at dawn on the side of a mountain, and held his aching limb in his hand. He had bound it up rudely with splints and deer-thongs, and now scanned the wide prospect before him for signs of human habitation.

Cartwright did not yet know that on September 3, 1783, a treaty had been signed in Paris, acknowledging the thirteen colonies to be independent states, and yielding them the lands beyond that high ridge to the west on which he now saw the first rays of the sun shine gold. These lands stretched on and on, westward beyond the mountains, to rich meadows threaded by rivers which ran into the Mississippi, and so down to the sea at the Spanish port of New Orleans. Somewhere amidst these meadows was Justurian's future home, if ever he could get off this mountain with his sprained ankle, and claim the benefits promised in the first American "G. I. Bill of Rights".

Jus was now traversing the area of the great wilderness nation, reaching through the mountains from Fort Pitt (now Pittsburgh) into Georgia, whose first creators were the generation of Justurian's grandfather. They were known as "Scotch Irish," but in the army Jus never came up against a Scotchman or an Irishman without realizing that he himself was neither. None of his folks had spoken Gaelic back to the beginning of time. Their talk was a somewhat Scandinavian version of the other language of northwestern Europe. They said *kirk*, rather than *church*, *skirt*, rather than *shirt*, with a rolling sound of the r-r-s. There were none of the Scotch and Irish *Mac* names in his tribe—McLeish, MacSparren. They had names like Randolph, Murray, Cartwright, which people who don't know the hereditary strains and tensions of the British Isles take to be English.

But Jus knew to the marrow of his bones that he wasn't English— not Saxon, Anglo, southern, redcoat English, with their idiotic servility to king and church. When his gorge rose at the sight of a redcoat, it rose from springs of bitterness gushing up from centuries back. When enlisting as a lad, in February, 1776, before Jefferson, the greatest genius of his mountain race, had formulated the Declaration of Independence, he had told himself that he owed no allegiance to the British king. Somewhere from the shadowy outlying parts of memory had come the cries and clangor of arms from far off and long ago.

In the aeons he had spent awake last night, lying on the wet ground, after he had tripped and wrenched his ankle on the slippery root of a tree, Jus had, for brief moments, escaped from worry about his predicament in wide-ranging thoughts about who he was, and what, now that the war was over, he was going to do with himself. Over and over in his mind he had churned the comments of his buddy, Dominie, at Fort Pitt. Dominie was the son of a learned parson in Pennsylvania. "Scotch parson" some said, but Dominie objected that he wasn't Scotch, and, in explaining that, he had explained Jus to himself.

For Dominie had told him of that belt of land between Scotland and "the King's England," north of the Humber, over the borders of Scotland, which had been settled even before the Saxons came to south England by sea-rovers from the Scandinavian peninsula, who had built the first civilization in the British Isles after the Romans left. Theirs was the first ordered life, with laws and arts and crafts completely independent of Latin or even Christian influence in all Europe. To celebrate themselves and their ways they had written the first long poem that wasn't done in Latin—the epic *Beowulf*. And they had lived there for centuries with kings sometimes called Norwegian, sometimes Danes.

So Dominie talked, recalling names that rang like bells in the far places of Justurian's mind—names like Cumberland, Northumberland, Lincolnshire. Dominie spoke of a far off city which was his ancestral home, and perhaps Justurian's. It was not London. It was Lincoln, 130 miles north of London—Lincoln whence Danish kings had ruled, with its old Roman walls, its grand cathedral, its Scandinavian traditions of free enterprisers in long boats and of little companies whose way of life had never led them to pack themselves together in an ordered totalitarian hierarchy of caste, with a leader at the top who had the attributes of God.

Jus had no way of knowing if all this was so, but it meshed with the lore that floated around among the so-called "Scotch Irish." It explained why they had named the new county beyond the Alleghenies where the soldiers would get land, "Lincoln County." Old Lincoln, though never conquered in mind nor altered in its ways, had compromised with the British crown. "But what our forbears couldn't do," said Dominie, "we've done. We've thrown off the crown. We're starting clean and clear with a new Lincoln over the mountains."

Among the foolish bargains their ancestors had made, growled Dominie, was the taking of northern Ireland as a gift from James I. Oppressed there by discriminatory taxes, they had come to America in waves of migration so large that they made the colonization of Jamestown, Plymouth, New Amsterdam, and Charleston look like mere excursions. They began passing through the port of Philadelphia in 1707 and were still coming. Now, at the end of the Revolution, they numbered one fourth of the whole white population of the United States, and had organized for themselves a territory virtually independent of the other thirteen colonies, and separated from them by a belt of uninhabited wilderness about one hundred miles wide.

From here on Jus needed no Dominie to tell him what had happened. His own grandfather's family and neighbors had landed in Philadelphia and started down the road the Dutch wagon wheels had worn across Pennsylvania to the Fort at the falls of the Ohio, later called Braddock's Road. They edged on bit by bit, hunting, fishing, building lean-tos and cabins, making friends with the Indians, if they could, fighting them otherwise, until they came into a valley which some of them named the Cumberland after their ancestral home. There they settled, made fair farms, and built good houses. But Cartwright's folks hadn't found what they wanted. So they kept moving south, following streams and the openings in the mountains till they came to the spacious valley that lies between the Blue Ridge and the Alleghenies—the Shenandoah. Here so many of the Scotch Irish settled that by 1738 the government they set up to rule themselves was recognized as the court of Augusta County, Virginia, at Staunton.

From the Shenandoah, the Scotch Irish had spilled east over the Blue Ridge, among them Justurian's father who had moved into Amherst County. But Justurian's friends at Fort Pitt—Dominie, Mac, Dutch, and Cherokee Bill—expected to extend the wilderness state westward to the Mississippi, with veterans of the Revolution as a nucleus of settlement in the most strategic areas.

But what is land without a woman? Jus had been tempted by the plump, blonde German girls riding up to Fort Pitt, in their white-topped market wagons, but these luscious German *mädchen* married or not at the behest of their parents, and when you married one, you were a son of her parents until you were old. But among his people, you married for love, and your parents had very little to do with it. The German girls worked in the fields, and the men didn't mind. But among his people your wife was your pride. You never let her work in the fields if you could help it, and whatever you had went to deck her out. In the eight years of soldiering, the Scotch Irish girls, back in the Shenandoah Valley, had become ever more lovable, till now his feet could hardly keep pace with his desires. Yet as the days had walked into weeks, and he had seen nothing but empty mountains, he had wondered whether he would ever see a girl again.

At Fort Pitt they had boasted of the great numbers of people who had settled these mountains. But where were they? The United States vaunted a population of 4,000,000 with perhaps a million in the mountain valleys between Fort Pitt and Georgia. A million! You could lose twenty million here!

2

For, as the log ramparts and thirty cabins at Fort Pitt had faded behind him, Jus had left not only man but the sounds of domestic animals—the barking of dogs, the crowing of cocks. Instead, there had been, by night, the howl of the wolf, the shriek of the panther, and the hoot of the owl, and by day, sounds even more solitary—the gobble of the wild turkey, the croak of the raven, the tap of the woodpecker. There were few singing birds, for these depend for their food on the labors of men; no bees and no flowers, even in the open spaces, for flowers and bees also follow and depend on man, or, more particularly, on women and their tastes and labors. Trudging southeastward, he fixed his course each morning by the rising sun, through undulating hills, under the shade of large forest trees, wading through rank weeds and grass. Descending into a valley, he would presage the approach to a spring or stream by noting the grapevines festooning the large trees, and gratefully feast on the sour fruit, purple at this time of the year. Otherwise, his food consisted of corn meal which he made into dough and roasted, or rather burnt, by winding it around a green stick and holding it over the fire. Meat he brought down with his gun.

At night he lay under the lee of a rock, or dug himself into the dried leaves and humus, against the shelter of a fallen tree, with a fire to warn off wild beasts. For the last five days it had been raining, and this was misery compounded. Two nights ago he had found one of those rude mountain shelters called "stations", where he had slept on the floor with twenty other home-bound soldiers. But they had scattered in the gray, drizzling dawn, on separate trails. Alone he had struggled on, a dried deerskin over his head for protection against the heaviest showers. At night he had slept without fire, his deerskin a roof against the downpour. His corn meal was gone. He still had in his tunic, where it bloused over his cartridge belt, forming an all-around roomy pocket, some hickory nuts and chestnuts. Green, but full grown, they were food of sorts. His main worry was neither Indians nor wild beasts, for these he could handle with a gun. It was that blind chance against which neither warrior nor mighty huntsman is wholly safe. He might step on a rattlesnake. He might get sick. He might hurt himself.

And now it had happened. He had hurt himself. That it was only a minor hurt made it all the more frustrating. A man cannot walk home to Amherst County from God knows where in the wild wet mountains on a sprained ankle! But at least the rain had stopped. Over miles of rain-soaked forests the morning shone crisp and sparkling. Against the sun to the east and the cloudless sky to the west, the woods rose, range on range, gilded by autumn but impenetrable to light, the bending shaggy boughs of great oaks, maples, and chestnut trees laced together with grape-vines and the bush rising thick between. But the long narrow valley separating eastern and western ranges, steaming in the sun, appeared to be more open. Now and then the mists would part, and waveringly visible like reflections in milky waters, were glimpses of a corn field and patches of felled trees.

"Damn that fog!" muttered Jus. Between one curse and the next the fog lifted, and below him he saw that there was a branch valley leading into the main one, and in it a log cabin with cleared fields rising in an amphitheatre behind it. With a whoop, Jus sprang up, and twisted his hurt leg under him. Of all damned fools not to handle himself better than that! There was nothing to do but sit back on the rock and rest his ankle and then try to drag himself down to that cabin. He thought he saw somebody moving down there.

3

Down in the valley, Mary Wilcox stood at the cabin door and gazed at the dark thickets yonder on the river bank by the blockhouse which had just swallowed all that was left to her in life. It had been such a treat for the children to go fishing with Dean after being cooped up by the rain. Mary had smiled to see them go off—Polly's little gold head bobbing above Dean's kind black face as she rode along on his shoulder. It was good riddance to bad rubbish, she had said. Now she'd have a little peace to get the cabin cleaned.

But she hadn't reckoned on the way emptiness would flood into all the places they'd filled with their chatter and need of being tended. Mary had been born to the terror of aloneness. Perhaps it was that she had been an orphan and nobody had wanted her. And she'd been bound out, and nobody had loved her—till John came. Now John was gone! Dead! Fighting Tarleton's men, trying to defend Governor Jefferson and the Assembly, in the Valley of Virginia. Gone! Dead! Dead and nobody to bury him! When familiar faces were withdrawn, or familiar voices stilled, as now, terror came out of hiding and filled the universe. The morning sunshine seemed pitiless and the wide world in its beauty utterly alien.

But Mary was not one to take any nonsense from herself. Giving herself a shake and a push, she carried out bed gowns and linsy woolsy skirts and baby's shirts and small boys' deerskin pants and hung them on the rail fence. She shook out bearskin and deerskin. She dragged out, loosened, punched, and shaped neat and square the corn husk mattress and the feather bed. She washed linsy shifts and sheets in water from the rain trough which stood slimy, mossy, and brimming over under the eaves. Finally she swept her doorstep and front yard with a broom made of twigs bound together by deerthong.

Her dark, slightly wavy hair loosened itself from the smoothly whittled wooden sticks which held it in a knot at the nape of her neck, and fell below her waist. The sun beat hot on her forehead and her bare feet were puckered with wetness. But when the messier part of the house work was done, she ran into the cabin and re-appeared with her hair neatly skewered up, and her small, finely featured young face shaded by a linsy sun bonnet. Her linsy woolsy gown was trimly belted to her flat waist by a cartridge belt in which was stuck a knife and a pistol. Her feet were shod with deerskin moccasins, fastened with thongs that crossed around her ankles. Mary didn't intend to be caught looking like a witch if anybody should come.

If anybody should come! She'd been saying this so long, and nobody came. But this was a fine day, and some day he'd have to come, for Mr. Asbury was sending a circuit rider into these mountains. What a circuit rider was she did not know. But all the help she had had in the days that had passed had come from Mr. Asbury and these strange people called Methodists. The little help they had given her had left a constant hankering for more.

She scanned the hillside. There he was! Coming down the side of the mountain! And then she knew that a circuit rider wouldn't look like that—dirty, with long tangled hair and beard, limping along. Bitterly disappointed, she cast a chill glance at the man and turned away.

"Seems like I can't stagger on much further," said the stranger in a pleasant easy drawl. "Do you mind if I rest here awhile?"

"Suit yourself."

Knowing it was but right that a decent woman should be uppity with a strange man, Jus sat down and began to unwind the bandage. Mary said grudgingly, "It wants washin'. There's water in the rain trough yonder." He started to limp toward the trough. She picked up a bucket which stood nearby, full of water, and set it down by him.

"Thank you kindly, ma'am," he said softly.

Without responding, she moved away. He washed his foot and began to bind it again with deerskin. Mary had disappeared in the cabin. She re-appeared with a length of unbleached linen. "This is better next the skin," she said, and threw it at him.

He stretched the linen between his big hands and remarked admiringly, "Some of your own spinning and weaving, I reckon. You can tell a smart woman by her weaving same as you can tell a smart man by his gun." He was rewarded by seeing the lips under the sun bonnet soften with the faint promise of a smile. "If she'd stop ducking under that roof o' hers, she might turn out to be a right pretty girl," he thought. Then he heard the twitter of children. "Oh Lord! She's married! She's got young uns!"

Three little children burst into sight, followed by a broad shouldered black man with a fine string of trout. "Pol fis, Pol fis," crowed the baby girl, pitching forward and falling headlong at Justurian's feet.

"She aims to tell you she's got fish," said the older little boy gravely. "Poll—that's her name."

"Looks like we're goin' to have a fish fry," said Jus, picking Polly up and setting her on·his shoulder, and limping over to the black man. "When it comes to cleaning fish, my knife's always sharp."

And forthwith he was cleaning the fish, while Dean built a fire and broiled it, and Mary darted in and out of the cabin, bringing trenchers and planks, and maple syrup in gourds, and begrudging every move that took her out of ear-shot of the men. For Jus was directing at Dean and the children a steady stream of comment and stories whose ultimate target was the sun bonnet.

It didn't seem right to Jus to be as happy as he was when he had figured out that the girl's husband was dead. His spirits rose. His small dark eyes flashed fun. He now felt free to give Mary's person the kind' of going over a decent man would shrink from if the woman was wedded to a living spouse. His eyes kept traveling over her shoulders and bust and from the moccasins up to where the slim, neatly laced ankles were lost under the full linsy woolsy skirt. As for Mary, her blood ran warm with biological pride, and life was suddenly high and exciting as it had never been when John was courting her. John had been a boy. But this man was no boy, and with the surety of experience he was engaged in discovering that there was a woman under the cold exterior of this little mountain girl, and a woman neither dead nor sleeping. He was living for the moment when she would get that damned sun bonnet off her head.

The lunch over, every scrap was burned, leaving hardly a smell to tempt a wild animal to the cabin. Dean went off to turn over the corn fodder, and Jus limped after him and was gone all afternoon. Jus was curious about this man, Dean. He had noted his cultured speech and dignified, self-respecting manners. Mary didn't treat him like a slave or a servant. You'd think he was some neighboring landowner come to visit—the way they behaved. How come this little mountain woman had a black like that?

4

Jus returned to the cabin about sunset, none the wiser. The black man was polite. But he could sure hold his tongue. However, Jus was able to tell Mary that, with Dean's help, he had fixed up a little camp for himself, and had hired himself out to Dean to shuck her corn and make her a new plank table. He assumed so serenely that Mary could have no objection that she was powerless to raise any. Instead, after supper, as the night fell suddenly cold, she asked Jus to come in and sit a while by the fire. Then, with far more graciousness than she had shown Jus, she turned and asked Dean to come, too. Dean hung back a moment, and then quietly accepted the position of chaperon.

Jus had been maneuvering all afternoon to get inside that cabin.

Now that he had done so, he was amazed. On the frontier it was the custom to hang the whole family wardrobe on wooden pegs around the cabin, and social status was most surely indicated by the number and quality of the garments. Turning his admiring eye from linsy woolsy skirts dyed yellow brown, green, red, and yellow with juices of butternuts, leaves, and berries, and boys' deerskin pants decorated with beads like Indian work, he contemplated the big well made bed. "I declare," he thought, "that gal's got sheets on her bed and clean ones, too." He said aloud, "This is pleasant, Madam." Mary almost smiled.

Now at last she took off the sun bonnet, and in the late red rays of the sun, through the one open shutter, Jus could see her face. Mary had the looks that among the rich are called "aristocratic." There was what is called "race" or "breed" in her chiseled features, well moulded head and forehead, deep set eyes, fine grained skin, neatly put together body with long slender bones, small hands and trim ankles. In colonial Virginia girls like that were born as often among the poor as among the rich. They can be found now in America among those who never had a lord or big landowner in their ancestry back to the beginning of time.

A quiet respect came into Justurian's manner, which Mary was quick to feel. She began to have the courage to lift her eyes and look at him in a natural friendly way. Each time she did so, Jus found it so pleasant that he bent every effort to make her do it again. Sitting by the fire, with the boys at his feet and Polly asleep in her mother's lap, Jus was suddenly anxious that this young woman should know that he was not a tramp or an adventurer, but came of a respectable family and had a home of his own to go to. "I haven't been back to my folks in Amherst County for nigh on eight years," he said. "Started fighting red-coats from the time I sprouted a beard." Getting no further with her, he paused, and added heavily, "Haven't met anyone who knew my folks in years. You don't come from down Staunton way by any chance?" he asked, trying to pry the door open a bit further. "No," said Mary shortly.

"My mother died and my father married again," he volunteered. "Name's Martha Patterson. Reckon she's a right nice woman. Has a baby named Sally. Might be little older than your Pol." Seeing her pay closer attention, he went on. "I have a sister Annie. She's most growd up. Have an own brother, too. Name's Peter." Here his face lighted up. "I did see him once. He enlisted in 1780 and was with Colonel Gibson at Fort Pitt. Things change a lot in eight years. I'd left him scrawny and all out of his breeches legs, like a young cockerel half feathered. And here he was all filled out fine, a man grown."

This was received in silence by Mary and Dean, but Jus could feel the social, temperature warming by several degrees. Dean battened down the open shutter, and put a big log on the fire. Jus made haste to help him despite his swollen ankle. By wordless mutual consent, they were settling down to an evening of comradeship. In the room, now fitfully lit only by the red dancing flames, the many garments on pegs assumed the forms of shadowy persons closing in around them. The fire made the little boys' faces soft and rosy, and quieted their fidgets till they both fell asleep against Justurian's knees as if he were a long absent father. Dean sat somewhat apart, his dark face vaguely limned out of shadows, his large earnest eyes lit with an almost phosphorescent glow. Mary's rather tight, chill features relaxed in the firelight into a soft rosiness.

Jus talked. Sociable, used to yarning around campfires, the talk flowed out of him.

"And you think the fighting is finished and done for?" asked Mary, skeptically. "But how are we to get hold of a man like Girty and string him up?"

Simon Girty was the renegade white man who had organized and led the Indians under the British flag to attack the settlers in the bloody year 1778. Her eyes rested on her smaller boy, Edmund, asleep where Jus had now gently laid him on a bearskin near the hearth. Mary had borne Eddie on a wild night of fighting against Girty's Indian troops, at the blockhouse, as she was trying to put out the fire-tipped arrows the savages kept shooting over the walls to burn them out. Hands raw from beating out flames, hair singed, she had been rent by an earthquake of pain, and bore Edmund right amidst the fires. Dragged to cover under a rain of blows from many hands trying to extinguish the sparks that covered her, she had fainted into an oblivion not so deep that it did not continue to have in it something of the horrendous fire of Hell. ·

Jus caught the fulness and fierceness of feeling in Mary's eyes as she gazed at her sleeping boy, and thought, "There's a lot of warmth in that little girl." Less interested now in stringing up Girty than in lassoing the girl, his easy drawl raced on to attack, though his words were still impersonal. "The fighting's done for from Fort Pitt on down south. The trouble is further north, above the Ohio River. That's what my friend Dominie says. He was out in the West with Clark."

She came to attention. "George Rogers Clark? John—my husband —wanted to go with him. Clark was here looking for men to go down the Ohio on flatboats. John wanted to go the worst way, but it wasn't for a married man to do." She retreated into herself, thinking, "If he'd gone, he wouldn't have been called to fight Tarleton's men, and may be I'd still have him." Justurian, sensing something sad in her withdrawal, wanted to comfort her. But he stayed on the impersonal levels of conversation.

"Well, Clark and his men rooted the British out of the Northwest," he observed. "But they arn't going to stay out unless we get in there and keep them out. They'll keep on making trouble for us north of the Ohio, but my friend, Dominie, who was out there with Clark says south of the Ohio through Kentucky, there's a belt of land where we'll be strong enough to hold. Thousands of folks have got out there now by Boone's trail, and they're bringing in blooded horses and building brick houses. Beyond there, across the Green River, we Virginia soldiers are fixin' to set up, just as fast as we get our land warrants."

Mary said skeptically, "They were going to give grants to those that won the war in 1763, when they drove the French out. Did you ever hear of anybody that got one?"

"Yes, ma'am. They're getting them now, in the court at Staunton. And let me tell you, Ma'am, what we fought for we're going to get, too."

Mary cast a sidelong glance at him, still slightly dubious but admiring his spirit. "Have you got a grant in Kentucky?"

"No. But I expect it. Joseph Jones, the member of Congress from our district, has been writing General Washington and Mr. Madison about it. And General Russell's not letting any grass grow under his feet. He says the Virginia soldiers of the continental line, and all others who want to join us, are going to settle that land out beyond the Green River, or we'll know the reason why. They'd better pay us in land. They can't pay us in money. Take me. They owe me 153 pounds, 17 shillings, and 9 pence."

"153 pounds!" said Mary in awe. "That's a lot of money."

She was figuring that soldiers' widows got from fifteen to twenty-five pounds for winter's living. Though she had never studied arithmetic, she arrived, by a reckoning of her own, at the idea that, on this princely sum, a soldier's widow could live almost till the children were grown enough to help keep her.

"It's a lot of money some places, and again it isn't anything," answered Jus. "I've seen where they'd charge seventy-five pounds for a bushel of corn, and you'd pay it. Else you and your horse would starve."

"Soldiers pay for corn!" exclaimed Mary. "We always give it to them—else they'd take it anyway."

"Not under General Russell we didn't," said Jus. "We paid fair and square. General Russell said he wasn't going to rob the people on the excuse of fighting for them. As for our pay, no money's good now. What the government can give us has nothing behind it, and what folks make change with is half of it counterfeit. The safest thing is to take our pay in land. Mr. Jefferson is always talking about a Bill of Rights. Well, that's the main right—a piece of land under your feet, all your own."

"But why traipse all the way to Kentucky? Land's good enough here, and you can get it by putting up a cabin and laying claim to all you can work." She was thinking, "He's just like John. They're all alike. The land over the hill is always better." Remembering John, a tolerant, wry, amused sense of what a man is softened the look she turned on this stranger.

Jus answered the look by launching on a lyrical description of the far off Kentucky land—no rocks, no hills, no trees to break your back felling them. "They call it 'the Barrens'," he explained.

"The Barrens!" protested Mary. "You might know if they gave land to anybody under a commissioned officer, it would be bound to be barren."

"But barrens doesn't mean what you think, Ma'am," Jus hastened to assure her. "Dominie says it's called that because it's got big stretches bare of trees—just meadows, open, sunny, grass man-high everywhere. And it's a mild climate—winters short, summers hot, autumns long— a full growing season. A man couldn't ask for better."

So he went on. As she listened, a tenderness came into Mary's face. So John would have talked. Jus answered her softened look, caressing this spunky girl with his eyes, telling her a soldier's dreams. When the quartermaster had no food to give them, they had dined on roast meats and puddings with which their tables would some day groan in Kentucky. When he had no boots to issue them, they had shod their bleeding feet in the comfort they would one day feel in treading the rich brown earth and crushing the tender green grass in Kentucky. To farms in Kentucky they had fought their way through eight years of war, and now they were ready to pick up wife and gun, and go to take those farms. Mary listened, not really believing, but fascinated. Believing or not, if it had been John who wanted to move out to dreamland, she would have picked up and gone with him, leaving the snug comfort of this cabin.

But, incorrigibly realistic, she asked how far it was to this Eden, and where was the nearest settlement. Jus made small of the impossibles. The tract allotted the soldiers was only 200 miles southwest of Boone's settlement in Kentucky, and a mere 500 miles thence south to New Orleans by the Chickasaw Road, through lands hunted over and fished over and camped on by the Chickasaw Indians, and regularly traversed by traders swapping rum, powder, and guns with them for furs. "They're making surveys out there right now," said Jus, like any realtor, trying to sell lots. "General Buford already has his 1000 acres laid out. I've heard that down at Richmond soldiers and officers are camping all along the James River and on the islands, waiting to get their grants."

For further assurance that life out there would be safe, he reminded her that those two heroes of the mountains, the great Regulators, John Robertson and John Donelson, who, in 1774 had led the mountain men against Governor Tryon of North Carolina, because Tryon was back at the old tricks of the lords and tried to build himself a palace by taxing the people—these brave men, when forced to flee, had taken two parties out to this very land

Bounty Warrant entitling Justurian Cartwright to a grant of land in Kentucky. From the Archives of the Commonwealth of Virginia.

Sum due Justurian Cartwright at the end of the American Revolution. From the Archives of the Commonwealth of Virginia.

that had now been granted the soldiers. Robertson had gone first with a body of settlers and sent back word that the land was good. Thereupon Donelson led a party of 120, with women and children. They floated down the Ohio on flat boats, and poled themselves up the Cumberland. "My friend Dominie says they have a big block-house out there, right on the edge of the Military Tract, and are doing fine."

Here Jus came to what was in the back of his mind. "You know, Ma'am, you might go yourself. They're fixin' to give grants to soldiers' widows same as to soldiers. Dominie tells of the widow, Elizabeth Murray, wife of an ensign in the war of 1763, who's been granted 2000 acres somewhere west."

He eyed her penetratingly. Mary's face sparkled. But she said, "I'm well off here, and all the land I can work in this valley is ours. Let the boys grow up to make a good life where they are, instead of traipsing off chasing a light on the far hills which, like as not, is only witch-fire." She paused, and looked at him shrewdly. "Seems like you know more than most about land surveys and courts and such."

"That's true, Ma'am, because you see I'm fixin' to be the lawyer for all soldiers' land claims out there. I haven't much book learning, but I can do what most soldiers can't, I can read. And Dominie, who's crammed to the gills with education, is helping me. By the time we Virginia soldiers line up with our wives and children, stock and chattels, to go West, I'm fixin' to be admitted to the bar. They're going to be right glad I did, 'cause they don't know how much trouble they'll come up against about land titles. There's a whole tribe of buffalo hunters out there as thinks the land's theirs, and it's going to be one sweet time getting them off."

So Jus and Mary talked long and late that night, till the walls of the cabin melted away, and in imagination the moon rose over the prairies where dark and dreadful fears lurked and stalked the silvery ground, but where nevertheless there was to be wealth untold, and a life of comfort and pride. When Jus left for his own lean-to for the night, it was with a sense of positive hurt, of desolation, in tearing himself from this warm nest of home. And Mary lay awake on her big bed the rest of the night, while all that he had talked of— buffalo hunters, settlers—raced over wide golden prairies toward a splendid dawn.

The autumn days slipped by, bearing Mary headlong on a high tide of living. She woke eager for what the day might bring, and went to bed to lie awake for hours thinking over looks, and words, and tones between her and this man.

Jus was less happy. Every day it seemed harder to tear himself away. He loved everything here, from the children's chatter to Mary's squirrel stew. But careless gallantry had given place to a mixed and troubled feeling. He couldn't lead the girl on when he had nothing to offer. Better see to getting his land warrant. Then he could talk. So he would tell himself. Yet from day to day he stayed on because of the way Mary looked at him that morning or something she had asked him to do tomorrow.

He was consumed with curiosity about this little family and its past. Neither Dean or Mary told him anything. Impeccably courteous though he was, the black night of Dean's disapproval enveloped Mary's self-invited visitor. Mary felt no such distrust. She was used to accepting or rejecting folks at sight, in accordance with an intuition which, ignorant of the world as she was, had never yet failed her. The only reason she did not tell Jus about herself was that she didn't know how. She was quite unused to general conversation because there was no social life for women in the mountains. The men had some common life in the militia, to which every male over sixteen belonged. The women met only during Indian raids when they fled to the blockhouse.

When Mary talked, it was to distill hours of meditation in some sharp-edged aphorism, or to lift the shutter for a second on memories of pain, fear, and rare, intense happiness. These all concerned the intimacies of wifehood or the agony and drama of childbirth. Outside of these she had no experience, and of these she naturally would not speak to a strange man. But when, unawares, she gave

Jus glimpses of them, they were so strangely moving that he found himself hankering to talk with this woman even more than he hankered to touch her—which, in his experience as a male, was strange indeed.

2

He got a rare chance to satisfy this hankering one day when Dean again took the children fishing. Mary sat alone on the doorstep, combing flax. Jus brought out the planks he was sanding to make the table, and seated himself nearby on the ground. Mary was excited but embarrassed. She had a feeling that Dean and the children had vanished for ever, and she was alone in the universe with this man. With heightened color and small rudenesses she at first resisted Justurian's attempts to draw her out with only laconic replies. But now and then she would flash into vividness of description and intensity of feeling, from which Jus patched together the main facts about her marriage. At the outbreak of the war she had been given the "freedom clothes," the household linen, the cow and the calf, to which she was entitled by the terms of the agreement binding her out, and had gone free. She had sold the cow and calf and bought a horse, and had eloped with John Wilcox across the mountains to take up cabin rights. Cabin rights meant that he must build a cabin, and then could take title to all the adjacent land he could work.

Here John joined the militia. Of the three fronts of the Revolution—the Canadian, the sea-coast, and the Allegheny—the Allegheny was the most constantly and brutally active. Day and night the militia stood guard against attacks by Indians led by British fur traders. John took his turn as sentry, stretched out for hours, amidst impenetrable foliage, on the limb of a tree. He worked his own land and that of other settlers in a squad guarded by armed men, acting alternately as laborer and guard. Neither day nor night did Mary and her first baby, Jackie, venture beyond the cabin, and there, when she was not personally guarded by John, she was protected by a sentry nearby. Day and night she kept her cartridge belt with knife and pistol close at hand. Again and again she was wakened by the hoot of an owl or the howl of a wolf or some other agreed on signal. Then she picked up her baby and fled down the trail to the blockhouse. During the bloody year of 1778 she spent most of her time in the blockhouse. There, on a wild night she bore her second son, Edmund.

"But at least I had John near," Mary said, with a little throb in her voice. "My heart was in my mouth all the time. But I felt safer than in all my born days—just knowing he was yonder in the trees or in the blockhouse tower." She lifted her eyes to Justurian's in helpless, involuntary confession, then dropped them and turned away, her lips quivering. Jus wanted to say that a woman like her had no call ever to be alone. A man would be proud—. But he felt unaccountably shy. The clear, stark intensity of her memory abashed him. Then Mary said, with a sighing sound in her voice, "So it was for five years. So I thought it might be to the end. But Benedict Arnold came to Richmond." She fell silent, and for some time made only laconic replies.

Again Jus pieced out the facts. Arnold intended to capture Governor Jefferson and members of the legislature which had moved from Williamsburg to Richmond. Following Arnold, the British Lt. Colonel Tarleton, with 180 cavalry and sixty mounted infantry, chased the Assembly to Charlottesville, and then over the Blue Ridge to Staunton where, in June, 1781, it opened its session in the Episcopal Church. Into the Valley of Virginia came Tarleton, and there was nothing for John and the militia to do but go to the defense of Jefferson and the legislators, leaving the trans-Allegheny settlement to the protection of the older men and boys. But when the militia tried to defend the legislature, it was beaten back, and the delegates had to flee. Patrick Henry leaped on his horse in the night, with one shoe off and one shoe on. Mr. Jefferson's place had already been ravaged by Cornwallis. His blooded colts had their throats slit, and his Negroes were carried off.

Jus said gently, "And you were left alone with three children?" He was wondering whether Dean had been left to take care of her.

"With two," she said softly, a flush staining her pale cheeks, "and—and one coming."

She was silent for a long time while Jus wondered what she was thinking. She was remembering that summer when she did not hear from John. Her heart had sickened, and the burden of her child was heavy within her. One of the militia brought word that the Methodist woman, Sister Belle, would come to help her, for being a Methodist gave you license to meddle in other folks' affairs. It pained Mary to remember how ungraciously she had replied that there was no use in the woman's coming till there was need.

As she was thinking about this, Mary saw Justurian's eyes fastened on her with deep kindness. Suddenly, unexpectedly, all barriers were down between them. She raised her eyes to his and said confidingly, "It was night when my pains came—all unexpected. I reckon the sentry heard me moanin'. Or may be he heard Eddie whimper." She stopped, the scarlet flaming into her face. What was she thinking of to talk like this to a man!

She was silent, but she couldn't help remembering. In the dawn, writhing helplessly, she had seen Sister Belle leaning over her. In a great thundering, leaping pain, she gasped sharply, "The baby! It's come!" Sister Belle took the baby, and Mary dozed off. Then she heard Sister Belle say, "Here's the baby, all clean and diapered. And it's a bonny girl." She felt the soft little mouth nuzzling at her breast. She opened her eyes and looked into Sister Belle's kind blue eyes and loved her with all the starving intensity of her heart. She had known there was security in the world when she married John. Now she knew there was kindness.

Sister Belle stayed with her for days, and it was like having a mother when you'd never had one before. Sister Belle used to kneel and say a prayer at Mary's bed every night. This was strange, but Mary liked it. It was as if a mother had sung her to sleep, and she dozed off contentedly with her baby at her breast and a higher opinion of God than she had ever had, now that she knew Sister Belle was His friend.

Thinking of Sister Belle, Mary regained a little poise. She lifted her eyes to Justurian's earnestly. "I don't know what I'd a done without Sister Belle." Then she added, "She's a Methody. It was the first I'd heard tell of Methodys."

This gave Jus the chance to ask what had been in his mind all along. "But you had Dean to help you?"

"No—not then."

Jus prompted her. When Cornwallis surrendered in the fall of

1781, the militia had come back? Yes, but John didn't come. Nobody knew what had happened to him. Warm days she'd sit in the doorway watching for the first sight of him. Stormy days when the cabin had to be boarded up, she'd sit in the dark by the cabin fire, steadying herself by making the flax wheel whir till she could bear it no longer. Then she'd run out and peer through the flying flakes to see if John was coming.

Stumblingly, Mary recalled that stormy afternoon when she opened the cabin door, and caught her foot on the body of a man on the doorstep, covered with snow. She was scared. She slammed the door shut quick and cowered inside. Then she thought, "It might be John." She stepped out and peered down through the whirling, grayish whiteness. It was a Negro. His eyes moved a little. He was alive yet, but in a stupor. She knelt, and, with repugnance in every nerve, shook him roughly. "Wake up. You've got to get in by the fire." She tugged at him desperately and then gave him a sharp kick. "Pull yourself up. You've got to. Lord God Almighty!" she wailed. "I can't drag you. You're too big." The wail quickened him. He rose, stumbled a few steps, and reeled to the floor inside the cabin. The baby began to cry. Eddie hid in a corner, his blue eyes staring out of it like those of a frightened kitten.

The black man lay on the floor. Mary covered him with a bearskin. Then she picked up the crying baby and holding her with one arm began to nurse her. She held out her other arm to Eddie. He crept to her, making a big circle around the fallen man. She hugged the little boy to her. This gave her back some steadiness. It was strange to sit here in the dark shuttered cabin, the wind howling outside, the fire sputtering and sparking, and that creature on the floor. She wondered desperately what she should do. Could she feed him? Was he sick?

At last he stirred, opened his eyes, and said, in a voice like a Squire's, "You are very kind, Ma'am, to shelter me." Mary made him sassafras tea, sweetened with maple syrup. He drank it gratefully, but seemed unable to eat.

For three days he was in a stupor. Night after night Mary lay down under the feather bed in her clothes, with Eddie and Jackie on one side, and the warm little chunk of Polly on the other, and, thus barricaded, fell asleep. The fourth morning she woke to find thin lines of sunlight sifting through the cracks in the boarded up window. The stranger had been up and out and had brought in a load of wood and built up the fire. Now he lay quietly wrapped in his bearskin.

"I owe you my life, Ma'am," he said in his cultured way. "Now I can take myself off your kind hands. But I wish there was something I could do for you. May I ask do you live here alone?"

Then Mary told him that John had gone with the militia to Staunton. And he said he had been with the militia there, too. He'd been one of the slaves Cornwallis had captured, but he had escaped and got to the militia, who asked no questions but gladly put a gun in his hands. . . .

Mary's story of her meeting with Dean broke off abruptly. She choked. And then she began to cry, the tears flooding down over her cheeks as if they would never stop. Jus made a motion to take her into his arms for comfort. But she turned away, sobbing desperately. Finally, through sobs, she managed to say, "He'd been the last to see John. He saw him lying dead on the old last year's oak leaves, and his light hair all bloodied." She added, her eyes staring through her tears, with intense horror, "They had to leave him there—all unburied as he was. Nobody could go back to bury him." She repeated, shaking with the horror of it, "He wasn't buried. Never buried at all."

It was some time before Jus soothed her sufficiently to learn more about Dean. But at last Mary pulled herself together and told him what Dean had told her. He had been a slave to a lady whom he had loved so much that he would have gone back and been a slave again just to serve her. But she was dead, and, when Cornwallis ravaged the plantation and killed her only son, there was no one left Dean need call master. He had talked to John, and John had told him where his wife was. Starting out to find Mary and do for her if he could for John's sake, he had fallen ill, and collapsed at Mary's door.

"He's the best man I ever saw," Mary told Jus. "Nobody could do more or ask less." And she added, "He's a Methody, too. Like Sister Belle. Like Mr. Asbury. All the good I've known has come to me through Methodys."

Jus rose and picked up the plank he'd been sanding. He had

come to a solemn decision. A quiet exaltation possessed him. "Well, I'd better be doin' something else that's useful," he said, and tramped away. The look he gave her in leaving stayed in Mary's heart all day, stirring and warming it. She never noticed that he strode off without a limp.

3

Jus was determined now to talk to Dean. Toward night he trailed him to a thicket high on the mountainside. He was kneeling on the yellow fallen leaves, tears flowing down his face, praying for grace to start down the trail of freedom alone, and telling the Lord what he thought of Mary's future husband in candid but not unkindly appraisal.

When Dean rose, wiping his eyes, with a look of peace on his dark face, Jus spoke to him softly, "Dean, I couldn't help hearin' you just now." Dean drew back. His eyes flashed. He lowered his head as if to charge. He clenched his huge fist to ram it through the white man's face. But he had prayed for the grace of God, and, remembering that, he checked himself and stood trembling with rage and pain, while Jus talked to him.

How the wall between them melted Dean hardly knew. But they were sitting side by side on a log, in the late afternoon, discussing the obstacles to Justurian's marriage. Dean didn't know anything to do about them except work and pray. Jus said he was ready to work, but prayin' wasn't in his line. And it didn't seem right to begin now because it was pretty nervy to ask the Lord to do you a favor when you hadn't been payin' any attention to Him before. "It's different with you, I reckon. You've earned the right to be heard."

Jus seemed to assume that Dean would be coming to Kentucky, too. That Jus wanted him to come moved Dean profoundly. As he and Jus made their way down the mountainside, in the chill autumn twilight, he felt more at peace than he had for a long time. He did not know that Jus felt more at peace, too.

Next morning, when Mary went out to get a bucket of water from the rain trough, Jus came striding up. His step was rapid and purposeful and without a trace of lameness. "Wish me luck," he said, in a cheerful, impersonal tone. "I'm off to Richmond to get me my Kentucky land."

Mary felt as if a big hand had reached out and taken the sun out of the sky. She lifted her eyes to his. Her lips quivered. "Going away," she half whispered, half sobbed. "Oh no!" That little gesture, so helpless, so self-giving, was Justurian's undoing. He strangled her in his arms. When he released her, she was reeling and dizzy and alight like a forest fire. But before she could gasp out a word or even look at him, he was gone. As she peered out through her long black hair which had come loose and was flooding her like night, she saw his broad shoulders receding down the trail. At the point where the forest swallowed the trail, he turned and waved at her, and called, "I'm coming back, Mary. Keep yourself careful till I come."

4

The conflict between the tension Jus had created in Mary and her still aching grief for John was torment. Night after night, after the children were in bed, she'd walk the floor, moaning to herself, "He's waked me up. I had three children and I never was waked up before. He's waked me. God help me!"

She had moments of utter shamelessness when she pushed the thought of John out of her mind. "If Jus comes back—if he ain't made a fool of me—I'll wed him as fast as he can get a preacher." But her strong, confused, untaught moral sense struggled to assert itself in loyalty to John. To retain this loyalty she threw herself on her bed and relived the weeping and raving of the hours when Sister Belle had come to comfort her for John's loss. Sister Belle had taken her hand and tried to pray. Finally Mary said fiercely, "You just shut up about God. He's like all the great folks. Only He's worse because He's bigger."

For weeks after that nothing was real. The fire had no warmth, the food no taste. She nursed Polly. She fed and dressed the little boys but pushed them away when they came near her. For her imagination was the prey of those ancient heathen beliefs which were still the dominant religion of the frontier. In this religion death had a peculiar horror. The worst horror was that when you seemed to be dead, you might not be, really. After you had been put away in the earth, you'd struggle and fight, trying to get out, till at last you were choked by the dirt and really died. But nobody died completely. Something was left, a lone, miserable wraith that howled down the wind, and hung about the place of its former abode, and materialized sometimes as a misty white form and haunted the living. There were places these hants wouldn't leave—old broken down houses, and a spot where a man had hanged himself. Such localities were to be given a wide berth. If you went near them something worse than death awaited you, though nobody said what. The best that could be hoped was that the dead would lie quiet. And so they might if they were properly buried. But one that was not buried could never rest. It roamed about perpetually, crying and moaning.

As Mary had begun to recover from her first grief, she had thought of these things lying awake nights, scared of the moaning of the wind and the rattling of the cabin door, thinking, "Is John buried?" She wanted some one to tell her where John had gone and to make her less afraid of the forest gloom all about, where shrouded forms seemed to lurk behind every tree. And she wanted something to protect her in the dark. As night came on, she'd lock herself in and keep the fire burning bright and never stepped out for anything. On summer nights when she had to unboard the windows for coolness, she felt that bad, grinning faces were looking in. Then she would leap into bed without undressing, and pull the quilt over her head, and lie there with her heart pumping and pounding as if it would burst.

Remembering this, it seemed to Mary that she would have died of horror if it had not been for Dean. Dean had brought her a comfort of which she had never since quite let go. For one evening, when he brought in the wood, she had asked him suddenly, "Arn't you ever afraid?"

"Why should I be afraid when God is holding me up, and wherever I go and whatever I do, beneath me are His everlasting arms."

"I don't see what God knows about poor folks like us," said

Mary. "He's big and high and knows everything and nothing can hurt Him. How should He know what it's like to be sick and poor and have your bones ache and your heart ache and not to know—" Here she started to say, "And not to know whether John is buried." But she choked this off and added resentfully, "I reckon God don't know because He's got no experience, and because He don't know He don't really care."

"That might have been so, Mrs. Wilcox," replied Dean, "if it had not been for Jesus who was the son of God. Jesus knew what it was to be hungry and tired and cold, and to have no bed, and finally to be tortured and killed by those he'd tried to help. . . Now He has gone back to God and is one with Him, and there's nothing of sin and suffering and lonesomeness and doubt that He doesn't know all about, and all we've got to do is to turn to Him, and let Him take our burdens and rest in Him."

In her rebellious but enforced exposure to Church services as a bound girl, Mary had always wondered why there should be "two of em—God and Jesus." This explanation made sense. But she only answered wearily and hopelessly, "It sounds right good the way you say it, but somehow I don't take no stock in it."

But Dean persisted, "There's a prayer for that, Mrs. Wilcox. It's a prayer I was taught when I didn't believe—back there when my lady mistress was so sick and nearly blind. She'd taught me to read so that I could be eyes to her as her sight failed, and I used to read the Bible to her by the hour. But I didn't believe. Even when she was so good to me and gave me a chance more than most white men have, I was resentful against God for making my skin black. The more I found how easy it was to learn the fine ways gentlemen have, and that books and culture came easier to me than to most of them, the more resentful I was. My mistress was a good Church of England woman, but the parson was a poor sort."

"I hear all Church of England parsons get stinkin drunk."

"Ours didn't get drunk. But he was a cold, worldly man. My mistress was a true Christian woman. Hearing that Mr. Asbury was nearby, gathering people into societies within the church to seek religion for themselves, she sent me twenty miles to bring him to her. He was a tall thin Englishman, gaunt as a skeleton, and so sick he could hardly sit his horse. Yet he came with me, and knelt by her bed. There was such a light in their faces as I will never forget. On the way back with him, I said, "It would be a comfort to believe like that, sir. But I can't!" Seeing into my heart, he said, 'Every night before you sleep lift your eyes to the stars, or, if it is cloudy, to the dark, knowing that the stars are just behind and say, "Lord, help Thou my unbelief".' So I did, through all those nights when my dear mistress was dying. And the night she died—the very moment her pure soul took wings to God—that moment—I believed."

So Dean had told Mary, and two years after, struggling with her conflict between her old love and her new, Mary could remember every word so vividly that it seemed like something she had lived in her own person. And she remembered what she had done after Dean had left. She had stood in the cabin doorway in the afterglow and looked at the eastern horizon piled high with cushiony, gilt-edged clouds, and wondered if beyond them there could be the fair fields of Heaven and John at rest there for ever. Suppose she should say those words, "Lord, help Thou my unbelief." But she had drawn back in superstitious dread. It was as if the prayer was a dangerous charm and might commit her irrevocably to she knew not what.

5

But a passing reference by Dean to the meaning of the word Methodist had taken her fancy. She could see the good of living by *method*, organizing her day, keeping herself going right along, for as a bound girl she had lived all her youth within the framework of set tasks. So, as she found strength to struggle out of the first nightmare of grief, she drove herself like a hard mistress, to plant the flax, to plant the truck garden, to break the flax, to spin and weave endlessly, to make endless clothes. She was thin and strained and jumpy. She told herself, "I've got myself in hand," but she was even more bleakly unhappy.

On a warm, rich, buzzing day in late June, 1782, Dean brought a wonderful piece of news. He said Mr. Asbury was here, and would hold a preaching in Sister Belle's double cabin. He offered to take care of the children and let her go under the escort of some armed Methodists from over Holston way.

This had been the most memorable experience in Mary's life. Never before had she been further from the cabin than the block-house. Never had she undertaken any movement or adventure entirely on her own. Into that ten-mile ride she crammed a thousand miles of new experience, riding along on her loose-jointed mountain horse, shaggy, lean, limber, his flexile body rippling along, up hill and down dale, more like a snake than a four-footed beast. The great trees arched overhead. The fallen leaves of centuries were thick and spongy below. Save for the mosquitoes which rose in clouds from the wet floor of the forest, it was beautiful, and most beautiful when Mary came out into an open space and saw the wide sweeps shimmering below, and eastward and westward the piles of the Alleghenies.

When they came to Sister Belle's big double cabin, folks were already sitting around outside, waiting for Mr. Asbury, eating corn pone and roasting bacon over fires. Then somebody said, "He's coming," and they all stood up and looked. Down the trail came Mr. Asbury on horseback, escorted by five armed men—a tall, lean man in a black coat and small clothes, wearing a round black hat with a broad brim. He took off his hat in greeting, and with his handkerchief mopped his smooth fine brow, and smiled at them out of his kind, intelligent gray eyes. Mary was disgusted to hear a titter run through the crowd, for Mr. Asbury wore a wig, and many of them had never seen a wig.

Mr. Asbury began to talk in an intimate, kind, real way about God and Jesus, as if they were any two folks there at the meeting. But somehow they were also One Person, infinitely great and good, filling all heaven, filling all earth, loving you, holding you up. You could tell them anything and not be afraid. And when you crept to them, so small and no account and ashamed to be what you were, all you had to do was to believe that they loved you and could lift you up, and you were lifted up.

In the midst of it all, when the shade of the mountain was growing long and cool, but the sky was still smiling, she had to break it off and go home under the guard which was leaving early. Riding back, with the clouds faintly pink like wild roses floating off into the blue, blue sky, Mary was in a dazzle of enchantment. If it could only be true that God was right there, riding along the trail with her, simple and warm and like folks. She raised her eyes, and it was like the time when she was heaving in the birth-throes with Polly, and there were the kind eyes of Sister Belle looking down on her. She raised her eyes to the blue above, and, for a trembling moment, she saw the same look, large as the heavens, wide as the sky.

The experience had not stayed with her, and yet it had not wholly left her. Ever since she had been looking for the Circuit Rider to come and lead her further on this path to security and peace. But instead Jus had come, and plunged her into a torment of longing, and of remorseful thinking about John—John unburied and doomed to wander without rest for ever. If only she could be sure that there was a Heaven, and John at peace there in a great glad company of angels. Then, if she married again, he wouldn't be in a way to feel that the only person on earth that remembered him had gone back on him. But even if John was in Heaven, her problem was not solved. For some day she would die, and meet John again. And then whose wife would she be— his or Justurian's?

One day Dean told her that a new family had taken land at the upper end of the valley. He had met the man in the militia. His wife was a big, stout red-faced woman they called Ma. They were Dutch. She'd belonged to a Methodist class back in Pennsylvania. This gave Mary an idea. Why couldn't they start a Methodist class, she and Ma and Dean, and Sister Belle and her family?

So, as autumn froze into winter, they used to meet at Mary's fireside. They had no Bibles, but Sister Belle's mind and Dean's were well filled with Bible verses, and Ma had a beautiful voice and could sing one hymn—"A Mighty Fortress is our God." They met and prayed and took one Bible verse after another and talked about it. Gradually Mary worked into the talk most of the problems which were troubling her. She asked what would happen if a wo- man married again and then met her first husband face to face in front of God's throne. Sister Belle quoted the verse which says that in heaven there is no marrying or giving in marriage. "Marriage isn't for all time," she said. "It's just for this world—for helpin' each other with the trials of livin' and for the makin' and rearin' of children. You grow out of it, same as you grow out of being a child. And when you meet in Heaven, you're not man and woman any more but just pure grown up souls, all lovin' each other and happy together with God."

It was always a help to Mary when Sister Belle could come to meeting. One had a feeling that neither trouble nor pain nor wickedness could touch Sister Belle, because she lived beyond reach of them, deep within herself, in a fair place where the rain never fell and the wind never blew, but a clear sun shone quiet and peaceful for ever. When Mary said something like this, Sister Belle smiled and answered, "It aint where I live, Honey, but it's sure where I aim to get to, for it's where God is."

Finally Mary found courage to bring up the really crucial question. Was it true that an unburied man could not rest? Dean said there wasn't a mite of truth in it, for not a sparrow falls to the ground without God knowing all about it. "Everything in the world that can't look after itself God looks after," he assured her earnestly. "We are all His and we rest in His arms."

"Sure, honey," said Sister Belle, "if a man aint buried, God buries him. He sends the leaves to make a blanket, and the snow to make a feather-bed. And then over the dead He makes the ferns to grow, and the little wood flowers, and so lays over them a bedspread of living things for ever."

After the third of these class meetings, Mary had a dream. She dreamed that she was lying with John on a bed of moss, and leaves began to fall on them and cover them, and after the leaves came the snow. Then a tree started growing over them, arching its roots above them like the rafters of a roof. On the tree, a hand was cutting a heart. It seemed as if it was John's hand, and then it seemed it was her own, and then, strangely, it was Justurian's. Inside the heart the hand carved with a knife the words *John* and *Mary*. She looked at it, and she felt sad and content to think of herself lying there for ever with John, and the tree growing over them. Then she felt herself walking away and leaving herself there.

She woke with a strange sense of relief, and lay thinking, "It's like when I was married to John I was somebody else, and she that I was is dead now. It's like I died with him that long time when

I was so low in my mind. Now I'm not the same woman. I'm some-body else now." From that moment the fierceness and shamelessness of her new love was tempered into a steady hope, and she tried to discipline herself and fill her days with activity and her mind with plans for the future against the longing that possessed her. Jus had said that he would come back, and she never really doubted it.

So October passed into November, and November into December. The winter had set in dark and snowy. The great backlog Dean had rolled in glowed and made the only light in the heavily shutter-ed cabin. Outside the wind howled, and the drifts were piling up to the roof. On the hearth the corn mush was cooking. There was a violent pounding on the door where Mary had drawn the latch string in. "Who's there?" "Justurian." The latch flew up. A great storm of wind and snow and bearskin blew in. When Mary came out of it, she was sitting on Justurian's knee by the fire, her head loving-ly pressed against his big chest. "I've got my warrant, Mary. 466 and two-thirds acres in Kentucky!"

6

Mary wanted to be married by a Methodist minister. So the next day Jus set off through the snowy woods on the horse his father had given him to track down a Methodist, carrying as a charm against the crisp cold, a burning in one cheek. He chortled and rubbed the stinging area. When, for a moment, in bidding good bye he had forgotten himself and presumed too far, she had hauled off and struck him a blow which made him reel, big as he was. What a woman! Spunky was no name for her! She was one that could hold a man in leash, no matter what the favoring circum-stances, and do it so he knew she meant it, while all the while something in her was giving him the most powerful come-on! This was what a frontier gallant admired in a woman he would marry. Jus was beside himself with pride and delight.

Jus was moving in the general direction of the Holston Valley because a sentry he had spied in a tree had told him there was a whole nest of Methodists down that way. As he rode, he observed the tracks of animals in the light powdering over the hard crust that had formed on yesterday's wet fall of snow. He noted the tracks of wolves who could slip lightly over a crust and never break through. And he saw places where the small sharp hoofs of deer had pierced the crust. In these cases deer might be an easy prey to wolves, and it was the business of a good woodsman to look out for them and shoot the wolves. Riding watchfully along, his rifle in hand, he found he was following the fresh made tracks of a horse.

His feelings were divided. If the other rider was friendly, it would be pleasant to see him. But the good horse he was riding was a liability. The horse being the most valuable property on the far-flung frontier, there were always those who would lie in wait to murder a man for his horse.

He rode along cautiously till the tracks turned off at a right angle. Looking sharply, he saw a stirring in a thicket. A horse was tied there! There was a man on the ground! Was he hurt? Or kneeling in prayer? The crunching of horses' hooves startled the man. He sprang up, facing Jus, gun in hand, but said pleasantly, "Good day, Brother. What can I do for you?"

"Well, I don't know as there's anything you can do, Stranger," replied Jus politely, "unless you can tell me where to find me a Methodist parson."

"I can tell you that easy. Look straight ahead."

Jus looked at the stocky figure and frank, fresh, clean face under the coonskin cap. "You don't mean to say you're one?" An idea struck him. "Are you the Circuit Rider my gal's been looking for?"

"I can't say till I know who your gal is and where. But a Circuit Rider I am, by the grace of God and Mr. Asbury. But how come you want a Circuit Rider? Is anybody dyin'?"

"Not dyin' but gettin' married. I want a parson to hitch me to my gal. And she says he's got to be a Methodist."

The Circuit Rider's face fell. "I'm sorry, Brother. But marryin' is one thing I can't do. I've no license for it—neither I nor any other Methodist."

"Then how do we get married?"

"You'll have to find a Presbyterian, but you'll have to take your gal to him. You won't find Presbyterians traipsin' out in the snow the way we Methodists are God's fools enough to do." Then, seeing Justurian's downcast face, he asked, "Have you eaten?"

"Not since morning. But I've got corn-pone and cold venison my gal gave me."

"Come and have a bite with me. I stayed at a Methodist sister's house last night, and she loaded me up with a heap of victuals."

While they were building a fire, Jus observed, "You let that smoke go up free and bold. Arn't you afraid Indians will smell you out?"

"Indians have sense the same as Presbyterians. They stay home when it's snowy. But I don't worry about Indians. There's two Delawares up the creek I converted. They most generally know when there's to be an Indian raid, and they tell me."

"It's a pretty good proposition you have, this being a ciruit rider," remarked Jus. "You convert a man here and a woman there, and then, wherever you go, you have friends. A sister feeds you. An Indian looks after you. It's a pretty good thing all around."

"Well, you know there's a Bible verse for that. 'Seek ye the Kingdom of Heaven and all these things shall be added unto you'."

Jus looked at him quizzically, "I have a feelin' that in your time you might have done some good healthy sinnin'."

"Sinnin'!" The tone in his voice made Jus jump.

The man's eyes flashed fire, and some deep feeling flamed hot and red in his face. "I swore. I lied. I did wrong and let others take the blame. I drank myself stinkin', blind, swinish drunk every night. I laid my first girl when I was fourteen—God forgive me! It's ten years from that day to this, and I don't forgive myself now, and I never will. If God can, it's His everlasting mercy, and the least I can do is to give my soul and heart to Him for it for ever. Amen." He paused and then said, still violently, "There's nothin' to do with sinnin' except stop. Stop dead in your tracks and turn and go away from it at a fast run. You can't fool around with sinnin' and stop easy. The day comes when you come head on against Hell and perdition, and then God help you if you don't turn tail, and run.

"God gave me one last grain of sense, and I turned plum around between one drink and the next. And I ran away from it till God stood square in my path, and He held out His hand to me, and He said, 'Son, why so scared and miserable and self-torturing?' I said, 'Because I'm such a skunk. I can't forgive myself.' He said, 'You don't have to forgive yourself. There's One that has taken your sin on Himself. Just leave it to Him, now, and don't you worry any more.

Just walk with Him, and trust Him, and do the best you can. And He will hold you up.' Then I understood that it's not so much good works that saves a man as love and faith. I reckon God knows as well as I do that I'm only a man, and, as such, a poor, ignorant, sinful creature, and always will be. But that don't make any difference. I don't have to save myself. He saves me. All I've got to do is to stay fast by Him, and rest in Him, and do the best I can."

Jus was so absorbed in the man's confession that it occurred to him only slowly that he was being subjected to the famous new kind of preaching of the Methodists. It was so frank and personal that it got hold of you before you knew what was happening to you, like a story. He looked curiously at the Circuit Rider. Was this just a smart new kind of preaching? Or was it God's truth he was telling? His shrewd eyes raked the man's face. With profound respect he decided it was God's truth.

But Jus didn't want his soul saved just then. He wanted to get married. So he asked the man why he could not perform the marriage service. The Circuit Rider explained that Methodist preachers were not ordained clergymen as yet, but only converted laymen, and Methodist church members belonged to "societies" of the Church of England.

"But I thought when the war broke out, they threw the old church out. I've seen many a church with its doors nailed up," said Jus.

"That's right. In Maryland and Virginia and parts South, wherever the old Church was established as part of the royal government, we Methodists are about all that's left of it. So we stick together and do what we can."

"But if you fellows can't perform lawful wedlock, who does it?"

"The county courts have been licensing Presbyterians."

"But suppose folks don't want to be married by a Presbyterian?"

"A lot of 'em don't. They're kinda scared to start their wedded life off under the threat of predestination and eternal damnation. They want to be married safe and sound in the old church doctrine."

"Then what do they do—live in sin?"

"Too many of them do just that."

Jus had lived in sin more times than he cared to remember, and the passion that flamed between him and Mary was fierce, earthly, and coarse. But he had been brought up in the eighteenth century tradition which established between those who lived in lawful wedlock and those who did not, the clear, clean difference between white and black. Though he was not consciously religious, he felt obscurely that this woman who excited him as he had never been excited before was still different from all other women because she was dedicated in his mind to the position of wife, and he wanted to consecrate that position.

The Circuit Rider had been observing Justurian's face. "Look-ee, Brother. So far as the general situation goes, there's nothing much to do about it. We Methodists are all working on it. It's about all we talked about last quarterly meeting. We've told Mr. Wesley he's got to do something to help us set up in America as a regular church, with the sacraments and an ordained clergy. For if he don't, we'll fix it ourselves, with our own sanctions before God. But that don't help you get married now. However, there's no call for you to worry. Just bring your girl down to the county seat, and I'll set you up the prettiest marriage you ever saw, with a Presbyterian to tie the knot, and me to do the real consecrating with prayers and a sweet tuneful hymn. And we'll have the Methodist brothers and sisters of the county thereabouts present—all five of them."

Jus was silent. He hadn't counted on bringing Mary down through all these miles of snowy woods. Would there be a private room for a new-made man and wife down in the county seat?

"How big's your town?" he asked.

"Oh we're a great city, we are. There's all of three cabins there together, and one of them's double. The double one serves for county court and liquor saloon and general store on week-days. Old Bill, the county clerk, he's the bartender and storekeeper, too—and on Sunday anybody that wants it can have it for a preaching. And we've got a wagon road, near a mile long. It's five feet deep in mud in spring, and five feet in dust in summer, and in winter it's frozen into mountains and valleys."

"I don't suppose there's a stopping place for wayfarers?"

"There's Si's Station. Five in a bed, and twenty sleeping on the floor. Filth on the floor you can shovel out with a spade, and bugs itching you."

"I'd rather build me a lean-to," said Jus, musingly. "A lean-to, with a fire burning in front of it, and a spruce-bough bed, and bearskins—it wouldn't be half bad."

The Circuit Rider hesitated. "I've got an old cabin with a fire-place. No bed, but spruce boughs on the floor by the fire, and bear-skins on top of them. If I had my girl," he stopped, and then said frankly, with a warm, rising blush, "I've got a girl I'm fixin' to mar-ry when she can get out to me or me back to her. The little old cabin isn't much. But when I can I do something to it against the time I might be needing it. There's plenty of wood stacked up along-side it, from the clearing I've been making, and you're more than welcome to all you can burn."

"But what will you do?"

"Oh I'll be around to see you married, and then I'll have to be off again. Most likely the night you're wedded I'll be sleeping with the Delawares up there in their wigwam."

Justurian said nothing. He was too deeply grateful.

7

He was more than grateful ten days later when, after swearing that he was over twenty-one, and Mary swearing that she was over twenty-one, and producing his military land warrant to show who he was, and a statement from John's colonel to the effect that he was dead, he stood up with Mary before a Presbyterian minister in the dirty log cabin courthouse bar and general store, amidst smells of tobacco, skunk grease, and corn whisky and was married. Then the Circuit Rider prayed, and one of the Methodist sisters raised a thin, sweet voice in a hymn, and the others tried to sing with her and failed. The five Methodists fell on their knees, dragging bride and bride-groom down with them. With tears flowing down their faces, and choking explosions of "Amen," they prayed in turn for the wedded ones, beseeching God to see to it that they had a long and loving life together, and stood fast by each other through good fortune and bad, and had a large family of children to the glory of the Lord.

Jus thought the recommending them to God was a little too long drawn out. But he was deeply touched. While he was still in that state of nature where he might have preferred to celebrate with whisky, fiddling, and whooping, he was bound to admit that this "slopping over," as he privately called it, was well meant and might be better for all concerned.

At any rate Mary liked it. She looked very ladylike in her best suit of clothes, the one that had been given her eight years ago at the end of her term as a bound girl. In response to the prayers her pale cheeks took on the color of a wild rose, and her usually cool blue eyes lighted like stars.

At last it was over, and he brought her to the Circuit Rider's cabin. The good sisters had cleaned it and hung ground-pine to decorate it, and the good brothers had brought in wood, and piled it roof high in the corner. The fire was lighted, and on the hearth a kettle of hog and hominy was steaming against the far off time when they might be hungry. On the floor the nuptial couch had been built up thick, high, and fragrant with spruce boughs, and piled with bearskins. On top of it lay a single sprig of mignonette from the only flower pot west of the Alleghenies.

CHAPTER 3

Amherst County, Virginia
June, 1784 to August, 1785

They'd never have enough of each other until Jus could get his land in the West and settle down. Realizing this drove him out, all that winter and early spring, to ride forty miles a day, up and down the mountains, organizing veterans for the westward march. But again and again, when he'd left, telling Mary he'd be gone for two or three weeks, he'd beat his way back to her in six days, in a kind of ravening anticipation, against wind and rain and driving snow, pounding on the door in the middle of the night, shaking the whole place like a thunderstorm. For this Mary gloried in him. He suited her.

But from the first they argued. Mary opposed his proposition that, as soon as the snow melted, she should go to his folks till they could get off to the West. She had no mind to leave the snug security of her property here for a dubious betterment in Amherst

County. "But, Honey," said Jus, with a twinkle in his eye, "it's the lot of a woman to follow her husband. And his people shall be her people."

"Not my lot, it isn't," she flared.

"Well, it's in the Bible," persisted Jus. "You ask Dean."

With an ironic gleam on his handsome dark face, Dean replied, "My Bible says a man should leave father and mother and cleave unto his wife."

But Amherst County had one lure. The Cartwright property there was on the main trail from Richmond to Fort Chiswell, at the lower end of the Valley of Virginia, which was the taking off point for the West. And, what was more important to Mary, Jus could begin his legal education by attending the sessions of the Amherst County court.

So, in the late spring, while Jus went back to Amherst County to arrange for his wife there, Dean negotiated an exchange of Mary's cabin and cleared fields with a trapper for his winter's catch of furs. The furs he traded at Fort Chiswell for three good riding horses and two pack horses. With these they set off in June, down the narrow mountain trails to Fort Chiswell, and east from there on the Richmond trail. The war over, everyone was on the move, and stations for travelers were springing up every forty or fifty miles. Mary readily found log shelters where, with their own bedding and food, they could make themselves as comfortable as mosquitoes, bedbugs, and the presence of whisky and tobacco-flavored fellow guests would allow. When, after passing the solid log fortifications of Fort Chiswell, and getting through the traffic of 'movers' caravans on both sides of it, they turned up the Richmond trail, Mary stopped somewhere near the still indefinite borders of Amherst County, and bathed the children in a stream, and put on the fresh clothes she had saved for their first appearance at Justurian's home. Then she arrayed herself in her own good suit of "freedom clothes."

His horse reined up on a rise of ground, Jus was looking out for them. Before Mary could be sure that lone horseman far off was her husband, he let out a wild Indian whoop, and bore down on them at a furious gallop, and snatched Mary off her horse and set her on his saddle in front of him, and tore off toward a cluster of cabins over the hill, yelling, while the children, shepherded by Dean, clattered after.

From one of the cabins a large man ran out, at the sound of the yells, and sprang on a horse standing there saddled, and rode toward them. "It's Pappy," said Jus, reining up and hugging Mary close. Mary felt dismay falling on her like a cold dark cloud. Looking at the large, loose figure, slumping in the saddle, she thought, "Will Jus look like that thirty years from now?" And then with a sharp click of her will, she mentally answered "No." But she was immediately disarmed, when John Cartwright's bright brown eyes looked into hers, and he held out his big coarse hand, with an almost courtly gesture, and said, "Welcome, my daughter." His eyes surveyed her ladylike figure in the well made bodice and skirt, the neat children, the dignified black on a good horse, the well laden, carefully strapped pack animals. Surprised but pleased that Jus had brought home such a lady, he said, apologetically, "I wish we had more that is fittin' for you." Touched, Mary smiled into his eyes. He added wistfully with a sweep of his hand toward the ragged acres rolling away on all sides, "I've done the best I could with the boys away at war. But the land and all—it's kind a got away from me." Then he wheeled his horse and started toward the cabins, and Jus, with one arm still around Mary's waist, spurred his horse and followed.

Coming to the cabins, Mary found the rest of the family lined up there to greet her, and recognized each one from what she had heard of them—Martha, the young stepmother, pink, plump, and sandy-haired, with baby Sally at her pendulous breasts; Annie and Peter, all legs and foolish laughter; and Peter's girl, Christian Garvin, hair frizzled with curling tongs, flaunting moist red lips, and high-heeled slippers with buckles. Hardly had she received their shy, offhand greetings, when there was an ear-splitting yell and Peter jumped on a horse and tore off to meet a crowd coming over a hill to the north. "It's some of the neighbors," said Jus. "You wouldn't believe it, Honey, but, from the time you left Fort Chiswell, somebody along the way has been keeping track of you for us. Now that the word's been got around you're here, they're bringing the wedding feast."

Mary cast a longing glance toward the cabin under a chestnut tree which Jus said was to be theirs. She would gladly be spared this wedding feast. But there was no help for it. Twenty or thirty people were bearing down on them. She could only consign children and packhorses to Dean, noting, with a sense of humiliation, that he realized how Justurian's people impressed her and was sorry for her, and turn away to be the center of their social uproar.

But the children liked it. They gorged happily on fried chicken, cold ham, apple butter, rhubarb pie, wheat bread, and other delicacies they had never before tasted. When the feast was over, Mary almost relaxed, and she even smiled when Peter tuned up his fiddle, and they began to sing and dance. But her sense of personal dignity recoiled when the men threw the girls around, and laughed as their skirts flew over their heads, and when, grabbing girls in the dance, some of the gallants moved their hands up to rest against their breasts. And though she didn't understand the songs very well, she realized with distaste that most of them were bawdy, the favorite one being about a maid who went in a maid and didn't come out a maid. And while whisky flowed like water jokes about maidenheads, horns, and cuckolds became more and more explicit. Since it was the time-honored right of the older men to kiss the bride, she submitted to prickly, wet fumblings from lips dripping with tobacco juice. But when, amidst those toasts to the prospect of a large family of children, which etiquette demanded, one old man poked her slender waist and asked Jus, amidst loud guffaws, how come nothing was started there yet, she could hardly keep her clenched fist from tangling with the old goat's white hair and long white beard.

In their own cabin at last, Mary was pleased but embarrassed by the glaring publicity of undressing by candlelight. Turning her back on Jus, she began unfastening her bodice, while he moved around casually, stealing glances at this procedure. She was thinking that some folks weren't in bed yet. "Is Peter fixin' to marry that girl?" she asked.

"Oh they'll get spliced when they get around to it. She puts him off. She says, once they're hitched, they'll start havin' young uns, and Peter's in no hurry. He's drawn 100 acres in Kentucky. Says he wants to see us all off first."

Mary wondered how Chris was going to put off having young

uns—with what she'd heard going on in the honeysuckles. But it was none of her business. She merely observed, "Seems like if I loved a man enough to marry him, I'd want it finished and done with. I couldn't stand it to be kissin' and slobberin'—and—and not gettin' somewhere."

"No?" His tone was half teasing question, half exultant comment. "Honey, Honey! My gal's not like Chris. My gal's another breed o'cats." And with a rich and happy laugh he blew out the light.

2

What Mary saw of the Cartwright way of life during the next months dragged down even her courage. Instead of the small, neat, well worked clearings in the mountains which had so a-bundantly sustained her little family, the ragged acres here rolled away endlessly over low country whose red and yellow soil had been churned up and ravaged without being adequately cleaned and tilled. There were acres of blackened stumps, and ragged, fresh-springing young bushes where the forests had been burned, and the cattle turned in to graze on the growth that came up in the ash. In other places more trees had been felled than could be cut up for firewood and building timber. The wood lay rotting amidst rank, young brush in which the cattle would lose them-selves and have to be hunted for days. An upper branch of the James River ran through the place. The innovation of "contour plowing" which Mr. Jefferson had introduced not far to the north, was not known here. The main purpose of plowing seemed to be to provide troughs by which, in a thunderstorm, all the good soil could be carried down and deposited like huge clots of blood in the narrow and rutted path which served as public highway to Richmond.

There was a whole village of log cabins on the place, all falling apart. The barnyard was rotten and spongy with manure. The hog pen could be smelled a mile away. The cabin Mary and Jus had was the best and stood a little apart under a huge chestnut tree. But it was not as large as her mountain cabin nor so well made. It shook on its foundations. The puncheon floor was rotten in many places. The roof leaked. The flies buzzed all the long, hot day. The mosquitoes buzzed all night. And if they weren't eaten alive by bedbugs it was only because Mary could smell them infallibly and kept after them all the time.

Mary's impatience with disorder threw her into a frenzy of activity. "The trouble with you all," she said to Jus, "is that you don't know what it is to root hog or die. And it's something you'd better learn before you set foot in Kentucky." She waved a disdainful hand at the Cartwright acres. "Do you want your 466 and 2/3 acres to look like that?"

Jus replied mildly, "But how can I study law and clean up this mess? And, besides, I have to get the veterans together to go to our acres."

"But why do you have to let Peter loaf along with you? Let him stay back and put his shoulder under the farm-load."

At this Peter raised a howl. "But you have to eat," said Mary. "And where do you get something to eat? Right out of the ground, Honey, by the sweat of your handsome brow!" She laid her hand on his arm with one of her rare winning smiles. Peter, who was the soul of good nature, melted.

Left behind, he worked well for a few days. Then, from the leanto he had built for himself, she heard the strumming of his fiddle, and his voice raised in one of his not too decent love songs. And there was a crowd of young people, dancing, whooping, kicking up their heels, and passing around corn whisky! At first they'd ride over only after dark. Then they came in the afternoon. Finally they embarked on an all day hunt in which Peter joined them. When she told him that one day off, right in the middle of summer, would have to do him for a long time, they didn't turn up for three days. Then they arrived again after dark, and she knew that the round of worktime wasting was beginning again. She was relieved to see that Peter was so busy with the fiddle that he had little time to drink. But he'd kiss some other girl if Chris was not by. This led to quarrels with Chris which went on for days, ending at night in the honeysuckles with results as inconclusive as ever.

If Jus returned in the midst of one of these social sessions, and good-humoredly joined in, he drank too much. One day he found

Mary sewing up a corn husk mattress. "I'm keeping it against the time you have liquor on you," she said grimly. "Times like that I sleep by myself."

The first time she used it, he picked her up and tried to put her back in the big bed. But she pounded his chest, pulled his hair, and clawed his face, leaving marks for days. "I'd as soon sleep with a hog," she said coldly. "You stink. You snuffle. You bumble. You snore. You belch."

Next morning Jus was contrite. "Honey, I just naturally don't like the stuff. It tastes awful. It burns my insides, and I haven't time to waste on a head like I have this morning."

"Then why drink it?"

"Oh, I get to talking, and some one hands me a gourd, and I drink out of pure absent-mindness."

"That's why I think nobody has a right to be handin' it around."

One night, after Mary had put the children to bed, and Jus had strayed over to join a party of Peter's friends, Mary sat by herself in the cool of the night. Looking up at the stars, she was trying to recall a Bible verse to cling to, and to sharpen again that sense of God which was fading into utter discouragement, despite the tactful efforts of Dean to keep it alive. She had assumed that here she could find a Methodist class. Though Asbury was in Amherst County that year, and assigned Thomas Foster and William Jessup to the Amherst circuit, the hurly-burly at home had prevented Mary from hearing about them. And here, under the eyes of so many white folks, Dean avoided those talks which had so often helped her before.

Her desperate attempt, alone that night under the stars, to find some cosmic reassurance was broken into by a high, shrill voice above the voices of the young people across the field. Leaping the space between her and them like a deer, she saw her boy John drunkenly dancing a hornpipe in a circle that laughed and clapped his every move. Then she saw that Edmund was there, too, and that one of the older men held Polly on his knee, his hand feeling lasciviously far up her fat little thighs. Mary stormed into the center, boxed John on both ears, and, snatching Polly into her arms, drove John ahead of her back to the cabin. Eddie followed of his own accord, whimpering. A snub-nosed little fellow, he was protected by his plainness from the attentions John and Polly drew as honey draws flies. Nobody bothered to liquor Eddie to enjoy his jaunty performances when drunk. Nobody cuddled him.

Mary burned up the rest of the night in fury, telling Jus that they'd pay in sorrow to the end of their days for throwing John and Polly into this mess of whisky and loose living. Child of a godless generation for whom the old sanctions and codes had been disrupted by social upheaval and long war, Jus had never put his mind on what had so shocked his wife. Startled, he soothed her, but felt her tumult hardening his will to speed the Kentucky migration. He hid from her the insuperable obstacles rising on the path to Kentucky. He was not one to give up before the insuperable. With time he knew he could figure a way around it.

3

As summer ripened, and the James River shrank, and horses could go for miles over what in June was swamp, the reports came back that Boone's trail was also dry. Then the movers came down from Richmond way—sunburned, stringy-haired, harrassed mothers, fathers with guns, tomahawks, and pistols, barefooted children walking by packhorses or riding three to a horse. Night after night parties camped in Mary's yard, or thunderstorms drove them into the cabin. Men could sleep in the outbuildings, but Mary would never hear of this for the women and children. But the thunderstorms always seemed to come on the rare nights when Jus was home. It was pretty hard to push him out and sleep with three women in her bed! She'd ask, "Will we all look so much like poor folks when we've been a few days on the trail?"

Jus said, "No." The veterans were seeing to it that, when they set off, they'd be properly supplied and guarded and have something when they got there. He said no more, but Mary was troubled that his pleasant brown face settled into harsh, worried lines.

One day a rider came clattering up the trail from Fort Chiswell with an appalling report. A party that had stopped to buy green corn from the Cartwrights a fortnight ago had been completely wiped out by Indians before they reached Cumberland Gap! Two days later came word that another party that had got past the fort before it could be warned had also been destroyed. The need for turning back or halting the movers brought into the councils on Kentucky two people to whom, till now, Mary had found no occasion to say more than "Howdy," when she met them at the spring. They were Hiram and Molly, who sheltered themselves in an old cabin and worked the Cartwright acres on shares.

Now Mary learned that their two families had started for Kentucky the previous year, with seven children between them. His wife and children had been killed, and her husband and children. Clinging together in this terrible catastrophe, they had struggled back to safety and had been living together, unwedded, ever since. Seeing the man's eyes, pale and watery above the scar that twisted one side of his face, resting on the plain face of this woman, Mary's usual prudishness melted in the thought, "God's brought them comfort in each other. It looks like He's joined them without need of preachers."

The dangers of the Kentucky trail, sending tremors up the mountain valleys even into Pennsylvania, brought the organizer of the Pennsylvania Dutch veterans down to consult with Jus. With him came his dark-eyed wife, Brenda, and his two little dark-eyed, white-haired sons, Otto and Hans. Dutch and Jus, having fought side by side for eight years, wanted their wives to know each other and go west together. One look at Dutch, huge, with bulging blue eyes and pasty pale skin, speaking in a thick, gutteral voice and scrambling his syntax, and Mary knew that here was a tower of strength. One look at Brenda, and she knew that here was no weak sister. The first day in the cabin Jus assigned to them, Brenda had everything out in the sunshine and was washing and scrubbing it. The second day Dutch was in the cornfield, doing the work of three. Brenda picked a bushel of summer apples and had them stewing over a fire outdoors. "I'm fixin to make you apple butter, quick as Dutch can find me some sorghum," she told Mary. "You've got to take summer apples when you can. They're ripe one day and rotten the next."

Mary, who had been shocked by the ease with which Jus adapted himself to those below him, was now delighted at the way he pulled himself up in good company. When he sat talking to Dutch, she saw a new man, a man of dignity and stature and sense. Here at last were people who didn't pull you down. When Dutch, pulling at his long pipe stem, said with decision that "to Kentucky is the way shut like a door for this year, not so, and for next year also perhaps?" she could strike bottom in her despair because she knew that if and when they did get off to Kentucky they would be going with people like these. When she said this to Jus, he replied with a slightly injured air, "But Honey, they're all like that. Dominie, Mac, Cherokee Bill—all my friends. You'll see."

"Then it will be a sight for eyes that looking around here has made sore," she answered.

At first Mary found in Brenda a kind of romance she had never found in friendship with a woman, and was as happy as a school girl with her first "crush." Slender, neat, with long, finely modelled face, and eyebrows like glossy wings above her glowing dark eyes, Brenda was an exotic contrast to the freckled women of the frontier. Mary, who, as an unwanted waif, knew nothing of her own parentage and longed for a family background, found Brenda's tales of her forebears most romantic. Her grandfather had been a member of Wesley's congregation in Savannah in 1736, though she did not know he was one of those Spanish Jews of whom Wesley wrote "some . . . seem nearer to the mind that was in Christ than many who call Him Lord." When her mother married and moved westward in Georgia, and then up the long valleys to western Maryland, she retained enough memory of the family's contact with Wesley to attend one of Asbury's early meetings and to become a Methodist. Brenda had been reared a Methodist and converted at fourteen and had joined a class. But under the infrequent ministrations of a Circuit Rider the little class languished and was taken over by the Baptists. Brenda was reconverted and immersed in a dark flowing river between high banks of snow on a day when it was five degrees below zero—an experience which had, for her, a drama, an intensity of mood and sensation, and a finality nothing Methodist could offer.

Mary had never heard of Baptists. What Brenda knew was only what she had heard at preachings, but, even so, a fairly clear picture of the kind of people the Baptists were was transferred from the vivid mind of one woman to the vivid mind of the other.

Through the century and a half of colonial government, the Baptists had been a poor, despised sect, claiming Roger Williams of Rhode Island as their founder, and distinguished mainly by their refusal to pay taxes to the established Congregational Church of New England and the established Church of England in the southern colonies. They represented pure democracy in church government. Each group organized itself and ruled itself according to its own laws. Preachers were the equals of their parishioners, living in the same kind of cabins with dirt floors, supporting themselves by farming, and distinguished only by their devotion to the very strict Baptist code of behavior which forebade slave-holding as well as the more generally recognized sins.

When, at the outbreak of the Revolution, the Church of England was repudiated in the southern colonies, the Baptists moved in even more successfully than the Methodists, for their extremely equalitarian and democratic procedures suited the rising sentiment. During the Revolution they grew from a small sect of the poor to a large and powerful body with many wealthy members, rigorously self-organized, with the strongest group discipline of any well-doers in this fluid, unorganized world.

Mary was charmed with what Brenda told her about Baptists till Brenda tried to convert her by telling her that Asbury was a Tory. "He's been sent over to drag us back to the King," she averred.

Mary was horrified. During eight years of war she had brooded over the Kings and Tories who caused it. Her husband had been killed. Who killed him? Kings and Tories. But she had to have something to look up to. The equalitarianism of pigs in a pigsty was not for her. "Seems like I couldn't be a Baptist," she told Brenda, "and have folks no better than me meddling with my soul." But Brenda was persistent. She had brought her Bible with her and read it aloud, and phrased her remarks in the Bible words which had such power of enchantment over Mary. They were two bright but abysmally ignorant young women, who had grown up in a new world, like beings born into a new heaven. The light in their sky was not the light of Europe. They breathed new air, looked out on new trees, new water. And in them new souls were struggling to expression.

When Brenda left, Mary felt let down, confused, irritable. Her faith in Methodists had been shattered, but no new faith had been put in its place. As her faith failed, and her spirits flagged in the loneliness after Brenda's going, her old superstitions revived. She had as yet no promise of a child. She knew that her failure to have a child now when she had had three by her first husband was a source of anxiety to Jus. Day by day horror was growing in her. Was John, unburied, putting a blight on her? The wet, mild, disagreeable winter set in. The cabin was drafty. The rain leaked in. The snow sifted in. The coursing in and out of the family kept it dirty and disheveled. The outside was as depressing as the inside. Here there was none of the high pure majesty of winter in the mountains. As fast as the snow fell, it melted and mixed with the red earth till it sometimes seemed that it was running rivers of blood. She'd look down the narrow churned-up wagon road that led to Boone's Trace and shudder at the day they would be traveling it to Kentucky. "I declare," she thought. "It looks like a trail of pure murder."

They saw the year 1784 out with fiddling, dancing, and shouting, and so much drinking that Mary did what she had not done for many a night,—slept on the corn husk mattress on the floor. After sleepless hours she rose early, wrapped herself in a bearskin, and went out into the cold, clear dawn. Above, in the sky, the morning star shone like the face of one trying to speak to her. But her heart was hard and bitter. There was no use trying to be good or do good when everything pulled you down. She looked at the star and asked it, "Is there a God?" She answered herself, "Yes, there's a God, sure enough, and He's up there, but he just don't care for poor folks like us."

She went in and banged the door on the star. 1784 was gone, she told herself, and she was glad to see it go, even though it had given her Justurian. She had no hope that 1785 would be better.

4

Miraculously it was better. On a howling March day when Jus had stepped over to his father's to help put back a piece of the roof which had blown off, a tall, lean, weather-beaten stranger knocked at the door and asked for shelter. Mary wanted to refuse. So long as she had only a one-room cabin to sleep in, she just wasn't going to put up any more folks for the night. But she couldn't refuse, for the stranger was a circuit rider. As Jus said when he came in, there wasn't anything they wouldn't do for a circuit rider, seeing what a circuit rider had once done for them. The stormy afternoon wore into night, and the wind rocked the cabin, and the rain poured in. But they didn't care, as hour after hour the three of them sat by the fire and talked. Mary begrudged every minute that took her away to get mush and milk for the children, or to bring venison for the men to broil, and potatoes to cook in the ashes.

The Circuit Rider had attended the historic Methodist meeting in Baltimore on December 24, 1784. He told them that sixty-nine traveling preachers and Mr. Asbury had met Doctor Coke who had been sent over by Wesley with power to ordain Asbury as Superintendent, and to set up the independent Methodist Episcopal Church of America. This done, a hierarchy of elders, deacons, and ministers had been ordained to serve under Asbury.

"So now," said Jus, "you're going to save the back woods from eternal damnation by the Presbyterians."

The Circuit Rider was a serious man, and he answered seriously. "Nobody could favor the Presbyterians more than I do. For I was raised a Presbyterian. They have a learned clergy, and in the settled parts of the country their learning means a great deal. They start the schools. They keep book-knowledge alive. Many a leader in our country now, like Patrick Henry, or Tom Jefferson, owes his start, off in the back country, to some Presbyterian parson who doubled as schoolmaster. But the hitch in it is that a man can't spend all his young days studying books, and still get the knowledge to stay alive out in the forests. As things are west of here, it takes all a man's young days to get so's he can dodge the Indians, and follow a trail marked only by notches in trees, and shoot to kill, and hold his own against bears, horsethieves, and weather.

On that account these book preachers arn't much good away from the settlements.

"Now the way we Methodists figure is this. Most people for years to come arn't going to be where learning can do them much good. They're going to be spread around, lost in woods and swamps and hills and hollows over thousands of miles—millions of folks lost that way. And somebody's got to go out and find them and bring them to where learning, when they're exposed to it, will take. That's what we circuit riders are set up to do. If Brother Asbury has his way, there'll be a circuit rider ahead of every westbound caravan. Henceforth one of us aims to be wherever they lay a human creature in the grave, or a newborn babe in its cradle."

As the Circuit Rider went on to outline plans for breaking the West into conferences, districts, and circuits, Jus listened shrewdly. "What is a circuit?" he asked.

"It's ground a man can cover in a given time on horseback. There's three, four, and six weeks' circuits. The man who covers a circuit is a circuit rider."

"And a district?"

"A district is a number of circuits under a presiding elder."

Jus ruminated. "If you put one of your fellows on some wild patch of country out there, he'll know more about it than any man living. This presiding elder—he'll be a pretty big chief, sending riders hither and yon on his own say so."

The Circuit Rider smiled. "We aim to get in before there's any law and order. For a time I don't doubt we'll be all the means of decency there is. We'll break ground for courts, schools, and churches to follow."

"But you'll be pretty scattered. How do you think to hold together?"

"Well, we've been working in America since 1766, and we've laid out our plan of itineracy by studying what worked, and doing more of it, and what didn't work and doing less of it. Every three months all the riders of a district meet in one place and thrash out their problems. This is called a quarterly meeting. Every year delegates from the districts in some big area get together, in an annual conference. We've got the land on this side of the mountains cut up into four conferences, and all the land on the western side is the western conference. We don't know yet where it stretches to and what's in it. But we'll send men to explore. Then we'll put riders on it here and there, wherever we find folks, and break it into circuits."

"But how will you hold together with the folks back East?"

"Brother Asbury aims to get over the mountains into the West every year and cover every circuit we set up there."

"That's a powerful lot of traveling for one man. He must be strong."

"Did you ever see him?"

"I have," Mary broke in. "He's peaked looking." She was remembering how she felt that July day when Asbury talked, and the kind look in the sky as she had ridden home. The hard freeze in her heart was melting.

"He is peaked," responded the Circuit Rider. "Most of the time he's so sick he can hardly sit his horse. He's plagued with the flux. His bowels are like water. What with cold and wet and bad food all the time he never gets over it. And lots of times he's dizzy with fever. Moreover, he's one of your reserved and particular Englishmen and he don't like us much over here. He hates forests and wild empty places. He's never going to feel easy outside a little garden in a town with a fence all around it. He can't bear not having a clean bed, and he don't get one from one year's end to the other. Barking dogs and howling young uns get on his nerves, and he almost never preaches except against their racket. He loves books and quiet. He almost always has books in his saddlebags, and his aim is to read 100 pages every day. And he loves to write. Wherever he is, he writes down what happens, though how he does it, the good Lord only knows."

Jus whistled. "Readin' 100 pages, and writin' every day, he still gets around?"

"Rain or shine, snow or ice, swimmin' swollen rivers, laying out all night in the wet, he makes from ten to forty-five miles a day regular. 6000 miles a year, year after year, that's what his comings and goings add up to. Sometimes he preaches as much as five times a day, and come Hell or high water, he turns up where he is expected. I've seen him preach when he rocked on his feet from pain and weariness till he got going with his sermon. And then the

Lord would take hold of him, and there was few that listened the Lord didn't take hold of, too."

"What does he do it for? What does he stand to gain by it?"

"Nothing on this earth except to fall in his tracks alone in the wilds, and have the buzzards pick his bones."

"Well, it don't make sense to me," observed Jus.

"It don't make sense to any man till the Lord touches you. And then you pick up and go out and pray day and night to endure to do what Mr. Asbury does," responded the Circuit Rider, with a quiet smile into Mary's speaking eyes.

The talk ended with prayers led by the preacher. Jus listened quietly. He was not irreverent, but he remained untouched. Not so Mary. Her heart was breaking. She knew it now—what she had never known before—the overwhelming experience of conviction of sin. She'd been bitter and hard and cursed God in her heart. She'd been low down and shameful in all her feelings, and there was no health in her. In broken words she began to tell God so, tears pouring down her cheeks. Jus was astounded. He knew little of the passionate inner life of this woman. He had merely felt in her "a mighty power of lovin'" which made her infinitely desirable as a wife. Now he was divided between embarrassment and aching tenderness. He was still more amazed when, struggling with sobs and prayers, she seemed suddenly to be illumined with a bright light—he could have sworn afterwards that it shone around her like a sun. She stopped crying, and raised her face, with that inner light making sparkles of her tears, and said in a glad voice, "It's gone. My sin has rolled away." She covered her face and prayed silently. The preacher began an evening hymn, singing softly so as not to wake the children. To Jus it was a strange experience.

5

Almost simultaneously with her great change of heart, Mary knew that the hope she had been concealing, hardly daring to cherish it lest she be disappointed, was indeed justified, and she was going to have a child. It seemed to her the ultimate proof of

God's mercy that he had given her this baby not now, when she was broken and contrite and trying to be good, but back at the turn of the year when all her feelings were reckless and shameless. "God is too good to us. It aint fittin' that I should a had such a blessing," she said to Jus when she told him, with a quivering look.

For Mary, spring had never come so beautifully. With every new flower that opened her own happiness bloomed anew. Jus was never tired of noting the changes in her and was inordinately proud that he had accomplished this miracle. In his long rides away from home on veterans' business he thought incessantly of the coming child. "My Kentucky Boy," he called it, because the child's life and the life in the new country would begin together. Mary thought it was just like a man to assume that the child would be a boy. A daughter would suit her just as well. Polly had been more of a comfort than Jackie and Eddie. Whatever it was, it would be her baby, a creature in the nature of things peculiarly her own, and she'd be able to nurse it and keep it by her for two years.

She had joined a little class formed by the Circuit Rider. Each time she attended it she learned Bible verses—the Twenty-third Psalm, "In my Father's house are many mansions," "He will gently lead those that are with young." She had no books and no music. These beautiful words served instead. They gave shape and color to all her aspirations.

One day Jus brought her a Bible. In those days Bibles were not easy to get, for there was as yet no Bible Society to sow them broadcast. When she was bound out, contracts for bound boys provided that they be taught to read, but no such provision was made for bound girls. But by listening in on the primer lessons for bound boys she had learned her letters. Now the class leader, who was slightly literate, marked in her Bible each verse that she learned. By studying these, she gradually memorized the appearance of the words and ranged far and wide in the book seeking whatever she could decipher, opening windows into strange worlds, and finding sayings she did not understand but could think about for hours, and other sayings as uplifting as music.

As the summer wore on, with its heavy and sagging heat, it was good to sit still for hours and leave it to Annie and Chris to do for the travelers who came by and the neighbors who dropped in.

The affairs of the farm had receded and become part of a dream. She did what she had to automatically, and was happy when Martha or Jus said she had done enough now, and she could slip away to her own thoughts.

CHAPTER 4

Amherst County, Virginia
August, 1785 to November 1785

Again, with the shrinking of streams, the movers to Kentucky crowded in on them. But Jus, coming home from the county court more strained and worried than Mary had ever seen him, said General Russell had put his foot down. None of his veterans were going to move west this year. Mary was glad that September which would see her baby into the world would not see her on the move. But, even in her new-found state of grace, she let fling a tart question, "How come all these folks get off to Kentucky, and soldiers are bid by their own general to sit down and wait?"

Jus replied that there was no law against folks going on their own and getting killed if they'd a mind to. But the veterans were counting on Mr. Jones, the Richmond politician, and Mr. Madison, General Washington, and General Russell to fix things up.

"What things?"

Jus cut a quid of tobacco, put it in his cheek, and drawled, "A lot of little things—safe conduct on the way out; a county court we run ourselves instead of the rascals that's out there; a way down the Mississippi for our goods; sound money to trade with; a government back home to do what the Continental Congress can't seem to, which is to keep the British and Spaniards out of our hair; and peace with the Indians."

"And when will they get this fixed?"

Jus shifted his quid to the other cheek, and spat as if he were spitting frustration out in one brown, bitter stream. "Oh, about the time our Kentucky boy's a man grown."

But the movers to Kentucky kept passing by, including some in those "gentry clothes" which marked them as a higher species.

One night a gentleman in a broad Spanish hat asked for shelter. When Jus said that they'd not a roof that wasn't covering movers already, he said that he'd sleep outdoors in his "poncho," but asked to buy a chicken and some green beans for his black servant to cook. For this he paid with two English shillings.

Mary was delighted with the money. Silver coins almost never came their way. Jus examined the coins carefully, clinked them on a stone, and dug into them with his fingernail. "Seems to be good silver," he said. Mary put the coins away for some special occasion.

The occasion came when that strange new species on the mountain trails arrived—a peddler on foot, with a cloth square filled with notions from "down Carolina way." When, before Mary's dazzled eyes, he spread needles, nutmegs, a nutmeg grater, and coffee in quarter of a pound packages, she hoped he might pay for food and lodging with these treasures. But he said he could trade only for money. When she offered him the paper bill she had taken from a mover earlier in the day, he demurred. "It's no good except around here. And I aim to travel far." Determined to have at least a needle and a nutmeg, Mary finally offered him one of the silver coins. He looked at it carefully, pursed up his lips, and, still holding it, said, "Ma'am, that coin's counterfeit." To Jus, who had strolled up, he explained, "That coin's what they ran Philip Alston out of Raleigh for three or four years back."

"Who is Alston?" asked Jus.

"Who going up and down here, trading, doesn't know Alston? He had a line of trade clear out to the Mississippi through the Indian nations, selling them goods he imported in exchange for furs— a better way out and better marked if you knew how to find it than this bloody path Boone made, and safe for anybody under Alston's conduct. Many a good trade I've made through Alston."

"And you say he's a counterfeiter?"

"Well, now, there's lots that don't like paper money. Alston had to have hard cash. Coming on a vein of silver in the mountains, through Indians who wore silver ornaments, he brought in some queer dark people called Portyghees and set them to making money. The state of North Carolina didn't like this and ran him out of Raleigh as a counterfeiter."

"Where's he gone?"

"I don't know. All I know is the fine house he had in Raleigh is sold and his business done for. Seems too bad." He threw up the coin and caught it. "I'll keep this for the needle and nutmeg," he said. "There's places where it will serve."

2

A few days later Mary heard a furious clatter of hooves outside her cabin and ran out to find Sandy, one of the militia officers, there. "Where's Jus?" he asked.

"Most likely at the courthouse."

"Send Peter to hold him there. We're mustering out the militia. And, John," to the older Cartwright who, hearing the horse, had come up, "You follow me." He wheeled his horse to go, then wheeled him back. "Somebody'd better be on guard here."

"Dean and Hiram will guard us," said Mary.

"You'd better seek shelter where you can wait it out in safety," said Sandy. He spurred his horse and was off like a thunderclap, with John after him. Peter, summoned by Mary, asked no questions. He got his firearms and finished the saddling which she had already begun, and was off. Only after they had disappeared in clouds of dust, fire-bright in the late hot sun, did it occur to any of those left behind to ask why the militia was mustered out and what they were to guard against. They had all been trained from infancy to spring to arms and ask no questions.

The late lingering light of that day, August 30, 1785, sank to dark while Mary waited. Martha, Annie, Dean and Hiram and Molly, the scars of last year's Indian raid still raw on face and soul, joined her, saying nothing. The children, who had got quite out of hand lately, were now still and obedient, sheltering themselves beside the nearest grown-up, as young sandpipers crouch down when danger threatens. On the frontier the first sign of danger meant retreat into silence. Women bore their children with lips clamped tight; old people died without a moan; even babies repressed a whimper under the hand held hard over the mouth. This dead silence in which they met danger and mortal fear was the reason why, when they were secure, in social or religious gatherings, the frontier people let go in such an orgy of noise—whooping, yelling, weeping, and crying out.

So silence came down on the Cartwright cabins, and when two families of movers stopped for the night, the men quietly took their guns and stood guard, and the women fed their children in stony stillness. The morning came and the white, hot, silent, empty noon. Then they saw Jus and Peter and their father riding up the trail, slumped in their saddles, one horse lamed, the other two obviously dragged out. They all stood waiting, eyes one desperate question, saying nothing. Jus looked down into their faces, and brushed the back of his hand over his forehead, where the sweat was making rivulets through dust and grime, and said, in a dead tone, "Si's family was murdered—every one, Si, Jenny, the boys, little Sue—all lying dead."

"Shot?" asked Mary.

"All except young Jo. His head was cleaved through with an axe."

The word was not uttered. But in amazement and perplexity Mary asked herself "Indians?" It was years since the Indians had been on the warpath east of the Blue Ridge. There'd been peace with the Indians so long that there was not even a blockhouse near enough to flee to.

Dropping from their saddles to the ground, where they slumped in utter weariness, the men reported briefly. "Si's family wasn't the only one. There were three others—all wiped out. A surprise attack in such force as to kill all instantly. Not one left to tell the tale."

"But every thing left as it was," added Peter. "Fires burning, mush cooking. They just took horses and guns."

"That ain't Indian fighting," said Mary.

"No," observed John Cartwright, grimly. "It's a white man's, one that just wants horses and guns."

"That counterfeiter's behind it—Sandy says. The one the peddler told us about—Philip Alston. He's workin' from somewhere west." Answering the horror in Mary's eyes, his easy voice tense and tight, Jus added, "Once you get into the great open spaces west, beyond the law, there's two things you must have—a gun and a horse. So there's a mighty profit in putting the Indians up to bringing in guns and horses to trade with the settlers out yonder for furs."

"Whoever's in the way of their business, they kill, so they can tell no tales," added John.

Jus rose heavily to his feet, and looked at Mary. "Honey, you've been asking what was keeping us off the trail west. Now you see it. It's been going on right along west of the mountains, but nobody expected they'd push their murder so far east." He looked around. "We're in no state here to stand siege."

"Siege!" Mary's lips did not shape the words, but the brain wave bearing the question reached him. He looked at her and said briefly. "I got a queer message from Cherokee Bill. I don't know where he is. He got word through to the courthouse to say be on guard tonight. I couldn't make it out till I saw what had been done to Si—and the others. We'll have to get the children away to the woods, with Martha and Annie and Molly."

Again his eye sought Mary's. Mary was thinking, "The baby's about due. O Heavenly Father, keep him waiting!" Aloud she said, "If Martha and Annie and Molly can take the children, I'll hide myself by the river." She did not say, "It wouldn't be fitting for the children to be close by if my pains start." But that was understood. Jus did not object nor acquiesce. This was beyond one who never was a father. Molly said, "Martha and Annie are enough to tend the children. I'll stay and shoot with the men. I've got a score to pay." She raised her cold blue, red-rimmed eyes to Jus and added, "You ain't told me what we're to stand up against tonight, but you don't need to. It's the same kind of crittur that last year killed all I had in this world!"

Conflict on the frontier being a battle of disguises, they prepared to meet the enemy that night without seeming to change any of their usual routines, Annie took John and Eddie to round up the cows. It wasn't noticeable to any who might be spying that when the cows came home the children were no longer visible. Martha took Sally and Polly to paddle in the little rill that ran off from the spring, and then melted away into the woods. Items for Mary's comfort were assembled in the hidden hollow by the river, one by one, inconspicuously, after a search of the surrounding bush to make sure no eyes were watching—a bearskin for protection from the damp ground, a bucket of drinking water from the spring. The movers who had stopped overnight were encouraged to move on, but a detachment of the militia arrived looking like movers, two disguised as women in sunbonnets and calico gowns. Grim humor pervaded the preparations.

3

At dusk they were ready, in sweet pastoral quiet, the cow nibbling outside Justurian's cabin, doors to cabins open to the sweet night air, smoke going up the chimney, hominy cooking on the hearth. But people, horses, guns, and knives had all melted away—all except Jus and Mary who sat for a while in their own dooryard in the dusk, Jus pulling on his pipe, and then started together for a little stroll around the place. As they began to descend the narrow wooded path to the river bank, under the dark roof of the oaks, Mary could feel Justurian's arm tightening around her like a blockhouse wall, and she settled a little within that strength, fighting down a desperate wish that it could stay by her. "If it wasn't for the baby coming, I'd be by his side, come what might," she thought. To ease Justurian's mind, she had let him believe that the baby was not due yet. She had thought she still had a fortnight to go. She was saying nothing about irregular twitches of pain—most likely she'd just got tired tramping around on her feet, getting the children ready.

Because of the passing pains, and the ache in her thighs and feet, she sank down gratefully on the bearskin, in the dark. Jus whispered worriedly, "We should have got Molly to be here with you. I'll tell her you need her now. She'll come."

"You'll need every hand to help where you are," she whispered back. "Two of us might make a noise and show that somebody is hid here. Alone I can be still as a stone."

All the while she was clinging to him, fending off, for one more second, the time when his great, warm, reassuring body would be gone. He gently detached her clinging fingers and passed his great rough hand over her hair. "Well, if ever there was a time for prayin', this is it. Cuddle down, Honey, and talk pretty to the

Lord, and I'll be seeing you."

She tried to pray, but for a long time it was hopeless, for her thoughts were nervous, broken, spasmodic, like the twitches in her aching feet and legs, and like those occasional sensations within her that were not so much pains as biological worries. But looking up to the stars, she kept saying, "Our Father Who art in Heaven," as an incantation tò ward off evil. And slowly peace came, not as religious exaltation, but as dreamy awareness that the waters licked the reeds with a faint, swishing sound; that a cricket chirped; that the reeds rose tall around her sheltering her completely. And so she slept.

Some time after midnight, on September 1, 1785, she was awakened by a wild whoop and the crackle of shots. Her heart rose in her mouth and turned over, and her pains began. They began so uncertainly that, quieting herself, and looking deep into the night sky, as if she were looking pleadingly into God's eyes, she tried to believe that her time had not yet come.

But she could not believe it long, as steadily, regularly the pains accelerated. She now had but one thought. The baby must be born safely. She nerved herself to labor firmly, efficiently, and with moral calm, clamping her lips lest she should cry out. Doggedly she climbed a sharp hill to the knife-edge of agony, and shudderingly relaxed, and climbed doggedly again. And always she kept looking into that soft, kind sky slowly silvering into dawn, and she knew the face of God was there. He—God—would help. Was God only a *he?* Could he not also be a kind of mother? A woman can do a lot of thinking between birth pangs. Her mind was racing madly. Always when she was a little girl she had wanted a mother more than a father. She remembered Sister Belle, and her kind eyes when Polly was born. Now the sky had the same kind look. A faint, shuddering sob escaped her as she rose swiftly, relentlessly to the point of the unbearable. "M—m—mother God!"

The sky was gold and rosy with dawn. The waters ran twinkling under a low bank of mist. There were no more shots or shouts. The pain took her and shook her in an earthquake of torment. She wanted as she had never wanted anything in her life, to open her mouth and let the scream pour out. She locked her lips. She had just mind enough to pray, "God, take me—take me if you want, but save the baby alive," when the sun came up over the horizon. Then the whole universe heaved and broke asunder in blood, and she knew that the baby was born.

Instantly she came to, steady and resourceful. She must cut the cord. She felt for her cartridge belt, close beside her in the reeds, got her knife, cut the baby loose, and tied the cord. Then she seized the child by its slippery red feet, and held it upside down, and slapped its fat little back. It burst into a faint, kitten-like squall, almost indistinguishable from the small noises of wild creatures all around her. Now she must wash it. Could she reach the water, sliding along through the reeds? She could and did, all the while cold with terror lest this squirming little thing should slip out of her hands into the water and be drowned. But as the baby choked and spluttered and flopped about, she thought with delight, "It's beautiful. It's big and strong like it's father's son would have to be. What a fuss! What a fuss! What a little man!"

She sank back into the reeds, and thrust it under her linen smock against her breast, and lifted her eyes to the sky in unutterable gratitude. All the wide heaven was smiling down on her. She thought, "God gave him to me when I was being so mean. It's the least I can do to give him to God." She felt with rapture the little live thing nuzzling at her breast. "He's strong. He'll be a strong man. I want him to be strong and steady like a rock—a man always for God and the right. Strong like a rock." Then a Bible verse cross-ed her mind about Peter. "Peter—it means rock. On this rock I will build my church." She pulled the baby to her and buried her face in the sweet-smelling fat little body. "Honey, honey chile," she crooned, with a silent crooning, "Your name's Peter." She closed her eyes and floated blissfully away with her baby out of all space and time

4

She came to, bewildered, swinging twixt heaven and earth, the reeds scratching her face. She was being lifted on to an improvised litter made of branches of trees and a blanket. The baby! Did she dream there was a baby? The question was taking shape in her misty mind, when there was Jus, with the little naked thing in his big hands, putting it to her breast, and on his face—grimy, hollow-eyed, dark with two days' growth of beard — incredulous joy struggled with sheepish embarrassment. Her eyes glowed into his out of a face suddenly young and sweet, like that of a happy little girl. "His name's Peter," she said.

Then she saw Peter, his drawn young face lighting with amazement. "You're naming it for me?" She didn't have the heart to say, "No," for Jus, surprised at the choice of a name, but pleased, said, "I reckon he's earned it for the way he stood up to Hell's fire tonight."

They were carrying her back along the path under the oaks to the house. Her mind looked back over the tremendous experience of the night. "I heard shooting."

"Shooting! I should say there was shooting," answered Jus.

"Everything safe?"

"We drove them off."

"All except those that lie dead," said Peter.

"Dead?" She had already breathed the question when Jus said decisively, "Honey, your own bed's safe and waiting. It's for you to rest now. Talk will keep." He swung the litter around sharply. "The other path, Peter."

Mary, craning her neck above the blanket which rose on both sides like a hammock, saw that there was a crowd on foot and on horseback in the field to the right of Pappy Cartwright's cabin. "Any of ours killed, Jus?"

"Now, Honey," he said, uncertainly, "Don't you worry your little head."

She looked up affectionately, for it is good to feel that one's man wishes to save one from the evils of this world, even if he can't. "Come, Jus. It's no use keeping anything from me. I've seen worse."

"They're trying to identify the bodies of those we killed," replied Jus. "And that's all there is to it."

She refused to be silenced. "Were they Indians?"

"None dressed as Indians or had any Indian marks."

"Three of them are Indians, plain enough," observed Peter.

They swung around the big chestnut tree toward Mary's own cabin. In its shade lay a long, thin figure in a calico dress, a shawl over the face, and by it a man was kneeling. "Hiram!" Mary started to say, but the word was cut short by the stricken, sere, twisted face he turned on her. Then he dropped his head with a kind of muffled bellowing. "It's Molly," she thought. "She was all he had." Her compassion was almost unbearable.

Jus commented briefly, "It was Molly's chance, and she took it. She was set to get them."

"She brought down two before she fell," said Peter, his pleasant and weak young face grim with relish in that killing.

Battle triumph flared through Justurian's studied reticence. "And then we finished them. Seven fell dead. The rest turned and ran. The militia's out beating up the country for them."

"Was—was anybody else hurt?" asked Mary.

"Dean got hurt in the leg, running out to save Molly. Other than that the children and we all are safe without a scratch."

"But they weren't all Indians?"

"The two Molly killed were white men. There's two we can't tell —might be half-breeds or just dark white men, or those Portyghees that work for Alston."

The baby cried. Mary, settling back and cuddling it, relaxed into weariness and then oblivion.

5

She woke in the shuttered cabin, and saw through the open door the chestnut tree dark against the late sun. The baby, clothed and diapered, was asleep in a crib beside the bed. She lay listening to hammering and sawing, and the far off hubbub of horses and voices. Martha appeared in the door with mush and milk, which Mary ate gratefully. As Martha went around the room, tidying it, moving as if to the rhythm of the hammering, her slack, fresh-colored face was set in hard lines.

Mary smiled down into the crib, and said, "Thank you for dressing the baby."

"It's a bonny babe, but what's the use?" said Martha. "We nearly die having them, and then we die protecting them." She yanked the bedspread off and replaced it with tense hands. "When I married John Cartwright and came here, I was like you. I wanted to pull things up. It's no use. Everything pulls you down!" She stopped and looked at Mary fiercely, "What do you want to go west for? There'll only be more of this, and worse."

The hammering seemed to keep time with her words, which were not so much spoken as delivered, blow by blow. Martha saw the question in Mary's eyes. Suddenly all her heart was in her face. She choked, "It's Hiram. He's making Molly a coffin!"

Jus was at the door. Both women's faces relaxed, as Martha lifted the baby to its father's arms. "Looks like an Injun," observed Martha, in the pride of her own sandy coloring.

Mary said indignantly. "He looks like a Cartwright. He's the spittin' image of his Pappy."

"Well, the Cartwrights all look like Indians," said Martha, which was true.

But Jus asked what was the matter with being an Injun. There were good Injuns and bad white men. There wasn't a better man with a whiter soul than Cherokee Bill. If he hadn't got a warning to them, they'd all be dead. Peter, arriving to pay obeisance to the baby, agreed with him. He said the baby was Big Chief Squawk Ha, a name the baby promptly justified by a loud squawk.

Darkness fell as they talked. Martha went off to tend John, Eddie, and Polly, whom she was keeping for the night. Mary slept, but waking, from time to time, looked for Jus on the bearskin on the floor beside the bed where he said he'd sleep till she was better, and did not find him. Then she woke again and knew that he was there, sleeping the sleep of utter exhaustion. She lay awake, listening to his breathing, in the quiet happiness of a woman with her husband and her newborn baby safe at her side.

Then there was a shot. He was on his feet and at the door, gun in hand, almost before the sound died away. He turned back and placed her knife and pistol and cartridge belt by her side. "Don't stir," he said. "It can't be the gang coming back. There's been only one shot." Then he was gone. Mary lay there straining her ears for movements outside. She could hear people running. This was no stir of battle. She began to sense tragedy in the tones of voices coming to her. Before she could make anything out of it, Justurian's tall form was in the doorway, a droop and sag in every line of it.

"Poor Hiram!" he said. "Couldn't take any more. He shot himself by Molly's coffin."

6

Next morning the Circuit Rider came to the cabin, loud in an argument with Jus about holding a burial service before consigning the dead horse-thieves to their collective grave. "Shovel them in and to Hell with them," Jus was saying. "Hell's too good for those who'd murder human creatures for gain."

The Circuit Rider agreed. "But still they're God's business from now on. The service is just to turn them over to God, fair and lawful."

Here Mary presented her baby to the preacher. His troubled face lighted up. "After the buryin', we'll have a baptism," he said.

And so it was. The service was held over the dead horse-thieves with only Jus standing by, polite but unsympathetic, while all around the militia gambled and drank whisky under the trees, thus celebrating their triumph over evil in what they took to be a more fitting manner. But they all listened, with tears rolling down many cheeks, at the second service for Hiram and Molly, lying side by side in two coffins which the women had piled high with flowers.

Meanwhile Mary waited in the cabin, sitting up in a bed made up with her best linen and covered with a blue spread of her own weaving, and wearing her best bedgown with a becoming frill around her neck. The baby wore a long white dress and a ruffled bonnet. "Honey! Honey!" she said to him. "This day you set your feet on the way to being one of God's saints!" For answer the baby looked at her with what she could have sworn was a wicked, humorous glint in the black eyes, and a curl of derision in the soft, toothless little mouth. Hugging him to her, she protested, "Don't you look like that at your Mammy. You've got no say in it. All the sin you were born with is going to be washed away."

The Circuit Rider came in with some of his Methodist class, including Dean on crutches, glowing with delight in the baby. The preacher had invited two or three others at the burial services whom he knew to be Christians. But, being Baptists, they indignantly refused to have anything to do with such heathenism as infant baptism. Neither Jus nor Mary had ever attended a baptism. But Jus stood gravely tolerant, with his son in his his arms beside Mary's bed, and Mary's heart was full to bursting with an exaltation which turned to embarrassment when the preacher stopped in the middle of the service, and said that ruffled bonnet must come off the baby's head. What a heathen she looked not to have known that!

But her spirit soared again as the spring water touched the baby's head and was accepted by him without a squawk. All her frustrated aspirations went into the fervor with which she promised to bring her child up in the service of the Lord. Jus, taking the same vows, translated them into intentions that, so far as he himself could see to it, Peter should grow into an upright man and a respected citizen, equipped to hold his own not only against wrongdoers, but against fools.

7

Mary was up and around. Dean, still limping, was digging her a root cellar to store turnips and potatoes for the winter. A big swarthy man galloped up and said, with a warm, wide smile, "I'm Cherokee Bill, Ma'am, looking for Jus Cartwright." Her soul in her eyes, she said, "Cherokee Bill! You're the one that saved our lives." He answered with a look so frank and kind that after he clattered off to find Jus, she ran into the cabin to see what she could make a feast of for a visitor so very special.

That was an enchanted evening. They sat long around an outdoor fire in the autumn night, roasting the deer Cherokee had shot for them, while he kept Jackie, and Eddie and Polly hanging on his every word about his own wonderful boyhood in a Cherokee village. Mary was as absorbed as the children.

Out of the glow and smoke of the fire there seemed to form by magic the shape of that little Cherokee town somewhere west of the mountains and south of Boone's trail. It was not a wigwam village, or composed of log houses like the county seat. It was built solid, around a square, of stone and dried mud and planed wood, all brightly decorated with Indian pictures and signs. Cherokee didn't live in the village, though he told about trading there and Indian dances there. He lived in a large house which his father, an educated Scotch trader, had built for his Indian bride—a happy-go-lucky communal existence amidst a tribe of Indian relatives; blooded horses, hunting dogs, and tame wolves, all sustained by the fur trade.

Mary had never seen anybody so content with being what he was. A child of the wilderness herself, she had nevertheless been inoculated with the pride of being white. It was strange that one of Indian blood should be so satisfied that he was the top of the human tree. But this inner poise gave Cherokee a natural and fearless good nature which was as pleasant as the fire. It was only after the children had been sent to bed that she saw the other side of him in the cynical realism with which he took hold of the problems of going west. He said flatly that it would be suicide to set off under two years, and then they'd need an armed guard which he wanted to pick—veterans of Indian blood like himself.

"There's two different situations to guard against," he said. "One is straight Indian warfare. The Cherokees won't fight us. They ceded the land of Kentucky and they got paid for it, and they'll deal fair so long as they're treated fair. But the Creeks to the south and Wyandottes to the north are set to fight us to the death, and the white fur traders will see that they do it. We're a threat to a way of life that's been building for a hundred years—the Indians roaming and hunting at will, but able to bring their fur to the fur forts and get for them liquor, guns, horses, knives, and all the white luxuries they can use." But he and other veterans of Indian blood would go along with the whites and take up land and make farms and homesteads. And he didn't think the Indians had any real call to battle the white men for such lands as the white men could use, for there was enough wilderness westward and in parts no good for the plow to serve the fur trade for fifty years. "So I tell my father let them move on and leave room for us for farms and homes."

The other situation to be guarded against was what they'd already had a taste of. "You've put it down here," he said, "and I think for good, because you have a county government with a strong state behind you, and what force the Continental Congress can muster not too far away. But you can't meet it without the means of government, and in Kentucky that's still a long way off."

"You mean organized murder for guns and horses," said Jus.

"Yes." Tentatively Jus said, "I've heard there's a man named Alston behind it."

The cynicism under Cherokee's good nature hardened his face as he spat into the fire, and said, "I know Alston. He's been put up at my father's place more than once."

He knew Alston! The name had been so wrapped in mystery and conjecture that Mary sat up tense—finding it strange that Alston should be to Cherokee just another man that he knew in the flesh. "What's he like?" asked Jus.

"A grand gentleman—fine clothes, fine manners, book-learning, a Mason."

Mary was not content till she could see him with her mind's eye. "What does he look like?" she asked.

"Handsome in a peculiar way—tall, well made, black hair soft and silky as your own baby's, big blue eyes, skin on face and hands soft and white as a woman's." He paused, and looked at Jus, questioningly. "What do you know about Alston?"

"Only that he was run out of Raleigh as a counterfeiter?"

"Do you know where he went?"

"Well, they say he's running these horse-thieves from somewhere west."

"He went to New Orleans," observed Cherokee, "and cut quite a figure among the plantation gentry. Changed from being a Presbyterian to being a Catholic, put his girls in convent schools along with girls of other fine families." He stopped, and then added, with ironic emphasis, "But one day he stole a gold image of Christ out of the cathedral, and coined it into Spanish coins." He looked around, enjoying the expression on their faces, and answered their question before they could ask it. "He escaped up the Chickasaw Road, and now he's settled on our property."

"What! Where we're surveying?"

"For once he set up in an honest business—started to manufacture salt, which is as needful out there as horses and guns. Then he brought out some Portyghees, and set them up on Muddy River to make money. He hooked his line of trade out from Raleigh to the line south to New Orleans along the•Chickasaw Road, and now he's got a third line hooked to Louisville." He looked at Jus. "You know Louisville?"

"It's at the falls of the Ohio. Dominie told me when George Rogers Clark left, he set up twenty families with stores to hold this point."

"Yes, Clark's lived there ever since. And now it's the landing-place for goods coming down the Ohio from the East, to be packed overland into central Kentucky. And just above it is the main center of the river pirates who get most of these goods. Alston's third line reaches from them down to our tract, where he's set up his son-in-law, James Dromgole, in an Exchange, to sell all this stolen goods. And there Alston sits now, right where we're going, like a spider in the center of a net that's spun all over the West."

"But how come Alston and his lot are settled on our tract, when it's been granted to us?"

There was a sardonic gleam in Cherokee's black eyes as he answered, "It's been granted to us, but they've got it. That's the situation we've got to work out."

CHAPTER 5

From Amherst County to Fort Chiswell, Virginia November, 1785 to September, 1790

A nursing mother being a privileged character in the "better fixed" cabin families, Mary spent several months in blissful detachment from domestic and other worries. Lying at her breast, little Peter reached and relieved a deep-seated loneliness which even Jus did not touch, and served as a bulwark against the many things she did not like. To say she couldn't put the baby down was an excuse for not doing what she did not want to do. To say that the baby asleep in her arms must not be disturbed, insured that her inner life would be undisturbed, and that she could sit quietly with her child and think. Running through her mind, her beloved Bible verses flowed singing from her own soul to the baby's on the strong rhythmic current of her milk. Sometimes when she dandled him on her knee, she made them into a lullaby like a plainsong. "He leadeth me," she would chant softly, "leadeth me beside the still, the beautiful still waters." At other times she would sit, silent and un-thinking, with her child at her bosom, at rest in the elemental a-bundance of her womanhood, and deeply at peace with God.

With this never-failing fountain at his command day and night, Peter grew lustier every day—a big-boned baby, with rather small but very bright black eyes, skin the color of weak coffee, and hair like a smudge of soot on his round head. As he guzzled, Justurian would stand over him and make faces at him, now and then putting his big hand down to take away the breast and make him yell for it. Thereupon Mary would slap her husband, and, with an affec-tionate guffaw, he would make for the door. Choking on a gush of milk with the tears still wet on his cheeks, Peter would follow his father with his eyes, as if he would like to go with him and still have a river of milk running down his throat. Thus from the first the impulse to nourishment and security played havoc with adven-ture. It was as if the cool waters in which his mother had first laved him were identified with peace at her breast, and the sound of a gun which had started him into the world—the first sound whose impact he had felt, even before his own cry—were identified with his father, and the glory and adventure of being a man. Obscurely aware that there was something in the boy which responded not only to the mother's milk but to her croonings about God, Jus was determined not to let him be a Mammy's boy. He resorted to every trick and device to wean the child in spirit, if not in body, from the mother and make him a man after his own fashion.

Year by year, Peter's birthday brought them nearer to Kentucky. For on it the veterans assembled at the Cartwrights' to review their progress and plan their next steps. The date they chose was at the height of the migration season. The more movers there were, the more they learned about their own prospects. They chose the Cart-wright place because it was on the main trail west, and handy for getting political news from Richmond, and news of the road from Fort Chiswell.

Among the veterans who came on Peter's first birthday, Septem-ber 1, 1786, was Mac—a huge red-haired, red-bearded, red-faced fellow on a big red horse, who looked like fire and fury in action, but actually was good natured and rather stupid. Of the four organizers of the expedition besides Jus—Mac, Dutch, Cherokee, and Dominie—Mary had met all but Dominie. Dominie had gone west again with George Rogers Clark to fight the Indians north of the Ohio, whose attacks were endangering all Kentucky.

Peter had just abandoned the loping belly flop, with which he was wont to get around, for a reckless run. As the big men dashed up, whooping, his sturdy little personality was electric with excitement and he chattered at the friendly bearded faces in a language nobody could understand. His uncle Peter rescued him from the hooves of Mac's big horse, and set him in the fork of a tree for safe-keeping. Holding him there firmly, he remarked that the child was an Injun, and talked Chickasaw. When they finally settled down to business, Peter was curled up in their midst like a fat bear cub, sleeping off the effects of a few drops of whisky which some one had given him in a gourd half full of water.

The main business of the meeting was the commercial treaty with Spain for the opening of New Orleans as a port for their goods which John Jay had proposed to Congress on August 3 of that year. A politician from Richmond explained it carefully. "Now you just sit on the tails of your delegates to Congress and see that this gets through," he counseled. The veterans were fast learning the art of lobbying. Following this, Jus read aloud a list of military surveys already made. "Wm. Green—Moate's Lick. Gabriel Long's and Thomas Slaughter's—Laurel and McAdoo Creeks west of Muddy. Stribling's between Wolf Lick and Muddy River." The names rolled off like music, and, as each was read, they yelled and whooped. But Jus threw cold water on them. "A survey don't guarantee they'll get this particular land. That will be for the land office to decide, and Virginia hasn't opened its office yet. All we've got is warrants when and if—" At this they all groaned.

Breaking up the meeting they took out their belligerency against Indians, Spaniards, and the still unopened land office, on little Peter. Jus plucked him out of a sound sleep and hurled him through the air to Uncle Peter, who caught him expertly by the heels, twirled him around his head, and threw him back. Then Mac stood him on his head and Dutch paddled him. When he was finally set upright on his stout little legs, he was as uproariously happy as the rest of them. When Uncle Peter tuned up his fiddle and caroled one of his bawdy songs, little Peter followed accurately an octave higher, in a weird, shrill, soprano chant. "See," said Uncle Peter to Mary, who had inserted herself into the uproar, like a bolt of lightning. "He has an ear for music."

"I hope not for that kind of music."

"What's the matter with it? It's a good tune."

"The tune the old cow died on."

She seized the child and began to drag him out. He kicked and bucked like a baby steer. "There's always a time when I have to put my foot down," she said, grimly. "I could tell by the sound of things you were all liquored up." She leaned over the struggling child to get a firmer hold on him, and grew cold with horror. For on his breath she plainly smelled whisky. "So help me God, it's the last time any man makes his sweet mouth a stink-pot. And if he's to sing," she added, with a final dark shaft from her eyes at Uncle Peter, "he's going to learn hymns!"

2

The next year saw so much progress that Uncle Peter and Chris stopped their fooling and got married, so that they might be ready to go west on a moment's notice.

The surveyors' office for the allotment of lands had been opened on August 1. By the time the veterans met on September 1, 1,000,-000 acres had already been allotted, leaving about a million and a half still outstanding in continental warrants. Jus read aloud the announcement that Colonel Richard C. Anderson was principal surveyor for the Virginia bounty lands, George Muter and Humphrey Marshall were superintendents for the state line, and William Croghan for the continental line. Now at last the veterans knew whom they were to deal with and had means for locating their lands.

But it was one thing to find their land. It was another to have security when they got it. So, the veterans listened keenly to a report on the two major political events of 1787 which, for the first time, offered them real hope of political protection in the West. One was the dying act of the Continental Congress in drawing up its greatest document, the Northwest Ordinance, working out on grand and simple lines the procedure for settling the West and organizing it into states and territories. Though the Ordinance dealt only with land north of the Ohio, it was important to the Kentucky settlers for two reasons. It guaranteed the use of Federal troops to stop the attacks by Ohio Indians on the Kentucky settlers, and it held forth hope that the British would be forced at last to give up their outposts on the southern side of the Great Lakes, in accordance with the provisions of the treaty of 1783 which they had thus far failed to carry out. The Kentuckians reported that these outposts were centers for arming and officering Indians for attacks on American settlers, in the hope of making the whole Mississippi Valley untenable, and so restoring it to British fur traders as their exclusive reserve.

The other event of 1787 which cheered the veterans was the calling of the Constitutional Convention on May 14, at Philadelphia, for if they were to go west in safety they would require a stronger Federal government behind them than the Articles of Confederation had provided.

Peter did not have much chance for manly education after the pattern of his father and his friends on the meeting of September 1, 1787, because they were too much in earnest to pay attention to him. They drank little and broke up quietly, conversing in low, serious tones as they mounted their horses. When Mary came out to see what had happened to Peter, several of them asked her solemnly to pray for them and so bring a blessing on all they had to do. As for Peter, she found him sound asleep, his breath untainted, in a mossy hollow between two big tree roots, overcome by the boredom of being unnoticed.

Peter's second birthday, September 1, 1787, was less a landmark for the veterans than for Mary. She had set this as a date when she would be finished with weaning, and finished she was. In a frontier family, weaning, usually at the age of two, was a major operation, with much yelling and cramming of mush and milk through stubborn, locked lips, and, for the mother, caked and aching breasts, a frayed temper, and a deep sense of desolation.

However Mary accomplished the weaning in record time, pitting her will relentlessly against the will of her strong stubborn child.

Then, according to primitive custom, she turned him over to his older brothers and sisters. Henceforth John, Eddie, and Polly brought Peter up. John, at the age of ten, slender, erect, with his mother's chiseled features, had heard so often that he looked like a gentleman's son, that he thought he should act like one. Hence all menial tasks that fell to his share he turned over to Eddie. Stocky of body and formless of feature, Eddie looked like a plebian, and, being responsible, unselfish, honest, and strong, was naturally to be put by the gentleman of the family into the way of being his hewer of wood, drawer of water, and carrier out of the family slops. As for Peter, John cuffed him when he answered back, and swore at him. But when Peter swore back, he rubbed wood ashes into his mouth to punish him. Day by day he taught the gentleman's law of property which was that whatever Peter had belonged of right to John, but nothing John had belonged to Peter. Henceforth the fundamental fact in Peter's universe was social injustice as represented by John.

So far as he could, without direct conflict with his overbearing elder brother, Eddie took Peter's part. And what Eddie didn't do, Polly did, more or less. Though, when Peter didn't mind her, she spanked him, he never had the slightest impulse to hit her in turn. But sometimes under the rain of her soft pats on his soft posterior he would yell, just for the drama of it. If he yelled long enough, Polly would ultimately kiss him and give him some maple syrup. She fed him mush and milk devotedly, and let him eat green apples and blackberries when her mother wasn't looking. She dressed him with repeated and exasperated attempts to make him dress himself, and glowed with pride when people admired the vivid and saucy child.

3

At their meeting on Peter's third birthday, September 1, 1788, the Virginia veterans listened with a troubled sense of inferiority to Dominie's report from Fort Harmar in Ohio of the settlement there by the Yankee veterans. Early in the spring of 1788 six boat builders, a blacksmith, and four workmen had gone to the site of the proposed settlement, each with an axe and a hoe, a good small arm, a bayonet, six flints, a powder horn, a pouch, a priming wire and brush, half a pound of powder, a pound of balls, and one of buck-shot. The men laid out the lots, started to build houses, and planted 100 acres of corn. Meanwhile 22 boat builders were busy at the point where the trail across Pennsylvania reached the Ohio, con-structing vessels on which to move the settlers and their livestock. So, when the settlers had packed themselves to the Ohio, they found the new boats waiting to take them down the river to farms and homes already started. By July 4 the clergyman had set up a church and a school; their stockade was the strongest in the West, and they sat down to a lavish public dinner to celebrate. After hearing what Yankee capital, mechanical skill, and long established technics of communal cooperation had done at Marietta, the Virginia veterans sat for a while in gloomy silence. Then Mac shuffled his big feet and said heavily, "They're not like us. When they git goin', they git."

But along with the activities of men trying to get off to Kentucky, the life of the women and children cut its own channel. Peter now had a new baby sister whom they called "Sis." To help Mary feed and tend the men, Mac brought his big, flaxen haired wife, Emmie, with her latest child, Sylvia, a little blonde darling who nursed blissfully and sat placidly. Occasionally' she would essay a brief journey on her soft little legs, and then sit down to reflect on her achievement in silent delight. Some times she spoke a few words—"Pappy," "Mammy," "give," "mush"—in a chirping, mechanical little voice, like a talking doll. To Peter her advent was a real event. He had almost burst with delight when his baby sister was born, but had been frustrated in his relation to her because she was so tiny, squawlly, and tied to his mother. But Sylvia was all he could dream of. He lugged her around. He gave her pieces of apple on which to try out her sharp little teeth. He watched with never failing interest when her mother bared her great creamy breasts and thrust the pink nipple between Sylvia's pearly teeth, and he superintended her toilet with assiduity.

Mary found no less satisfaction in Emmie than Peter found in Sylvia. Emmie had a large, deep-bosomed, deep-bodied figure, a homely round freckled face with deep dimples in her cheeks, steady blue eyes, a broad, good natured looking mouth full of large, strong, white teeth, and big strong freckled arms with dimples in the elbows. On another woman her hair might have been beautiful, the thick, long, flaxen braids falling well below her waist. But in Emmie it was merely the crowning detail in the look of healthy female abundance.

Mary admired the way Emmie did things. When she scoured a kettle, it shone. What she cooked had flavor. Mary perceived that the reason for this was a kind of philosophy. Emmie was full of sayings like: "Use your head to save your heels," and "A few pains taken at the beginning will save a heap of pain at the end." She had a serene sense of her dignity as a woman. One night, sitting with Mary in the warm, star-pointed dusk, in the cabin doorway, nursing the babies, Emmie gently removed her breast from Sylvia's sleepy mouth, and said softly, "It's a right worthwhile thing to be a woman because a woman's got so much use and meaning in her own flesh and blood." As Mary looked across at her startled and inquiring, she went on musingly, "There's nothing in nature of so much good use as a woman's body. It pleasures a man and keeps him going steady and coming back to her o' nights. It makes new folks to fill the earth right out of itself, and then it feeds them and keeps them alive till they are able to fend for themselves. It's a proud thing"—her voice was soft and reverent— "to be able to do good and give good, just by being the kind of crittur you are."

Nursing their babies together in the darkness, the two women shared their memories. Emmie told about her grandfather who had come to Germantown, Pennsylvania, as a pastor. He had books. He could write music the way other folks write words. The people he ministered to made beautiful cloth, and silverware, and furniture. They had stoves made of china, like china teacups with pictures on them, that warmed the house day and night. Her grandmother had lovely things in a big carved chest, among them the gold chain Emmie wore around her neck.

Emmie's mother had been bewitched by a Scotch Irishman who had just landed in Philadelphia, eloping with him to the western bounds of Pennsylvania. Where Emmie grew up there was neither church nor school. Though her mother had been well educated, she couldn't teach her children to read or write because she knew only the German script. But she had told Emmie about the fine ways in her mother's home, long ago in Germany, strengthening in her the will to work her way back to civilization. "That's why from the day I heard tell of the soldiers' bounty lands in Kentucky, I kept after Mac to get his. From all I hear, Kentucky's a place where a body can build a good life—not like the mountains, all rocks and boulders, with roaring floods carrying the land off in the spring, and always a wall as high as the sky between you and other folks. I aim for our children to have book-learning, and be decent church members, and eat off a table with a white cloth on it and china dishes, and wear gold chains around their necks."

Emmie had had one unforgettable glimpse of the kind of life she wanted. As a young woman, a fine family, traveling north, through the mountains to see a great tract of land the "Squire" had bought in the wilderness, had taken Emmie on as a servant, and with them she had gone back to Charleston for one glamorous year. The year ended when Mac docked at Charleston, and persuaded her to strike west and then north, looking for land of their own, which they ultimately found in western Maryland, and which they would sell when Mac took up his Kentucky grant. Emmie had been well treated in the big white pillared house in Charleston and had exercised a degree of authority over the black slaves. She was full of details about the long midday dinners, with black servants handing around the silver dishes, and the gentlemen sitting around the mahogany table in the late afternoon after the cloth was removed, cracking nuts and eating raisins and drinking wine, and about the young ladies of the family, in silk petticoats and panniers, with laced bodices, and high heeled slippers and silk stockings, daintily descending the beautiful stairway while their gallants waited in the hall below.

Though Mary didn't like something in Emmie that bowed down and worshipped at the feet of the rich, she found in her a warmth of affection and admiration which made her the perfect friend. All that she had hoped for in Brenda she now found in Emmie.

4

At last the Virginia migration took shape on large though simple lines. On September 1, 1790 there would be 200 families, including about 1000 persons, ready to start with their cows, and with their household goods and food for man and beast on packhorses. Jus and his family, including Peter, Chris, and their baby, and Dean, would wait at their place for Mac's family coming down the Richmond trail. Starting together toward Fort Chiswell, they would pick up twenty families who would be under their charge. At Fort Chiswell they would meet the main body of settlers, coming through the Valley of Virginia by a trail that led to Philadelphia, and including a group of Baptist families led by Dutch. Turning west they would travel about 100 miles to the Watauga Blockhouse. There they would find the last contingent of families, recruited from among settlers west of the Alleghenies, and a special guard of 100 single men, all experienced Indian fighters, some of them Indians themselves, under the command of Cherokee Bill.

As the last summer days of his fifth year slipped away, Peter was wild with excitement, scrapping with small boys from other veterans' families as they passed by, helping to carry dried hog's meat, cornmeal, hominy and maple sugar to the puncheon table under the big chestnut tree where Mary, Chris, Martha, and Annie made them into compact bundles for the packhorses.

The Circuit Rider stopped on his round every four weeks, with news from the circuit riders that had been sent to their territory. One of these was killed, but from the other two—James Haw and Benjamin Ogden—he had learned that there was quite a cluster of log cabins at Nashville, which was over the Kentucky border about twenty miles south of their Military Tract. So far as he could judge there were enough folks out there, scattered around a few miles apart in the tall grass, to get together for horse races on the Sabbath when they should be praying. God-fearing folks were as scarce there as hens' teeth, but such as there were were all Presbyterians. On one of his stops he showed Jus an excerpt from Asbury's report of a journey to Kentucky in April of that year. "How glad I would be of a clean plank to lie on as preferable to most of the beds. And where the beds are in a bad state the floors are worse. The gnats are troublesome. The people . . . are of the boldest cast of adventurers . . . The great landowners who are industrious will soon show the effects of the aristocracy of wealth by lording it over their poor neighbors, and securing to themselves all the offices of profit or of honor."

"There speaks the Englishman," observed Jus. "It's what happened when a new place in Europe was settled. We're seeing to it that it won't happen here."

Peter observed that for a while after the Circuit Rider left, his father would walk around in thoughtful silence. But before the day was out he'd be whooping again, and rolling Peter over in the dirt and saying, "Li'l ol Kentucky boy, you're goin' home to your own land." Then Peter would lift his eyes to the fine, high, clean azure line of the Blue Ridge, which shone with a steady crystalline blue all these summer days, and his thoughts would go on a far journey. "It's like it was made of sky stuff," he would think dreamily, and then "Over there's Kaintuck."

So his unconscious babyhood passed, and his conscious memory began. In old age he would be able to recall every detail of that westward journey but nothing before it. And through all his mighty and legendary career in the West he would be putting into practice upon thousands and tens of thousands of men the lessons he would learn on that journey beyond the Blue Ridge home to his own country, Kentucky.

5

Early on the morning of his fifth birthday Peter was feeling tall, strong, and manly. Fingering the edge of his tomahawk with a grim expression playing around his full childish lips, he saw John cantering toward him. John at thirteen was a tall, erect boy, with a fine, slim figure. Turning toward Peter a face in which one eye was swollen and black, and the lip twisted and torn, he asked amiably, "Want a ride?"

"No," said Peter shortly, turning his back.

It was the black eye which made Peter feel so big this morning. Last night he had celebrated the passing of his babyhood by giving that eye to his brother. The chain of events leading thereto began when Cherokee Bill, galloping through at top speed to take command of their guard at the Blockhouse, stopped long enough to give Peter a birthday present. It was an Indian, beautifully moulded of maple sugar, even to the feathers of the ceremonial headdress. While Peter was admiring it, alone and happy, John swooped down on him, snatched it away, and bit off its head. Peter knew better than to yell. He had already learned that such matters boys settled strictly among themselves. But for the next three hours he brooded darkly. "How can a small person get justice against a big one?"

At two o'clock that afternoon the question was unexpectedly answered. For when some veterans' families came by, very noisy and snarling among themselves, Peter heard his father say firmly but mildly, "All right. You fight it out right here. We ain't going to be plagued with your rows later on. It's got to be settled now."

Thereupon men, women, and children formed a circle, growling and looking very mad. In the circle, Jake, a big, stout, hairy man, and Jo, a little thin man, stood up. "Do you aim to fight fair or *rough and tumble?*" asked Jus.

"*Rough and tumble!*" shouted the crowd. "They must fight *rough and tumble.*"

At the words *rough and tumble* Peter felt himself seized by his mother's small, strong hand and dragged away. He yelled in protest. His father turned, snatched him from his mother, and started walking back with him to the circle where the fight was. "But," protested Mary, running after them, and speaking in a sharp whisper, "I don't want him to see *rough and tumble.* It's no bettern heathen savages."

"Savage or no," said his father, "It'll be justice this time. And Peter's got to learn to see justice done the only means it can be done the way we're fixed here, or are likely to be fixed for a long time in Kaintuck."

He set Peter down, making a place for him on a rock, in the midst of the circle, and the fight began. The little man, Jo, contracted his whole form, drew up his arms to his face, stiffened his hands till they looked like claws, and pitched himself into the hairy bosom of his opponent. The shock of the attack knocked the breath out of the big man and brought him to the ground. The little fellow, digging his knees into his stomach, instantly fixed his claws in his hair and his thumbs in the man's eyes, causing the eyes to start out of their sockets. This was called *gouging*. The crowd cheered, and one yelled, "Three to one that Jo blinds him!"

The big fellow on the ground roared aloud and like a boa constrictor wound his huge arms around little Jo and rolled over and over with him on the ground. When Peter could again see the big man's face, he saw, with a feeling between relief and regret, that he still had his eyes, though they looked very much distorted. The crowd was arguing whether Jake or Jo would "give out," with the odds in favor of Jo, when Jo suddenly got his enemy under him again, and his clawed and bruised face turned upward to the sky. Then, with a deft turn of his hand, he snapped off the big man's nose, so close to his face that no projection remained. "All that's wantin' now is for him to bite off his ears," observed a satisfied voice.

But Jake decided to save his ears, and "gave out." Whereupon the whole crowd gathered cheering around the victor, and two of the men made a chair of their hands, and lifted him high and carried him off, the rest following and calling for whisky to celebrate. Jake, mutilated, slunk away.

What it was all about Peter did not know and nobody told him. But he grasped some fundamentals which illumined his personal problems with a fierce white light. Against strength, you could pit skill; against size, quickness; and, if finally put to it, you must aim unerringly for the soft, weak, exposed parts of the body.

So much whisky flowed that night that it was not hard for John and some of the other boys to make off with a bucket of it, unnoticed by their elders. Peter, stalking his brother, found him in a convivial group in a thicket on the river bank, and springing on him, like a wild cat, in exact imitation of the spring he had seen Jo make, he knocked John over—unawares and half tipsy as he was— dug his knees into his stomach and, planting his thumbs firmly under his brother's eyes, started to gouge them out. He was hauled off by the others but not before he had seized John's upper lip in his teeth, yanking at it as he was pulled away. Then he squirmed like a wet eel out of their hands and took to his heels.

Next morning John was most amiable. Taking Peter aside, he spoke to his small brother for the first time like an equal, with the best possible imitation of the manner and diction of the few "gentlemen" he had seen. "Peter, you'd best not speak about that fracas last night. I wouldn't want Father to give you a flogging for it."

"Happen he· knew you were drunk, he'd flog you," said Peter, shortly, "And that's what I'd laugh to see."

At that moment Peter's father came by, laid him over his knee, and spanked him five times for his birthday and "one to grow on," and then turned him over and kissed him on his laughing lips, and made him give five guesses what he was going to get for a birthday present, in the midst of which John was glad to slip away, postponing questions about what had happened to his face as long as possible.

6

While Peter was standing idly looking down the trail and still enjoying his reflections on John, he was scooped off the ground by huge, red, hairy, freckled hands, and lifted aloft, and there he was on the saddle in front of Mac. Mac cleared the space to the Cartwright cabins in a few flying leaps, and rent the heavens with a yell which brought Jus out whooping. Mac then plucked Peter off the saddle, and tossed him into his father's arms, and everybody was in a great noisy tangle, shouting and laughing.

The tangle resolved itself as rapidly as it had formed. Mac went off with Jus. John went off with the three red-headed Mac boys, boasting that he had got his black eye in a gouging fight in which he had left the other fellow with his eye completely out. Polly disappeared with the Mac girl, Delphine, who, like her, was seven and had two teeth missing. For a moment Mrs. Mac loomed over him, giving him five spanks and one to grow on for his birthday—grave, full bosomed, with her rope of flaxen hair. Then she was gone and his mother was gone.

Desolation fell on Peter. It was too outrageous to have everybody go off and forget him when he had a birthday and had been the center of the stage all morning! Though he could hear them all talking and yelling, and knew well enough that they were putting the packs on the horses and getting ready to go, it all seemed far off, and he felt alone and forlorn and neglected. He wouldn't run after them. He would crouch here and let them go to Kentucky without him. And when they were on their way, they would miss him and think the Indians had got him. Then they'd be so worried they'd all turn back to find him. They'd be so glad they would make a great fuss over him, and when they started to Kentucky again, they'd have him riding up in front of them and wouldn't neglect him again for anything.

The unfolding drama in his mind came to a sudden stop. A small girl with soft light hair, and soft light blue eyes and a soft round face was standing in front of him and looking at him gravely. Peter gulped and said impulsively, "Want to see me hit that ash tree with my tomahawk?"

He threw the tomahawk. It did not stick in the tree, but Peter said with assurance, "I hit it. You just run and see. You'll find the tomahawk right there at its foot. Run! See!"

The little girl ran obediently, found the tomahawk and held it up gleefully. Peter was suddenly giddy with happiness. To have someone to boss, instead of being bossed by John, Eddie, and Polly, to have some one to show off to, some one life-sized and intelligent, not like baby Sis! He reached into the deerskin pouch which swung from his shoulder and in which he was to carry needfuls for the journey, and drew out a sling shot, two stones, and the remnant of the maple sugar Indian, dirty, with hairs clinging to it. "Suck," he said benignly. She sucked. Generosity flowed through him. "You can have it all," he said, putting the sticky stuff into her sticky little hand.

In the midst of the hurly burly of getting off, it was a relief to Mary and Emmie to find their young uns playing so peaceably. They had an inspiration. Why not set Peter to minding Sylvia all the way to Kentucky? "Nothing makes a child be good more'n' givin' him a littler one to tend," observed Emmie sagely. "I've seen times when it would well nigh make him sprout wings."

"Peter could sure do with an angel feather or two," answered Mary. "I've been lookin' every day to see him show up with cloven hoofs and a tail—he's been such an imp of Satan."

At this point Dean came up with a handsome offer. Why not separate Peter from John, Eddie, and Polly, and Sylvia from her three brothers and her sister who mauled her like a wee mouse amongst a whole mess of kittens, and let them ride one horse? "But where do we get the horse?" asked Mary. For Mac's family had only two horses to ride, "leastways till we eat the packs off the pack horses," said Emmie. At the outset, she and Mac planned to take turns on one horse, and let the five children take turns on the other, two or three of them riding at one time. The Cartwrights had three horses. One Mary would ride, with Sis swinging in a basket on one side, balanced on the other side by a basket full of a mother's needfuls. One Jus would ride. And one had been assigned to the four children. Jus knew that John would be riding most of the way, and that Peter, as the youngest, would have to walk to Kentucky. "Not my L'il Ol Kentucky Boy," said Jus to himself with a scornful look at John, and planned to take Peter up on his own saddle.

Now Dean brought out his gray mare, "Lady," old, but tough and gentle. He'd be proud to give her to Peter for a birthday present, if Sylvia could ride her, too. Dean could afford to make gifts. Of all the migrants he was "best fixed." All these years he had farmed the Cartwright acres on shares, had sold his share carefully and saved the earnings. A good business man, and an honest but shrewd trader, he often said, "The only one that can be cheated is a cheater." As he seated Sylvia on the horse with Peter, the black eyes and blue eyes were raised to him, as if to some great beneficent god.

7

A little after noonday they finally started for Fort Chiswell, Pappy Cartwright looking wistfully after them, and Martha and Annie waving their aprons until they were out of sight. Peter, riding his own horse, with the soft little body of Sylvia in front of him on the saddle, was in a glow of self-importance and happiness. The little girl had for him all the values his first puppy has for a small boy —and much more. She looked at him with trust and admiration more than could shine even in a dog's eyes. He was released from slavery to John, Eddie and Polly. He was his own man now, and had something to love and to care for. Liberty and love—even at five a man may begin to know these.

All that golden afternoon they went south and west, with the Blue Ridge appearing and disappearing on the right, and camped that night near a rushing waterfall, and slept with the dry, resinous breath of pines in their nostrils. Next day they went on, through wooded, shaggy country, up hill and down dale, the children looking out for the open spaces to whose sunny edges the blackberries clung, luscious and over ripe. Here they stopped while the cattle grazed. Starting again they overtook five other families who henceforth strung along with them in one caravan. Toward evening some of the men brought in wild turkey and fish. Peter was to remember that night, for it was the last good time they were to have.

For a while, in the early evening, he was running about, gnawing turkey bones, greasy and happy, watching a wrestling match between boys of John's age, and competing in tomahawk throwing with the small boys. But as the evening wore on, he began to feel the lonesomeness that comes to small boys with sleepiness, and looked around for his mother. He found her sitting apart with Emmie, little Sis asleep in her lap and Sylvia asleep on the ground with her head in her mother's lap. Mary reached out her hand and drew Peter down between Sylvia and herself. He cuddled in, quiet and dreamy, but he did not go to sleep. Instead he became increasingly wide awake, with a kind of secondary sight, different from the sight by which he saw by day, and keener. The stars shone down, so bright that they seemed to pierce him with a prickling sensation, stimulating and pleasant. The silhouette of the trees against them was so clear that he felt impelled to examine every twig and leaf minutely. And then he saw amidst the leaves a fat little porcupine, sitting there and looking down on them with a metallic gleam in its round eyes, like the shine of fire on a piece of polished hard coal. He kept watching the small, still body up there in the leaves. "He don't know I see him but I do," he thought. It made him feel big and important to see that porcupine when no one else saw him.

Far off he heard the subdued roar of a waterfall, and distinguished it from the soft stir of wind in the pines, as a musician might distinguish the viola from the cello in an orchestra of many pieces. Nearby he heard the dry buzzing of insects, and isolated one small sawing sound and determined to catch and examine the crittur that made it. He heard a faint, frightened chirping and thought, "Something's caught something. Sounds like a bird, but it can't be a bird because nothin' can catch a bird this time of year. Their wings is grown too strong. Only when they're baby things and don't know enough to fly." He wondered whether the something that caught whatever it was might be a skunk, and sniffed the air for the familar odor. He was a boy of the wilds and conscious of thousands of stirrings and activities in the world about him to which the preoccupations of the modern child leave him blind and deaf.

In the faint glow of the distant firelight he saw Sylvia sleeping beside him, her small, creamy brown legs thrust wide, her delicate fair hair scattered against her mother's butternut colored linsy skirt, her sweet little face warm, bloomy, relaxed in sleep. He listened to her breathing and felt with companionly comfort her leg alongside his. There was something so soft about Sylvia—like little new chicks, like pussy willows. She stirred in him a strange gentleness of feeling, and a poignant wish that nothing should ever hurt her.

Lying so, quiet, but intensely awake and aware, he was at the same time listening to his mother's efforts to bring Emmie to religion. Emmie didn't take much stock in this talk about God and Heaven. "All the life I want is right here," she said.

"But how about when you die? What happens then?"

"What happens to anything when it dies? It happens to us the same as to the flowers, and the ol' cow. It's stoppin' when you've been goin'."

"And is that enough for you?"

"Yes," said Emmie, with grave stoicism, and added, "Seems like all I can find to stretch after is things I ain't got in this life, and don't intend to stop till I get them."

"What things?"

"Things for the children mainly. I want they should have learnin' to their heads, and fine clothes to their backs, and tools to their hands, and gold chains to their necks."

Mary sighed. "The best of earth is poor to what I want. There has to be a Heaven."

Peter listened, registering their talk as if a hand were writing it on the soft clay of his mind, to harden and stay for ever. It was as if he were no longer Peter, but someone looking down on himself, everlasting, universal, inhabiting all, knowing all. "If I was to die," he thought, "I'd just be shet of myself. I'd drop myself there like my old pants and moccasins, and then I'd go away, up there, everywhere—into everything." Dreamily he felt himself go away. He slept.

CHAPTER 6

The Wilderness
September, 1790

As they began to see the two storey log towers of Fort Chiswell against the dark wall of the forest, they were joined by some twenty dashing persons on horseback. Hearing the soft, light chatter and ripples of subdued laughter behind him, Peter nearly gave himself a "crick in the neck", trying to see the "critturs" that made such unwonted sounds. But not till a stop was ordered under the great log stockade did he have a chance to scrutinize them. Then he saw women as big as real women folk with faces soft, white, and delicate as young babies—no freckles, no coarse red sunburns, no brown patches, none of the marks of female maturity as he knew it. And on this hot day when Mary, Emmie and Chris went barearmed and barefooted, these women wore kerchiefs around their necks, gloves, small tight shoes, and bonnets.

"They aim to look like a potato that sprouts in the spring in a dark place," observed Mary, sourly.

"Their complexion's beautiful," answered Emmie. "Do you see that young one there? It's like she was made of apple blossoms." Mary stared unhappily at the lovely girl's delicate skin, and long-lashed violet eyes. She had always taken pride in her own fine grained skin and was neat and dainty beyond most frontier women. Now she knew herself for what she was—a coarse mountain female.

Peter, having thoroughly examined the women, turned his attention to the men. He was fascinated by their leather boots and their neatly brushed-back hair tied up in little black silk bags behind. Even more amazing were the children, quiet little replicas of their parents. But most exciting were the horses. They seemed a different race from the shaggy, lean mountain horses, with their low, dragging heads and shambling gait. These creatures had compact, shapely bodies, polished coats, slim, long, dainty legs, and proud, high-held heads. Even when they stood still, it seemed as if they were trying to dance on their delicate hooves. With sharp distress he heard his mother say, "Wait till they strike the mountains. Those critturs' feet will dance another tune." He did not want those beautiful things to be hurt.

Then he heard his mother ask his father. "How come this Tidewater gentry's joinin' up with us? They won't be able to stomach us, or us them."

"They're veterans same as we all," replied Jus. "That one in the middle—the one that acts like a lord—he was a major. They've got some ol' gentry clothes on their backs and some right smart horses. But they're as poor as we and worse. Their plantations were burned by the redcoats, and their niggers ran away in the war—at least their young niggers. Some of them had old faithful niggers they wanted to bring along. But I told them they couldn't. We can't have old folks, black or white."

"Well," said Mary. "I pity them when we strike the wilderness. Their fine feathers will sure be draggled."

Jus strolled over to talk to the Major, who was a personable fellow, with neatly cut curling hair, frank brown eyes, a ready laugh, and a way of seeming familiar while inwardly keeping his distance. Jus returned, smiling grimly. Peter heard him tell Mac, "He remembers I was sergeant, but I clean forgot he was major. And the way I laid down the law to him a general couldn't have done better. His Tidewater folks listen to him like he was God Almighty but I made it clear he'd listen to me like I was God, because I'm going to command the company he'll be in, and it will be a matter of life and death to mind me. He means well, but there's a heap of things he'll have to learn before he hits Kaintuck."

Peter had been so absorbed in the Tidewater folks that he didn't notice how his family's caravan was being swallowed in the great, trampling, shouting mass of men, women, children, horses, and cows, crowding in from every direction on the big blockhouse. Militia men stood at the huge log gate, holding off the masses from rushing inside and shouting answers to questions. From the two storey towers at the four corners of the fort, voices were directing caravans to camp sites, warning them not to dirty the water, and reminding them that even here, in the shadow of the fort, they weren't safe from Indians. Hence each company should put the women, the children, and the stock in the center of their camp, and the men, well armed, as guards and sentries around the outside. All around the fort as far as Peter could see, the people were camping. Toward evening the sun looked like a red ball through the smoke of their camp fires.

The only one to penetrate the social wall around the Tidewater gentry was Emmie. She took the first opportunity to drop around to see how the apple blossom girl was making out, and to ask if there was anything she could do for them. Alternately protesting and saying pretty *thank yous*, the ladies let her do most of the work of settling them in camp. She returned all aglow with her social adventure, and at supper Peter heard her telling his mother about it.

Emmie said that, though they called the apple blossom girl "Miss Eugenia," she was married—a bride of a few months. That young fellow with the round pink face, and blue eyes with hollows under them, was her husband, and so lovesick it was pitiful. He stood around and waited on her and worried over her and made sheeps' eyes at her all the time. Miss Eugenia had never done a thing for herself. Her Negro Mammy had always tended her like a baby. She had wept on Mammy's bosom when she had to leave, and almost every night now, sleeping out under the open sky, she'd wake up at two or three in the morning, sobbing and calling for Mammy like a babe for its mother, till her young husband was quite beside himself trying to comfort her.

"Poor soul," interrupted Mary drily. "It must be right hard to have to take a fresh and handsome young man and what he has to give in trade for the heavenly comfort of an old nigger woman's bosom!"

But Emmie went on, speaking with a rapt look. It tore at Miss Eugenia's heart, she said, to have to cross a river. Every river they came to she felt the tears come to her eyes, and her heart to her mouth, and though she tried to be brave ("I reckon so," interpolated Peter's mother, sarcastically) she'd think, "One more river between me and my beloved home," and then she couldn't keep back the tears. Everybody was sorry for her and petted her, and the men all tried to make it easy for her. If they had to cross by swimming their horses, they'd go across in a company, and see that she was landed safe first, before anybody, and then swim their horses back for the other women and the children. If it was a shallow stream they could cross by wading, two of the men would make a chair of their arms, and set her on it, and march her through, laughing and singing.

"It would pay anybody to be homesick to get all that attention paid you," remarked Mary.

Before Emmie could answer, one of the gentle boys from the Tidewater camp looked in and said politely, "My mother presents her compliments and wants to know if the good woman who was with her this afternoon can come right over. My little sister is sick." He added, with round, frightened eyes, in a more natural tone, "She's deathly sick. She's having convulsions."

This softened Mary, for a frontier woman was used to thinking that sickness in any cabin, even in that of her worst enemy, was the same as if it were in her own. She got ready some frontier medicines—slippery elm bark, flax seed, oil of snakes, oil of racoons, and mixtures of maple syrup and wild cherry and other juices and sent Emmie off, saying to the Tidewater child kindly, "Come back and tell us how the poor babe is getting on, and if there's anything the rest of us can do."

But next day, when Peter heard Emmie telling about the baby, he saw that his mother had again soured on these Tidewater folks. Emmie said that all that ailed the child was that it had eaten green apples. She got it to vomiting by sticking her finger down its throat and soon it felt better. The mother hadn't known what to do because she had never taken care of the child. She was the elder sister of Miss Eugenia and had had the same Mammy.

"And so," observed Mary, "They're all bent on making a Mammy of you."

"What a thing to say! I'm only too glad to help them out."

"You sure are. But those kind of folks can't live without some-body takes care of them and does their work for them, and if they aint got niggers to carry them on their hands they'll never rest till they find some poor simple white folks to set in the place of nig-gers."

"I declare I never heard such talk," said Emmie, angrily. "There's nobody on earth that can make me do a thing unless I want to."

"The more fool you to want to."

Emmie was so hurt that she didn't speak to Peter's mother for hours. Peter was discomforted by the arctic temperature that sur-rounded the women in whose motherly ministrations he was wont to bask, and asked anxiously, "Are you mad at Aunt Emmie for always?"

Mary said with a trace of a smile, "I'm not mad, Peter. I just think it's for Emmie's good to come to her senses."

By noon they were friends again, but rather than risk Mary's coldness a second time, Emmie found an excuse for not going over to prepare the ailing child's lunch, as she had planned to do. But she could not resist passing the Tidewater camp at a distance and listening, with hankering to be among them, to their soft, rippling chatter. When she turned back to her own camp next the Cart-wrights, she was thinking that, though Mary was a wonderful wo-man, the price she set on being friends with her was almost too much.

2

At Fort Chiswell, Dutch and Brenda joined the caravan, with their praying, hymn singing contingent of Baptists. But while Mary often saw Brenda at a distance, and pointed her out to Emmie, she had only one brief chance to speak to her. Then she was interested to observe that, since she had seen her last, Brenda had had a pecu-liarly winsome little son named Jerry. "He must be about Peter's age," Mary said, laying her hand gently on the sun-bleached blond head, and smiling with an instinctive impulse of love and concern into the child's appealing gray eyes. "I'm glad Peter's to have him to play with."

But Peter was not to have Jerry to play with, until they should come to the end of this journey, at Crab Orchard, in central Kentucky, where the level lands began, and where they could make arrangements for going on, for another 200 miles, to their Military Tract. For keeping count of each person, in the great hurly burly at the fort, and assigning each group to its place in the line of march west, required that you stay strictly with your own group of families.

During the thirty-six hours they spent at Fort Chiswell, getting organized into one expedition, Peter had to look after Sylvia, and keep her from getting lost or hurt or frightened amidst this welter of people and beasts. At night he helped to bed her down next himself on the dividing line between the bare ground his family slept on, and that on which the Mac family slept. After she was tucked in, he squatted beside her, to watch while she went to sleep, looking at the small face, pearly in the glimmering dark, with loving eyes, until, succumbing to sleep himself, he fell in a heap beside her.

Early on the second day after they arrived at Fort Chiswell, the long line began to snake its way westward, twelve miles, to a rude stone mill, and thence, eight miles, to a collection of run down cabins called "Boyd's station," where they stopped for the night in a large trampled clearing, littered with old saddles, bones, and other trash of those who had gone before. This first twenty miles lay through country which had been spoiled by man without any real attempt to cultivate it. Here and there stringy-haired, weather-beaten people waited for them with butter, milk, and Irish potatoes for sale. This was the Watauga Settlement, made in 1771, and was the southern end of the thinly populated trans-Allegheny frontier on which Mary had had her cabin.

Next day they set out before sunrise, to cover the eighty miles to the Watauga Blockhouse in four days, by a narrow but well marked bridle path into ever wilder and shaggier country. When they climbed a high mountain, the limber old horses clinging to the mountain wall, stones and boulders loosening under them and rolling down, Peter put both arms around Sylvia and pushed her forward. "In climbin' you lean forward. That helps the ol' horse." When they went down, amidst crashing undergrowth, he drew her back, "Goin' down hill, you lean back."

He liked to have Sylvia cling to him as they went through a deep gloomy wood. It made him feel large, brave, dependable. He liked coming out on a sunlit windy height, and seeing the wide world of wood and valley shimmering below. Above all, he liked to swim Lady across a river, Sylvia clutching him, the water washing cold around his bare legs, and splattering up and wetting him all over. He shivered pleasantly when the wind blew on his damp garments, and relaxed in steamy warmth as they dried in the sun. He didn't stop liking it all even toward night when his thighs began to ache, and his back itched in a place where he couldn't get at it to scratch.

Usually the caravan tried to reach a camping place before dark. Then John and Eddie and the Mac boys would milk the cows and Peter, after seeing that Sylvia drank her milk, would gulp a gourd of it himself, warm and smelling pleasantly of grass and cows, and would fall instantly asleep.

The hardest part was getting out in the morning, cold, cramped, shivering in wet clothes, and starting before it was light. In the morning Peter felt cross and babyish and selfish even with Sylvia. But Sylvia awoke bright as a sunbeam, and seemed a year older at dawn than at sundown, and would even admonish him, in a motherly way, to fasten his clothes and drink his milk, instead of being admonished by him. But once they were on the back of "Ol' Lady," Peter's spirits rose to giddiness. The first rays of morning sun on his back and gleaming gold along the upper slopes of the mountains ahead, while the valleys below were still shrouded in fog, seemed to light a fire of joy in him. He wanted to tickle Sylvia, or to kick the old mare and make her jump, and staying on the horse and behaving himself was pure torture. When they came to a river crossing where, in waiting their turn at the ford or the log rafts, they could build a little fire and could get some hot mush or a crisp hoe-cake or a bit of burnt bacon rind to munch on, Peter would feel himself mellowing into responsible, daylight steadiness. And as the day wore on, and Sylvia got tired and sleepy, he grew inwardly in stature and grave protectiveness.

3

They came to the Blockhouse on schedule and found the trans-Allegheny caravans assembled there, quiet and solemn under the guard of Cherokee Bill and his 100 men. Without loss of time the heads of families assembled to hammer out the rules for their 200 mile dash through the Wilderness, in a meeting which began in the afternoon and lasted into the night. Once they left the Blockhouse and plunged these hundreds of living creatures into danger, there'd have to be an iron law for all till they arrived safely at Crab Orchard. Cherokee Bill, as commander of their guard, would have the last say, and each company and sub-division of a company, down to the individual family, would have to be under the absolute rule of its head, who in turn would be under the rule of the head of the next largest sub-division, and so on up to Cherokee Bill. But before such obedience could be enforced, there was much to argue and explain. "Nobody's goin' to act in the dark," said Mac. "They've got to know why."

So patiently for nine hours they discussed whether they would stop for eating, whether they might have fires at night, whether they might change places in the line, what to do with unruly members and the sick. Through hours of wrangling it was settled that there would be no stops except to cross rivers. Then there would be a natural pause which could be used for eating or the satisfaction of other needs because they'd have to be guided or ferried over in small parties. They might have no fires at night. Even a little fire could be seen for miles from the mountain tops and would guide Indians to the spot. They might not change places in the line because, as Cherokee Bill said, "Those of us who are charged with the safety of you, must know where each and every one of you is at all times." Those that raised ructions would be escorted by the guard to some spot a mile or two away from the line and left with powder and food to go backwards or forwards as they saw fit. As for the sick, they'd have to be carried on by those nearest to them, no matter what.

Peter heard all about the meeting when his father crept in beside his mother in the darkness. Separated as Mary and Jus usually were by the children and the concerns of the household and the migration, almost all the real talking they could do together was done at night in whispers under the bearskin. Peter, as was the custom for the younger children, had always slept next his parents, at home in the cabin on a trundle bed, and now here on the bare ground. Often he would wake up after his first sleep and listen, in perfect stillness, with the most intense curiosity, to what went on between his parents. This was an important part of his education.

Jus whispered that the Major had stood up and made long speeches and challenged every plan they tried to make. He said he had it on the best authority that Indians seldom attacked in numbers of more than fifty. With 300 stout men—200 heads of families, all veterans of the Revolution, and 100 special guards— he thought they were proof against Indians. He couldn't see any need for arrangements so hard on the women and children. To expect them to go day after day without fires, without regular meals, without a chance to clean up and be decent was an outrage. In the darkness Peter could hear his mother sniff. "It's amazing how when those gentlemen don't want to do something themselves, they get worried about the poor, tender women folks!"

"We voted the Major down," whispered Jus, "and he was so mad he said he was going to turn his party around and go back. We said he'd have to turn back if he didn't mind what we'd all settled on for everybody's good, his includin'."

"Did he go?" whispered Peter's mother, eagerly.

"Oh no. I guess the truth is they haven't anything to go back to. So pretty soon he changed his mind, and they're coming along, quite peaceable."

"I wish they'd turned back," murmured Mary. "They'll do us no good."

For a while after there was silence under his parents' bearskin, Peter lay awake thinking of all he had heard. He was only five, but few students in college listening to a lecture on government would be given so much real insight into what is involved in governing men, nor would lay it away so securely for future reference.

Next morning before sunup, Cherokee Bill and his men went the rounds of the camps looking everything over. "If there's anything amiss with your packs, fix them now," he said. "Feed yourselves and your cattle to last all day, fix up the babes and the littlest ones. Change into clothes you'll be ready to wear day and night till we get to Crab Orchard. Be sure your powder and shot are enough and at hand, and your guns oiled. Boys and women that can use rifles, pistols, or tomahawks, have 'em at hand and ready."

Peter had slipped around to the Tidewater camp, because he felt worried about the horses and wanted to reassure himself that the beautiful, proud, delicately built things looked fit to stand the journey. Lingering by a horse whose leg had been bound up, he heard the Major's voice lifted in light comment on Cherokee's orders. Cherokee stopped, his swarthy face looking suddenly all Indian, and said, "Major, the road we're entering on is lined right now with folks like you, lying dead. And there'll be times when the stench of them will be in your nostrils, and over your head will be flapping the wings of vultures, hoping to see you lying like them. And I tell you now, and get it straight, either you take my orders, or you turn tail with your folks this minute, and go back to where you came from."

The Major answered placatingly. But as soon as Cherokee Bill was out of sight, Peter heard him remark to Miss Eugenia's husband, "The man's an Indian himself, and I for one don't like his look. Did you see how hard and shifty his black beady eyes were when he spoke? I wouldn't put it past him to deliver us over to his tribe himself." Then Peter heard the ladies exclaiming and fluttering, and the Tidewater gentlemen reassuring them, telling them how they'd watch Cherokee Bill, and take command of the expedition themselves if this Indian showed the least sign of betraying them.

4

The sun rose darkly at their backs, as the Blockhouse disappeared behind them, and the long, silent line moved into the foggy shadows ahead. All day there seemed no brightness in the sun, though the September sky was cloudless, for loneliness hung over these mountain solitudes like a pall, and the only sounds were the voices of desolation, as the vultures rose black against the sky, and underneath there was the steady shuffle, shuffle of the horses' feet. Holding Sylvia close, Peter warned her against stepping on a snake when she dismounted, and said snakes give off a poison which makes you die or go crazy. That night the howling of the wolves kept Sylvia awake. Peter put both arms around her, and, clinging together, they fell asleep.

The way they were following had been blazed by Daniel Boone in 1775, but not improved since. Taking them down the Powell Valley, it brought them, on the second day, in sight of Cumberland mountain, which henceforth for fifty miles stood like a wall across their way—a vast ridge of dead white rock, inaccessible to man or beast, gloomy by day and utterly desolate as the sun went down. On the fifth day after leaving the Blockhouse, they passed through the high swung Cumberland Gap, 1600 feet above sea-level. From this point for fifty miles Boone's trail would follow the Warrior's path, an ancient trail, north and south, made by the going back and forth of the Indians from the Miami and the Scioto in Ohio to the southern mountains.

Suddenly out of the fear and silence which hung between them and the clear, sunny sky, a shriek rent the air, long, ululating, full of terror, protest, and pain. The line halted abruptly. Cherokee came crashing through the underbrush alongside it, whispering tensely as he rode, "Stay where you are. Don't move. Don't speak." Mary, clasping Sis in her arms, rose in the saddle and tried to peer forward into the forest. Peter, holding Sylvia tight, crouched down on the old mare.

In a few minutes Cherokee came riding back, looking furious, and spoke to Jus. The line ahead started on. But at the point where the Cartwrights were it was still stopped, while Jus and Mac conferred in whispers. Then Jus came back and said to Mary, who was riding ahead of Peter and Sylvia, "It's only that fool Tidewater girl Eugenia. Just as we got through the Gap, she shrieked, 'The gates have closed for ever on all that I have loved,' and fell into a dead faint. They haven't got her out of it yet. They're callin' for Emmie. They say nothin' will do them except to have Emmie back there to hold up the women folk. Cherokee's as mad as Hell, and he says if there's one more word from them, he'll dump the whole gang. But he thinks the best thing is for Mac's whole family to move back in the line and travel next this outfit, and try to steady them, seeing the women hang on Emmie so."

Mary saw two pairs of eyes, the gentle blue ones and the bright black ones, raised to hers in apprehension and appeal. "Let Sylvia stay where she is," she said. "She and Peter go along together with less trouble than either of them would be apart." She turned to appeal to Emmie. "Emmie. Where's Emmie?" But Emmie had already rushed back to take care of Eugenia.

Jus consulted Mac, and said with the natural obliviousness of the heads of families to the emotional drama of the women and children, "Mac says Sylvia will have to go with her mother. He can't have her apart from the rest of them."

With that Mac took hold of Sylvia. But she sobbed and clung to Peter who hung on to her like a young wildcat, and fastened his teeth in Mac's big hand. She was ripped away. He started to scream, and felt his father's hand, hard over his mouth, clamping it shut. "Easy, Son. We've had more than enough noise as it is."

One of the guards rode up and whispered tensely, "Cherokee says get goin'."

Then Ol' Lady was moving again, and Peter was behind Polly on the horse, forced to hang on to her as they plunged down hill. She turned her head and whispered, "Shut up, Pete. Don't be a cry-baby."

Through Peter's fury and frustration an idea began to form. He'd drop off the horse and hide in the bushes till the horse bearing Sylvia came alongside. Then he'd jump on it, and rather than stop the line or make a fuss, they'd let him stay with her. Where she was he knew. He had the formation of his part of the line by heart. There were twenty families with their pack horses and cows between him and the Tidewater folks, and the Macs would be with the Tidewater folks, either in front of them or behind.

As they plunged into deep woods, Peter caught a low-hanging branch and swung himself off into dense underbrush. Ol' Lady, pushed by the horse behind, continued straight on. He could hear Polly's muffled scream as she found he was gone, and her agitated, "Petey, Petey." He scurried away under the bush on all fours. Reaching forward, he grasped something that felt like raw meat. There was a clap like thunder, and the whirring of great wings.

His heart leaped to his mouth. Then in the dim light, he saw that his hand was on the torn face of a woman lying dead there, her tangled bloody hair spread on the wet leaves, her dress ripped open showing her white breasts, one filmy grayish eye, like a fish's eye, staring up at him, and where the other eye had been, a raw red hole. Above, he saw what had made the noise. It was a vulture, so close he could see the reddish gleam on its black feathers like rust on old iron, and the cold, wicked face with its round bright eyes. "Looks like a bad old widow woman," he thought. His hand felt poisoned where it had touched what was on the ground. But he was not frightened or even horrified. He was thinking clearly, with a sense of utter outrage, "All a human person's made of is *meat*—just old stale meat."

Then he felt himself lifted up, a hard hand on his mouth, and the next thing he knew he was on the horse again with Polly, and Cherokee Bill, leaning over him, was saying, "Pete, you stay on that horse from now on, and I don't mean maybe."

Peter gasped, in a whisper, "There's a woman there—a white woman. She's dead."

Bill leaned over him and made him look down at his big hand, as he silently snapped his five fingers, one after the other. Peter, as a frontier boy, understood such signs. He knew Bill meant that there were five people there, but didn't want even to whisper it, lest Polly hear. Bill, seeing that he comprehended, said, "We take care of such things." He put his finger to his lips. Peter nodded eagerly. His submerged ego swelled with gratitude and restored self-esteem thus to be made the great leader's confidant. Bill leaned over impulsively and kissed him. "Be good now, son, and stay on your horse. L'il ol' Injun boy, mind your Injun Pappy." He dug his heels into his horse's flanks and was gone.

Feeling himself imprisoned on his horse behind Polly, while dark wood, valley, steep mountainside, brook, and river went by, and the golden September day turned to frosty moonlight, he kept thinking, "Sylvia wants me. She's cryin' for me." And all the while the dead woman's face was in front of him, so that he couldn't help staring at it, and the feel of that face where he'd touched it wouldn't leave his hand.

5

A rumor went down the line that the guards were always stopping to bury the remains of those who had gone before. But nobody knew that it was really so except Peter. Nobody else had seen one of these dead. The knowledge gave Peter a dark sort of satisfaction, making him feel important against everything else that made him feel low. He took a morbid interest in vultures wheeling overhead. "There's something down there," he would think. Once he smelled a strong stench. "There's a dead one!"

On Saturday evening they stopped a little before dark, and held a meeting to decide whether to travel on the Sabbath. On the frontier the Sabbath was generally observed, even by those who had no other religion, from a superstitious feeling that it was unlucky to work on that day. After some discussion, the leaders agreed with Mary. She said it would be good to rest on the Sabbath if they'd spend it prayin' to God to bless and guide them. But seein' they were all heathen except a few Baptists, they'd be drunken and whoopin and layin themselves open to Indian attack. "So," said Jus, "we're bound to sin either way, and gettin to where we're goin instead of settin' and darin' the Indians to come down on us seems the most sensible kind of sinnin'."

So before dawn they were on their way, aching, cold, and hungry. Their wet clothes, sticky with the dirt and sweat of long wearing, clung uncomfortably to their chafed and itching bodies. The golden weather had vanished. Though it was still warm, heavy gray clouds hung between them and the sun, and sudden frosty chills pierced the humid, balmy air. The horses were tired. Men, women, and children were tired. Food for man and beast was running low.

After nightfall they came to an open place where, palely visible to eyes used, like Peter's, to the cloudy dark, the fallen trunks of trees lay all about, and the brush was beaten down and the ground worn and rutted as if with the trampling of many feet. "This," said Bill, "is Camp Defeat. An emigrant train that went through here not a fortnight ago was all murdered—every man, woman, and child down to the smallest babe."

"Do we camp here?" asked Jus. Even in his father's easy voice

Peter could detect a distinct tremor.

"There's no other way out of it," said Bill.

In the dark they made up the camp with the greatest care, the men in charge moving like ghosts, talking only like the whisper of the wind. Weary, but tense and watchful, they fell into their accustomed places like automata, cows, horses, women and children in the center, older boys round about, the heads of families around them, and guards outside in the brush and the forest. Bill selected the most experienced Indian fighters among the heads of families, and added them to the outermost guard. Peter heard his father being provided with one of the best rifles and instructed to take his place in the hollow of the old beech tree out yonder, and howl like a wolf if he detected signs of Indians.

Shivering in a damp bearskin, less from cold than from excitement, trying to ease the gnawing in his stomach with a cold corn pone, Peter registered with smell and hearing what he could not see. It had begun to rain. In the drizzle the odor of cow-dung hung heavy crossed with the stench of a skunk disturbed by one of the guards. The camp hummed with a subdued unhappy sound. Squalls of babies stifled by hands of mothers held over their mouths, the muffled sobbing of somebody in pain, the hissing of commands and admonitions, the anxious asking of questions in whispers mingled with the whinneying and stamping of horses, and the soft musical note of a cow bell.

In Peter the general anxiety became an overmastering obsession. He must get to Sylvia. If Indians came, he must drag her into the bushes and hide her. Stealthily he crawled out of his bearskin and, worming his way amidst prone people and the legs of horses, he came to a point where, in the low murmurous complex of sounds, he could distinguish the light music of the Tidewater voices. He crawled to a point where they could not see him in the wan darkness, but he could hear what they were saying. The Major was telling the ladies that these stories about burying people were a put-up game on the part of young men who wanted their way paid to Kentucky. He did not deny that there might have been scattering attacks by Indians—just enough to give plausibility to the stories. But nothing like what they'd been told by this Indian rascal, Cherokee Bill.

Contempt swept Peter like fire. The face of the dead woman rose staring in front of him. His hand crawled with the memory of what he had touched. There was a roaring in his ears like the flapping of that great black bird. All his little being was shouting, "You fool! I saw the dead one. I saw the vultures eatin' her!" Stealthily he crept nearer, like a small panther. Then big arms picked him up, a hand was held over his mouth, his kicking limbs were tied together, and he was carried back like a trussed animal and dumped on his mother.

"I was lookin' for Sylvia," he whimpered from the bearskin in which he was wrapped like a papoose. Mary's heart was sore and heavy. The only woman friend she had ever had, bewitched into being Mammy to that fool Tidewater girl! She whispered gently. "It's a sore trial for us, Honey. But we must pull through the best we can. It'll be over and you'll have Sylvia to play with again in Kaintuck. And her mother will have learned her lesson, and not go workin' her fingers to the bone for these kind of folks any more. Lie still, dear, and I'll whisper comfort to you."

She began to whisper "Our Father who art in Heaven." Peter didn't understand the words, but they had a soothing sound, and he knew there was magic in them, the power of incantation to ward off evil. The bearskin was warm. His mother's hands were light and gentle. He relaxed. He could battle no longer. And like a small bird in the rain and the dark before dawn, a small hope was beginning to sing in his heart. The journey was almost over. He'd have Sylvia again in Kaintuck.

6

Peter woke with a violent start. The howl of a wolf was dying on the air, and there was a shot. He heard the tense whisper, "Indians!" and the voice of Cherokee giving orders. Slipping out of the bearskin, he began to slide on his belly to the center of excitement. "It was an Indian, I tell you," his father was saying in a strong, earnest whisper. "I saw him move and I raised that howl. He turned and right against an opening I saw him like a black lump. He seemed like he was going to spring on me. I fired. I hit him. He flounced around at a terrible rate and then he was still."

Then Peter heard the Major, not whispering but speaking low, in his light, airy way, "He hit a cow." There was a muffled titter. The Major said to his father, "Come, my good fellow. Own up. You were scared out there alone in the woods, and glad of an excuse to come back to camp."

Jus said, "Major, nobody calls another a coward in these parts, 'thout he can prove it."

Cherokee Bill said to the three of the guards who were with him, "Boys, take charge of the Major and bring him along. Every other man of you stay at his post, and that," he added, with acid emphasis, "goes most particularly for them from Tidewater."

Peter heard them go out. Tense silence settled on the camp. "I hope an Injun gets him," thought Peter, angrily. "I'd laugh to see a tomahawk hit him square between the eyes."

Ages passed. Peter heard them returning. He crawled to where they were. The Major was saying amiably, "Mr. Cartwright, I owe you an apology. There was an Indian and you hit him."

"An Indian with a tomahawk and a rifle, in the act of springing on me," said Jus.

"An Indian with a tomahawk and a rifle. But whether he was going to spring on you or not I don't know. However, any satisfaction you wish to demand I will gladly give, so far as your personal truth and courage are concerned. But I must point out that one Indian is not an Indian raid, and I have yet to see proof of these wild stories of dead people lining our path with which you have been poisoning our ears."

Cherokee Bill said roughly, "To your post, Major. And shut your trap. We'll argue all that when we get to where we're goin'."

Then there was silence, and the next thing Peter knew Polly was shaking him and telling him to get on his horse quick. "But it's dark," said Peter, digging his fists into his eyes.

"Dark or not, the orders are to get going."

Two days later, peering into a mass of mountain laurel leaves, to see what animal was moving there, Peter saw a face staring at him. At first he thought it was another dead face, because the jaw was broken and bloody. Then he saw the eyes moving and actually smiling at him, and a hand waving up from the bushes, while through the bloody mouth came a sort of shout. Instantly Cherokee's guard closed around him, and that was all Peter knew till he heard Jus tell the whole story to his mother that night.

This man had been one of seven white men returning to Virginia from Kentucky, all well armed and mounted on fine horses. They were fired on from the bushes, and three of them fell. The four dismounted, shot into the ambush, and killed three Indians. Four Indians seemed to be left, and the white men were four. The Indians shot and two white men fell. The white men shot and two Indians fell. There remained two Indians and two white men. At the third fire of the Indians, one of the white men fell, and the last, whose name was Baker, was hit in the mouth by a ball. He wheeled and ran, loading his gun as he went. Finding a large hollow tree, he crawled in feet first, holding his rifle ready to fire and expecting that the two remaining Indians would look in, and he could shoot them. But though he heard the Indians cross and recross the log twice, they did not find him. Meanwhile, lying there, he heard a cowbell.

As soon as the Indians went, he crawled out of his log and followed the sound of the cowbell to the emigrant line. Hearing his story Cherokee's young men rushed to the battle ground and found the white men and the Indians lying dead. They dug two separate graves, one for the white men and one for the Indians. Peter saw some of the guard come up to Cherokee, leading four horses, with excellent saddlebags. They came quietly, but Peter could almost hear the whoops bursting inside them, for one of the prerogatives of the guard was the right to strip dead bodies and to take all stray horses. "Got four horses," said one, grinning. "May be we can pick up the rest in the woods."

But even for the guard, property rights must yield to other considerations. "Go through the bags and take out the valuables," said Cherokee. "Then take the horses along the line, wherever there's one sick or footsore or fainting. We can sure use some fresh horse-flesh." Seeing the men demur, he added, "We'll have to let them that needs them most borrow them. But for ownership we'll cast lots later." They still hesitated. "Go," he said. They went.

When darkness began to settle next evening, they were only

seven miles from Crab Orchard and the end of their journey. They were footsore, hungry, and dirty. The horses could barely stumble. Every human being had come through alive, but many were racked and embarrassed by dysentery, and several were so dizzy that they could sit on a horse only if some one walked alongside and held them up. The children had ceased to fret, and were dumb and drooping. Mothers trudged on foot carrying heavy children three and four years old. Boys were carrying on their own backs the packs the horses were too weak to carry longer.

For days there had been no chance to clean up. Their hair was long, straggling, and matted. Their faces were sunburned, streaked, caked with dirt, and scratched with briars. Several miles from Crab Orchard the line stopped. Man and beast sagged to the ground where they were. Peter heard his father say, "We're takin' a vote. Do we go on to the fort where we're sure we'll be safe? Or do we stop here and run the risk of Injuns one more night, and then straggle on most of tomorrow."

Soon there was a stirring in the dark, and one by one they got to their feet. "We're goin' on."

Cherokee Bill rode up to Peter's father. "The god dam idiots," he said. "Those Tidewater folks won't come on. The Major says the women and children ain't moving till they get a good night's sleep. And what's more they're going to strip off their filthy clothes, and light a fire and wash up, and get something hot into their stomachs. He says its just plumb foolishness to think Indians will attack seven miles from a fort."

"He don't know Injuns."

"But Mac— Mac and Emmie—they're coming on," cried Mary. "They wouldn't be fools enough to stay behind without a guard."

"No, Mac figures that if these Tidewater folks won't come on, he's got to stay by them. If Injuns did come down, he'd be all they have between them and scalping. He says the men are all brave and can shoot, even if they haven't much sense, and in case of attack he thinks he and his two older boys—Robyn and George—could manage to direct them so they could put up a fight or get the women to safety. And Emmie understands Injun fighting and can shoot."

"It's downright madness," said Jus. "Mac knows better'n to do this."

"Well," said Bill, "if it was me I'd come on to the fort if it killed me, because any death is sweeter than scalpin'. But those folks have reached the end of their rope. The young bride's so tired she's going from one hysteric fit into another. And there's two young uns sick to death. Mac says they've got to have somebody stand by them."

"Let the young Macs come with us," said Mary. "We'll take Delphine and Sylvia." At this Peter hurled himself off his horse, and ran and caught at his mother's feet where they hung in the dark from her horse. "Mammy, Mammy, make them let us have Sylvia," he wailed. "I don't want Injuns to get Sylvia!"

Had the men really attended to what Mary was saying, they might have agreed with her. But they were too weary and preoccupied to reexamine the masculine dogma of the frontier that, even in the worst danger, small children were safest with their mothers. So, as usual, the heads of families made up their minds what was best for the women and children without much heed to their protests. The argument ended. The Macs, including the little ones, were staying behind with the Tidewater gentry. The line started forward. Somebody picked Peter up and put him on his horse, where Polly held him firmly.

They were going on seven miles to Crab Orchard. Seven miles. Seven hundred miles. Seven thousand miles. Inch by inch the suffering line edged its way through the dark. It was three hours before they saw the blessed lights of the fort, the first light they had seen at night since they left the Blockhouse. It was four hours before the last of them dropped in their tracks under the safety of the great log walls. Peter, asleep on his horse, was gently lifted off and laid on the ground. For a moment he felt himself sinking into everlasting emptiness, and then he knew no more.

7

"God Almighty!" A roar like a stuck bull! Peter started up. It was his father making that dreadful sound! A muffled shriek from his mother, desperate, anguished, "Emmie! Sylvia! Oh dear Father in Heaven—no!" Peter's heart turned over, and in that moment he knew it all, and what followed was only commentary on the dreadful certainty.

In the light of a flaring torch, Mac's next eldest boy, Robyn, stood there, panting, perspiring, a streak of blood running fresh, bright, and unheeded down his face. "All of them except me. Every one dead. Father and George and me—we stood sentry duty—but they were all undressed and asleep. I don't know how many Injuns. There were a lot. They came down on us, more and more. We tried to get Jim out to get word to you. The Tidewater boys all tried to get out to you. They were as brave as they make 'em. But every one was caught and killed by the Injuns before he got out of hearing. The Tidewater men stood their ground. But they didn't know how to fight Injuns. They just stood and were shot down. The women had plenty of pluck, even Miss Eugenia. But it was no use. They was like chickens with a whole mess of foxes comin' in. Mammy tried to organize them but it was no use—they wasn't used to our way of managing. And trying to get them out of the way, Mammy was more exposed than she'd have been if she'd had anybody who knew anything to help. And the children. It was just no use. Every time an Injun came across one, he strung it up, like you'd kill kittens, just to get 'em out of the way. And the older children they killed because they fought back and tried to hide the little ones. It was just no use I tell you. We done all we could. Pappy held out to the last, and George and I stood by him, and we must have killed ten Injuns ourselves—me and George. Just at the last, when we knew there was nobody left alive except us, George fell, and then of a sudden, a bullet hit Pappy, and all he could do was gasp, 'Quick, Son, save yourself.' So I ran, and twenty Injuns after me, and the bullets comin' like hail-stones, but I got away."

The paralysis that had taken Peter broke into a howl as of a dozen animals. Somebody seized him. He kicked. He yelled. It seemed impossible that so small a body could pour forth so much rage and pain. "Sylvia! Sylvia! They killed Sylvia!" He stopped at last, utterly exhausted, and found himself limp, and unutterably weary and hopeless, in the strong, gentle prison of Dean's arms.

The whole fort was boiling over with excitement. Lights were being carried flaming hither and thither. Horses were trampling. Orders were being shouted. Held tight in Dean's arms, Peter saw a light flaring on a strong, brown, grizzled face that seemed immeasurably old, and heard a voice saying, "Mr. Cartwright, I'm William Whitley. I command the fort." Too miserable to feel his usual curiosity about what the big folks were saying, Peter heard no more until, through black suffering, some words penetrated like a red flame. Whitley was saying, "This is to show you at the outset what the word Kentucky means. The Injuns say in their tongue Kentucky means *dark and bloody ground*." "Dark and bloody ground, dark and bloody ground." The words began to toll like a bell in Peter's mind. "Dark and bloody ground."

A soldier had brought up Whitley's horse. Behind him was a troop of horses, rearing and champing at the bit. Whitley sprang into the saddle, "We're off to get those Injuns. We can't bring back the lives of the dead, but we can kill them that murdered them, and recover the property. We know that outfit and the way they come. We'll fix 'em."

"We're fixin' them ourselves," said Jus doggedly. 'Cherokee's rallying the men now."

"But you're all tired. We can take care of those yellow-bellied sons-of-bitches. We're used to them. That's what we're here for."

"Thank ye kindly," said Jus. "But nobody does our fightin' for us. We do it ourselves. You lead, but we're following, and when we come to those Injuns, it's us they've got to answer to."

They had to hold Peter under guard all the rest of the night, and all the next day to keep him from going after the Indians himself. He cried. He stormed. His black eyes shone with a maniacal light. His mother, heartbroken and bitter, understood the gleam in those dark eyes. Only by constant prayer was she keeping down the mad rage in her own heart. She distrusted every mood of the strong and wily child, even when he was quiet out of sheer weariness. "We can't have him runnin' away into the woods," she said to Dean.

The personality of the big, gentle black man surrounded the boy in those hours. Three times Peter ran away, and three times Dean carried him back, holding him till his kicking legs were still, and the tangled curly black hair rested quietly on his broad chest. To Peter he seemed irresistible and universal like God. In the intervals when Peter was quiet, he kept up a soft, running talk about

Sylvia being alive and happy and beautiful for ever there at God's feet, waiting for Peter to come to her. "When she went away from you, off Ol' Lady, back to those Tidewater folks you knew where she was. Now she's just gone a little further, and she'll stay longer. But the difference is that you don't have to worry about her where she is now, for she's in the best of hands for ever and ever."

While Dean was still guarding Peter, there was a whooping and a shouting, and the men rode back into camp. "We got them all," said Jus dismounting, sombre, dirty, and so tired he could hardly stand. "There were twenty-five Injuns, and they had all the horses and property they'd made off with. We got every scrap of it and brought it back. And they're dead and buried where we found 'em, and," he added heavily, "Mac and all of them, we buried them, too."

"Buried," said Mary, in a small, choking voice. "Emmie—buried in the dark and bloody ground."

Jus took Mary aside. "I don't know if you'll want to look, but I have Emmie's things here, and the children's. There's this." He held out the gold chain Emmie had worn around her neck.

A storm of thoughts went through Mary's mind. Emmie saying, "I want us to be the ones to wear a gold chain." It was the value she set on nice things that made it so those Tidewater folks could bewitch her! But where was there justice in the world if the weak could so undo the strong? God in Heaven, could this be right? O gentle Jesus, could you let this be? But she only said, in a small, tight way, "They belong to young Mac. They're all he has. Give them to him."

Jus hesitated. "And I brought something else. I hate for you to look at it, Mary. But one of the Injuns—I shot him myself, damn him—had this hanging from his horse's bridle." He held up a thick braid of flaxen hair, and added quickly, in answer to the horror in Mary's face, "No, she wasn't scalped. None of 'em were. It was just that the fellow had cut it off, and was taking it home to his girl, most likely, as a curiosity."

Mary took the hair in her hand, and, for the first time, the tears gushed from her eyes, washing down over her cheeks in a steady, warm flood. She felt all broken up inside, as if, once she had started crying, she could never stop. "It's for young Mac," she said.

"I'll give it to him myself. It'll be for remembrance."

Jus went on. "And the Indian had a little curl hanging by the braid. Mary, I don't know whether you want to look—it breaks me up, kinda—but there!" He held out a soft curl, the color of corn silk, but much finer. Mary had thought she could feel no more. But to see that poor little girl's hair. The hurt was like the stab of a thin, fine knife, indescribably poignant. Her tears stopped suddenly. Her hands trembled. Her knees trembled. Her mouth was dry. Should they give this to young Mac, or quietly put it away?

There was a howl and a spring like that of a young tiger. And Peter seized it. "Good God!" said Justurian, "I didn't know the boy was listening." He laid his hand on the child, "Steady, Son." He tried to unclasp the small, rough, brown fingers. The boy's eyes burned. His curly hair seemed to stand up and crackle. He bared his white teeth in a snarl like an animal clinging to its prey. "It's mine!" His tongue struggled with the word he had just heard. "For—for—rememberance!"

Mary's eyes met Justurian's. She said to Peter gently, "Keep it, honey, but we must put it away so it will be safe." She had an inspiration. She took out of the pouch swinging from her shoulders the small Bible in which, since Emmie died, she had been reading constantly to steady herself. "Here, we will lay it away in the Holy Book, and it will be like we had laid it in God's hands, and His kind Almighty fingers had closed over it."

Peter looked at the book, and something that had been hard and unbearably painful deep within him began to relax. His mother's Bible was the only book he had ever seen. He supposed it was the only book in the world—a unique object, out of which by a magic he could not understand, she could draw strange and wonderful sayings. Even people who didn't understand religion knew there was power in this Book. Robyn had told him that it was a lucky thing his mother had it on her person, for an Injun arrow could never kill her, but would be automatically caught by the Bible and turned aside. And he had said that if you laid your hand on the Bible and made a promise, you'd have to keep that promise if it took your life, for if you didn't something so awful would happen that Robyn didn't even dare say what it was. All of which confirmed Peter in the mystical sense of security and of personal prestige which he associated with his mother's book.

He half yielded the curl into his mother's hands, and yet he could not quite let it go. "Lay it here," she said, "right over these words: 'Blessed are they that mourn, for they shall be comforted'." With the feeling that he was performing a mystic rite, he placed the soft wisp of gold between the pages. She closed the book. Then she had another inspiration. "Take the book in your arms, Honey, and hold it awhile, and let God's goodness flow out of it into you."

She left him sitting with the Bible in his arms, a sad, rapt look that was almost peace on his small, wan, dark face.

8

All that night, waking fitfully from sleep that pressed like dark pain on head and limbs, Peter was aware of his parents' sleeplessness, exploding in little gusts of whispered talk from under the bearskin.

"If it hadn't been for that fool Major," Jus was saying. Mary cut in—

"It was all of them. They killed Emmie, more'n the Injuns. They weren't bad, but they were weak, and being weak like they were is worse'n being bad, for they made themselves weak to be waited on, and saved trouble, and to put on others the load they was meant to tote themselves."

"It's what comes of owning niggers like they own mules and dogs," said Jus. "It's not only that the niggers do all their work. They do most all their real livin' for them."

There was silence while they tried to readjust their bodies to sleep. Somewhere, beyond the murmurous stir of the camp, Peter dozing off, could hear Sylvia crying, and started up, and then, remembering, sank back as if into a bottomless pit. His father, giving up the effort to sleep, was talking again.

"Yes, they make themselves weak to be waited on. And the trouble with that is they can't feel comfortable about it. They have to have something to make themselves feel big and hide from them what miserable trash they are. So they work themselves up to think they're something special in the way of God's creation, and have been given a right to have it easy when other folks have it hard, and to sleep warm where other folks sleep cold, and eat when other folks are hungry."

"But what I puzzle about," whispered Mary, "is what happens when honest folks like Emmie comes up against these butterfly do-nothings. There's something about folks that sets themselves up high and fancy—a kind of bewitchment they have—and it works on some of the best kind of people like Emmie who wants nice ways of living and never had a chance at them. It's as if they thought some good flowed from these folks just by being near them, and betterment from serving them. And so she let herself be made a Mammy, a body servant. Emmie had sense. Yet she did it."

"Honey, try to go to sleep," said Jus, soothingly. "What Emmie did is something we'll never do, we nor our children for ever. Amen!"

BOOK II

1790 - 1796

George Washington, President

CHAPTER 7

Crab Orchard, Kentucky
September, 1790

On the southeastern side of the settlement of central Kentucky stood the log fort of Crab Orchard, under the command of William Whitley, brother-in-law of George Rogers Clark. Here, in the autumn of 1790, the young settlers coming over Boone's trail met the northern settlers who had come across Pennsylvania by Braddock's Road to Pittsburgh, from Pittsburgh to Louisville by flatboat, and thence by foot, horseback, and sledge to Crab Orchard. From here they scattered among the log cabin villages of Harrodsburg, Danville, Stanford, Frankfort, and Lexington, which were all within easy reach of each other by horseback. Here, in what was known as the "Western District of Virginia," they incorporated themselves into a community of some 73,000 people, who, separated from the eastern settlements by 300 miles of savage wilderness, ruled themselves, and protected themselves without help against the constant attacks of the trans-Ohio Indians.

Otherwise there were only two settlements in these western wilds. One was the tiny settlement of the Yankee veterans at Marietta, on the north bank of the Ohio. The other consisted of a log courthouse, some eighteen feet square, a distillery, two log taverns, and some cabins and shanties, surrounded by a fence to keep off the buffalo, on the bluff above the Cumberland at Nashville, in what is now Tennessee. Eleven miles north of it was the big blockhouse of the Donelsons, who, with their numerous relatives and retainers, constituted a village in themselves—and not a village only, but practically a miniature state, self-ruled, self-sustained economically, and self-protected.

Northward and westward of this stretched the wide open buffalo lands, the grasslands, the Barrens, which had been granted to the veterans and were known as the "Military Tract." Between it and the settlements of central Kentucky there was a trail 200 miles long, infested with horse-thieves. On this trail John Donelson, father-in-law of Andrew Jackson, was murdered and his horse taken. Here Abraham Lincoln's grandfather was killed by an Indian arrow. There was here a force, pervasive and intangible, which resisted settlement. From the Military Tract the quickest and surest way out was down the Mississippi to New Orleans or down the Chick-asaw Road, a narrow trail, with single tree trunks laid over streams for bridges, which led through the hunting grounds of the Chicka-saws. Hence the Military Tract had already been preempted as the main headquarters of horse-thieves, river pirates, and counter-feiters. If pursued from any part of the West, they could escape from here down the Chickasaw Road to the Spanish port of New Orleans and be out of reach of American justice.

To Mary, as she took her wooden bucket, and wearily jostled and dodged her way to the spring, that September morning, Crab Orchard was just another stop on the way to the Military Tract. She was not prepared for the amazing new world that met her eyes. The shouting of men and shrilling of women, the squalling of children, the cries of auctioneers and hucksters, the whinneying of horses, and the clang of cowbells made the kind of din she had heard at Fort Chiswell and the Watauga Blockhouse. But there it had rumbled and hissed under the lid the military guards put on it with their admonitions not to give away their presence to an enemy by noise. Here the noise poured out in a fierce, exuberant flow. Mary thought wonderingly, "The Indians killed Mac and Emmie seven miles from here—wiped out every living soul. And yet they can laugh and holler." Then she thought, "They've been through

William Whitley's brick house, which was the first domicile not made of logs west of the Alleghenies, still stands near Stanford.

the worst and come out alive. They're beyond being kept down. So are we all." And with that she felt new strength.

But that wasn't all there was to the strange new spirit here. For one thing there were the goods for sale, which the northern settlers had brought in. On the road across Pennsylvania the large Dutch wagons, drawn by two, four and even six stout horses, could carry the riches of Europe and the products of Yankee mills and handicrafts, and the flatboats could carry them down the Ohio, if they could escape the robbers on every island. What was left, after running the gauntlet of murder and robbery, was spread out here on miles of plank tables to dazzle with cambric, crockery, lace and tinware the eyes of young people from the log cabin world of the Appalachians, who had never worn any cloth but linsy and linsy woolsy, or drunk from anything but a gourd, or eaten from anything but a wooden trencher.

For another thing there was a lively friendliness and talkativeness. While she waited for an hour in the long line that had queued up at the spring, Mary listened to the chatter. A man next her who looked no older than Jus was one who had got through with Boone's party, back in 1771. When he first saw this ground, now so littered and trampled, he said it was all an open grassy place, with springs leaping and glancing amidst leaves and flowers. "The Garden of Eden couldn't have been sweeter," he said. There were but nineteen years between what he told and what was here now, but his story had the heroic coloring of a prehistoric age.

A group came alongside heatedly arguing. Should the folks out here try to join the new Federal Union, or should they bargain with Spain on their own to float their goods down to New Orleans? A lean, hatchet-faced dark fellow whom Mary recognized as one of Cherokee Bill's guards said, "We didn't fight the British to tie ourselves up with the Dons." A man with a long beard, wearing a broad hat and gentry clothes, drew out a small, crudely printed sheet from his breeches pocket, and began to read an argument against the new constitution. Thereupon, a stranger observed in a nasal drawl, "I'll be God dass it! If they ain't got a newspaper out here! Stranger, do you mind if I look at it?" The other man surrendered it, and it was passed on from hand to hand, till a man in a preacher's black coat took it and brought it back, saying in a mellow voice, "Thank you, my friend. A newspaper is the first instrument of civilization. We had not expected to find one in these wilds."

"There's the newspaper office," said a hearty looking young fellow, pointing to a plank table under a tree, at which, on an up-turned stump, a young man sat making notes with a quill pen on a long sheet of foolscap. "John, come over and show yourself to these folks." To the crowd which had now gathered, he said, "I'm Fielding Bradford, and this is my brother John, and we're editors, proprietors, and printers' devils for *The Kentucky Gazette*. Line up to pay for your subscriptions right here, folks. All the latest news of who's coming and going, and what's for sale, and arguments for and against the federal constitution, right off the press, and any news you've got to tell us guaranteed to be in the next issue. Step right up here, folks, with your names, your money, your advertisements, and your news."

And then John Bradford told how he and his brother had brought their printing press down the Ohio to Louisville, and packed it down the trail from Louisville to Lexington, and had some type cut out of dog-wood, and so produced the first newspaper west of the Alleghenies in August 1787. Mary listened wonderingly. It had never occurred to her to think how print might be put on paper. This was the first of the many new matters she would be forced to put her mind to in this new world.

2

When, at last, Mary started back with her water, she was halted by a sound piercing the cheerful din—thin, high, like a long drawn wail on a fiddle. "Somebody's died," she thought, her primitive soul responding to the primitive message. Then she thought, "It's a hymn—from hearts that are broke." She set her pail down under a clump of bushes, and walked to where the hymn was coming from, going along with many other people, some with heads bowed, some weeping. Then she was kneeling on the ground in a mass of kneeling people, many of them sobbing aloud.

Mary sobbed, too, with an unutterable sense of release. The sorrow for Emmie, the shock, the bitter, burning sense of injustice dissolved in a great healing flood. After the hymn there was a long prayer for those cruelly murdered, and a reading of " 'Vengeance is mine,' saith the Lord, 'I will repay.' " And then another hymn. All the while Mary did not ask who had died. She only knew that this was what she wanted—to lay down her burden before God, and let the pain in her heart flow out.

It was only when the preacher, tall, thin, in a straight linen coat and black stock, stood up and began to talk that she found her mind released enough to piece together the facts. This was a memorial service for a flatboat full of people who had been foully assailed and murdered near Cave-in-Rock on the Ohio River. These were the friends and relatives of the victims who had been on another flatboat. The two boats had started together from Pittsburgh, and had gone along together, anchoring at night, building big campfires on shore, visiting back and forth from one boat to the other. Near Cave-in-Rock they were hailed by some women who said they'd been left by their own boat, and could they get a ride down to Louisville? When the first boat tried to maneuver itself to where they were, it was taken by the current and swept on. But the second boat got into position and took them on board.

The people on the boat ahead, looking back with concern to make sure those poor stranded women were all right, saw the second boat explode in a wild volley of shots and shrieks. Then a whole attacking army was pushing out from the shore in boats. The horrified watchers on the first boat saw a child flung high in the air and hit the water with a splash. And they knew those "women" had been river pirates in disguise.

But what were they to do—those folks on the first boat? Through all the weeping and praying there ran the torturing question. Had they done enough? Could they have done more? Some wanted to anchor and try to fight back. But if they did, wouldn't they put all aboard their own boat in jeopardy? But when they had been carried out of sight around a bend, some of the men landed and went back along the shore to see what had happened and to rescue any who might have got away and be in hiding there.

They returned with one lone survivor, carrying him on a stretcher because both legs were broken. He was here, at this memorial meeting, and was lifted on the shoulders of his friends, and, in a weak voice, which broke down every few phrases, he called the roll of every man, woman, and child on that flatboat, thirty-five in all, telling how each died. As he finished with each name, they prayed in chorus, "Lord, have mercy."

It was finished. They rose from their knees, and stood dabbing their eyes and lifting their faces to the sky, as they sang the last hymn. A slender young woman who had been kneeling next to Mary, quietly weeping, turned and looked at her. Meeting the blue eyes under the smart straw bonnet, Mary thought, "She's like that Tidewater girl. Wears a bonnet to keep looking like milk and apple blossoms." But the antagonism that came with this thought gave way as the young woman said, "My brother—my only brother —was on that boat." The tears welled in her eyes. She wiped them away with a fine linen handkerchief.

Mary said awkwardly, "I know what it is to have ones that are dear—murdered." She choked, thinking of Emmie.

The other young woman, regaining her poise, said, "You speak like a Virginian. Are you one of those bound for the Military Tract? My sister, Barbara, is engaged to marry a man that has a grant there. He would have been on that boat, coming down to join your party here, but an Indian raid kept him at Fort Harmar."

"Fort Harmar!" exclaimed Mary, "That's where that friend of Jus —Jus is my husband—Justurian Cartwright—his friend is at Fort Harmar. Dominie—"

"Dominie! He's the one that's marrying Barbara. So you are Jus Cartwright's wife!"

Some people circled around the girl and cut her off from Mary. Freeing herself and laying a slender, well kept hand on Mary's arm, she whispered, "The captain of those river pirates—they call him John Wilson—is really Sam Mason. He has a grant of land on the Tract. He's in league with the counterfeiter Alston." She was pulled away by an older woman, who said, "Come, Lydia."

"Wait," said Mary urgently. "Where's your camp. Jus will want to see you."

"Over there," the girl pointed. "But we're going to Harrodsburg to-day." She was pulled away but turned back for a last word. "Tell your husband to look into it. It's life or death for you."

3

Jus, rushing off to talk to Lydia, returned sparkling with excitement. "What do you think of old Dominie—marrying into the quality? Lydia and her husband Fred aim to settle north of the Ohio when the land's clear of Indians. But till then they've bought land beyond Harrodsburg—they and all the folks on their flatboat. They'll clear it and make improvements, and raise horses and then they'll sell out and set themselves up handsomer in Ohio. That's the Yankee way. They're smart."

"Not like us," said Mary, sourly, "who just go on from one tumble-down cabin to the next that's no better."

"Honey, don't talk like that. It's going to be different now. Listen!" A new authority sparked from Justurian's black eyes, and gave a set to his head. "Do you know what's happened? Just as soon as I can get cleaned up, I'm called to go into conference with a dozen other of the heads of companies in our outfit, about what's to be done with the situation down there on our Military Tract. And do you know who I'm going to sit down with? Isaac Shelby. And do you know who he is? He's going to be the first governor of Kentucky. And do you know who's going to teach me my law, and admit me to the bar? It's George Muter himself, and it's all fixed that he's to be Chief Justice of Kentucky. Honey, the social heap's turned over now, and we're sitting on top."

Despite her chronic feminine impulse to stick briar thorns into men's bubbles, Mary was impressed. "It's like you were hand-in-glove with Mr. Jefferson and Mr. Madison," she said, trying to stretch her mind to the wonder of it.

As Mary helped Jus to cool and heal his face in the bloody wake of the razor, Jus suddenly asked where Peter was. He was taking him to the conference about the Military Tract, at Ranger Whitley's house. "Whitley's got a brick house—two storeys," he said. "It's time Peter begins to see a house that isn't a log cabin."

Mary protested. "Peter's in no state to be dragged around. Leave him with Dean."

But Jus walked off and found Peter sitting on Dean's knee, listlessly watching a tomahawk throwing match among the little boys, and brought him back on his shoulder. Unprotestingly, Peter let himself be stripped and stood in a bucket of water and scrubbed, and clad in clean linen shirt and breeches. When he was clean, he looked a little brighter.

There was a rush of dust and noise outside and Dutch clattered up, with his small son, Jerry, on his saddle. Mary cast a motherly eye over the slight child, with his long pointed face, limpid, almost colorless gray eyes, and hair streaked light brown and burnt yellow white. "He's one Peter could be happy looking after," she thought. She could see where the empty place Sylvia had left might be filled.

When Jus set Peter up on his saddle, and the two men started off for the Ranger's with their little sons, she could see that Peter was already "waked up" a little, and admitted that Jus had been right to make him go. The wifely happiness of yielding the palm to Jus was warm in her heart, as, shading her eyes with her hand against the sun, she watched them ride away.

4

Emerging from the tangle of human and animal creatures around the fort, Jus and Dutch turned west on the bridle path which led through the forest to Stanford. The path was wide enough for two horsemen to pass each other, and hence was no longer a path but a "road," there being as yet nothing else of that name in this country.

Going on for a mile or two, they came to the clearing, surrounded by walls of forest where, huge and astonishing to children used only to one-room cabins, there rose the square, two-storey brick mansion of the Ranger, William Whitley. When Jus and Dutch reined up in a trampled place where several horses were hitched to trees, Peter and Jerry slipped from their horses, and ran forward, dodging between groups of strange men, to examine this marvel at close range. They felt of the strange red rock, cut so regular and square. They had never seen brick. They studied the windows, two on each side of the doorway, made of small panes of glass. They had never seen glass. "It's hard, like it was stone," said Peter wonderingly, "and yet it's like there ain't anything there, no more than it was air."

The Ranger had come out on the steps in front of the house, and was calling to them to look up over the door. The men roared with laughter. Peter and Jerry looked up, uncomprehending. The red wall went up and up far beyond where a roof should be, and above, there were other windows. Jus, seeing that the children were puzzled, lifted Peter in his arms and walked back with him for some distance. "They're laughing at what the Ranger says about those two big letters over the door. See them?"

All Peter could see was lines of different colored brick above the door. Their shape was something like bent sticks interlaced. "They are the first letters of the Ranger's name," said Jus. "W. W. for William Whitley. He says he's done what most men haven't the guts to do. He's got his own name plastered in front of the house, and his wife's name in small letters, E. W., back behind over the kitchen door."

What interested Peter more was that a second house had been built on top of the first house. Clutching his father's hand, in a kind of fearsome awe, he mounted the steps and passed through the open door, Jerry following with his father. Here the children were transfixed by their first sight of a stairway. After some mutual consultation, they figured it was "kinda like" the ladder which usually led from the main room of a cabin to a sleeping loft at one end. Only, instead of bunks under the eaves, there was another house up there. Colonel Whitley invited them to walk upstairs. When they had gingerly scaled those heights, he set Peter on the bannister and told him to slide. After a frightened moment, Peter got the idea and came flying down and bounced to the floor while everybody roared.

By this time more men had ridden up. One was sturdy, stocky, a little over middle height, dignified and affable. His name was Isaac Shelby. With him was his brother Moses. Others were leaders of the veterans, among them Cherokee Bill.

From the hall they all entered the cool dim parlor. Less by sight than by a kind of electric shock, Peter was aware of a tall thin man, in a straight linen coat and black stock, standing there, his eyes like burning coals. "The Methodist Elder, Francis Poythress," said Shelby's voice. Next to him stood a young man, slender but strong-looking, with a sensitive, slightly surly, bronzed face. "This is Brother James Haw. Was on the Cumberland circuit. Is going back to your Hell's country, to fight Satan for you against the time you get there," said Poythress abruptly to Jus. The mellowness in his voice and the rapt look in his eyes kept his abruptness from seeming rude, and compelled attention.

But it did not prevent Peter from being diverted by a Negro, bare-footed and wearing only a linsy breech-cloth, who was passing around a large plate made of a shining substance Peter had never seen. It was a silver tray and on it were glittering receptacles filled with red and gleaming water. These were wine glasses, and the liquid was wine. Peter and Jerry stared, for they had never seen either.

Poythress waved the liquor aside. Haw said, "No thank you, I'll take the children's drink." And lo! the black man was offering Peter the tray, and on it were three of the glittering containers full of a golden liquid. Haw took one of the golden drinks and told Peter and Jerry each to take one. Peter held his in both hands, scared lest he should drop it, and imitating Haw, tasted it gingerly. It tasted like the juice of a summer apple. Jus was looking at the drink curiously. Haw said, "It's a good Methodist drink. Made of honey and vinegar. We call it *metheglin*. It's a considerable improvement on what you're drinking." The others roared derision.

Whitley was telling how, after the Revolution, he and his first wife, Elizabeth, and their three children had come out with his wife's brother, George Rogers Clark. "It's to him we owe the claim to all we've got out here," he said. "But he's not getting his dues, which is to be head of all the armed forces of our state when we set it up, and it's not likely he will."

"Where is he now?" asked Jus.

Whitley shrugged. "There's always another wilderness to conquer, and always more to do of what you didn't get thanked for last time. He's south of here, helping to make good the white man's hold on the Chickasaw country. More fool he!"

Diverted to pleasanter subjects by Isaac Shelby, Whitley was soon telling about those early days. 'We had nothing but a gun, a plow, an axe, and a kettle. But there was a lot of fine land nobody was laying claim to. Later, when we got patches of it cleared and thousands of folks began coming out here, I traded one farm for brick and masonry to put up this house, and another for enough liquor to prime the laborers on it and keep them happy, and a third for the talents of Mr. Swope who did all the carving."

He pointed with pride to the carved panels in the walls, and the thirteen panels over the fireplace representing the thirteen colonies.

Asked if there were any other brick houses out here yet, Whitley said there was the Robards' stone house over in Harrodsburg. "Her son, Lewis, is married to Rachel Donelson. She's the daughter of John Donelson, one of the two founders of the Nashville settlement. That's your nearest neighbors," he said, turning to Jus, "right over the line from your tract in what is the western district of North Carolina." He added, "Rachel's a right sweet girl."

Moses Shelby said, "Even if she's eloped from her husband."

"Who could blame her?" said Whitley. "Lewis Robards is a skunk."

"Is it true she's gone off with that red-haired son of Satan, Andrew Jackson?" asked a voice.

Young Haw interposed severely, "We've law-breaking and wickedness enough. There's no use adding to it by making up scandal. The girl was unhappy, and all Jackson's done is to take her home to her folks." To Jus and Dutch he added, "When you've been down in your Hell's country as long as I have—it's three years since I started to see if I could break it for God before it broke me —you'll thank God every night on your knees that there are folks like the Donelsons down there."

Elder Poythress took a large gold watch out of his cartridge belt, and snapped it open. "Whitley, while I wait there's a man going down to Hell. I have to get back to him. Let me say what I was sent for to say and be off."

Silence fell. Poythress spoke solemnly. "Isaac Shelby has asked Brother Haw and me to put our weight behind what he has to propose, because we know your Hell's country. And we do it unconditionally. *You must not go down to the Green River country with wife and child now.*" He turned to Shelby, "And now, Brother, let Haw speak for both of us. I must get back to Micajah Harpe. He's got one of his crazes on him." With that he shot out of the door. Jus, Dutch, and Cherokee looked at each other in dismay.

"You mean," said Jus to Shelby, "you want us to give up our Tract?" Give up the Tract they'd fought their way to, through eight years of war, and seven years of peace, and three hundred miles of bloody wilderness! Give up when it was so near? Even Peter and Jerry, drinking glass after glass of *metheglin,* could feel the tension in the room, and crouched down like young creatures in the face of danger.

"Not to give it up," said Shelby. "But only to wait." More waiting! Hadn't they waited long enough? Shelby hesitated, unable to meet the looks that were turned on him, and added lamely, "Brother Haw can tell the reason. He's been down there."

All eyes were turned on Haw. "The reason is that your land's become the seat and fount of authority for the most hellish banditti that have bloodied the earth since Cain."

"We know that," said Jus coolly. "And we're going down in such force as to fight 'em down. We've got 300 men, and there can't be more than 100 of these banditti there all told." He looked at Haw. "Isn't that so?"

"It's likely you couldn't count a hundred at one time," replied Haw. "But it's the center for the coming and going of every bad character from the Ohio to the Gulf of Mexico, and the Alleghenies to the Mississippi. They're all hooked together in one net by Alston, and counting them all, there may well be thousands. If you start fighting them, out there, 200 miles west of all means of law and order, you'll start a system of perpetual feudin'." He looked around. "Who that has fathers or grandfathers that came from the borders of Scotland doesn't know what feudin' is? Do you want to start it again over here?"

Every Scotch Irishman in the room answered, "No."

"There's another choice you have if you insist on going down there now," said Haw. "You can accept the rule of these outlaws and pay them tribute—make your surveys only on land they're willing to leave you, turn in your skins and your crops to them for whatever they want to pay, and take their counterfeit money in return, and buy your goods only in the thieves' market they set up to handle the goods and the horses red with blood from every trail coming west. So you can help set up a robber baron society by the time-honored means by which the nobility of Europe was established."

His eye rested on Dutch. "Does any one whose folks fled the robber baron society of Germany want to see it set up again here?"

"Gott in Himmel, nein!" roared Dutch. And every German in the room said, "Nein."

"Well, then," said Shelby, "there's the third choice, and that, I take it, is the true American way. We've laid out Lincoln County to include your Military Tract, with the county seat at Stanford. If you will tarry near Stanford, you can work with us who are trying to cut off from Virginia and be admitted as a state. When that's done, you can go down there with some law and order behind you."

"How long will that take?" asked Jus, feeling hopeless.

"About two years. Seeing we didn't get admitted as a state before the old Confederation broke up, we've had to wait till the new constitution could be ratified. Now that's settled, we expect Congress in the next session will pass the enabling act to admit us. By which time we hope to work out a state constitution, and draw up a good slate of officers to be voted on."

"But where do we live?" asked Dutch. "What do we live on?" asked Cherokee. Whitley replied that they could get the use of land anywhere here by agreeing to break a few acres to the plow. With the timber felled in clearing, they could build cabins and barns, and when they turned the land back, they would be paid for these "improvements" and could take any stock they had raised with them to their new homes. During the winter to come, no one need starve. All they had to do was to organize a hunt and bring in not only enough meat and skins for the family's use, but some to exchange for anything else they might need. "In this country," said Whitley, "the soundest legal tender is a buffalo skin, and fifty miles west the buffalo are still so tame you can walk up to one and slit his throat."

While they were discussing this, Moses Shelby took Jus aside, and told him that he might read law with George Muter, who was in charge of the soldiers' land titles, and would probably be Chief

Justice. "Hearing from Whitley that you aimed to handle the land titles," he said, "we've found a place for you to live right near the county seat. You can have it as long as you want, and all you've got to do for rent is to leave it with five acres cleared."

As they talked, Jus underwent one of those transformations which Mary loved to see—when he was pulled up from his careless, amiable, frontier slackness to his latent best. He sat up straight. His black eyes flashed with intelligent response, instead of being veiled, shifty, and Indianlike. He even took the quid of tobacco out of his cheek and wiped his mouth. When he picked Peter up out of his deep sleep and set him on the saddle, Peter sensed the warm power flowing out of his father's big body, and nestled against it in drowsy security.

5

Peter and his father soon found the scattering cabins under huge trees which formed the new county seat of Stanford. Stanford had been built three years before in 1787 on a tract of land given by Benjamin Logan, one and a half miles east of Logan's Fort, or St. Asaph's, which was one of the two earliest settlements, the other being Boone's fort at Boonesborough. Though Stanford had some two hundred inhabitants, including Negroes, tucked out of sight in the woods, the only sign of a town as yet was the new courthouse. This was built of logs, and was thirty by twenty feet, with a small jury room at each side, which gave it the form of a T. Near it was a log jail of two rooms, each twelve feet square. Jus took Peter into the empty building and pointed out the platform behind a high desk of puncheons set on up-ended logs, where the Judge sat; the seat below for the clerk; the puncheon tables on each side for the attorneys of the plaintiff and defendant; the puncheon benches with log supports for the jury, close to the witness box; and the bench enclosed by a strong palisade of heavy logs for the prisoner, guarded by the sheriff. He also pointed out to Peter the large iron stove and explained its working. He had seen these modern miracles in Pennsylvania when he was a soldier. But in the courthouse in Virginia the only heat came from fireplaces.

They then rode through the cedar woods above the Dick River. Peter stared wonderingly down on the water lying far below, walled on each side by solid perpendicular rock, three or four hundred feet high, of limestone and marble. They found the land Shelby had offered Jus, with a half finished cabin, and corn growing between charred stumps. Jus reckoned that by winter he could finish the cabin, break more ground for corn and truck patch and flax patch, build a barn, fence the horselot, lay in a winter's store of venison, bear's meat and buffalo meat, and get enough skins to trade for anything they might need. Then he could spend the winter months attending the county court and studying law. He was so pleased with this prospect that he clattered back to Crab Orchard in high spirits, trying not to think how Mary would "take on" when she heard that it would be two, perhaps even three years, before they could settle on their own land.

Mary met him looking neat and pretty, her freshly washed dark hair becomingly braided around her head. "I know all about it," she said, with a clear, radiant look. "I reckon it's for the best to stop here."

Not till the confidential midnight hour together under the bearskin did Jus learn that Elder Poythress had called on Mary. At first she'd been embarrassed because he found her washing her hair. But by the time she'd got it tied up in a long roll of clean linsy, in a turban on top of her head, he'd made himself at home on an upturned stump. He told her about the dangers of going down to the new land, and the farm on Dick's River, plans for getting Jus admitted to the bar. And then he had pictured what she might do meanwhile for the seven poor wandering preachers who were all there was of the Methodist Church west of the Alleghenies.

Homeless, allowed to keep only $64.00 for themselves out of their collections from their scattered converts, using the rest to build the church here up from scratch, a kind Christian woman was to them the only hope of comfort. She'd cook them a hot meal, after they'd lived for days on mouldy corn pone or game shot while riding from one preaching to the next. In her home a tired man could sleep under linen sheets of her own weaving, and a quilt of her own patching, instead of on a buffalo skin on the bare ground.

As yet there were few log chapels. A Christian home could be a warm, clean, well furnished substitute for a church.

So he talked, holding out to Mary the hope of leadership in religion as the Shelbys had held out to Jus the hope of leadership in the law. "And the Lord will bless a house of which one pillar is justice and the other mercy," said Poythress solemnly. "He calls on you to start under your own roof a woman's society for Christian service."

Repeating the events of that wonderful day, Jus and Mary hugged each other in the awareness of a miracle accomplished. No longer were they lowdown folks beyond the edge of civilization, living no better than Indians. They had come into a new world where they would be leaders, and would build their own civilization with heart and brain as well as hands. Peter, listening, registered it all. He had an intense, precocious curiosity about life. The hours in which he strained his ears to catch the whisperings under the bearskin were a kind of hothouse in which night by night his own heart and soul were continually forced to an awareness beyond his years.

CHAPTER 8   Stanford, Kentucky
                                        September, 1790

In the new home, the nearest neighbor on one side was Dean, and on the other Brenda and Dutch and their family which, besides Jerry, included Gretta, a plump girl of ten with flaxen braids and dark eyes, a sunny winsome small boy, named Heinie, and Hans and Otto, two big boys about John's age, with bulging blue eyes and bulging muscles on their strong young arms.

The friendship between Mary and Brenda, begun and broken off before Peter was born, was now renewed. Brenda hadn't changed much. In a world where women sagged and aged early, she was still the same trim, fiercely neat young woman. The excitement of Mary's life, the first winter in Stanford, was the mental clash with a feminine mind as keen and untrained as her own. Most of their arguments concerned Baptists and Methodists. Central Kentucky was at that time a Baptist stronghold. Squire Boone, Daniel's brother, had been a Baptist preacher. While there were only a few

Presbyterians, and a few hundred Methodists here, there were thousands of Baptists organized in hard, self-isolated, self-disciplined, equalitarian units, with one of their members as leader and preacher, living by the Bible according to their lights, scorning those weak souls that must have a bishop, a clergy, or any organization outside themselves to tell them what to do.

"Your Methodist circuit riders," said Brenda, "don't know it, but when they sign up with Asbury, that's the last of being free men. The day when they wake up to that ends the Methodist Church here. They didn't cross the mountains to be anybody's slave—least of all that old sickly minded, sickly bodied Englishman's."

Mary tried to answer this, but she lacked ammunition. But just wait till the Circuit Rider came around! She'd get enough intellectual gunpowder from him to blast Brenda into dumbness on this subject for all time!

More stinging, more deeply disturbing, were Brenda's observations on Mary's son, John. At thirteen John had little of the crudeness of the frontier boy. He stood when Brenda came into the room, and set a chair for her by the fire. These attentions Brenda dismissed with a curt "That's nice of you, John," and, when he was out of sight, remarked, "You'll have to watch that son of yours, Mary. He's just cut out for the Mystic Band."

What was the Mystic Band? Brenda explained in horrendous detail. It was a secret society, said to have been organized by Philip Alston, to snare young people into a life of crime. "Those that have fancy notions about themselves are those they get easiest. Some fine-talking gentleman spies a boy like John who likes to keep his fingernails clean and have everything fine and fancy. And he says, 'Son, I can show you how to make $50.00 if you'll keep your mouth shut.' Without the boy's knowing what he's doing he gets him to be a go-between for the killers and stealers. Then he says, 'If you squeal, you're a dead one. If you keep your mouth shut, there'll be money in your pocket.' They've all sorts of secret signs, and oaths, and ways of scaring people and they have regular services in which they worship the devil the way we worship God, and burn a fiery cross in the Devil's name."

Mary was horrified. "John wouldn't have any truck with things like that," she said, with a confidence she did not feel. The heart and soul of her eldest son were shut to her. There had been a wall between them ever since—She pushed into her deepest subconscious a question she would not face. Had John Wilcox, unburied long ago, snatched from her his eldest son and namesake when she married Jus?

When Mary told Jus what Brenda had said about the Band, he said there was evidence of such a secret society, and it might be Alston was back of it. The problem was to get through the mess of rumor, and rule out the stories people make up for lack of anything else to talk about, or for spite and self-righteousness, and get what could be *proved*. However, he pooh poohed any danger to John. He also pooh poohed the Baptist taboos. Where cards, liquor, and women were concerned, the thing to do was to teach a boy to take 'em or leave 'em. He would take John in hand and keep an eye on him. Mary was reassured. She had observed that Jus could sway John where she couldn't.

2

Justurian's first assignment as future attorney to the veterans was to go over a petition which Muter had received asking that the Military Tract be set off as a separate county, and check the signatures against the veterans' warrants and such names of outlaws as could be supplied by Cherokee Bill or James Haw, the circuit rider. The first name that met his eye was Sam Mason who, Lydia had said, was John Wilson, the captain of the river pirates. When Jus told Muter this, he answered uneasily, "Every one of the names and grants has to be looked into. Some of them are forged. About Mason, you'd better see Whitley."

When Jus told Whitley what Lydia had said, his grizzled face set in lines so deep they looked as if carved in oak. "I've met this Mason," he said. "He stayed at the fort a few days. A big, pleasant fellow—seems quite a gentleman!" He added angrily, "If those Yankees know so much, why don't they come across with proof? They've been raising Cain saying that some of George Rogers Clark's men have got themselves holed up in Cave-in-Rock and are robbing and murdering."

"Do you think that's true."

"Could be. You can be a hero and conquer the Northwest, and still not sprout angel feathers." He shrugged. "No use talking to me about it. I've got my hands full with Boone's trace. I've recommended they put a Federal fort up on the Ohio to take care of pirates. I understand they are doing it, at the mouth of the Cumberland. It will be your mainstay. As for Sam Mason being John Wilson—I just don't know."

The next legal chore Jus undertook was going with another lawyer to the bedside of a dying woman to write down the woman's deposition that a slender, gentle, beautiful quadroon, named Jassamine, who was nursing her, was free. Jassamine had been put up, as a child, on the slave-block in Charleston, and had been bought by the woman's husband, a Quaker, on a business trip there, and taken north to Philadelphia and freed, and brought up in their household as a daughter. Now her mistress, dying, wanted to make sure that she would remain free. Jus got his first legal experience drawing up the proper papers.

This dying woman and Jassamine were all that was left of a party of Yankees who had been attacked by robbers on the road from Louisville to Lexington. All the men were overpowered and killed. Jassamine and her mistress were the only women in the party. In the cold November dusk a big highwayman with one protruding tooth loomed over the girl and held her as in a vise with his big hands. "Easiest thing is to shoot 'em all, and leave 'em be. Dead, they tell no tales," said a voice. But the big man with a protruding tooth said, "Damn you to Hell for a lowdown butcher!" To Jassamine he murmured, "Calm down, my honey-colored wench. I don't want your life, and I don't want your virtue."

Expertly he bound her hand and foot and tossed her into the bushes. Then there was a crash, and she knew that her mistress had been bound and thrown in after her. They could hear the clatter of hoofs receding. Then night, cold, and utter aloneness settled down. All night Jassamine struggled to free herself, losing consciousness now and then in sleep but waking to struggle again. Her mistress never moaned or complained, but spoke reassuringly, and Jassamine answered with reassurances. Early next day Jassamine managed to free herself, and then to cut the rope that bound her mistress. Aching and hungry they then started to walk over the frozen, crusty ground to Lexington, till her mistress sank to the ground dizzy with fever, choked with phlegm, brought on by cold and exposure. Jassamine made a bed for her in the dried leaves, and broke the thin ice on a pool to get her water. Her mistress could eat nothing, but Jassamine found some black walnuts which she cracked for herself and a few chestnuts. For two days they lived thus alone in the woods.

The third day a horseman appeared on the trail. Jassamine braved the danger that it might be another robber, and ran out and hailed him. It was Elder Poythress covering his circuit. He rallied out help from a Methodist family a few miles away, who brought the sick woman on a sledge to Masterton's. Masterton was a Methodist brother who kept a clean and commodious station five miles from Lexington which served as a headquarters for the Methodists. There the Quaker lady was put to bed between clean white sheets, and was nursed by Jassamine, while her life ebbed away. She used her last strength and consciousness to have the papers made out for Jassamine, certifying that she was free. Then she died.

Everybody was concerned for the graceful, ladylike girl. The Mastertons said they'd be proud to have her stay on and help them with the station. Mary called on her and found that, though brought up a Quaker, she had been baptized a Methodist. Thereupon Mary invited her to the next class meeting at the Cartwright cabin, to which Dean also came. There Jassamine told of the day when she had heard Asbury preach, back in Pennsylvania. Into the clean, bleak, and, to her, cold emptiness of her Quaker upbringing there had flooded the warmth, the kindness, the redeeming love of the Saviour. Kneeling and weeping not so much for her sins as for her great need for love and guidance, she had felt Asbury's slender hands laid on her head in blessing. To her the ceremony of baptism and her first communion had been soul-shattering experiences in which her Quaker benefactors had taken a remote, kindly interest, opposing no arguments or barriers.

While Jassamine told her story, Dean's large, magnetic eyes never left her face. When the next class meeting met, she and Dean rode up together on two of Dean's excellent horses, from Elder Poythress's preaching station ten miles away, whither they had gone to have him make them man and wife.

To Peter, the home Dean made for Jassamine was second only to the Ranger's in splendor, though it was only a log cabin. Reared as children in wealthy homes, they had in common a vision of domestic elegance such as neither Mary nor Brenda had even seen. Among the household goods that had come down the Ohio and were auctioned off by people who needed money or had found them useless on the frontier, Dean acquired a mahogany chest of drawers, an Oriental rug brought to Philadelphia by a sailing ship, some delicate porcelain teacups, and two tall brass candlesticks in which he burned candles with an extravagance not elsewhere known in the cabined darkness of that primitive land. The gleaming richness of Dean's cabin by candlelight and firelight affected Peter like a sunset or the golden light of an October afternoon, sifting through the colored leaves of the forest, making him feel solemn, but uplifted and deeply satisfied.

With Jassamine to work for, there was a stimulus to Dean's capacity for attracting material wealth and to that innate social authority in him which, in a white man, would have been the mark of "aristocracy." Concerning his status, whether slave or free, no one asked questions. It was enough that he lived in association with the Cartwright family. In early Kentucky there were a good many Negroes of personality and superior culture who lived in lifelong relation to a white man which was more of a partnership than a relation of slave to master, leaving the black man free to acquire property and sometimes to develop a business or professional career. Henry Hosier, the small, very black man who went everywhere with Asbury, was preferred by some congregations as a better preacher than Asbury himself. So in that raw world on which the blight of the cotton slave-economy had not yet fallen, Dean and Jassamine were personages, and were treated as such.

One point in Jassamine's story had fixed Justurian's attention. It was her description of the big highwayman with a protruding tooth. "If we could ever get one of these cases to court, it would help to know that one of these sons of Satan looked like that," he reflected, and rode over to see the Ranger, to ask "Is Sam Mason, by any chance, a big fellow with a tooth that sticks out?"

"Yes, that's Sam," replied Whitley, in surprise.

"That's all I want to know," said Jus.

But, riding home, he was forced to consider the limitations of the law which Whitley, though no lawyer, had accurately pointed out to him. "All you've got for testimony is the single unsupported word of a nigger girl. How long will that stand up in court?"

Sometimes it seemed to Jus that the law was rigged to let the criminal out. Yet, as he scowled at the rights that men like Alston and Sam Mason had—the right to be represented by counsel, to be considered innocent till proved guilty, the right of *habeas corpus,*—the experience of three centuries of resistance to Catholic church and feudal overlord stirred in him. It had to be like that. Else there was no protection for the innocent against spite, greed, mob violence, or power in high places. "All that's needed is patience," he reflected, "and we'll get those fellows. We'll have to out-wit and out-wait them by due process of law."

"Due process of law"—a respect for this has been virtually unknown in societies far more complex and polished than that of early Kentucky, but on this, and on a crude evangelism which these young settlers created for themselves out of the application of the Bible and their own ideas of right to their barbarous situation in an unbroken wilderness, they were to build the unique American civilization.

With this deep, bred-in-the-bone respect for "due process," Jus made a rough and ready attack on the inherited body of English law. The main project of the years 1790-1792 was to read through Blackstone's Commentaries and try to make sense of them. He had to do his studying in a one-room cabin shut up with his family on cold winter days, the wooden shutters closed, and no light save that of the wood fire and of one precious, sparingly used candle. But worse than the lack of light and privacy was the lack of writing materials. Paper was scarce and very expensive, and available only for official use. Jus needed something on which to practice writing and to scribble rough notes. For a while he used boards whittled smooth and sanded, writing on them with pokeberry juice and a goose quill pen. He was rejoiced when he got a piece of slate and a slate pencil.

Night after night Peter's last vision as he sank to sleep in his trundle bed was his father sitting close to the fire and reading the law book by its flame, copying words on the slate, painfully and slowly, with the big rough hand that looked more fitted for a gun than a pen.

Like most primitive leaders of savage tribes, who must function without help from the printed page, Jus had a well trained memory. As a scout in the frontier militia he had learned at sixteen to carry messages by making a knot in a thong of deerskin for each name or fact he wished not to forget. By fingering his knotted cord every few hours he could keep his message in mind. Now, learning out of a borrowed book, writing notes which he must erase to make new ones, Jus efficiently consigned all pertinent legal details to the safe-keeping of his own head.

It helped Jus to understand a difficult legal passage if he translated it into simple concrete words and tried it out on Mary. But she didn't take much stock in all this man-made law. Who had made it anyway? The gentry and the parsons to suit their own selfishness. The punishments were brutal. It was biased against debtors and mortgagers. Its doctrines of criminal conspiracy, seditious libel, and inalienable allegiance were outrages against the free soul of man. She looked for the day when they'd chuck those old law books into the fire and start new with only the word of God to guide them—both the word He had written in His Book, and the one He had written in men's hearts, if they'd only forget their own selfishness long enough to heed it. To all this Jus listened with some amusement, not assenting but not actively dissenting, either. He was not the only frontier lawyer on whose own rudimentary ideas of law the earnest, unlettered evangelism of his nearest and dearest was having a certain effect.

But the main part of Justurian's training was attending the county court and sitting afterwards by the fire in the log tavern, chewing tobacco, drinking whisky, exchanging jokes and raw stories with members of the Kentucky bar, and taking an increasing part in an argument which went on and on, from one meeting of the court to the next. In this argument the majority of lawyers, including Jus, maintained that the common law of England was too barbarous and antiquated to serve as the basis for American law. They wanted to start new and build American law on the statutes of the Virginia Assembly, on the laws to be made in the future by the Kentucky legislature and the Federal Congress, and on the eternal principles of right and justice as expressed by Thomas Jefferson. The minority group held that the Common Law was the indispensable basis of American law, and that those who had not mastered it could never hope to associate on equal terms with lawyers outside of Kentucky. But so strong was the objection to taking laws from England that it was generally forbidden to cite an English precedent in a Kentucky court.

Peter often listened to these arguments, registering fragments of them in his retentive mind, for Jus and Dutch took their small sons everywhere, as men take favorite dogs. So Peter was quite used not only to the county court, but to all the side shows, like horse races, wrestling matches, shooting matches, drinking bouts, and violent arguments beginning with words and ending with fists. Mary used to object when Jus rode home through snow or sleet after midnight, and lifted Peter down from the saddle, sound asleep in his cocoon of fur. She said if Jus couldn't get the boy home at a decent hour, he'd have to leave him behind. Jus wanted to know why one hour of the night was decenter than another and what was to prevent Peter from sleeping late in the morning to make up. The only concession Mary could wring from him was a pledge that Peter should never drink whisky. For that promise which Jus faithfully kept she had to sacrifice all other objections.

3

The sense of prestige which Peter derived from his father's legal activities was enhanced by his mother's position with the Methodist clergy. The future superb organization of the Methodist Church existed at that time only in the head of the frail Englishman who drove his protesting body over the Alleghenies every year. And Asbury's ideas had been only imperfectly communicated to the half dozen headstrong earnest young men who comprised the whole of the Kentucky District. Though Poythress was called presiding elder, actually no such title existed till 1792. But Mary saw it all with something of the vision of Asbury himself. The Church was to her a great transcendent entity, and its ministers more than human, to be welcomed at her house with something above daily fare.

Though the cuisine was normally limited to meat, more meat, and still more meat, Mary acquired small amounts of such imported delicacies as coffee, China tea, lumpy brown cane sugar, New Orleans molasses, ginger, and wheat flour which Peter looked on as a kind of food of the angels, reserved exclusively for preachers. Not for many years did these items cease to have, in the western cabins, a peculiar odor and taste of sanctity. With the super-celestial smell of the cookery, Peter associated an unwonted state of cleanliness in his own person. His round brown face shone with scrubbing. His hair which had been sticky with dirt and prickly with burs had been washed and slowly and painfully reduced to a cloud of soft, dark curls. He couldn't see the curls, but when his mother's eyes rested fondly on them, he would put up his hand and touch the delicate light stuff with a feeling of mingled pride and well being. Having been stood in a wooden tub, and thoroughly and ignominiously scrubbed while he struggled and yelled, he felt light and free and somehow superior in a clean linsy shirt and pants of a brown butternut color. He even enjoyed contemplating the unwonted cleanness of his bare toes, calloused and criss-crossed as they still were with ingrained lines of dirt.

The first winter the visitors were mainly Poythress and Barnabas McHenry, a tall, commanding, courteous, but frank and natural man with brown eyes and reddish hair. They both filled the cabin with a kind of unearthly energy, barely held in leash, and awed Peter so that he could hardly bear it. He felt more at ease when Benjamin Ogden turned up. Ogden was a stocky man of twenty-five, distinguished from the usual gang of wrestlers and gun artists who hung around the county court only by his earnestness and his greater personal cleanliness, and his way of correcting himself when he had made a slip of grammar. He had been sent with James Haw in 1787 to "break" the Green River and Cumberland River area into circuits. Peter listened, entranced, while Ogden told how he had come down the Ohio River, and had gone ashore at Maysville with the names of Methodists who had gone west, on a piece of paper in the blouse of his hunting tunic. He'd located Simon Kenton three miles southwest of where he landed, and then he located the Stevens sons, Methodists from Maryland, and going on in a southwesterly direction, he had found himself beyond all settlements, on the banks of a river he knew must be the Green River. There back in 1781, a man from Virginia named Abraham Lincoln had filed claims for 2000 acres, and way off here he'd built a log house and started clearing. But one day three or four years before Ogden came, he'd been killed by an Indian arrow while he was working in his corn patch. Then his family had all gone away. Ogden slept in his empty house, but he prayed all night, because there were so many noises and stirrings. But he knew they were only apparitions of Satan to frighten him back. So he prayed till at dawn there came peace and quiet, and he slept.

Then he had gone on into that sea of light which is the Barrens, and which, though he kept describing it, Peter could not imagine, because he had lived all his life in the forest shadows. Ogden had traveled day and night up and down that country, and wherever there was a little nest of human beings he found them. Some he married, some he christened, and some he buried. Some he comforted, and a few he saved from going mad or killing somebody. And a handful of them he brought to Christ.

What Peter found most exciting were the maps Ogden drew in the ash on the hearth with the point of a stick, showing how the streams ran in that country to which they were going, and where there were "knobs" or sudden outcroppings of limestone rock, making sharp isolated hills and hillocks, and where the buffalo had made and kept open from year to year, time out of mind, those paths through the long grass they called traces. And he was interested to hear about those strange dark people, the Portyghees, whom that wicked man, Alston, had enticed there.

"They're niggers, ain't they?" asked Jus.

"No. So far as the county courts have had occasion to pass on the matter, they're held to be white. But they look like they were white, Indian, and Negro mixed. Some say they're the lost tribes of Israel. Some say they're descendants of a Portuguese ship that was wrecked years and years ago on the Carolina coast. But the thing that's against this is that they have English names, and none of them can remember a time when their folks didn't speak English. The likeliest story, I think, is that they're descended from the lost colony. You know way back before there was a permanent settlement in Virginia, there was a colony of English that just disappeared. It was thought they had all been killed by Indians. But I think they just started going west, the way we're doing. So now all the way west from the Carolinas, you'll find these nests of dark people called Portyghees."

"I think you're right—they're the lost colony," said Mary, decisively, her vivid imagination quite untrammelled by historical evidence. To think of these folks that had been thought to be lost turning up on their very own land! "You did say that there's some of them down where we are to settle?" she asked, afraid lest it shouldn't be so, and the drama of it all be imperfect.

"Yes, there's a little nest of them on Muddy River—I'm afraid they're all Alston's counterfeiters."

Mary was disappointed that people with so romantic an ancestry should be so wicked. "Arn't there any good ones at all?" she asked anxiously, and was relieved to hear that the Baptists had got in among them somewhere and many of them had been "redeemed."

"It takes the Baptists to get hold of folks like that," commented Ogden. "I hold we won't get where we ought to till we take a lesson in democracy from the Baptists. At present there's too much pulling us all around, like bear cubs on a leash, by Asbury, who's a foreigner and hasn't the first idea of what we think is democracy over here."

At this point Peter lost interest. He was lying on a bearskin before the fireplace. And while Jus and Ogden went off on a discussion of democracy in church government, he thought dreamily about those lost people wandering by themselves in the wilds. The next thing he knew it was night. He was in his trundle bed, and the preacher had gone.

But Mary listened with a sinking heart, for all that Brenda had said about Asbury and his "Lord and Tory" rule, Ogden was now repeating. As she sat staring moodily at the young preacher, she felt a deep foreboding. If the Methodists started breaking up, they'd end by being hooked in by the Baptists. She could not bear to give Brenda that satisfaction!

4

By spring Mary had made supper and laid open clean beds for all six preachers then on the western circuits. But the preachers that rode up that warm April day were nobody she'd ever seen. The door stood open on the soft bloomy outdoors. Suddenly a big man filled the doorway with blackness—broad black hat, long black hair, long and very heavy black beard, black clothes covering his heavy bulk, and, dominating all this blackness, a pair of large black eyes. He tramped in and set his gun in the corner and seated himself on the bench at the table without removing his hat. "I'm a Methodist preacher, Ma'am," he said and looked from the table to the bubbling iron kettle that gave off a nourishing savor.

Mary hastily pinned up a stray lock of hair, and came forward, smiling. "You're hungry. There's always a place at our table for the servants of the Lord."

The big man gave a kind of snort, and rose, and tramped to the door. "Come in, Red," he called into the outdoors. "The sister's got food."

A slight young man, with red hair, and beard, and blue eyes, clothed in identical black habiliments, now entered. "Put your gun there," said the big man, jerking his thumb toward the corner, "unless you aim to shoot the lady."

Used as she was to preachers' humor, Mary found something strange in these servants of God. Peter crouched in the corner by the fire, his bright eyes observing the two men. "Come here, young un," said the big man. Usually Peter went to preachers willingly Now he clung to his mother's skirts. "So you're afraid of me?" asked the big man, with a wild, leering look. "Scairt! Plumb scairt! He turned to his red-haired companion. "Brother Wiley, what do you recommend for a young un that's scairt?"

"Slit his throat," said Brother Wiley, speaking for the first time

The big man took out his knife. "You heard him. You hear my pious brother. You come, or else. I'll count three. Come One, two, three—"

Mary always kept her pistol at hand. Now, while seeming to g toward the bubbling kettle, she swiftly laid her hand on the pile c linsy that concealed it, and her lips said soundlessly to Pete "Dean. Get Dean."

The big man ostentatiously sharpened his knife against his leather boot. "I give you a second chance, but no more. I'll count, and if you arn't here on the count of three—"

Peter started toward him, but on the count of three he was out of the door, and running at his top speed to where Dean was working in the fields. "Two men—they look like preachers but they ain't. Quick. Go to Mammy. Quick."

"Run and get Dutch," said Dean, and with great loping steps he was off for the cabin. Peter was out of breath. He had a stitch in his side, and his heart was pounding. But he ran.

When Peter reached the cabin with Dutch, the big man lay groaning on the floor, one of his legs limp or broken in a pool of blood. Dean was grappling with the little man. "Now," he said, holding Wiley as in a vise, "who are you?"

Wiley did not answer, but the man on the floor said, "Splint my leg, and help me on to my horse and I'll tell you." While Wiley was held bound by Dean, Dutch bandaged the big man's leg, and helped him outdoors and into the saddle of one of the two horses that were tethered there. "My gun," said the big man.

"We keep that till you are too far away it on us to turn," said Dutch. "You can get it at Masterton's to-night." He turned to Wiley, whom Dean had practically carried out to the other horse, and added, "We're seein' you to your horse. Up you go." Dean picked him up like a child and set him in the saddle. Dutch gave the big one's horse a push. "Get goin'!" he said.

The horses bounded forward. The two men yelled in unison, "We are the Harpes!" and rode madly away.

The post-mortem on this strange affair continued for weeks. Mary said that, when Peter ran out, she tried to find out whether the men were really preachers, or at least to appeal to their better natures by asking them to read a passage from the Bible by way of grace before meat. She pretended that she couldn't read herself, and never lost a chance to hear the word of God read to her. The big one took the Bible, but instead of reading it, he began to look at the records of births and events, beginning with the birth of Peter. The last entry had been made by Jus. "March 4. George Washington was inaugurated President of the United States."

The big one stared at this soberly. "George Washington was a brave man," he remarked. "But a mighty rebel against the king."

"Against the King," exclaimed Mary. "Why! We were all against the King!"

"And you're all to die for it, and roast in Hell," said the big man so violently that Mary stepped back swiftly to where her pistol lay under the new-spun length of linsy by the spinning wheel. Just then Dean's big form darkened the door way. "Mike," said the little man urgently. "Mike, look!"

Mike turned to Dean, startled, picked up the knife, and went toward Mary with his arm lifted and its point turned to her heart. "You've sent for that big nigger to spy on us."

Mary whipped out the pistol and aimed at his leg. He fell to the floor, with a howling curse. Afterwards she explained. "I didn't figure to kill him. I aimed to break his leg, so he couldn't do mischief."

He kept howling with pain, and dropped the knife. Mary darted toward him and grabbed the knife away. He rolled over and over trying to get at her. The little one flew at Dean and grappled with him. The big one turned over and dragged himself toward Dean, tried to grab his leg and throw him. Dean kicked him off, while struggling with the little man who, though small, was tough and wiry. Mary by this time was out of the door, and looking at the two horses the "preachers" had left saddled and tethered there, wondered whether to jump on one and go for more help when Dutch galloped up, with Peter on his saddle.

All this made talk for weeks as one after another heard of it, and added some new story to the tale of the Harpes. For these two were already a legend on the frontier. Mary had heard of them several times, but had paid little attention to the name. Micajah and Wiley Harpe, known as "Big Harpe" and "Little Harpe" were sons of a British Tory who had been killed in the Battle of King's Mountain, in North Carolina. As children of a Tory, following the Revolution, they had been scorned and ostracized and finally had taken refuge with the Indians. Besides the Indians, their only helpers had been Presbyterian ministers, for in that section of the mountains the only church was Presbyterian. Latterly the Methodists had taken up their cause, and Elder Poythress had at times had hope of doing something with Big Harpe. The preachers tried to build up their self respect, and combat weird rumors that followed wherever they went. There had been several morbid murders in and around Knoxville, in western North Carolina (now Tennessee) where they were most often seen and best known—children found with their necks wrung like young chickens, bodies cut open, filled with stones and dropped into a stream. When suspicion fastened on the Harpes, they had left Knoxville and gone into central Kentucky. Now it was said that they had some part in the crimes of Cave-in-Rock. There was the story Lydia and her party told about seeing one of the robbers pick up a child by the legs, and twirl it about and fling it far into the river. That, folks said, was what Big Harpe might do. And there were the two figures that stood naked and howling on a height by Cave-in-Rock, taunting a party that was being killed below. That, folks said, might well be the Harpes.

The tendency of such talk was to make good folks answer, "Micajah and Wiley were well nigh ruined when they were children with evil speaking against them for what wasn't their fault. And are we to give them their last push into Hell now? Hold your tongues, and let us help them all we can."

When Mary heard the whole story, she was filled with compunction for her shooting of Big Harpe, the more so when Elder Poythress sent word that Harpe was lying ill at a Methodist sister's house, with his wound greatly inflamed. She and Brenda and Jassamine immediately rode over to see him, taking some of their precious tea, coffee, brown sugar, and ginger, and clean sheets and bandages. But when Mary tried to tell Big Harpe that she was sorry she had hurt him, he looked at her scornfully. "Don't be a mealy-mouthed Methodist fool. It was what any woman ought to have done, if she'd had a gun." He added, sardonically, "If you hadn't shot, I'd have ripped you with my knife." And with a realistic sweep of his hand he drew a line in the air from just above the parting of the breasts to where her full skirts covered the fork of the legs.

Mary gave up, but to the Methodist sister, who came in just then with a bowl of buffalo meat broth, she said, "If there's anything we can do for him, we will."

To the Methodist sister Big Harpe said, ignoring Mary, "I don't thank her for what she does now any more than for what she did then."

Jus wanted to bring Big Harpe to trial for threatened molestation of Mary. But Mary was aghast at the idea. In her world such an affair was a "fracas" which those concerned settled among themselves. Jus then proposed that Big Harpe bring action against Mary for shooting him in the leg. "In such an action, we could clear up a lot of talk, and find out what he was up to, coming on to you like that." At first Mary was outraged by the idea that an action could be brought against her for what was obviously self-defense. But when she understood what Jus had in mind, she agreed reluctantly. "Well, if he thinks he was wronged, it's his right. And I'll stand up for myself for doing what anybody in her senses would, even though I know I'll be struck dumb if I have to show my face in court."

When Jus suggested the idea to the injured Harpe, the big dark man glared, and shook with fright, and pleaded with him. "Let be. She did what was right. Next thing I'd ha' ripped her from throat to crotch."

Shocked, Jus looked into his great brown eyes in which a maniac gleam was giving place to the beseeching of a helpless child, and remarked dryly, "It sure would be interesting if you were to stand up and say that in court."

Following this interview with Justurian, Big Harpe begged so earnestly for a preacher that the Methodists dashed about on horseback, to locate Elder Poythress and bring him to the bedside of the suffering man. And meanwhile their hearts were softened, and they prayed singly and in unison for his soul's salvation. But Poythress' report of what came of his ministrations was disquieting.

"I sat up through a whole night with Micajah Harpe, and all that time he kept talking to me about predestination, saying he knew for sure that the Almighty had destined him for a life of crime since before the beginning of the world, and Hell was before him. No matter what he could do, he must run his appointed course. I said I didn't believe any of this. He said, 'To Hell you don't! Why?' I said, 'I am a Methodist. I believe in the freedom of man's soul, and the everlasting love of God.' Then he rose from his sick bed, and pointed his pistol at me and his eyes glittered like a maniac, and he said I was a damned heretic, and get out of there. He said, one more word from me, and he'd blow me right through Hell to the wastes beyond that were worse, for there were gentlemen in Hell, but beyond, where I'd go, there was only scum. I drew my pistol, and I backed out. But outside I knelt in the wet forest, and I prayed for well nigh an hour for that man's soul." He hesitated, and added, "A man who suffers in his spirit like that isn't all bad. And I am not ready to say that what is alleged about him is true. But he's on the edge of madness. And unless his soul is saved and he finds the peace of God, I pity him and all that come his way."

It was a relief to all when Harpe's fever abated, and his leg appeared to lose its pain, and his small red-haired brother, who had hitherto not shown himself, suddenly appeared to take him back to Knoxville. They said good-bye politely, and, with thanks, rode away. "The queerest pair!"

But, as Mary told Brenda, "If you don't treat children right, that's what you raise up for yourself. It's like Micajah ain't all bad. There's real good in him. But he has a nest o' rattlesnakes inside him, and you never know when one of them will rear its head and strike."

But Brenda wouldn't agree that it was in the "raisin'," for the Baptists were predestinarians. She didn't want to hurt Mary by saying too much about John—more than just a warning to be careful. Mary and Jus had certainly raised that boy with care and love. "But look at him," she reflected. "He's as much possessed of a devil as Micajah Harpe. It's not an angry devil. It's a cold devil, but it's deeper. There's just no opening in that boy's hard soul for prayers or human love to get through." And, as usual, she marvelled that Mary and Jus should be so blind to what was perfectly plain in the reports of Peter and little Jerry.

CHAPTER 9

On February 4, 1791, Congress passed the enabling act, providing for the admission of the Western District of Virginia, as the fifteenth state, with the name of Kentucky. The date set for the final admission was June 2, 1792, by which time Kentucky must provide itself with a constitution, a governor, and a legislature. Following the admission as a state, the Military Tract could be organized, with its own county court, and the veterans would be in a position to impose order in an area growing daily more menacing. Meanwhile the federal Fort Massac had been established at the mouth of the Cumberland. Jus and the other veterans were holding meetings to make sure that the principles of Thomas Jefferson, plus various radical ideas of their own, were written into the state constitution, and to make plans for dealing with the *de facto* government of the illicit society that was rapidly forming on their own land.

For detailed information about the state of affairs on the Military Tract, the circuit riders were still the best source. From the reports of Ogden, Jus was making a kind of names and places dictionary for the new county to which every talk with a preacher added some detail. The latest circuit rider to go down to the Cumberland was Peter Massie—a slender man of thirty, too slight for rough riding. Mary worried about him from the time he left. She did not know that Polly was worrying, too. At the age of ten, Polly's heart had received its first romantic impression. Used to being indulged because she was pretty and appealing, Polly already aspired to something finer than she saw all around her. And one of the finer things she aspired to was a man who wasn't bristly with hair, stained with tobacco juice, and malodorous with the whisky-flavored aroma of the unwashed. The first faint impulses of adolescence turned to the beautiful young preacher. She surprised her mother by asking to go to Peter Massie's preaching, and fell on her knees and prayed. At this there were tears of joy in her mother's eyes. She had no idea that Polly was praying not to God but to Peter Massie.

But when Polly crept close to him by her own fireside, hoping he would put his arm around her as the other preachers did, Massie rather abruptly pushed her down into a kneeling position, saying, "Polly, it's time for family prayers." There was a storm in the child's heart as she knelt there, wanting to snatch him from his absorption in God, wanting to keep him in the cabin always. Next morning he departed with hardly a glance at her, leaving her a dream tinged with resentment which absorbed all her waking, and some of her sleeping, hours.

Mary never knew how Polly's heart broke when word was brought that, in December 1791, Peter Massie had died, four miles west of Nashville. He had insisted on going on, from one preaching place to the next, in the first bitter weather of winter, though he was so dizzy and weak he could hardly sit his horse. He could not have kept going as long as he did had it not been that a tall, powerful young Negro, named Simeon, whom he had brought to God, came to his help. Simeon begged him to stop traveling, through the bad weather, and get a rest. But Massie said, "If I am not well enough to travel, I might as well die." He died, and Simeon said the burial service over him. And then Simeon took up his work, and went from one convert to another that Massie had made, encouraging them to hold fast till another circuit rider could be sent to them. Hearing this, Polly's heart quietly broke. What she went through no one knew. But she would never fall in love with a preacher again, nor yield herself even for a moment to preaching.

Almost as disquieting as Massie's death, to Mary, was the visit she received from James Haw. "Send your prayers with me, Sister," he said. "I'm going down to the Cumberland for good."

Joy broke over her face. "Oh, then you'll be there when we come."

"I'll not be too far away," he replied, his cloudy face taking no gleam from the light in hers, "but not on your Tract. I'll be over the border in the western district of North Carolina, which is to be organized as the territory of the United States south of the Ohio."

"You mean—near Nashville?"

"Between your Tract and Nashville."

"Oh well, that can't be more than a dozen miles from us. But I thought you took in as much as 300 miles on a circuit."

"I'll not be on a circuit. I'm *locating*."

"Locating!" She'd heard the circuit riders speak scorn of weak souls who fell out of their rough riding ranks and *located*.

"I'm locating, and I'm getting married," he said sullenly. "I'm done with being one of Asbury's monks on horseback. Henceforth I take my orders only from God. There's a congregation of those I converted that are setting me and my wife up with 600 acres, and a log house and chapel." He kicked a log lying on the hearth, waiting to be heaved into the fireplace. "What's wrong with that? Hasn't a preacher a right to home and wife and land like other folks? Can't I serve God staying put as much as being on the go?"

Mary had no answer to that. She knew what the other circuit riders would say to this renegade. But, as a woman, she could not but be glad that he was to have wife, acres, and home, instead of dying like Peter Massie.

2

The tenth and last constitutional convention met at Danville April 19, 1792, and settled on a constitution which was not submitted to popular vote but was generally accepted as the best that could be done at the time. Jus and other radicals who followed Jefferson won two concessions. One was universal suffrage for all white males over twenty-one. This was the first state constitution which did not set a property qualification on voting. The other was representation in the lower house of the legislature by *numbers*. Otherwise the "aristocratical principle" represented by the speculators and big landowners, triumphed. However, when the electors chose Isaac Shelby as governor, and he appointed George Muter as Chief Justice, the veterans were generally content. On June 4, 1792, Shelby was escorted to Lexington by troops of horsemen, and after a noisy welcome to the Governor, the legislature convened in Lexington on June 6.

All this meant that the Cartwrights could soon go down to their new home. Jus was assured that he would be certified by the Supreme Court as one fit to practice law. The first county court in the new county of Logan, which they were going to make out of the Military Tract and name for General Logan, would meet in the autumn. So, after the noise and shouting were over, Jus, Dutch, and some twenty other veterans went down to spy out the land, taking Dean, and guided by Cherokee Bill, who had been down there all winter and was already set up with a silvery-blonde little Chickasaw girl he had lifted out of a convent somewhere down the Mississippi. With them went Peter and Jerry.

When Mary and Brenda objected, the fathers argued, as usual, that the sooner boys got used to the hazards of their world, the better they'd be able to cope with them when they grew up. As usual the women were helpless against the masculine solidarity of father and son. But Mary's resignation was tempered with resolve. "So long as it's only danger to life and limb they run Peter into," she said to Brenda, "I'll hold my tongue and hope for the best. But when it comes to danger to his immortal soul, I pray God give me strength to stand fast and fight."

They started about the middle of June, along the bridle path under great oaks and beech-trees which led from Lexington to Nashville. After riding for days in the warm, silent shadows, they clattered through the shallow waters of a river that ran creaming and brawling around their horses' legs. When they had climbed the bank on the other side, the men stopped, and took off their hats. "Well, boys," said Jus, "this is it."

"Honey," said Dean to Peter, "Set your feet down on this earth. We have crossed the River Jordan, and this is the Promised Land."

Peter was disappointed. The Promised Land looked just like the land they had come from. He responded more to his father's exaltation than to his words when Jus explained that they had crossed the Green River and were riding on the Military Tract.

But before the day was done Peter saw the Promised Land. For, ten miles beyond the Green River, they crossed the Little Barren River, a small stream, thirty or forty feet wide, with high, rocky banks. When they had scrambled up its steep sides and through thickets of Virginia cedar, double-leafed pines, and black oaks, they came out into an ocean of green and gold that made Peter dizzy with light—that immense grassy meadow, sixty to seventy miles long, fifty to sixty miles wide, known as The Barrens. For hours Peter could see nothing but the walls of green grass rising higher than his head on both sides of the narrow channel the buffalo had made, and the great spread of the sky above, blue as periwinkles and crossed by slow-moving clouds, like great snowdrifts gilded with light. The air was sweetly warm but not hot, and of a marvelous freshness, as if all things that rot and decay, all creatures that grow dirty and spread defilement, all disease, all sickness, and all death had vanished from the earth, and there was nothing but life, young, full fed, and happy.

Most of the time Peter and his father rode just behind Cherokee. Against the blue sky Cherokee's face looked as if carved from sandstone, for he was always lounging sidewise on his horse, turning to talk to the others. Behind Jus and Peter were Dutch and Jerry. If Peter stood up on his horse and Jerry on his, they could see each other over Dutch's head, and discuss the world beyond the green walls. And this they did till their fathers made them sit down. Of the marvels that could be seen by standing up there was no end. As far as the eye could see the plains were covered with grass ten feet high, and cane and pea-vines rolled away like green sea-billows, swept into silvery washes and swirls by the light wind, and dotted with buffalo like black rocks. Sometimes they would see a "knob" rising abruptly, its limestone sides terraced and carved and covered with the silver spray of water disintegrating into mist against its gray sides. Sometimes they saw herds of buffalo quite close—great humped beasts with low, glowering heads. Sometimes they saw deer, skipping like creatures of air whose light legs need never touch the ground. At night they camped beside a clear stream, dancing over smooth pebbles, and ate a supper of fresh broiled trout and wild strawberries.

Going on, in a generally southwesterly direction, they came to an area where the level lands rose at intervals to wooded ridges of blue, gray, and white limestone, and were crossed with creeks which cut a channel through the clay, often leaving yellow clay on one side and red clay on the other. The highest ridge, which was later to be called Pilot Knob, had other ridges extending from it, like vertebrae from a backbone. Some of these ridges were real hills, some were only slight rises in the ground, but they were all high enough to form the dividing lines between the waters of Red River and Muddy River, and Muddy River and Gaspar River, and Gaspar River and Drake's Creek. From Pilot Knob the land descended gradually to the western and northern boundary of Logan County, and to Drake's Creek on the East, and the Red River on the South.

The northern part of Logan County was poorly watered and lightly timbered, but the remaining two thirds was covered with large and stately trees, in magnificent groves, interspersed and surrounded by grassy fields which, when Peter and Jerry first saw them in June were great flower gardens and strawberry patches. The trees were the largest the boys had ever seen, their trunks as big around as a fair sized room, crusted with moss, wrinkled with age, the branches waving far and high above.

For three days the veterans kept clear of their ultimate destination—the place which Ogden called Cook's Station, down near the state line, but which Cherokee said was formerly Big Boiling Spring, at the head of Muddy River. North of Cook's station, they rode up and down the buffalo traces, locating the streams and finding here and there a group of veterans clearing land. Meanwhile Peter and Jerry made a survey of the timber resources and of the population of wild creatures. The trees were oak, beech, black and white walnut, ash, hickory, hackberry, sugar maple, wild cherry, poplar, chestnut, and buckeye. Wherever they went, quail whirred up from the grass, and wild turkeys gobbled at them, and the male pheasant, proud and vain, stood up in full view and said, "Honk! Honk!" Peter and Jerry caught five or six wild pets each day, and reluctantly released them, planning to have a whole menagerie when they settled down. But the birds which interested them most were those they could never catch—the eagles that wheeled in the sky above or stood, lone and high, looking down on them from the top of a dead tree, and the parakeets that flew squawking and scolding in flocks above the meadows and filled the groves with their noisy protests. They saw herds of elk, deer, and buffalo, and heard the bellowing of buffalo like thunder across the grassy plains. They lunched on broiled young turkey and wild honey, and dined on venison, and ate strawberries all day long. They drank from a score of crystal springs running over silver sands and white rounded pebbles, and fringed with great ferns. They dipped their bare toes in a score of creeks where the water ran clear over clean rocks and sparkling sands. The air was full of the song of birds, and fragrant with the odors of beautiful and gaudy flowers.

3

But when they turned south one morning, with the sun on their left, Peter and Jerry knew from the change in their elders' manner that the less they said and did the better, and erased themselves from notice, crouching down so quietly in front of their fathers that a stranger, seeing the cavalcade, would not know there were two small boys in it. Only their eyes seemed alive—the limpid gray eyes of Jerry, the brilliant black eyes of Peter, observing every detail with a sharp, concentrated attention unknown to the children of a secure civilization.

Staleness had come into the air. Swarms of gnats flew out of the grass. The trail roughened and widened. In some places the grass was beaten back, as if many horses had been there. After they had gone for some time through open prairie with no tree in sight, there loomed ahead of them a vast poplar, nine feet in diameter, reaching far off to the heavens. Just before they reached it, their buffalo trace joined another at an angle, and they saw that the ground under the tree was trampled and a horse without a rider was tethered there. Warily they rode down the more beaten down of the traces. "That's the place," said Cherokee. "This is Cook's Station, and the future county seat."

Peter stared at the tent of cane or reeds, littered all about with bones, most of them dried and white, but some of them still dispensing a carrion smell. Bloated blue flies buzzed over them, and a great black vulture rose noisily. Peter's heart turned over, and he clutched his father. "It's a bad place, Pappy. Go away."

"Quiet, Son," said Jus gravely. "The man's a buffalo hunter.

They're but the bones of the critturs he's killed."

Cautiously Cherokee dismounted and approached the hut. For one minute Peter saw the hard brown skin that hung over the opening of the reed tent drawn back, and a witch looked out. Her sharp eyes glared through the tangled black mat of her hair, and she said something in a voice shrill and mean. Cherokee turned back. "The Missus is there, but she says she don't want no truck with us."

Just then they heard hoof beats and a man rode up alongside them. Peter recognized his horse as the one that had been tethered down by the big tree. He stared at the rosy young-looking face above his full gray beard. "He looks like a governor," he thought, remembering Isaac Shelby in his stockings and buckled shoes, instead of the hunting tunic and pantaloons laced close around the ankles with deer-thongs which was usual among backwoodsmen.

"Good day, my brave young warriors," said the handsome gentleman in a rich voice. "We've been busy here getting ready for you."

Jus eyed him speculatively. "How do you mean—ready?"

"Well, we're setting up a county government."

Jus started to speak. Then he turned and looked warningly at Dutch and deliberately spat a charge of tobacco juice into the blue distance. Wiping his mouth with the back of his hand, he said, in a small, quiet voice, "That's right thoughtful of you. But we are aiming to set up the county government ourselves."

The gentleman looked a bit taken back. Then he smiled genially. "The old spirit of '76. Freedom, independence, self-government—how good it is to have you brave fellows with us. But of course you know that the land has a number of old settlers, and we were assured that the military surveys would not infringe on their properties. Because of their prior possession and their long experience, it seems advisable that they should take the lead in setting up the county government, expecting, of course, to associate you with them."

Here Dutch said bluntly, "What are the names of these so important citizens?"

"Well, as one of the large land-owners here, though a comparative newcomer, I have been acting as leader. My name is Burwell Jackson, sirs, from your own glorious state of Virginia. With me I have associated quite informally, pending elections, two of our most promising young men. One is Young Ewing."

"But seems like I heard the Ewings are newcomers, too," observed Jus.

"Yes," said Mr. Jackson. "They are, like myself, persons of education and a little capital who have been attracted by the great opportunity for the development of enterprise and all the arts and comforts of civilization, with the opening of this beautiful land to you heroes and your families. The five Ewing brothers, Robert, Reuben, Young, Urban, and Finis came up from south of the state line two years ago but already they are becoming a power for good here. Hence I have associated Young Ewing with me in working out plans for the county government."

"It looks to me like you old timers are not, as you say," observed Dutch, "But speculators rushing in to snatch from us beforehand the fruits of what we to this land will do."

"Far from it," answered Jackson, genially. "Your interests are ours. But you will need services, a means of purchasing goods and of sending your goods to market. For this you will need help from persons like myself and the Ewings. However, the old timers are being provided for. The third person associated with me on the committee of temporary government is Wesley Maulding. Do you know the Mauldings?"

"Old James Maulding is a buffalo hunter—used to keep a station for hunters," responded Jus, consulting the list of names he had got from Ogden. His eyes traveled down the page. "Four sons—Ambrose, Morton, Richard, and Wesley." He did not add that after Morton's name there was a note in Ogden's writing. "Morton was formerly Alston's partner in counterfeiting, robbery, and, it is believed, murder."

Jackson was saying effusively, "They are all nature's noblemen. Wesley, the youngest, is a most manly and ingratiating lad."

Peter could feel something in the cavalcade of men like the rising of hair on the backs of animals. Jus said, disarmingly, "Ain't you kinda neglecting your most distinguished citizen? How come Philip Alston's not on the board that is going to set up a government for us poor, ignorant soldiers?"

A faint shadow of anxiety crossed Jackson's pleasant face. "Ah. Alston—there is an interesting man! Do you know him?"

"A little," lied Jus. "Back in Raleigh. But he wouldn't remember me."

"Mr. Alston's business interests are of longer standing than any here."

"So I undertand," said Jus, dryly.

"His business requires his presence elsewhere. So he is not in these parts at present. But his son-in-law, James Dromgole, is a partner of big Bill Stewart, the hunter, who boards with Cook and his wife there in that wilderness mansion." Here he made a large gesture in the direction of that wigwam of reeds, while Peter's eyes met Jerry's. Peter was thinking, "She isn't a witch. She's just a man's wife." Burwell Jackson was going on. "Dromgole and Stewart are setting up a store to provide for you and your young families. William Reading, our attorney here, tells me they anticipate such a profitable business that they have persuaded him to invest in some shares in it."

Jus was examining one of Ogden's notes. "Peter Alston, Philip's son, is a pirate on the rivers. His brother-in-law, Dromgole, is the receiver of the stolen goods." He said nothing. The silence was embarrassing. Finally Jackson remarked uneasily, "You seem to have quite a document there."

"So I have."

Used as he was to frontier tricks, Peter expected Jackson to make a spring and snatch the paper from his father. But he only smiled and said cordially, "You'll find the old timers a rough lot, in a way, but grand persons. They roamed this land after the buffalo and marked out estates for themselves where never white man's foot had set. Same as the old lords and aristocrats of England."

"Just the same," agreed Jus, dryly, adding, "The reason I have a list of these folks is that I'm acting as attorney for the soldiers in settling their land-claims. My name will come up for confirmation before the first court that meets here."

For the first time Burwell Jackson's geniality deserted him completely. He said, coldly, "I'm afraid you're too late. William Reading is to be confirmed as attorney here."

Jus eyed him and asked slowly, "The same William Reading that has shares in the firm of Dromgole and Stewart set up by Alston's son-in-law?"

For a moment the black eyes met Jackson's clear blue eyes. But the blue eyes were no match for the black, Indianlike gleam in the head of this frontiersman. Jus continued quietly, "I knew before I came down that Reading was to be confirmed. But I also am to be confirmed at the first meeting of the court upon the recommendation of the Supreme Court of Kentucky and with the personal backing of Governor Shelby. I don't aim to do general practice. But I do aim to look after the soldiers' interests."

Jackson exploded into cordiality. "In that case, welcome Mr. . . ."

"Cartwright's the name. Justurian Cartwright."

"My dear fellow," said Jackson, effusively. "I can't tell you what a pleasure it is to welcome an educated young man into our wilderness." He looked around. "But you must be anxious to locate your surveys. I notice most of them are south of here, on the way to Nashville. May I guide you?"

Peter and Jerry were aware of a closing in, a shifting into position of guns, a swift and silent organization for trouble in the cavalcade behind. And they knew Peter's father was lying as he said smoothly, "We'll be right glad to have you for the sociability of it, sir. But as for knowing the way, Cherokee here knows it like a book. And there's a whole force of us between here and where we're going. So we reckon we don't need a guide along the trace."

"In that case," said Mr. Jackson, with equal smoothness, "I'll just show you through our town here. It happens that Cook, who is the leading citizen of this metropolis, and most of the time the only one, doesn't like strangers."

Peter huddled down in the shadow of his father as they passed the reed wigwam. He still shrank from the buzzards, and the smell of the bones. And he judged from the quivering of the dried skin that served for a door that the witch was peering out at them. Jackson was saying in his full round voice and "eddicated" accent, "Gaspar Butcher lived there in that wigwam and was king of all this country, and lord of the buffalo. But in an evil moment he gave hospitality to two other hunters, Cook and Stewart. The place got over-populated and Gaspar moved. Then Cook picked up a wife— a wild thing who never sticks her face out long enough to let us see what she is like. And now Stewart is looking for other quarters. He doubts whether he can stand it to live in this town any longer.

It's getting too crowded."

"Crowded! Who else lives here?" asked Jus. Peter looked off across the plain. There was not a sign of habitation except the wigwam.

"Nobody yet. But I understand you fellows want to set up the county court here."

"Yes. We aim to start right in turning the traces into roads, and getting some kind of building up for the court."

Jackson eyed the young man. "You seem to be going ahead without consultation with the others involved."

"You said you expected our co-operation. Well, Sir, we expect yours." Again the bland blue eyes met the black eyes. Peter, understanding the language of eyes better than that of tongues, saw the blue eyes fall before the Indian gleam in the black eyes.

"Well, here is where I turn off," said Jackson, as they came to another trace. "I am delighted to have met you brave fellows." He swept off his hat and bowed to them all. But as he started to canter away, he drew up, turned, and asked, "Mr. Cartwright, is your land, by any chance, the survey with the two large caves on it?"

"Oh, are there caves on it?"

"Yes."

Jackson said effusively, "I am most happy to have made your acquaintance, Mr. Cartwright. Come to me at any time if you want help. And if you should want a little ready cash, I should be interested in taking the caves off your hands."

"Thank ye kindly, sir. I'll come—when I need it." Jackson looked at Jus, suspecting an edge of irony in the last words. But Jus was looking quite guileless. Again Jackson swept off his hat and bowed. Jus merely pricked his horse and said briefly to Cherokee, "Lead on."

When they had gone a few hundred yards, Cherokee slackened his horse and waited till Jus came alongside. "What did that bird want to guide us for?"

"Oh just for the sociability's sake."

Cherokee rolled his dark eye at Jus, and said, "All the same, we go watchful."

About nine miles south on the Nashville trace, a mile north of the state line, they came to the Cartwright survey. Jus said, "Stand up, son, and stretch your eyes to front and back and left side and right side, for all you see is ours."

Peter looked out on land that lay like a garden, rippling through grass and flowers to low hills. A little brook sang along under the grass. His father dismounted. "Slide off, Son, and stick your toes in your own earth."

They knelt and sifted the warm, light soil through their fingers. They walked in it and felt their bare feet sink in it. They lunched on the banks of the little stream from the wild strawberries in the grass. They climbed the low ridge, and Peter stood with his father in silence. His father was almost crying inside. Finally, he said, "Son, it's too good. I can't see how all this was ever left for such as me." They walked soberly down in the golden summer afternoon to the place where they had tethered the horse, and mounted to ride after the others who had gone off to look at the other surveys. With a last fond look at his land, Jus said, "I wouldn't have believed that I could ever make you the heir, Son, of 466 acres of such land as this. It's God's plenty—that's what it is. The graspers and the grabbers, the selfish and the cheats will never be enough to cope with such plenty as this. The earth and the sky here are bigger than man's greed."

When two weeks later Peter and his father burst into the cabin, Mary raised her eyes in apprehension. She was so used to hope that turned to despair. She knew that never was cup so sweet that the bottom of it wasn't all bitters. There was bound to be something wrong with the land. She felt it in her bones.

But Jus lifted her off her feet. He kissed her till she could feel herself reeling. "Honey. Honey. It's too good. It's more than I could have dreamed."

She whispered. "Nine years. We worked so hard—I was so afraid."

He laid his bearded face down against hers. She could feel his tears warm on her neck. "I'm blubberin' like a fool," he whispered. "But I just can't believe it. I'm so happy."

4

Late in the summer Jus and a troop of veterans were to go down to the new country to attend the first meeting of the county court and to set up the Commission of Peace as the executive branch of the local government. They were also to break ten acres on each of their holdings for winter rye, working as a crew, breaking one place and going on to the next.

Peter and Jerry persuaded their fathers to take them again. Jus, announcing this decision to Mary, added, "I'm thinkin' of taking Eddie, too. A boy of thirteen can be a big help." Eddie flushed with pleasure. He was a substantial unassuming, unaggressive boy of generally mediocre appearance, but steady and unselfish. But John protested, "Hey, that's no fair. I'm the eldest. If anybody's going, I am."

Jus, seeing a chance to discipline Mary's son, replied, "What we want is work, Son. And work is something I never see you do."

John said nothing more, but when Eddie set out in a cavalcade of teen age boys who had won the privilege of going, too, he was a very damaged piece of goods. Neither Jus nor Mary asked what the fight had been about or who the assailant had been. They knew.

John had fallen on his brother furiously. "You sneak, your white-livered, yellow-bellied liar. I'll teach you to go trucklin' up to Paw and stealin' my chances right out from under me!"

Under the shock of the attack, Eddie gasped, "If we fight, let's fight fair."

"Fight fair," roared John. "Fair with rats like you? There ain't no fairness where a varmint is concerned. I'll stomp you out! Say your prayers, you sniveling brat, you! I heard Mammy tell you how to say your prayers. Well, you'd better say them now, for this night you'll sleep in Hell. When I get done with you, there ain't goin' to be anything but red, bloody mash!"

At this point a stone, aimed by Peter, hit John near the eye, blinding him and bloodying his face. With the respite thus gained, Eddie saved his eyes, his ears, and his life, and John retired as badly damaged as he, for when he was on top of Eddie, both Jerry and Peter attacked him with stout hickory sticks, raining blows on his back and neck till he had to loosen his hold. Eddie slipped out and ran to the cabin, leaving a trail of blood. John turned furiously on the children. Jerry shinnied up a tree, and Peter led his already bleeding and exhausted brother a chase in and out of briars and thickets till they came to the river. In a flying leap, Peter went overboard and swam about, daring John to come in and wash off that blood. Unlike Peter, whose warm-blooded body was like a seal's, John hated cold water. A prolonged immersion which only left Peter sparkling and rosy, left him blue and shivering. In his weakened condition he couldn't face the water. So he slunk away, and was seen no more till Eddie and Peter got off on their trip.

Between June and September of 1792 a great change had come over the Lexington-Nashville trail. It was beaten down along the sides, as if five or six people had ridden abreast. There were big trampled areas at intervals, covered with piles of horse-manure, old rags, broken boxes, and skeletons of animals picked white by the vultures. They passed several caravans of "movers," most of them veterans going to take up their lands. But they saw fewer Indians and almost no buffalo. "There's two kind of critturs," said Cherokee, "that just naturally don't like the smell of the paleface. One's the buffalo and the other's the Injun. Injuns say the paleface dirties the air and dirties the ground wherever he is."

Peter thought about this, and it seemed to him it was true. It hurt and humiliated him. Finally he said to his father, "Is it true we dirty the air and the ground?"

"Son, it's true for a while. There's no gainsayin' that life, whether human or animal, is cleaner and decenter before it gets mixed up with us than it is for a long time after we come around. But that's something that will pass, Son. It's something savage things have to go through before they're really civilized."

"By the Eternal," said Dutch, suddenly, "Look what for a fracas is there!"

They were approaching the Big Tree, at the main entrance to their proposed county seat. As they came to the point where one trace joined the other, there came from the other trace into the path ahead of them a long sledge drawn by a string of five horses, piled high with logs. Peter sniffed the resinous air. "Must a cut a whole cedar forest." They could hear shouts and hammering, punctuated by roars of singing. Coming closer they saw the largest

log house Peter had ever seen—two big rooms and a smaller room.
The walls had been built to full height. But instead of the roof being laid on a slant, it was being laid level. "What are you going
to do there?" asked Jus.

"Build a second storey."

Jus explained to the boys. "It's like the Ranger's house. They
build one atop the other and the roof of the first is the floor of the
second." Both boys stared. They had thought that a two-storey
house must be made of brick.

Burwell Jackson came up, cheerful and self-important, in
breeches, coat, and a large beaver hat. "Welcome, young warriors.
We're setting up the county seat."

"Is this the courthouse?"

"No, we thought that had better wait till we had a meeting of the
court. This house here is one the old timers are putting up for
Wesley Maulding, for a tavern. We're hoping you'll all want to
join us in making Wes sheriff."

"We'd just as soon look him over first," replied Jus.

"Surely. Surely. Wes, come over here, and let the soldiers see
what the old timers' candidate for sheriff looks like."

"Sure thing," said a pleasant, hearty voice, and a good-looking
young man turned and came toward them. His buckskin pantaloons were ornamented down the sides with coins, pierced and
strung on deerskin thongs.

"This is Wesley, the youngest of the tribe of Mauldings," said
Burwell Jackson. "His mother—God rest her sainted soul—named
him for John Wesley. Wesley's the top and sum of all the religion
we have here."

An older man who looked like Wesley but was larger, browner,
and much rougher, said, "Yes, he says his prayers four times a day,
and Hallelujahs and Amens every other word, and he don't never
touch a drop of strong drink."

"No, Sir. Never," said Wesley. "All I drink is holy water. Hi,
there, Sam, give these gentlemen some nice cold water from the
baptismal font."

A slim, dark boy with a long nose came forward. "This is Sam
Morris," said Wesley. "Looks like a nigger, but he ain't. He's a
Portyghee. Who owns you, Sam?"

A flash of black lightening lit the boy's lean, ugly, dark face. "Nobody owns me, and nobody's goin' to. All the ownin' that's done I aim to do."

"Cool off," said Wesley, laying his hand on the boy's shoulder. "You don't want to rile Sam," he said to Jus and the others. "He murders as easy as he eats. Cool off, I tell you, Sam," he repeated, with an unexpected hardness in his voice, "And pass the holy water."

Sam passed around a big bucket of whisky. "All you want," said Wesley, hospitably. "There's more where that came from. The land grows grain if you just spit on it. And there ain't anything to do with grain after you've et a few bushels of it save make it into whisky. We swim in whisky. You don't ever need to drink water again." Then, as if remembering his manners, he turned to the larger, browner, rougher man who stood next to him. "Meet my brother Morton. We figger to send him to the legislature if you all is agreeable. The only trouble is," he continued in a confidential tone, his bright blue eyes moving from one face among the veterans to the next, "we just can't think of a job yet for Ambrose, and it makes him so mad that he ain't set up as a king-pin yet that we all here can't sleep o'nights. For Ambrose is so mean when he's been drowning his sorrows in whisky that he'd just as soon stick a knife into Morton and me as not. So we've got to fix him up."

At this a third man, still larger, browner, and rougher, with dark eyes instead of blue and a prodigious black beard, stepped out of the crowd. Wesley said amiably, "Ambrose, meet the soldiers. I was telling them what a murderous son-of-a-gun you was, and saying as how they'd better elect you to some office before you blow their brains out."

Jus thought this was a joke and started to smile. But he was met with such a black and surly look that he stiffened. Cherokee's dark eyes were fixed in a cold stare. Burwell Jackson said, "You must meet our other dignitaries, Mr. Cartwright. Here is your brother attorney—William Reading." A small, timid looking young man held out his hand. "I'm glad to welcome a brother member of the bar."

"Better look sharp," said Wesley, with the slight contempt a big-bodied man has for a small one. "You've got competition, Bill. If you don't keep us out of trouble, we'll hire Cartwright."

Cartwright fixed the laughing blue eyes with a level dark glance. "The price is high," he said.

5

Just then a big man with a strong animal smell, hairy as a great beast, pushed his way in. Even in this hot weather he wore a coonskin cap. Bare to the waist, his whole front was covered with a mass of red hair. His trousers were of buckskin ornamented with several jingling rows of coins.

Peter grasped his father's hand. "Look, Pappy, he's got money all over him, too."

"What does the young un say?" growled the man, so fiercely that Peter cowered against his father. But his father never let the child shrink from anything. Giving him a little shake and pushing him forward, he said, "Speak up, Peter. Tell him what you said."

"I said," repeated Peter, "that you've got money all over you."

The child's clear voice carried above the rumbling and grumbling of the men. Several stopped talking and listened. Then they came up to Peter, laughing and blowing blasts of whisky ahead of them like steam. One of them said, "Make him tell you where he got the money."

Thus prompted, Peter asked, "Where's the money come from?"

"I got a money tree," rumbled the man, looking at Peter, his eyes bright and almost kind behind his red hair. "I grow money same as some folks grow beans. Want some money, boy?" He pulled out a handful of coins. "Take some," he urged.

Peter looked anxiously at his father. Among his folks it was an axiom that no self-respecting person would take a gift of money. His father said firmly, "No, thank—ee. No money passes our hands except good money," he laid a slight emphasis on the word *good*, "in fair exchange for things honestly come by." He looked coldly at the man, who frowned so fiercely that Peter thought he would strike his father. Cherokee, Dutch, and half a dozen others closed around, their guns in their hands. Reading interposed, "Mr. Jackson, introduce Mr. Stewart to Mr. Cartwright."

Jus glanced at Stewart, with a sidelong glance that was keenly appraising. So this was William Stewart, partner in the firm of Stewart and Dromgole which proposed to keep a monopoly of the wholesale and retail business in these parts! He, like Wesley, was brazenly wearing and displaying the counterfeit money.

Burwell Jackson was saying, in his genial way, "This is Bill Stewart, Mr. Cartwright. He's one of our old timers—a mighty hunter of the buffalo. You remember that when you came through before there was a kind of pointed house of reeds here where Mr. Wesley Maulding's house is now going up. Mr. Stewart lived there. He was the original patriarch of our county seat."

"Never lived here," growled Stewart. "Never wanted to. There's no roof I'd call my own but the sky, and no bed I'd take if I could help it, but the bare ground in a place where no man's foot had ever been but my own. This here place was plum spiled from the outset by all the comin' and goin'."

Jackson explained in an aside, "Nobody came and nobody went before this but Gaspar and Cook and the Mauldings and Alston —not a dozen men and they not often."

"A dozen too many and much too often," growled Stewart. He continued violently, "Any god-damned-son-of-a-bitch who says I lived in that pig-sty—I'll smash his face in."

At this point two others who looked as wild as Stewart, bare and hairy like him to the waist, elbowed their way in. One laughed loudly. "He didn't live there. He just naturally crawled in alongside Cook's missus, when Cook wasn't to home."

"Pappy! Pappy! Stop him," shrieked Peter. It seemed to him that only he saw Stewart coolly lift his pistol and discharge it straight into the other man's face. The man crumpled and dropped. "Like a sack of meal. He went all soft like a sack of meal," Peter was thinking desperately. He began to cry. A cold shudder ran down Jerry's spine and his teeth chattered. His little face was drawn and white. Jus wheeled around with an oath. The veterans were drawn up with guns, ready to charge.

Wesley Maulding stepped forward coolly, and, with a re-assuring look at the veterans, took Stewart by the arm. "Bill, you're drunk. Get out o' here before I kick you out."

Stewart turned on him. "You son of a bitch!"

"No you don't," said Ambrose Maulding, snatching Stewart's pistol away. Morton took him by the shoulders. "Wesley's boss here. You do as you're told or never show your stinkin' carcass here again."

Morton and Ambrose pushed Stewart away. The dead man lay on the ground. Wesley said to the crowd of men, "Take him out, dig a grave, and bury him."

"Look here, Wes," said one of the men who had been laying a log in place on one side of the house. "Just because we're buildin' you a house is no reason for your settin yourself up so high and fancy. *Buryin'*—who ever heard of buryin' when there's more than enough buzzards starvin' for a taste of good salty human. Throw him out, boys, and the birds will fix him."

Wesley's pistol was out. "Nobody gives orders here but me. I'm sheriff."

Several roared, "You ain't yet."

"I'm goin' to be sheriff," said Wesley firmly.

"Whoever says he ain't answers to us," said Ambrose. He and Morton towered dark and strong beside Wesley, their pistols cocked.

Wesley said more quietly, "I said bury him, and I mean *bury*. Six feet deep and no cheatin'. Things is changing here. There's goin' to be law and order. And the first law is that whoever gets killed from now on is goin' to be *buried*."

Cherokee said to the veterans, "Let's get out of here." They started off with a rush, the wind blowing through Peter's hair. He clung to his father—not because the horse was going so fast, for the horse didn't live that he couldn't stick to at any speed, but in nervous reaction to the killing. "Let's go back home to Stanford, Pappy. It's a bad place here. They all are bad men."

"They're bad men, son. That's certain. But it's a very good place, and we don't aim to let them keep it."

6

They rode along soberly. There was the sound of galloping behind them. A slender lithe young man who appeared to be in his twenties reined up alongside Jus and Peter, on a sleek brown thoroughbred. "Mr. Cartwright, I am Young Ewing, and back there tangling with your company, is my young brother Finis."

Introductions were difficult on the narrow trail. But the cavalcade drew up, and Peter, standing on the horse while his father turned sidewise to talk to Young Ewing, saw the brother Finis come up on the other side. And the next thing he knew his eyes were on a level with the most re-assuring face he had seen since they crossed the Green River. It was young and shadowed also by a dashing large hat, with only the nose and the fresh-colored upper cheeks and the gray eyes showing between the brown hair and the brown beard.

Young Ewing was saying, "May I ride along and talk with you?"

"Ride along, Mr. Ewing," said Jus.

Peter wished that Finis would ride on the other side. But the trail was too narrow. Finis fell back to the tail end of the cavalcade. The withdrawal of this comforting human being from his side, here where everything was so fearsome, left Peter with a sense of desolation.

Young Ewing was saying, "I was back in the crowd, watching you through all that ghastly scene."

Jus responded with studied irrelevance, "You and your brother don't look like you belonged in the kind of company we saw up yonder."

"We don't. But my family are interested in developing this country. We're aiming to put up a fight against the Maulding-Alston outfit all along the line. But you see what they are. It's no use coming to a show-down with them yet. One misstep, and we'll all be murdered. But in time, as the state government strengthens, we may be able to prosecute some of them on criminal charges."

Jus said, "There ain't a jury in Kentucky that wouldn't acquit that big red-haired brute for shooting a man that said he was committing adultery with his pardner's wife."

Young Ewing replied eagerly, "I'm glad you see it that way, for may be you won't misunderstand me when I say that Bill Stewart is far and away the best of the old outfit here except Wesley. He and Wesley haven't got any morals, any more than the others. But they are manly by nature, and there's certain low-down things they won't do. I know Stewart looked pretty bad today. He was crazy drunk. But the fellow he killed is a much lower kind of beast than he is. He's been asking for what he got for a long time."

"H-mmm," said Jus. "And he's partner of this Reading who is to be confirmed as Commonwealth attorney here?"

"That's what I hear. And I'm afraid we can't stop it. All we can do is to make a trade with them to confirm you, too." Jus looked surprised. What should Young Ewing have to do with confirming him? Ewing answered the unspoken question. "Moses Shelby, the governor's brother, who, as you must know, is going to take up land north of here, put it up to my father and brothers and me to see to your confirmation. And we intend to see it goes through."

Justurian's face was dark with troubled thought. He spat a charge of tobacco juice with the sudden sharpness of a gun-shot. Peter, listening, sensed doubt and trouble. He sickened again with the memory of the dead man crumpling like a bloody sack. Horror swept over him. The sunshine was no longer bright, the sky no longer kind. He was tense, indrawn, like a frightened animal, his eyes large and watchful. He looked around for Finis Ewing but could not see him. He grasped his father's hand nervously. "Pappy! Pappy! They're bad men. It's bad, Pappy. It's all bad. Let's go away."

Young Ewing looked down kindly at the boy. "It's bad, Sonny —no mistake." He looked at Jus. "It's rotten bad. But we've got to be patient and get at it politically. And that's what I want to talk to you about. Burwell Jackson. . ."

"Yes," said Jus. "We've seen quite a bit of Mr. Jackson. Where does he stand?"

"Mr. Jackson patches things up and worries along, with whatever side has the power." He hesitated. "I can't keep you now, but my brother and I would like to bring Mr. Jackson to talk to you, when you are settled, perhaps in three or four days, and lay out political strategy."

"Any time," replied Jus, non-committal.

"Then I'll go along now." Young Ewing reined up his horse and waited in the bushes to join his brother at the end of the line. Peter tried to stand up to see them gallop off. But his father pulled him down and rode on.

Dutch came alongside. "Have not heard all the words," he said, "but the looks have talked so loud as words."

"I'll tell you about it later. It sure calls for some thinking."

CHAPTER 10

Logan Courthouse
September, 1793 to February, 1794

The nasty memory would not leave Peter for days. It rose between him and his food and made him sick. He dreaded to go to bed because the face of that man, leering foully as he spoke of Stewart crawling in beside Cook's missus, the crumpled body, and the red, red blood were printed on the blackness of night. But gradually, like soreness going out of a wound, the impression faded and brightness came back into the sun and taste into his food. Jerry never spoke of what they had seen. But he insisted on sleeping with Peter on their bed of leaves covered with bearskin out of doors, his thin little body pressed against Peter's sturdier and warmer one. One night he woke shrieking, "Don't shoot me! Don't shoot me!" Peter held him close, and when at last Jerry slept, Peter was wide-awake. But he was less scared to remember. He lay looking at the stars, listening for the howl of the wolves and the hoot of the owls, and thinking of the words his mother had taught him, "The God of Jacob is thy refuge and beneath thee are the ever-lasting arms," until he fell asleep.

It helped that they had the land to break. The brown noisy crew of men worked like an army, every day moving to a different stretch of land, breaking the ground for the seed they had brought in bags over their horses' backs. They'd ride over their acreage, admiring it and looking for water, and when they came to an open place, where the grass grew high, they'd dismount and sample the deep, rich, soft soil. When they had settled on the easiest spot to

reak, they'd set fire to the grass. Peter and Jerry loved to see
he red gold sheet of flames crackle to the blue sky, sending off
ungent whiffs of smudge. About once a day the fire threatened
o get away. The first time this happened, the men tore off their
hirts—and some even their pants—and tied them to sticks and made
nops with which, when dipped in water, they could beat out the
lames. Peter and Jerry, panting, black with smoke, ran back and
orth to the stream, bringing water and keeping the mops wet until
he fire was under control.

Barefoot in the ash, which was soft as down around their toes,
he boys dropped the seed and tramped it in. Efficiently organ-
zed by Eddie, a dozen of them did all the planting. At night, in-
tead of being sent to get this and that because "Pappy is so tired,"
hey were waited on and petted by the older men. "Seems like
hey've done most of the work," said Jus. 'It's their turn to be
lone for."

The men built a great log lean-to which served as a community
helter on rainy days. The lean-to was a wall of great tree trunks,
vith two side-walls of slenderer trunks sloping down from seven
eet in front to three feet in the back, with spruce boughs piled the
vhole length of it for about five feet under the eaves, and covered
vith bearskins. During a spell of wet weather what fun it was to
ie on the sweet-smelling pine and fir and watch the row of fires
uilt across the open front, crackling against the misty rain outside.
Here, on a wet day they were visited by Young, Reuben, and Robert
Ewing, who were all variations on the same general type—strong but
lender tall bodies, well cut features, gray eyes, brown hair and
eards—and all in their twenties or early thirties. They were ac-
ompanied by Burwell Jackson and a handsome man of about forty
vith noble features, and eyes that crinkled good-humoredly at the
orners. But there were some ironic cross-glances among the veterans when this personage was introduced as "General" Cauldwell.
A number of high army officers whom neither the boys of '76 nor
the War Department in Washington had ever heard were appearing on the Military Tract.

The political plan they brought had the neatness of a mathe-
matical equation, proposing that in the legislature and other
elected offices, four of the Ewings should alternate with the four

Mauldings, the Ewings representing the interests of the veterans, and the Mauldings admittedly being tied up with Alston who had coached them in politics. For all local committees the Alston-Maulding group should put up one member, the veterans one member, and the third should be Jackson, or Cauldwell, or one of the other speculators or non-veteran settlers on lands honestly acquired from veterans.

Jus said, "I don't understand just where the Mauldings come in. I've got the Alston lineage straight. Dromgole's his son-in-law, and Stewart and Reading, the lawyer, run the Exchange business with Dromgole; and Peter Alston, the son, is alleged to belong to the river gang, and to feed the loot into the Exchange."

At this the Ewings, Cauldwell, and Jackson exchanged glances. They had not expected the soldiers to know so much. Jus asked again, "But where do the Mauldings come in?"

"Some fifteen or twenty years ago," said Robert Ewing, "when the buffalo hunters first came in here, and Alston turned up with patents to most of the Red River country, and set up his salt manufactory, James Maulding came here to hunt, bringing his wife, Katy, who was a lady of a good Virginia family—the Tylers. Unlike most hunters, he was pretty well educated, could read, brought along two or three books, including his wife's Bible, and wrote a very fine neat hand. He set up a station about fifteen miles from Alston's. So far as I know it was just a rude tavern for hunters and a trading post for furs. It wasn't concerned in Alston's kind of dealings."

"Is Maulding still alive?" asked a veteran.

"Yes, and he's well off. But he keeps out of the way of us all. Says buffalo are better company any day than humans," said Young Ewing.

Here Robert Ewing took up the story. "As for Alston the Mauldings don't forget that he and old James were the patriarchs of this country. They look on Alston and his family as their own social circle, to be rudely loyal to against strangers like you, and like us, too. Only one of the Mauldings was ever suspected of having business dealings with Alston."

"That one, I understand, is Morton," said Jus.

This was met with silence in which the politicians and the veterans measured each other with their eyes. Then Young Ewing said, "Richard Maulding seems quite respectable. But to my mind the best of the lot is Wesley. He'll respond to appeals to generosity, and he'll fight his own kin if he feels like it. On the other hand, his three brothers will all stand by him, whatever he does, for the reason that he's their young brother."

"So you think he'll do for sheriff?" asked Jus.

"He's the only one that can handle the real law-breakers. If you all back him as sheriff, I think we can make a trade," said Young Ewing, "and put you soldiers on the election committees and the road committees. By keeping the Mauldings in but tying their hands . ."

"We might worry along," finished Jus, "till the worst of this outfit sees the wisdom of clearing out and starts loping west after the buffalo."

"Exactly," said Burwell Jackson, chuckling and rubbing his hands.

All of which so commended itself to the political wisdom of the veterans that the five politicians rode away, thoroughly satisfied.

Peter and Jerry and the other youngsters, lying on the pine boughs under the eaves, had strained their ears to this conversation. Peter was only seven, but what these men did mattered to him as no political conference can matter to a civilized child for he had to find out whether these men were "good." Good things were the things you didn't need to be afraid of—like ripe grapes and garter-snakes, and soft bunny rabbits. Bad things were things you'd better not touch or let them touch you, like berries of the deadly night-shade, poison ivy, and rattlesnakes. When the men had gone, he wiggled over the pine boughs to his father's side.

"They're good, ain't they, Pappy," he whispered.

"Seems like," said Jus, his big hand resting on the boy's tangled curls. Peter felt re-assured.

2

The first court met at Richard Maulding's—a well built cabin about eighteen by eighteen feet between Whip-poor-will and Elk Fork in Clay Lick woods. For Peter and Jerry playing outside the cabin it was fun to see the men ride up, fun to hear the buzz inside and the hammering with a large wooden sledge hammer and the shouts, "Order in the court-room," and the guffaws of laughter. A man lifted Peter and stood him on the window ledge. "Listen," he said, "They're talking about your Pappy."

Peter heard Burwell Jackson's full rolling voice, "Ordered that it be certified to the Supreme Court of Kentucky that Justurian Cartwright is a man of honesty, probity, and good demeanor." The man who had lifted Peter explained, "'The court has to give him a certificate of character if he's to practice law here."

But Peter soon lost interest when he found that nothing more was being done for his father. While William Reading was producing his license from the Judges of the Supreme Court to practice law, he jumped down and, seeing a freckled red-haired boy beckoning from the back of the cabin, he and Jerry ran around to him. The boy's name was "Red" Maulding. He had several fishing lines and some angle worms for bait. Peter and Jerry took no more interest in the court.

Meanwhile the men inside the cabin appointed a Commission of Peace, in accordance with the act of the Assembly authorizing the establishment of the local government. The Commissioners were Burwell Jackson, Young Ewing, and Ambrose Maulding. Samuel Cauldwell was appointed clerk; Young Ewing, assessor; Ambrose Maulding, magistrate; and Wesley Maulding, sheriff. On this first round, the Ewings were defeated in their plan to match every Maulding in public office with a Ewing, mainly because Ambrose had been so ugly that it was deemed wise to find an office for him. But the Ewings felt they could bide their time. Robert was already dreaming of something bigger than an illiterate Maulding could aspire to. He might even be United States senator from Kentucky! Peter, Jerry, and Red Maulding returned from fishing attracted by a savory smell of broiled venison, for a barbecue climaxed all political meetings. Peter was proud to see his father standing and talking with Burwell Jackson and Young Ewing. In his eyes some magic had been done inside to clothe these men in dignity. They walked as if wrapped in invisible robes of state. Even his father seemed changed—more grave and dignified.

On October 2 the court met again in William Harrison's house on the south prong of Red River, about a mile from its mouth. While the court was in session Peter and Jerry climbed up the side of the cabin, and peered through the chinks whenever there seemed to be some special commotion inside. On one of these explorations, Jerry heard the word "Cartwright" and shrieked, "Cartwright—that's his Pappy!" pointing down to Peter. "His Pappy is in there. They're doing something to his Pappy."

A man said kindly to Peter, "Come, son, I'll boost you up. Want to hear?" Peter could hear a voice intoning, "Statement of the earmarks of Young Ewing, Morton Maulding, and Justurian Cartwright."

"Must be giving him some kind of a political job," said a man.

"Who's this fellow Cartwright? Ain't never heard of him," said a voice. For a minute Peter was outraged. Why! Everybody knew his father! He was slightly mollified when another voice answered, "Cartwright—he's the big pleasant fellow that's attorney for the veterans."

Jus, Dutch, and several of the veterans returned to Stamford for the winter. In the spring of 1793 they went down to the military tract to plant corn and start building and stayed there all summer. Peter did not go back to Logan County again till after his eighth birthday, in the fall of 1793, when his mother, his brothers, Polly and Sis, with Brenda and Jerry's brothers and sisters, and several other families went down together in a long cavalcade, escorted by Cherokee, leaving Uncle Peter and Chris and the babies behind in a slovenly cabin on acres they were share-cropping. Having drawn only 100 acres Uncle Peter thought it not worth while to take his grant, and besides, he liked music better than farming.

About ten miles east of the new county they were met by Jus, Dutch, and other heads of families. As they approached the Big Tree, they saw, at the point where the buffalo traces converged, the imposing walls of Cedar House, now finished and open for business. From it led the first street in the new town, a narrow passageway lined by four or five new cabins. Wesley came out of Cedar House to invite them to a feast of welcome, and, as they entered, ladled whisky out of a big tub into glasses, which, to lips that had never tasted whisky from anything but gourds, was the height of sophistication. Ladies who frowned on whisky were seated at tables and served Hyson tea in china cups by a black slave who wore a loin cloth and a red calico jacket.

Mary had never drunk out of a china cup, but she could not enjoy this new luxury so long as Jus was standing by the whisky tub. Meeting Mary's severe eye, Jus set down his empty glass and, refusing a fourth refilling, strolled over to the wall where, on a large sheet of legal paper, the prices fixed by the county court were posted.

LIQUOR: One quart of RUM, six shillings

BRANDY: three shillings

BREAKFAST OR SUPPER: one shilling

LODGING: six pence

CORN PER GALLON: six shillings

STABLAGE OR OTHER PROVENDER: 24 hours, one shilling, sixpence

PASTURAGE: 24 hours, sixpence

The price of rye whisky was not included. That was given away.

"Hi, Wesley," shouted Jus. "Since when did you learn to write?"

"I'm taking lessons from Bill Reading right along now," said Wesley, proudly. He called out to a crowd who had gathered around a copy of *The Kentucky Gazette*, "It's against the rules of the house to learn to read from the latest *Gazette*. That's there for them that can read well enough to get done with a piece of print and pass it on to the next man. But there's old copies of the *Gazette* you can have to practice readin' on, if you handle them careful."

While they ate, Jus reported the local political news. At the third meeting of the county court on Christmas day, 1792, Abraham Raymour had been permitted to establish a ferry across Barren River not far from Bowling Green. On January 22, 1793, when the court met, Nathan Jones was appointed constable instead of George Herndon. On March 26, a man named Shaw had been allowed to start a ferry across the Cumberland River near its mouth, and one across the Ohio at the mouth of the Cumberland. Morton Maulding, Wes Maulding, John Huftssutler, and Alexander Guffy had been appointed to view a road toward Nashville. "Hear that?" cried Jus, pausing to address Mary. "We're goin' to get a real road down our way—not just a buffalo trace."

After dinner, Mary and the other veterans' wives went to "view" the new county courthouse, but, there being as yet no direct route between it and Cedar House, they had to go nearly a mile up one buffalo trace and turn back on another. The courthouse was a log cabin, solid and well built, retaining a forest freshness above the odor of whisky and tobacco which was, in Peter's experience, the characteristic scent of the law. "In time," said Jus, looking around at the beaten down grass and scattering poplar trees and bushes on all sides, "this will be a real city, and we'll give it a name. But for the time being the whole area round about is known as Logan Courthouse."

"That, Sir, is not what I hear this place called," said a long, lean, rangy, red-haired youth in a brown broadcloth suit and a linen stock, propped against the log wall of the courthouse outside, carelessly at ease, and yet tense, like a panther that can spring at a moment's notice.

"Mr. Cartwright," interposed Bill Reading, "meet Andrew Jackson, our distinguished colleague from over the border."

Jus acknowledged the introduction with a pleasant smile, and a keen appraising glance. He had heard much about this brash young man—as indeed who had not? "What's the name you hear our future great city called by, Mr. Jackson?" he asked.

"Rogues' Harbor," said Jackson.

Jus had lived for the moment when Mary would see their beautiful farm with the fields already broken, the tassels of corn waving high, and a horse-lot fenced in. Not presuming to pick the site of the house, he had cleared a space under the trees where the ground sloped to a spring and a little stream, handy for drinking water and for cooling the milk. Mary looked everything over with incredulous exactness, as if there must be a flaw somewhere. "The house could be there," she said, pointing to the place Jus had cleared.

"As you wish, Honey," he said gently. His dark eyes sought and held hers. Moments when they remembered each other as persons were few these days. But he still loved to see the chill blue of Mary's eyes warm from within. It seemed to him that when Mary's eyes shone it was with something higher than ordinary human gladness. Her deeply hidden soul opened and let you look into it. Jus was not mystical about anything but Mary. But something in her—her hidden intensity, her religion, the fineness of some of her reactions, and her occasional flashes of inspired observation—stirred in him a special kind of reverence. Now she raised her eyes to his, welling with light. "Honey," she said softly, "it's too good. God is more than good to us." Jus patted her shoulder. "We've waited a long time for it, dear heart. Now it's ours."

Peter stood by with Eddie and Sis. All three children sensed the solemnity, and triumph. Suddenly Peter let out a wild whoop and began running round and round. Then he turned half a dozen hand-springs. And finally he shinnied up the hickory tree and shook down nuts on Sis's head. One hit her on the nose and she screamed. Peter laughed and shook the branch more violently. He had to do something.

3

They stayed that night with Dutch and Brenda in their new house on lands the Baptist veterans had pre-empted near Muddy River. It was a beautiful house. The logs, instead of being left rough, in the round, had been squared off and the spaces between, instead of being roughly chinked with mud, were neatly plastered with clay, the wavering lines of white between the broader bands of dark wood making a handsome pattern on the walls. Along one of the side-walls were pegs for their clothes, each carved with the head of an animal. Dutch whittled these pegs evenings as he sat by the fire. Peter said wistfully, "We never had a house like this. I wish we could build us such a house."

Jus and Dutch laughed. "It's the very house we're building for you. All the men are going over tomorrow for a house-raising," said Jus. He laid his big rough hand on Peter's tangled curls. "Son, we're done with livin' in old, tumble-down cabins. This is what we've been waitin' for. This is your Kentucky home."

Next morning Peter, Jerry, Eddie, and John rode over to the woodlot where some forty veterans were felling trees. What fun to see the great bushy tops begin to sway a little against the sky, to hear the slight creaking, and the sharp yells, "She's comin'!" and then the mighty crash as the giant leveled all smaller trees and bushes under it to the ground. The dismembering of it seemed to Peter like cutting up a deer. First the side branches were cut off, stripped, and laid aside. Then the great trunk was neatly trimmed, cut to measure, and squared off. The main part of the house was to be 20 by 24 feet, but there was to be an extension at one end which Mary planned to keep for the visiting preacher.

They had no transportation except a home-made sledge which two horses unwillingly drew, for their horses were not trained as draught animals. The big logs were moved by up-ending them and throwing them over in the direction of the home-site. Big rocks for the foundation and the fireplaces were rolled, or inched along with a stout stick used like a crowbar. All the wood was trimmed and cut to measure where it fell, and stacked in the order in which it was to be used, so that the final rearing of the house was like putting up a prefabricated building. They were proud to have a skilled carpenter to make the window frames and door frames, and talked hopefully of the day when they'd get glass for the windows.

Peter ran in and out, leaping over the rising walls till they were too high to clear, and then walking round and round inside the quadrangular enclosure. The second day after they started all four walls were of full height, and the doors and windows were framed. The third day Brenda and Mary rode over to see the roof go on and made a feast of the rabbits John and other boys had shot. John was of little use as a carpenter, but he was a good shot and always ready to hunt. Eddie labored steadily at any job he was assigned. And when the time came to plaster the spaces between the logs, he contrived to make Peter and Jerry really useful, superintending them while they brought the clay and patted it in place.

The making of the roof was the most interesting operation. Peter perched on the topmost log of the side wall to watch, and when he was driven off, he and Jerry climbed a tree and looked down. The gables were made by small logs gradually shortened to the comb. It was fun to see them lay slender logs to form the roof and over these clapboards, fastened down by logs which were held in place, without nails, by timbers braced between them. At one end of the cabin was the wide chimney place, the chimney built up outside the cabin by rived sticks laid on corn-cob fashion, and plastered inside and out with clay. The most careful job was the laying of the floor. This was made of puncheons, which were logs, split with a wedge, the flat side rubbed smooth, the edges neatly trimmed. The doors were made of split boards shaved smooth with a drawing knife, and hung on leather hinges. The windows had similar doors hung on leather.

In four days the house was finished, and there was a house-warming which lasted far into the night, with whiskey and dancing on which Mary and the Baptists frowned in vain. "Times like this I miss Peter's fiddle," said Jus.

While Mary and the children settled themselves in the new house, Jus was off with the house-raising crew getting other families settled before winter. Left as the man of the family, John did little except look after the horses. Eddie had to do the milking. In John's philosophy a clean social line divided horses from cows. The care of horses was a gentleman's job; the care of cows a plebian's. John also busied himself fitting up the loft where he and Eddie and Peter were to sleep with a set of puncheon shelves which, he said, should be exclusively his. He put up pegs for his own clothes and hung them neatly, but left Eddie to put up pegs for Peter's. Mary had supposed that the boys would sleep on the floor of the loft on bearskins. But John objected to this and made himself a comfortable bunk under the eaves, with a spring mattress consisting of slender, resilient spruce boughs, covered with a padding of small cedar twigs, with a bearskin on top. Peter admired this so much that Eddie constructed one for Peter and himself to share under the eaves on the other side of John's bunk.

As it grew colder, the loft was very snug for the heat from the fireplace settled under the heavy roof. Peter loved to hear the rain beating on the roof, and the wind plucking at the shutter. He liked to open the window in the morning, and see the sky and the bright day framed in that little square.

After getting themselves moved in, they had to see to the corn crop, for maize was their staple cereal, and "bread" to them meant cornpone. Peter enjoyed going through the acres of shaggy, drying cornstalks and finding the golden ears inside the fine, paperlike husks. Before the kernels had hardened completely, it was grated to make a soft meal excellent for cakes and delicious as mush. The grater they made by punching a piece of tin full of holes, and bending it over a board with the rough side up. As soon as the corn was hard enough to pound, they made a mortar by burning in a stump a hole large enough to hold a peck of corn. Over this a wooden pestle was suspended by a spring pole, and the corn crushed into excellent meal. They made hominy by scalding the corn in strong lye made of wood ashes and rinsing it in the stream till all trace of ash was removed. The wheat crop had not been very good, for few of the early settlers understood the raising of wheat. But such as it was, it had been gathered earlier, before Mary and the boys came down, trampled out by horses, and winnowed and stored. Mary made cereal by soaking the wheat for three days in a bucket by the fire, and then boiling it endlessly with a little salt. Finally she poured maple syrup on it, and let the children exercise their teeth by chewing it. Chewing it was a lot of work, but the flavor was delicious.

Next to gathering the corn, the main thing was to store the wild grapes and nuts. Dutch made a pit in the side of a hill and stored the grapes there. They shriveled as time went on, but continued to be good eating till snow fell. But the great crop of the woodlands was nuts—walnuts, hickory nuts, butternuts, chestnuts. It was boys' work to gather these. Day after day Peter was out with other small boys, shouting and beating up the woods. Day after day as the leaves yellowed and fell, the store of nuts grew.

4

The most exciting things on the Cartwright acres were the two saltpeter caves, which Peter and Jerry were forbidden to enter lest they step on a rattlesnake or get lost. The little boys often wondered to see the veterans standing before these caves, engaged in earnest conversation, and men riding up and asking to look at the caves. All this gave the caves a mystery which was explained by John, who, on the rare occasions when he noticed his small brother, usually told him horror stories. John said that it was common for people to go into one of these caves and keep on walking, thinking they were going back to where they came in, but actually going the other way until at last they walked right out into Hell and were never heard of more. The only people who could go into a cave and not step right off into Hell, were murderers. Caves were full of people that had been killed there.

"I think I'll have Dominie's survey run where the third of the saltpeter caves is," observed Jus, one Indian summer morning. "If any one could turn that saltpeter to advantage it would be Dominie."

Mary bit her tongue. She wouldn't hurt Jus by saying, "Dominie and his Yankee girl are too fine for this place. They've settled in Ohio." She pitied Jus for his faith that this paragon, whom she'd heard him talk about for ten years, but who had never shown his face, would at last settle alongside them here. Jus went off on a train of thought which crystallized in the observation, "Or I might survey for him up to those unused cabins off the Nashville Trace between here and the courthouse."

Justurian's job, as attorney for the soldiers, was to get a survey made to the amount the warrant called for on some land to which the title was so vague that it could not be effectively disputed in court, then to get the veteran on to the land and furnished with a cabin, and to start breaking the fields. This done, the title could be registered at the county court, and henceforth the ownership of that land would be undisputed.

Since much of the land which had been granted to veterans was loosely claimed by "early settlers," there was much litigation. Sometimes surveys had to be made again and again before land could be found of which the veteran could take possession without too much strife. Even so, the veterans were forced to operate in armed companies of from fifty to one hundred, breaking disputed land and guarding it till the original claimants gave up. Many a "speculator" yielded thousands of acres rather than come to open war with these glowering troops of heavily armed men. Gradually it was being settled that if an early settler had put up adequate buildings and was working his land, the veterans would make their surveys elsewhere. However, if an absentee owner, with a claim prior to that of the soldiers, should try to evict one who had surveyed his land and settled on it, he must pay for all the "improvements" in the way of house, barn, fences, and fields broken, which the actual settler had made. These were rated at so high a price that the cost of evicting an industrious man was more than the land was worth.

Jus had had his eye on the lands surrounding the unused cabins said to belong to Wilson for a long time, and had been wondering how far they would dare to run the veterans' surveys into this acreage. Though he had been told they had been sold by the original builder to a man named Wilson, he could find no record of the sale. Rumor said that Sam Mason had built the cabins. But this both Stewart and the Mauldings denied. They said Mason had lived further west, but was a speculator not to be confused with the Mason who was said to be head of the river-gangs. Would Mason appear in court in person and challenge a veteran who might try to settle on this land? If so, could witnesses be found who would swear that Mason actually was the head of the river pirates, so that a warrant for his arrest could be taken out? Or was this talk about "Mason's gang" just hearsay?

While Jus was cogitating at the door of his cabin, Peter was building a dam across a small tributary of the creek. Seeing the small boy, a horseman on the trace drew up and shouted, "Is Justurian Cartwright to be found here?"

"He's my Pappy," said Peter.

"Run and tell him I've got a letter for him."

Peter had never seen a letter. "A letter, what might that be?" he asked, staring at the saddlebags as if he expected a strange animal to jump out.

"Ask me no questions, and I'll tell you no lies," answered the man solemnly. "You just git your Paw for me. Hurry! Git!"

When Jus heard there was a letter for him, he not only came running but called Mary. It had been less than a year since the first mail route had been opened from the West to the East, from Danville to Pittsburg. Mary and Jus had heard of this, but even in Stanford they had never seen a sign of it. When Peter's parents approached, the man on horseback said, "I was goin' through to Nashville, and the postmaster at Danville said there was a letter that had been settin' up there waitin' for you ever since you left Stanford. So I brought it along. The postmaster made me sign a paper for it. And now you sign here, and I'll give it to you."

By this time John, Eddie, and little Sis had joined the interested audience. All formalities attended to, the man drew forth a creased, dirty paper folded and fastened with a blotch of red sealing wax, accepted a drink of whisky from Jus, tucked two of Mary's corncakes into his saddlebags, pulled Peter's hair, chucked Sis under the chin and rode off. Jus had broken the seal and was slowly deciphering the script. A pleased smile broke over his face. "It's from Dominie! Mary, he's comin' right along, and he's bringin' a wife and baby!"

Mary did not hear this. She was peering into the distance. "Everybody is riding down the trace to Nashville. Look there! It's a man and a woman and a baby." She hastily wiped her hands and tucked up her hair. The air was rent with a whoop that seemed to ululate to the sky and shake the very clouds. Peter looked wildly to right and left, and then burst into a laugh as his father cleared three tree stumps in one leap. "Dominie! It's you, you old wildcat!" In the whirlwind of their meeting, Mary had only a chance to think fleetingly. "It's good Dominie's got brains, for he ain't got looks." For after one moment in which she peered up into the freckled, hawk-nosed, homely face above her, she was being propelled by Dominie on one side and Jus on the other toward the woman and baby on horseback. "She's sure is high-toned," Mary thought, looking into the face shadowed by a smart straw hat. But when the face answered her uncertain glance with a smile, Mary was instantly disarmed. Frank, pleasant, with a wide mouth and a wide smile, a turned up nose, green eyes set wide apart, and some freckles, nothing could have been plainer or more instantly likeable. "Mary," she said, not waiting for Dominie to introduce her, "I am Barbara. My sister, Lydia—you met her at Crab Orchard—said you were a lovely person, and I can see that you are."

Compliments were so rare in Mary's life, that she could have cried. "Lovely. She called me lovely!" she was thinking, in a daze, as Barbara handed down the baby to her, dismounted in a graceful leap, and, taking back the baby, walked with her to the cabin, like a long lost sister coming home. While Peter and Eddie took charge of the horses, and Jus and Dominie were lost in conversation and tobacco smoke, side by side on the puncheon bench at the cabin door, Barbara sat down companionably on the new rush bottom chair in the shade of the big chestnut tree, opened her stylish bodice, and nursed her baby. When Peter returned to observe this remarkable person, it gave him quite a start to see one who looked like that nursing a baby. He had thought that such fine females functioned in some other way, more impersonal and more delicate. He stood staring at the white breast with the baby tugging at it till his mother sharply ordered him away. But he came back and observed with equal amazement the removal of the baby's diaper. The lady's hands were white. She had worn heavy gloves to protect them. Yet with those hands she did all these things, just like an ordinary woman! Mary had much the same feeling. Never had she associated on the humble level of diapers and nursing with a woman with the dress and air of this one. Even Jus felt rather odd about it. He had given a slanting glance at the delicate white breast as it emerged from the smart bodice, and instantly turned his eyes away.

Looking into Peter's expressive face, Barbara said, "Why don't you show me the dam you were making?" She laid the baby away, fastened her dress, and pulling up her long skirt for easier walking and bunching it gracefully over her hips, she followed the flattered boy to the stream. She returned full of plans for making a pool lined with smooth stones where clothes could be washed on fine days. And she told Eddie that he could run the stream in under a shelter, and set some flat stones like shelves just below the water where milk and other things could be set to keep cool. Explaining this to Mary, later, she was led to other suggestions. You could put food in an earthen dish, and wrap the dish in wet linsy. If you kept the linsy wet, the wind blowing against it and evaporating the water would draw the heat out of the food. She thought, in time, she'd have a deep cold cellar under part of their house where in summer food could be kept from being spoiled by heat and in winter from being spoiled by cold.

Barbara then followed Mary into the cabin, suggesting at least twenty ways of making housework easier, but showing such admiration for Mary's weaving and sewing that not only did she not resent the proposed innovations, but she felt quite exhilarated. Here was something as fundamental as religion. You didn't let mess and dirt defeat you. You went full tilt at it with your *mind*. She felt a strange new kind of security as Barbara, with her tucked-up skirts carelessly showing her neat white stockings and nice leather shoes, reviewed everything, with the directness and authority of a general planning strategy.

5

Jus was far less happy in his re-union with his long lost friend. Observing Dominie's face grow set and cold, as he told him about Logan Courthouse, he remarked with an effort at cheerfulness, "It's a bad situation here. But we'll weather it."

"It's worse than I thought," answered Dominie. "I'm half a mind to give up my claim here, and go back and settle with the Yankee veterans in Ohio."

Jus was aghast. He had counted so much on the support of his intellectual friend in this wicked place. And now that he had come, he had for a few bright moments felt so secure. Now he felt his world collapsing. But he masked his dismay with a question, "What's so infernal superior about Ohio?"

"A good many things," replied Dominie, thoughtfully. "The main thing is that they started off differently." And he went on to tell about that rainy day, April 7, 1788, when he and the others at Fort Harmar stood in the fog on the river bank and watched the Yankee boat, *The Mayflower*, bring down the Yankee settlers. He told how they landed with tools and skilled workmen, laid out their town, called a town meeting, made their laws and posted them on a tree, built themselves a stout stockade and put inside it a school and a church, and started both school and Sunday school. "They didn't straggle out alone, one by one, without proper equipment, pitting their sole strength as individuals, against the wilds."

"Well, we didn't either," said Jus. "You and me and Dutch—we all organized for years, and we've moved now as a company."

"And to that extent you are much better off than most who just come as they can. But even so, Jus, we haven't begun to think, like the Yankees, in terms of institutions. And we haven't their mechanical skill, by which I don't mean being able to make a knife or a bow. I mean the ability to invent machines which others can use to make things. The Yankees have a kind of spirit of progress . . ."

"I have heard," cut in Jus, masking the misery in his heart, "that the Yankees haven't the first notion of freedom. They've got a minister supported by taxes, and what he says everybody's got to do. That's clean against Jefferson's idea. And they don't leave a man free to bring up his children as he sees fit. They take money from him to set up a school, and then they make him send his children to the school."

"But nobody makes them. They make themselves. It's all settled in town meeting."

"Well, they can have it," said Jus, stretching out his long legs. "For me, give me my freedom—freedom to be poor if I haven't the gumption to get rich, and ignorant if I don't want to learn. I don't want anybody making me do anything, even if it's for my own good."

"I know how you feel," answered Dominie. "There's something here the Yankees haven't got. It *is* freedom—inner freedom and largeness of mind. But Jus, it can't last." He looked off morosely into the distance, his homely, large-nosed face set, his cold gray eyes hard.

Jus watched him for a while, and puffed meditatively on his corncob pipe. Finally he removed his pipe from his mouth, and said, "Dominie, it don't seem like you to want to clear out of here just because we're so low-down ignorant we can't make things like the Yankees do. Come now, there's a bigger bug than that eatin' you."

"There is," said Dominie. He paused, and then added, with something portentous in his tone, "Sam Mason stayed at Cedar House last night. He went by the name of John Wilson. But I recognized him. His brothers were with me on Clark's expedition."

Jus started, but observed cautiously, "They say the Sam Mason who's known down here is no relation of the Sam Mason that's said to be head of the river pilots."

"He's the same man," replied Dominie.

Still cautious, Jus asked, "What does he look like?"

"A big fellow, with one front tooth that sticks out."

"I'll be damned!"

In answer to Dominie's startled look, he told him Jassamine's story. He also told him about the cabins said to belong to a man named Wilson. "I'd thought of surveying the land up to them for you. And then I wondered if you wouldn't want the piece of ground with a saltpeter cave on it."

Dominie pricked up his ears. "Saltpeter!" Jus described his own

two caves, and the third one not yet claimed. Slightly relieved by
Dominie's interest, he ventured an observation that was really a
question, to lift the burden still weighing on his heart. "But what's
the use of talking to you? Now you know Sam Mason's to be your
neighbor, you won't be able to make tracks back to Ohio fast
enough."

An expression at once grim and enigmatic had come into Dominie's face. "I'm not sure about that. I find a neighborly opportunity to send Sam Mason to Hell where he belongs rather allur-
ing. Don't forget what he and his gang did to Barbara's sister, Lydia.
And what you say about the saltpeter interests me. Let's take a
look at these caves."

Word that the men were exploring the caves got from John to
Eddie and Peter, who had been absorbed in Barbara's ideas about
the stream, and they came running to share this new adventure.
With a feeling between curiosity and terror, Peter saw Dominie
light a torch and thrust it into the opening of the cave. His heart
beat violently against his ribs when he was allowed, himself, to
look in and see the light flaring on the sculptured walls of rock and
the things like stone icicles hanging from the roof, and the walls
dripping with wetness and crusted with a sort of rime.

Watched by the fascinated boys, Dominie spent the rest of the
day making a lantern out of a piece of old iron, shaped like a pail
with a cover and a handle to carry it by, and with a hole on one
side through which the light could shine. In the bottom of it,
below the hole, he put some bear's grease, and a twisted piece of
tow linen for wick. Then he made a long rope of tow linen and
wound one end of the rope around his waist and gave Jus the
other to hold, and took the lantern and went in to explore the cav-
erns. They weren't very large, and before night, first Jus, then
John, then Eddie, and then Peter had gone all through them, and
they seemed as familiar as any dark, damp rooms.

Dominie was quite excited. With saltpeter they could set up a
plant to make gunpowder. Sitting by the fire that night, roasting
a side of venison which Jus, fortunately, had hanging out behind
the house, Dominie talked about the part industry can play in
building up a new settlement. The secret of the Yankees, he said,
was that they did not depend on farming alone but balanced farm-

ing with industry, "so they are always rolling along on two wheels instead of trying to balance on one."

"We'll make gunpowder," he said, "and we'll trade it at Fort Massac for goods from their post exchange. If, as they say, the exchange of Dromgole, Stewart, and Reading is just an outlet for the goods Mason steals, this will make us absolutely independent of it. We'll never need to get a thing from them."

He and Jus talked about this excitedly till late at night, long after Barbara and the baby had been put to sleep in the preacher's room. There was no more talk of Dominie's going back to Ohio.

6

With the help of the other veterans, Dominie's cabin was up in a week, and he set about making "improvements" such as the Virginians had never seen. Among other things he built two barns, snug, neat, and warm as houses, one for horses, one for cows. Two thoroughbred horses, and two cows from the farm Barbara's sister, Lydia, and her husband, Fred, had taken near Lexington, were brought down by two Negroes, along with a sledge carrying household goods. With them came Lydia and Fred themselves.

Lydia rode over immediately to greet Mary. Looking into that delicate, piquant face, so like Barbara's but much prettier, Mary was overwhelmed for a moment with the emotions of that service for those killed by robbers on the Ohio when she had first seen Lydia. She could see that Lydia was remembering it, too, and even more poignantly. The two women greeted each other with conventional words, and in an offhand manner, but Mary said to herself, "It's like my being beside her there, when she was broke at the heart and weeping, made us sisters," and all the warmth of her heart went out to meet the look in Lydia's blue eyes.

Barbara had sent by Lydia an invitation to Jus and Mary to come over for supper. Mary, who had never supped with fine folk like that, wanted to refuse. They'd see what a lout she was at the table. They'd learn she didn't have any dress-up clothes. And that would be the end of their kindness and frank acceptance of her. Better not put herself in the way of being rejected. But Jus accepted heartily before she could demur. Mary spent the rest of the day washing her hair, remaking her old "freedom" dress, and trying to bleach and soften her hands and to shape her nails. It was hopeless! She wished the earth would open and swallow her before they got to Dominie's cabin!

The supper was finer even than she had expected. The table was set with a damask cloth, real china, and real silver. After supper they served sweet wine in stemmed glasses at the fireside, accompanied by nuts in a silver dish, with a silver nutcracker. They didn't notice anything strange when Mary hesitatingly refused the wine, but smiled with infectious friendliness when Jus reached over and set Mary's glass alongside his. After that, with laughter and jokes, Dominie filled both glasses again and again, and Jus drank for the two of them.

It was Mary's first contact with people who had never lived in log cabins, neither they nor their fathers and grandfathers before them. For three generations they had lived in brick houses in Philadelphia, and had known how to read and write! Theirs were the skills, the culture, and the graces of the native American urban civilization of the eighteenth century. But they had none of the fancy Tidewater ways. They were as comfortable as an old moccasin. Fred, Lydia's husband, was homely, middle-aged, and partly bald, and had a thickening waistline, but he was as easy in his ways as the others—matter-of-fact and quietly jolly.

Much of the talk turned on transportation, and their low opinion of the sledge. All they'd been able to pack on it had been a few dishes, some silver, and two or three rugs. Mary gathered that there were all sorts of chairs, tables, sofas, and bedsteads somewhere in the family which Barbara might have if she could only get them out here. Fred proposed to put it on a Conestoga wagon, and put wagon and all on a flat-boat at Pittsburg and float it down to Louisville. "But try to get it down from there," said Dominie. "Can you run it between trees two feet apart, five feet around, and standing trunk to trunk like a fence along a trail one horse can barely squeeze through? No, all of civilization we can move is what we can carry in our heads or our saddlebags. We'll have to begin new with that."

"By the time you've done what you'll have to do with that," observed Fred, "the folks back home won't know you. You'll be a new species in a new world."

As if they found this prospect of being new-made exhilarating, they vied with each other in planning the gunpowder industry. Jus asked what they would need for gunpowder besides saltpeter. Fred said they'd need charcoal and sulphur. Charcoal they could make. But there was no sulphur this side of Louisiana. How get it from there?

"Cherokee Bill has married a French Chickasaw girl," said Jus, looking at Dominie. "He can get anything up the Chickasaw road."

This information was received with as much delight as if Jus had contributed a million dollars to the project.

The climax of that wonderful supper came when Fred got so interested in the gunpowder that he said he'd sell out his acres near Lexington, and come down here and set up the plant for them. Lydia enthusiastically concurred. She didn't care for gunpowder, but she wanted to be near her sister.

Riding home, Jus and Mary confessed to each other that they couldn't understand why people who could sit in fine houses back in Philadelphia, and drink sweet wine and crack nuts before brass andirons after dinner, would come out here to live in log cabins and make gunpowder. But it was plain they looked forward to it with a gusto Jus and Mary and their friends had never been able to rise to.

7

The folks at Dominie's cabin stirred up so much excitement with their plans for improving life that it was with a sense of desolation that Mary and Jus saw Fred and Lydia leave to close out their affairs near Lexington. However, they were cheered by the promise that their new friends would soon be back, and by spring they'd have the gunpowder industry in full blast.

Dominie lost no time. He arranged with Cherokee to get the sulphur and with Dutch to accompany him to Fort Massac to get equipment and instructions for the making of gunpowder. While they were working out these plans, in secrecy, the new firm of Stewart, Dromgole, and Reading put on a preliminary promotion campaign among the veterans. To this end, James Dromgole called on Jus with an offer to take deerskins, bearskins, coonskins, and buffalo skins from the veterans in any quantity in exchange for anything they might need.

Dromgole was, in all outward respects, the type of the frontier upper class, with those plain, friendly, self-respecting good manners, and the clean-cut, racy, and reasonably grammatical speech which were to emerge as distinctly "middle western." As usual among middle westerners later, his dress was a careless compromise between neatness, comfort, and the natural desire of man to show off. To any one but an astute frontiersman of his own breed, like Jus, he would have appeared to be honest because he was bluff and without social pretense. Jus did not invite him in, but stood by his horse, talking amiably. After half an hour of polite fencing, Dromgole rode away, calling back heartily that Jus must come in and see him, and Jus answering just as heartily that he would.

Dromgole's call was followed by one from Stewart. Peter, playing in the yard when Stewart clattered up, recognized him as the one who had killed a man more than a year ago, but he was now so changed that the sick memory of that was lost in curiosity. Hair and beard trimmed, face clean and engaging, Stewart was dressed in a coat made of patches of yellow, scarlet, green, and blue velvet and brocade, with rows of gold buttons. His top boots were decorated with red tassels. A white silk handkerchief was passed through a gold clasp at the back of his neck and fastened like a stock. He wore a large beaver hat trimmed with a plume of red turkey feathers.

"Son, call your Paw for me," he said, drawing a handful of something from his saddlebag, and adding, "Some of these for yourself, some for your handsome lady mother, and some for your pretty sister."

"No, thank ye, Sir," quaked Peter, eyeing the silver and gold rings, earbobs, and bracelets.

"Oh, well, let the hogs root for them," said Stewart, flinging them off into the wet snow.

Justurian came out, with polite and even hearty greetings. But he did not ask Stewart to dismount and have a drink, and Mary refused to show herself. After he had ridden away, they all turned out and

helped Peter scrape away the snow and locate the rings and bracelets. "Give them to me, son," said Jus. "I want to show them to
Dominie."

When Dominie had studied the trinkets, he observed, "I don't
think they're stolen goods. They're of his own making. He must
have been bound out to a metal worker in his youth, before he came
out here to hunt buffalo and set up Alston's counterfeiting." He
turned to Peter, "Peter, when Bill Stewart gives you or Jerry a coin,
it's all right to take it. But bring it to me."

Peter looked questioningly at his father, who said gravely, "It's
all right, Son. But mind no honest man takes money unless he gives
it back with interest, or gives something in fair exchange. So when
you take it, say, 'Thank you, kindly. My father will pay it back'."

Peter didn't understand the amused glance which passed from
Dominie to Jus at this, nor the ironic gleam on the face of his mother
who, as usual during the men's conversation, sat quietly within hearing, stitching on a wool frock for Sis.

Early in 1794 Stewart, Dromgole, and Reading opened for business. Their store had no display windows and almost no goods in
sight. It was a substantial log cabin, with a well built fireplace, in
which the coals glowed purple and orange all day between the huge
backlog and the smaller hickory forelog. It looked more like a club
than a store. There was a wooden bucket of whisky, with gourds
hanging by it, where thirst could be slaked for nothing, a month
old copy of *The Kentucky Gazette,* and several well worn packs of
cards. Gambling began before the earliest rider passed along the
trace, and it continued by firelight long after all respectable citizens
were in bed. Business was carried on quietly among those who
were lured in by warmth, whisky, and sociability. If a man had
skins to sell, he would be enticed into the cold log lean-to behind,
double-barred and stockaded, and dazzled with Cashmir shawls,
lengths of broadcloth and satin, calico, silk, brocade, and velvet,
shoebuckles of every kind of fancy design, boots of fine Spanish
leather, Spanish saddles, copper kettles, silver-mounted pistols, porcelain, glass, and silver. By late winter luxuries of this sort were appearing in log cabins all over the frontier, and the determination
of the settlers to keep clear of Dromgole and Stewart was hardening
into a plan among the Baptists and the stricter Presbyterians for an

organized boycott.

Early in 1794 Dominie and Dutch, and some fifteen other veterans set out for Fort Massac, to exchange their skins for some of the twenty-five gallon copper cauldrons which were made at Liberty Town near Pittsburgh by an Alsatian Frenchman, and which were used for making salt by evaporation. Dominie planned to heat the scrapings of the saltpeter caves, mixed with water, in these cauldrons.

They planned to bring their cauldrons and other equipment back on a sledge drawn over the snow. "If they attack us," said Dominie, "we'll put up a good fight, and use what we learn from fighting them against them later. If they let us come through safe, we'll prove that what's keeping us from opening trade down here is more bluff than real danger."

They left on a morning so cold that the snow creaked under their horses' hooves, and their breaths froze to their beards. The cold abated. The sun shone earlier and earlier in the morning with a fresh hopeful light that looked warm even when it was chill, and the creek was in flood. But they did not return. Whenever they could, Brenda and Barbara rode over to Mary's to relieve their worry by asserting and re-asserting that it was too soon for them to be back, and if anything had happened, surely news of it would have got through. But every day it was harder to say this with assurance. Brenda was in a frenzy of worry. Did God require a man with a family to take such risks even against the hosts of Satan? But Barbara said gravely, "It's a risk I'd take myself if I had a chance. Life isn't worth living if you have to back down before bullies." The words spoke to Mary's heart like a trumpet. "Hear that, Peter," she said. "That's something you're never to forget."

Peter was sitting on the floor in front of the fire, gnawing on one of those lean, hard sides of venison which, at this time of year, were called "bread". The cornmeal, hominy, and wheat had given out. The venison served for "bread"; the fat bear's flesh for "meat." It was the season when frontier children would give all the four-footed and feathered creatures in the world for just one bowlful of mush and milk. Peter desisted from his attempt to appease the gnawing in his stomach and looked up, his dark eyes earnest in his greasy face. Barbara said, with a slight smile softening her gravity,

"Yes, never back down before a bully, Peter. For no man's a bully unless he's a coward or a fool. Since he's a coward you can scare him. Since he's a fool, you can pull the wool over his eyes. So you generally won't even have to fight him." How often Peter was to remember that and test the truth of it in after times!

While Dominie was away, Dean and Jassamine helped Barbara with the outside and inside chores. Dean had built himself a double cabin on land Jus had procured for him, and was farming the Cartwright acres on shares. No one among the veterans except Dominie had a home so neat and civilized. Since Jassamine had grown up in Philadelphia, she and Barbara had much in common. They would sit together for hours, sewing and chatting about old times.

Both Mary and Barbara felt something special—something almost pitying— in the concern Dean and Jassamine showed. There was a curious constraint in their manner when they asked, "No word from Dominie yet?" Often Jassamine would start to speak, and then choke off the words and change the subject. At times she would ask, as if the words hurt her to say them, "Your sister? You haven't heard from her yet?"

Barbara's "No" had an unwonted note of strain in it. She had not heard from her sister, though travelers came down from Lexington every few days and might have brought her a letter. Finally she sent a letter by a man who was going up from Nashville to Lexington. He sent back word that Lydia and Fred and their two Negroes had never returned to their place near Lexington. Telling Mary this, Barbara put on a brave front. "They must have changed their minds and gone to Louisville. There were things Fred wanted to order brought down from Pittsburgh by the Ohio boats."

But when she said this to Dean, he made no comment. There was a dreadful solemnity in his dark face.

CHAPTER 11

Mary had her own worries as the winter froze down solidly upon them. There had been no word from the Methodists since they arrived. This was the more strange since Ogden and Haw had been the first Christian preachers down here, and had been their source of information about this land all these years. Jacob Lurton had said that he was coming. But there was no sign of him. Dean and Jassamine were as puzzled as she. With no preacher to organize even a class, all they could do was to meet together—the three of them—and read the Bible and pray.

Meanwhile they saw persons with less experience of God's saving grace organizing themselves into congregations. The Ewings, the Burwell Jacksons, the Samuel Cauldwells, and others of the elite had formed a small Presbyterian congregation around John Grammer. This met in a cabin on Red River. Barbara and Dominie joined it, but admitted it was very dull. "What you all have got," said Mary to Barbara, "ain't religion. It's just a kind of high-toned feeling of being above the muck and mire of everything else around here." Barbara smiled. She could not deny it.

A more religiously "convicted" congregation formed around the strong live core of German Baptists on Muddy River. To this Dutch and Brenda belonged. The preacher was a horny-handed, picturesque, and literate eccentric whom the Presbyterian children called "Ol' Waterbug." Every Baptist was a missionary. By mid-December the Baptists had converted so many of their neighbors that they held a baptismal ceremony in the freezing river, and, as Mary said, "drownded them straight to Glory." Observation posts for this performance in nearby trees sold, among the heathen, for as high as a buffalo skin apiece.

A second Baptist congregation was formed on Muddy River by

William Morris, the Portyghee—a good and gentle man. Hearing rumors that his son, Sam, was a member of Alston's gang, and that the Portyghees all through the Green River and Cumberland country were counterfeiters for Alston, William Morris had walked from North Carolina, praying every step of the way for the regeneration of these and other denizens of Rogues' Harbor. Most of his congregation were Portyghees, but a few other neighbors met with him regularly—both white and black.

But when Jus wondered how the Baptists and the Presbyterians had contrived among them to get together three handfuls of Christians—less than forty in all—in a population scattered over a radius of twenty-five miles and not numbering 1000—Mary said shrewdly, " 'Tain't religion they're after. It's safety. They think that the ones that come to preachings regular are those least likely to cut your throat. So they make haste to tie up with a preacher—both to show they're well-meanin' themselves and to find others they dare trust."

Jus smiled. "Mary, you're smart enough to be a lawyer!"

All that winter the preacher's room in the Cartwright cabin stood ready, with a new feather bed, a bedside table with a candle, and a thick black bearskin on the floor. But no preacher came. Instead there came terrifying rumors, helpfully relayed by the Baptists, that the whole Methodist Church had collapsed. Jus rode back from the January court with news which he did not have the heart to break to Mary till next morning at breakfast.

"I saw Ben Ogden, the circuit rider, yesterday."

"Oh," said Mary, her face all alight. "They've sent him instead of Lurton. Well. Glory be somebody's come. Just wait till I give the lie to those Baptists!"

"Ogden's come down here to locate," said Jus.

"Oh!" she said. She was taken aback for a moment. Then she said eagerly, "Like James Haw! Well, at least we'll have him here to hold up the Methodys."

"No, not like Haw. Ogden isn't a minister any more."

She gasped. "Not a minister!"

"The plain truth of it is, Mary, he was *drunk*."

"Oh." She reeled from the news as from a blow. Then she reacted angrily, "I won't believe it. It's a Baptist slander."

"No, I talked to him myself. He was roaring, slobbering drunk."

"Ogden—that good young man, Ogden! Why he was the first circuit rider down here, he and James Haw, riding up and down, daring the Devil to come out and show his face, when nobody else hardly dared to look in here. Ogden *drunk!*"

Her world was collapsing in horror. Jus went on to tell how Ogden had told a drunken story about the Kentucky preachers rebelling against Asbury at the first general Conference of the Methodist Church that was held in the fall of 1792. A preacher named James O'Kelly had at last dared to raise the point that had been bothering some of them all along—that John Wesley was a Tory and the whole set-up of the Church was patterned after the English hierarchy of lords and bishops. We wanted none of that structure of privilege in this country, O'Kelly and his friends said. But when he couldn't fight Asbury down and get a democratic church policy, he walked out and a number of preachers with him. The secessionists called themselves Republican Methodists. Ogden was disgusted with the whole business. Preachers, he said, were no better than other sinners, back-biting and selfish and grasping for power. But at least the common ordinary variety of sinner wasn't a hypocrite. As for himself, he was going plumb to Hell. He begged Jus to find him a piece of land out west of the settlements. There he proposed to run a station for the buffalo hunters. "They're wild, and more often than not they're bad. But what they are, they are in all honesty. They don't cloak it in pious deceit."

"Poor soul!" said Mary. "You can tell his heart's broke." She begged Jus to take a message to Ogden, which Jus engaged to do the next time he rode to the courthouse for he was sorry for Ogden. A few days later he saw the young man, lounging in front of Cedar House, sober, but sullen. Ogden refused Justurian's invitation to come down and stay a few days in the new preacher's room. He dared not face the look in the eyes of the earnest little woman with whom he had prayed and sung hymns in happier days, nor the bright face of the boy Peter, to whom he had been a hero. Folks like that were being betrayed, just as he was.

For days after Jus brought this word home, Peter shivered under a sense of moral tragedy, like a black cloud between him and the sun. As for Mary, it was more than she could bear. Her mind sought refuge in any idea that would offer relief. She remembered

James Haw. He had been Ogden's partner in "breaking" the wild west back in 1787. John Grammer, returning from a meeting with Doctor Craighead, the Presbyterian minister at Nashville, had told Dominie that Haw had quite a following. So far as there was a Methodist Church in the region south of the border, it appeared to center in the vigorous, truculent personality of Haw. Hearing this, Mary began to rebuild her shattered sense of security around Haw. Come spring, he might be persuaded to go on a wide circuit up here north of the border and preach and set up a class. She was trying to get courage to send him a message when Jus punctured this bubble. Haw, he said, had also revolted against Asbury and had taken most of the Cumberland Methodists with him.

Mary was desperate. Her faith had strengthened with the weekly discipline of prayer and Bible reading and mutual confession at the class meeting in Stanford. "But even so," she told Peter, who listened with a solemn, though uncomprehending interest, "if your life in God isn't tended, and brightened with new fuel from time to time, it'll just naturally sink to ash." She read the Bible and prayed passionately, and had moments of illumination when it seemed God was calling her to mount a horse and summon the half a dozen Methodists among the veterans to gather at her cabin and reconstitute the church. The next moment she wondered how she could have thought of anything so presumptuous. "God will send Jacob Lurton," she thought, and prayed with ever renewed fervor. "God, don't let him fail us, too. Send him to us."

2

One mild, thawing day, Dean asked Jus to ride over the property and pick out trees to tap for maple syrup. When they were out of sight of the cabin, Dean reined up his horse and said bluntly, "Jus, I've kept it to myself as long as I can. I prayed God it wasn't so. But now I know it is." He hesitated, and then said gravely, "Lydia and Fred were murdered."

Stupefied, Justurian's lips barely framed a question, "Where?"

"Between Cedar House and Morton Maulding's cabin. They'd barely got on their way."

"And their two Negroes?"

"They were killed, too."

"How do you know this?"

"Jus, when there's dirty work to be done, who does it? Folks with black skin. And that goes for murder. There were three black skins and black souls on that job—Sam Morris, whose father is the Portyghee minister, and Pompey and Sambo.

"I know Sam," observed Jus. "But I've never heard of the others."

"They come and go," replied Dean. "But when they're here, they're very much at home in the Mason cabins."

"It might be easy enough to hang Negroes for murder," reflected Jus. "If there were anybody to testify against them."

"There's nobody," replied Dean. "Every Negro knows all about it, and every Indian. The Mystic Band never even tries to keep their doings from persons of color. It acts like they were horses and dogs, knowing they won't testify in a white man's court, and if they do white men won't believe them, and knowing they can punish 'em any time they want, in any way, and the law won't interfere."

Ruefully Jus admitted the truth of this. "But," he observed, "what did they think they could steal from Fred and Lydia?"

"It wasn't a stealing job. They were put up to it. There were two white men in it."

"Who were they?"

"I don't know. Some Negroes think—the Harpes."

"The Harpes! Are they down here?"

"They've been seen. They stay at the Roberts' cabin—you know —that dirty old man with an oaf of a son."

"And two daughters—Susan and Betsey. I know them," said Jus.

He was remembering what his law teachers had told him. "Establish a motive." Aloud he said, "If the motive wasn't stealing, what was it?"

"It's plain enough. These folks came down here with never a by-your-leave to anybody at Logan Courthouse. They were riding all over the place and planning big things, and it looked like they had the wherewithal to carry them out. But they weren't like the Ewings, and Jackson, and Cauldwell, honest enough, but ready to fix things up with the Alston-Mason-Dromgole gang. They just ignored them, and went about as if they had all the power in the world themselves. Look at it from the Mystic Band's point of view. If folks like Dominie and Fred came down here in numbers, how long would the Band last? They had to do away with them quick. It's Satan's logic, but it's logic."

Jus had to agree that it was. The horror of it—the dread of facing Barbara and Dominie with it—had been kept at bay while he was getting at the facts. Now misery overwhelmed him.

Dean said, "I haven't the heart to tell Barbara—now she's alone and worrying about Dominie."

Jus answered heavily, "Nor have I." He pondered darkly. Then he added, "We'll keep it to ourselves till Dominie comes to help her face it. I won't even tell Mary."

3

The sap was running in the maple trees. In the forests the fires glowed rose-red and orange pink in the fogs that rose from the melting snows. It was the time the children loved best. They went the rounds of the maple trees, collecting the buckets of sweet water. They stood around the boiling kettles, sniffing the fragrant steam, clamoring for the time-honored children's treat of the frontier —the boiling down of the first syrup to a candylike consistency, and pouring it out on the snow. There it congealed into a flavorsome gum which kept the jaws busy for hours. Peter, his own mouth deliciously glued together, had just inserted a wad of the sweet between the jaws of Shawnee, the "ol houn dawg," and was jumping up and down in silent merriment as Shawnee, trying in vain to yelp, thrashed with his tail and paddled violently with his four feet in the snow. Suddenly the air was rent with a war whoop. Barbara gave a little scream and started to run. "It's Dominie!" And there was Dominie and Dutch and the others, coming back safe and sound, dragging the sledge with copper kettles on it. But the tale they told was fantastic.

They had arrived at Fort Massac and thrashed out the situation at Rogues' Harbor with the commandant, who gave them cauldrons and other equipment in return for their skins. But in the future he could not take furs, because skins were the only things the Indians north of the Ohio had to trade with, and he must keep their good will by giving them a monopoly. But he would gladly take gunpowder. The fort had sent word to all friendly Indian chiefs that Philip Alston was to be brought in, dead or alive. Alston was certainly the man behind the whole network of robbery, counterfeiting, river piracy, and thieves' markets. About Mason he was not so sure. He seemed thunderstruck by Dominie's statement that he had recognized a man who passed as John Wilson as Sam Mason.

Well satisfied, Dominie's company started back. The second day, in passing through a heavy forest, they were attacked by a band of robbers, wearing white hoods over their heads and faces, and led by a burly figure in a large plumed hat with a black velvet mask over his eyes, who waved a sword and shouted, "St. Iago and at them!" Dominie sprang from his horse, wriggled forward on his belly, Indian-style, and shot this man from the back. In the scrimmage, two of his own comrades dragged him through the snow, leaving a trail of blood, and then, with shouts and roars, another band fell on them. Dominie, from behind a tree, saw that the second crowd was fighting off the first, and then a hearty voice called, "Dominie, old scout, come out and say Howdy to an old friend." And there was Sam Mason!

Dominie came forward cautiously. When he did not take Mason's proferred hand, Mason clapped him on the shoulder and said, loudly and cheerfully, "I've saved your life for you, damn you! And is this all the thanks I get?" He introduced his two sons —two well built, good-looking, fresh-faced young men named Thomas and John, and shouted to one of his party who seemed to have gone in pursuit of the robbers, "Come back here, Tom, and renew your acquaintance with your old friend, Dominie."

Thomas, Sam's brother, whom Dominie had known on Clark's first expedition, turned back, frank and friendly. By this time Dutch and the rest of Dominie's party had come out of hiding behind trees and had retrieved the sledge, with the copper kettles still in place. But the robbers were gone, leaving only the trampled snow and mud, faintly reddened with blood.

Sam and Thomas asked Dominie about friends at Fort Harmar, talked about General St. Clair's war with the Indians in Ohio, and finally invited the veterans to dinner at the cabin of a friend, Henry Havard. When Dominie declined, the Masons rode with them as a guard through the woods. Sam Mason, abreast of Dominie, talked about the Military Tract. "I've land and cabins down there," he said. "But it's been too wild to bring up a family in. Now that it's filling up with a good class of people, I'm moving down there this spring." He wanted Dominie to warn Cartwright to keep off his land. "In case you've forgotten it, I was an officer in the war, and my brothers all fought. Among us we've got warrants to cover our claims."

After escorting them through the forest, the Mason family clattered off, waving their coonskin hats cordially, and calling back, "See you in the spring."

"And so," said Jus dryly, when this tale was finished, "we're to have the Mason family as neighbors!" He looked shrewdly at Dominie. "What do you make of it?"

Peter, in his favorite place, at his father's feet, on the flat rock in front of the fire where the maple syrup was boiling, listened keenly. He had been trying to figure it all out. He was always studying the ins and outs of the barbaric intrigues and deceptions of his wild world and trying to understand men who, for all their apparent rudeness and ignorance, were complex personalities and finished actors.

Dominie replied, "The fellow I wounded may have been Alston himself, and Mason's performance a means to get Alston safely out of the way."

"But you said the man you hurt was big and burly. They say Alston's a rather neat, elegant figure."

"He'd stuffed out his figure. That's why my shot didn't kill him— too much stuff between him and the bullet."

Jus spat a stream of tobacco juice into the fire. "They sure are a prankish lot."

Peter heard Mary say to Barbara, and the words fell on his mind like seeds on deep rich soil in spring, "It takes a showoff, vainglorious type to lie and steal and think of fancy ways of getting something for nothing. You have to be more than half mad to take to a life of crime. A sane man knows what's good for him in the long run, and he's God fearin' and settles down, humble and patient, and really works for a livin'."

Through all this talk Dominie had felt a constraint in Jus, and something solemn and ominous in the look Dean had fixed on him. Now he asked, "How is everything here?" Jus hesitated. Dominie insisted. "Something has happened." His gray eyes and hawklike features grew tense. "Something bad."

Jus looked around at the eager faces aglow in the firelight. Brenda and Dutch were "verhuddled" with their children in a happy family group. Barbara sat placidly content beside Dominie on a fallen tree, the baby in her lap. With sticky faces and hands, the children were joyously running around, sharing their snow-candy with the returned travelers. He had not the heart to answer Dominie here.

"Something has happened," he said in a low voice. "It isn't good. It's—it's bad. I'll tell you when we're alone."

Dominie rose and walked away with him into the snowy shadows. Then he called Barbara. Something in his voice pierced Mary's heart like a knife. "I'll take the baby, Barbara," she said. Barbara, shaken by that tone, ran to Dominie.

They returned white-faced, cold, the life drained out of them. "I'll take the baby, Mary. Thank you. We're going home."

Jus answered the question in Mary's eyes. "Lydia and Fred were murdered on the path between Cedar House and Morton Maulding's."

All Mary's heart went out to Barbara in passionate protest. "Can God be just if He lets such things happen?"

4

Spring brought the Masons in state. Sam Mason and his company stayed at Cedar House for days while descriptions of their eyes, noses, and inches ran from mouth to mouth. With him were Mrs. Mason, a silent, rather dour woman, who looked as if she belonged in better company; his brother Thomas; his sons Thomas and John; a young man with a thin beak nose and narrow dark eyes named Kuykendall; Mason's two daughters—"Sweetie," and "Hon"— and John Mason's girl Marguerite Douglas. They were all richly dressed and handsomely mounted. A shower of bleached curls fell to Sweetie's plump white shoulders, earrings sparkled in her little shell-like ears, half a dozen rings shone on her white fingers, and her arms were covered with bracelets almost to her dimpled elbows. Hon had a dark structure of hair nearly a foot high, her languishing gray eyes were fringed with long black lashes, each hair of which appeared to have been separately stiffened and oiled, and her slender "elegant" figure floated in a cloud of fine muslin summer draperies. Marguerite was handsome in a sultry, dark, full-bosomed way, but her manners were rude and over-bearing, the familiarities between her and John scandalously open, and she was selfish, petulant, and self-willed.

Though no respectable veteran would help the Masons, there was quite a crew of whites, blacks, and Portyghees over there, cutting down trees, putting up buildings, and making furniture. After a few days the family staged a parade down the Nashville trace, and set up open house for all the young people for miles around in what Mason called "our villa." From behind the grove of trees which screened this country estate, passers-by at night on the trace could hear the sound of fiddles, punctuated by pistol shots and blood-curdling yells. Soon the matrons in cabins along Red River and Muddy River were saying that those girls at Masons "laid out" every night in the woods with one man or another. One story was that every night after Sam Mason and his wife were in bed, Kuykendall would come to the door. Hon would steal down from the loft where she slept, clad in nothing but her wide petticoat draped around her shoulders like a cape. She would bring Kuykendall in, with her petticoat thrown around the two of them, past her parents' bed, and take him up into the loft. Early in the morning she brought him down in the same way. This scandal came to a climax when on July 9, 1794, Kuykendall ran off with "Hon." Mason pursued the lovers up and down the buffalo traces, and across his neighbors' fields, trampling the crops. When the irate father failed to capture the run-aways, he vowed that any man who kissed a girl under his roof must marry her. This resulted in an announcement of two weddings. Sweetie was to marry a red-haired ruffian who was often seen coming out from the bushes early in the morning, and Marguerite was to marry John. John Grammer, the Presbyterian preacher, thought that, as the only one licensed by the county court to solemnize marriage, this would call for his services. But Sam Mason told him that marriages were made in Heaven, and did not require the hypocrisy of civil registry. A visiting clergyman, an "old friend," would perform the rites.

The night Sweetie was married, the guests found that their horses had all been stolen. Sam Mason called out his sons, and, with tremendous noise, they pursued the robbers and brought back the horses. Some said Mason had himself arranged the robbery as one of his little jokes. But this he stoutly denied. After the weddings, Sweetie rode off with her husband, but Marguerite stayed on as John's wife.

5

There was much speculation about the visiting clergyman. People said he wore a long white gown with a gold stole, and his face was covered. They said the ceremony was something Papish, with a sprinkling of wine for holy water, and the burning of incense. Some said a fiery cross had been seen burning at the Masons during the ceremony—a rumor which angered the good Scotchmen among the veterans who were outraged that the ancient fiery symbol of respectable clansmen in Scotland should have been appropriated by these outlaws.

Brenda told Mary that the Baptists had heard from William Morris that her son John Wilcox had been at the wedding. "I'd rather you'd told me he was dead," Mary said, bitterly. A few days later John rode up to the door, mounted on a good horse he had never found in his father's horse-lot, and wearing smart breeches and top boots. Dismounting, he entered with a new gentlemanliness and polish in his naturally fine bearing. Jus ordered Eddie, Polly, Peter, and Sis out of the cabin, and shut the door on himself and Mary and her son.

The children crouched with their ears against chinks in the cabin wall to hear what was going on inside. Then Eddie hoisted Peter to the roof, and he hung himself head downward from there and peered into the small, high, open window, seeing everything. When the voices inside were raised so high that a whisper outside could not be heard, he communicated everything to Eddie and Polly. Pretty twelve-year-old Polly had found the Masons glamorous, and was determined to look like those girls when she grew up and to have fun with dances and gallants. The prestige her elder brother had in her eyes was greatly enhanced by the romantic rumor that he had actually been at the weddings. She longed to know all the exciting social details.

When Jus asked whether John had been at the weddings, he at first denied it, but was forced, under cross-examination, to confess that he had. He said he didn't know who the visiting clergyman was. Forced finally to say that he was called "The Grand Master," he protested that he knew not one thing about him, except that he had been attacked by some ruffians and severely wounded.

In vain Mary tried to get John to promise that he would have nothing more to do with the Masons. John said they were one of the best families in Virginia. Most people here were such louts that when they were exposed to the ways of good society even at a distance, they began to tell lies and vulgar stories—which only showed the kind of minds they themselves had. What Jus said to this Peter did not hear, for, in his eagerness to see everything, he hung down too far and fell head first off the roof. Jus heard the noise outside and came out and angrily chased the children away. By the time they had stealthily crawled back, John came out and mounted his horse and rode away. His handsome pale face was flushed. His eyes were flashing. He held his head high and sharply pricked his horse to make him gallop.

And now Peter, who had rested secure all his life in the respect people had for his parents,—Peter, who had never seen faces turned away from him, but was used to a friendly response everywhere to his own cheerful smile, suddenly found something dark and chill closing down upon him. Clattering down the trace on one of the pack-ponies he was allowed to ride, he saw two of the Baptist boys. Pounding the pony with his bare heels, he shouted, "Wait for me. I'm comin' over to fish in your creek." Instead of waiting, and taking turns in riding the pony back to their place, as he expected, they ran and hid in the bushes. Peter was astounded. And then he was so ashamed that the blood came up in his cheeks. He turned and rode slowly home. A huge, cold, wet mountain was weighing on his spirits.

Next day Jerry came over with his father. Even Jerry was changed. He seemed shy, uneasy, strained. Peter asked him outright what the matter was. Jerry confessed that his mother didn't want them to play together any more. "She says you-all have too much truck with the Masons to suit her." But he added that his father had insisted on bringing him over, saying that the Cartwrights were going to have trouble enough with John Wilcox without their old friends going back on them. At these words the burden that had been weighing Peter down blew off in a great burst of rage. He could feel himself hurling himself on John and beating him to mash.

Jus heard that John had been playing cards at Dromgole's, and had won a horse from Ambrose Maulding which he was keeping in Maulding's pasture. And he had stayed overnight twice at Cedar House. "Wes Maulding don't put him up for nothing," thought Jus, worriedly. "I wonder how he pays for his lodging?"

He would have been even more worried if he had known what Peter and Eddie knew—that among John's things was a silver-mounted pistol and a white hood with holes cut in it for eyes. But they said nothing. It was not the custom for boys to "squeal" on their brothers, even brothers so little loved and admired as John. But when Jus said they'd better tell John that if he couldn't come home at a decent hour at night and take his share in the farm-work, he could stay away for good, Mary replied, "My door is never closed to a son of mine, whatever he does. It 'ud be the last kick to push him over into hell fire—to have his own mother slam the door on him." When John did come home, she put herself out to be gentle and sympathetic and to try to bridge, at this late hour, the natural gulf that separated her from this son. But one day she turned on Jus a hard, burning look, and said tensely, "Some day you men will learn not to have truck with the Devil—when he reaches his claws right into your own home, and starts pickin' off your children, one by one."

Peter heard this, and, moved by some obscure impulse of sympathy, he came close to her and plucked her dress. "Mammy. Mammy," he said softly. She flung her arms around him and hugged him fiercely.

When he saw his mother, looking colder, paler, and sadder every day, and spending every spare moment reading her Bible with a look as if inside herself she was praying and crying at the same time, Peter would often go and kneel beside her. She would draw his tangled, curly head to her, and then he knew she was comforted. One day he heard her say to Jus, "If Jacob Lurton would only come! If we could only have a preaching here."

"Well," said Jus, "I've not got much stomach for preachings. Seems like a man is a pretty poor sort if he has to have a preacher roar at him and pray at him and threaten Hell fire to keep him from lyin' and stealin' and doin' what no self-respectin' man 'ud want to do. But I'm bound to say it would be a glad day for us if Jacob Lurton should show up. Once we get preachin' here regular, it will be plain to all that whatever is done by some of the family, it's no fault of ours and we're showin' clean and clear where we stand."

To Peter these words came as a revelation. His mind had been racing around madly trying to find a way out of the sense of blame and wrong that had fallen on them though they had done nothing to deserve it, except to be kin to John. He seized on the mention of Lurton with unutterable relief. If the circuit rider came, if they had a preaching—there was the answer to it all!

6

It was a comfort that they had had the planting of the truck garden, and especially of the peach trees to fill the days and leave them too tired for anything but heavy sleep at night. The Yankees at Marietta, who did all things by plan and rule, had determined that, to get 100 acres of land, a family must agree to plant fifty apple and pear trees and twenty peach trees, besides breaking fifteen acres for crops. The Kentucky settlers liked their own way too well to make rules like that. But in the settled area around Lexington, they readily realized that peach trees were the orchard crop that promised the quickest return, and planted as largely as the Yankees. Dominie got some of the young peach trees from Lexington for himself and Dutch and Jus. Mary's pleasure in them was somewhat soured by her perception that the men's idea of the right use for peaches was to make peach brandy, which was selling for three shillings a quart. She was better pleased with the seed potatoes Dominie brought. She and the children cut the potatoes into the smallest possible pieces, one eye to a piece, and planted them carefully, all the children except John helping eagerly with work which promised to relieve the nauseating boredom of their wild meat diet. Their only vegetables these spring days was a fuzzy plant called "bear's lettuce," which the children picked in the woods, and which they ate raw, without salt. They had no cereals left. It was pure frustration to have all the new maple syrup stored away and no mush to eat it on!

Eddie, Polly, Peter, and Sis watched over the truck patch with mouth-watering anticipations of roasting ears and new potatoes. But neither Mary nor the children would take much interest in the crop which engrossed the men—the planting in a rich patch of ground of the tiny, black tobacco seed, and the care of the seedlings. Mary said with the need they had for grain it was pure foolishness to take all the trouble to raise tobacco. Jus said tobacco was a cash crop. You could sell it for money. Mary wanted to know what they would to do with money if they had it—the way they were fixed there. "You'd think," she commented to Barbara, "that with our gorge rising at the very smell of the ol' stale meat, and getting up from the table more empty than when we sat down, the men would see the need of planting something to spread a good board and put some flesh on the children's bones. But no! All they think of is liquor to addle their brains and tobacco to burn up their insides."

May 1794 was a busy month, for, besides all his farming activities, Jus was deeply involved in politics and court business. Despite active campaigning by Young Ewing, supported by all the more respectable veterans, Morton Maulding was elected to represent all of western Kentucky in the legislature, which would meet in the fall at Frankfort. Morton Maulding's inability to read and write would make little difference since two thirds of the other legislators would be equally illiterate. He was shrewd, quick-witted, determined, aggressive, and, in his amiable moments, uproariously and indiscriminately friendly. If it had not been for a taint of association with Alston about him, most frontiersmen would have regarded him as an ideal person to represent them. But, as it was, there was such a determined objection that the elections had been fraudulent that, at the May 17 court, Jus, with James Ross, James Herndon, James Wilson, and William McMillan, had been appointed as commissioners to take depositions for contested elections. This gave Jus little satisfaction. Even if the elections were fraudulent, they'd have to go pretty carefully in proving it. They weren't fixed yet for a real show-down with the Alston-Maulding-Dromgole outfit!

7

One day Peter saw a broad-chested man, on a black horse—a man with lean, wiry legs, a bushy black beard, and a mane of bushy black hair falling all around his face. Under his craggy brow and bushy black eyebrows, his dark violet eyes shone stormily blue. It had been more than a year since Peter had seen him. For a moment he stared, unrecognizing, and then it was as if the sky had opened, and God Himself had ridden down to their aid. He ran into the house shouting, "Mammy! Mammy! He's come! Preacher Lurton's come!"

Refreshed with a bath in the brook, his dirty ragged shirt replaced by a clean new one of Mary's spinning, weaving, and sewing, his hair and beard neatly trimmed, Jacob Lurton, the Circuit Rider, sat down with the Cartwrights to enjoy the first good meal he had had in a month. And tonight, for the first time in a month, he would sleep between two clean sheets. On the table by his bed were neatly stacked the four books in his saddlebag library—his Bible, Watts' *Psalms and Hymns,* Taylor's *Holy Living and Holy Dying,* and Blair's *Rhetoric.* Gratefully he thought—but did not say aloud—that if the church survived in these savage wilds, it would be by the grace of a Christian woman. When the last minister of God fell in his tracks, hopeless and foredone, there would still be one last Christian woman to succor him and lift him up.

In the last month Lurton had broken 800 miles of bridle tracks south of the Green River and along the Cumberland. He had buried ten people, of six different parties, who had been attacked by robbers. He had fought twelve battles with fist and cudgel and three with pistols. He had slept out all but five nights, and had eaten little except what he had killed with his gun or fished with his line. Finding this little family so snug and well furnished, with such a fine stretch of cleared land turning gold with harvest, he could at first think of nothing but sheltering himself and licking his wounds in this unwonted peace and security.

But after dinner, Dean and Jassamine and Dominie and Barbara came for prayers under the maple trees by the brook, and shocked him out of his sense of peace with the latest word of what Satan was up to here. Dominie told of the disappearance of Lydia and Fred, and listened with averted face while Dean repeated what he had heard among the Negroes. As he spoke, Jassamine reached over and took Barbara's hand in hers, and they sat there in silent sympathy, hand in hand. When Dean said the Harpes were said to have been in on the killing, Jus observed, "They've been seen here—there's clear testimony to that. They stay with Roberts." Dominie told what he had known of the Masons when both they and he were with George Rogers Clark, and Jassamine said she recognized Mason now as the big highwayman who had saved her and her mistress from being killed, and had trussed her like a turkey for roasting and thrown her into the bushes. Dominie added that he was pretty sure that the man he had wounded on the way back from Fort Massac, and the mysterious "visiting clergyman" at the Masons' weddings were both Philip Alston.

Lurton, listening intently, said to Jus, "But it doesn't add up yet to a case you can bring to court."

"Not yet."

"Then," said Lurton, "it's a case for Almighty God and the thunders of His righteousness."

So far Mary had held back the matter which had filled all her prayers—the way in which her own son, John, was getting himself mixed into the doings of the Dromgoles and the Masons.

Lurton pondered, his rugged face cloudy with thought. Just then Peter came clattering up with Jerry on the horse behind him. Mary had encouraged Peter to get Jerry over to play with him because she wanted Brenda to know that the preacher was staying with them. As the boys slid to the ground, Lurton turned his eyes on Peter. How long-legged the boy was getting! He'd be a fine figure of a man in no time. Now that the blanks left where his baby teeth had fallen from his full lipped, smiling mouth, were filling with permanent teeth, one could see his bright, comical face firming into the promise of the man to come. A strong boy—full of life! Full of the devil! And smart! From behind the Indian gleam in his black eyes, there looked at times a soul much older than his years.

Watching Peter, Lurton said thoughtfully, "There's no saving them from the lures of the Devil with anything flesh and blood has to offer. Neither man nor woman can fight the Devil. Only God can do that. You've got to bring a boy to see God, and then his eyes will be opened, and he'll know the Devil's trash for what it is."

"I pray for John with every breath I draw," said Mary.

"Pray for them all," answered Lurton, still watching Peter and Jerry. He called to the boys to come and join in a hymn and a prayer. They came willingly enough. Hymns and prayers were still a novelty on the frontier, and where there was no theatre, no circus, no shows of any kind, they had some dramatic appeal.

Kneeling, with the children on their knees beside her, her own thoughts full of John, Mary realized, with a shock, that Lurton was praying, not so much for John, as for these two innocent children. "Those bad men could never get hold of Jerry and Peter," she thought. "No, no! Not Peter! Dear God in Heaven—not Peter!"

They talked there under the trees by the brook all afternoon. Mary, looking for the wherewithal of silencing Brenda and making her feel shamed, asked Lurton about the lies that had been going around concerning the schism in the Methodist Church. "They arn't lies," responded Lurton, soberly. "Of the 65,000 Methodists east and west of the mountains, it looks like 20,000 are going with O'Kelly, and that means most of the thousand or so members in the West. Of the western preachers, Poythress, John Page, Northcutt, and McHenry are standing by Asbury, but William McKendree—you don't know him—he's a big raw-boned fellow from Virginia—who's our best hope of a leader that can hold the West, is standing out against Asbury for a democratic re-organization of the church."

As for himself, he said, he was completely won over when, late in March, last year—1793— Asbury crossed the mountains to talk to the Kentucky preachers. Sick with fever and a heavy cold, he rode over steep heights slippery with rain, and swam his horse across flooded valleys, weary, wet and hungry. "I'm free to say that when I saw the condition he was in, and how he'd just picked up and come out to us regardless, I thought, 'He's earned the right to be a Tory if that's what God made him and he can't help it.' For, Tory or not, he's a man, and more than that he's one of God's saints, if not God's angel in the poor aching fleshly garments of a man."

"Well," said Jus, discharging a stream of tobacco juice into the clean water of the brook, "Good or bad, I'm agin all Tories. I'm for democracy, pure and unmixed."

"So am I," said Lurton. "But all this talk about democracy is just a manner of speaking so far's we Methodists are concerned. For we arn't a state, and I hardly blame any Presbyterian or Church of Englander who says we arn't a church either. There's only about five of us preachers that are able to keep going steady, and who knows when one of us will be bumped off. Though Asbury hasn't the first idea of what we west of the mountains mean by democracy, I don't think that matters a tinker's damn. He's got the message straight from John Wesley, and he's got the guts to hold us together and keep us going. And I, for one, will wait to argue about government till we've got some to argue about."

"But how do you think you'll make out here? I understand Haw not only has taken all the Methodys with him, but says he and his will stop any Asbury man from comin' out here," observed Jus.

Lurton smiled grimly and shook his black mane like a lion. "Haw has it spread far and wide that any one who stands by Asbury is a traitor to our country. However, I've fit my way through this summer, and now Barnabas McHenry is on his way to relieve me, and we'll just keep going till we have both Haw and the Devil licked."

CHAPTER 12   Logan Courthouse
                                              Summer of 1794

Early next morning Peter was sent to invite the neighbors to a preaching to be held after supper that night. Since it was thought he'd be safer if he had some one with him, Mary told him to ride first to Jerry's house and ask Brenda to let him take Jerry up behind him on his horse. Turning northwest, through the tall grasses and jointed reeds, sometimes twenty feet high, fighting his way through tangles of pea-vines, Peter noted the great puffs of smoky dark clouds piling up on the eastern horizon and spreading into the clear blue morning sky. Sniffing the bright fragrant air, he isolated a little strain of chilliness in the warmth. "Goin' to rain," he thought. "Us Methodys will be just as wet as if we was Baptists!"

When he rode up to Dutch's cabin and whooped, Brenda came out, her long handsome face looking very friendly. She said Jerry might go with Peter, and gave the boys a reed basket containing cold turkey legs and wings for their lunch. But she told them to see the Baptist preacher first and find out if he was willing his flock should be exposed to Methodist preaching.

Walt or "Ol Waterbug" the Baptist preacher lived up a zig-zag trail half a mile away. As the boys clattered up he came down to the rail fence to talk to them. A big man, with long, prematurely gray beard and gray hair and twinkling blue eyes, he was smoking a long stemmed pipe which he had fashioned himself, and hospitably offered each of the boys a tug at it. When they invited him to the preaching, he frowned and roared like a thunderstorm. Did they know John Wesley had supported the King—yes, the King—against the liberties of free-born Americans? Did they know he was a follower of Arminius, and flouted the true doctrine of Calvin?

Then he pulled Peter's ear and said he bet him three chaws of tobacco he didn't even know what the doctrine of Calvin was. Peter admitted he didn't know. Secretly he didn't care because he didn't want three chaws of tobacco. Ol Waterbug said that the doctrine of Calvin was that if you are predestined to be damned, there's nothing you can do about it, and if you're elected to be saved, you're bound to be saved sooner or later.

"But that doesn't leave you anything to do about it," said Peter.

"Sure it does."

"What do you do?"

"Do your damndest to be good and hope for the best!"

This didn't make much sense to Peter. He was still more puzzled when Ol Waterbug said he didn't have much use for Lurton or for any preacher, including himself. "A man's fate in Heaven or Hell is betwixt him and his Maker. It's up to every man to get busy and work on his own salvation." And with that he unexpectedly told Peter to tell Lurton that he was coming to his most heretical and seditious preaching, and bringing his flock with him. "And tell him," he said, turning his bright eyes on Peter, and speaking in a thunderous tone that had something quite make-believe in it, "tell him my flock's the greatest collection of ruffians this side Hell!"

As the boys started to ride away, he called after them that they mustn't forget those Portyghees up the river—William Morris, Goins, Portee, and Bird. "And very odd birds they are," he thundered.

Then taking his pipe out of his mouth, and leaning over the fence, he blew out a strong stench of tobacco along with a stage whisper. "They got into those caves up east of here that lead into Hell, and they got nearer and nearer to the door into Hell, till Hell-fire leaped out and singed their hair and beards and sooted their faces. Then they ran and they ran till they came to Muddy River, and there they said they wanted to set up a Baptist Church. So I helped to set them up, with William Morris preaching to them. And I tell them so long as I've got anything to do with them, they've got to be good. I don't know whether they'll be saved or not, but saved or damned, they've got to be good!"

Leaving Ol Waterbug, the boys proceeded rather timorously up the path that led through the woods to the Portyghees, until they came to a big cabin with several smaller ones around it. A slender youth with a broad high brown forehead and penetrating, wicked-looking eyes came riding toward them. Peter remembered him. He was Sam Morris, and he had been at Cedar House when Bill Stewart killed the man that spoke scandal of him and Cook's wife. The memory dimmed by time but still intense, made Sam's face like something in a nightmare. Hearing Peter's message, Sam laughed, and rolled his eyes. "You tell that son-of-a-bitch preacher to go to Hell, and if he shows his dirty face around here it'll be mashed in," he said, loftily, riding on and switching Peter's horse to make it jump.

But a grave, kindly man, dark as a Negro but without Negro features, who Peter knew was Mr. Morris, said without raising his voice yet making every word count, "Sam, you go about your business. I mean it," he added, with a sudden flash of his eye. "You get out of here and stay out till you can behave yourself."

When Peter explained his mission, Mr. Morris said he would come and bring as many of his people as he could. "It's not often that we have the chance to hear the word of God," he said.

Peter was staring curiously at the Portyghees. Some had dark skins, kinky black hair, and dark eyes, and yet there was something about them not quite Negro. Some had coarse straight black hair and bronze skin, and yet were not quite Indian. Some had smooth yellow skin, curly dark hair, and slightly slanted dreamy small eyes. Some had rather fair skin, curly brown hair, and blue eyes, but all shadowed and faintly smudged.

"You seem to find us strange, my boy," said Mr. Morris.

"Yes," said Peter, with shy candor, "I don't know what kind of folks you are."

"We're Portyghees," said the man. "We belong here same as the Indians do. We're Baptists and try to serve God. We're a separate branch of His people, same as the Jews are. We marry only among our own kin and try to keep ourselves unspotted from the world."

This made little sense to Peter, but as much sense as these strange dwellers in the southern mountains have made to anybody to this day.

2

Following traces and paths that led to the salt licks, the springs, and the river banks, where the new settlers almost always built their cabins, and where the buffalo and the Indians had marked out the way before them, the boys notified every one they saw of the preaching. But when they came to a path that led through a swampy place, under low-hanging dark branches, Peter drew up, brushing away the gnats and screwing up his face at a stale smell that came from in there. "Yonder is ol man Roberts' place," he said. "I wonder should we go in there?"

Next to the Masons' the Roberts' place was most mistrusted, though no one said why. Peter and Jerry had been forbidden, in the past, to go near it—which gave it, of course, a peculiar interest. Now Jerry considered. "He's just the kind of man preaching's for."

He added piously, with an unconscious imitation of his mother's solemn way of talking, "There's none so low but God can lift him up."

"Hark!" said Peter. The two boys listened. A thin sweet voice as of a child or a young girl was singing, tunelessly, but rather happily, "Sing a song of Sally Ann. She ran off with a bold young man."

Peter whispered, "Turn the horse around, so's we can get away quick if there's need, and I'll just crawl along here and look in." He slid off the horse, turned it quietly, holding fast to the bridle, so as to make as little noise of trampling in the bushes as possible, and then wriggled on his belly to the edge of the clearing. Peering through the bushes, he saw a large cabin, pretty well built, but to reach the door one would have to wade through horse-manure. The offal of dead animals was decaying amidst bones and rubbish. A lean black pig was rooting in the mess, and two brown "houndawgs" were rather restlessly pricking up their ears and growling, without moving from their comfortable berths on some rotten hay. "They kinda suspicion I'm here, but they're too lazy to come after me," thought Peter, carefully taking the dogs' measure. Satisfied on this score, he fixed his fascinated gaze on the singer, who was beginning, for the third time, her tale of Sally Ann.

She was perhaps thirteen, her feet bare and crusted with the horse-manure, but dressed in a rumpled silk dress. She sat on a stump, holding a broken mirror with one slim hand, and with the other adjusting the end of a pink ribbon bow in her thick, light brown curls. The face that looked back from the mirror would have been better for more careful washing. But some washing had evidently been attempted, and the face was pretty, in a thin, young, pert, blonde way. Seeing a crittur so harmless, Peter cautiously stood up and stepped a few inches out of the bushes. One dog lazily rose and growled but made no move. The girl noticed this and turned. Seeing Peter, she gave a slight scream, which she instantly suppressed with an apprehensive look at the cabin. "What do ye want?" she whispered, sharply.

"I just want to tell you there's a preaching—to-night—at the Cartwrights. You're invited, and everybody else of your folks."

She looked somewhat taken aback, but rather pleased. It occurred to Peter that it must be pretty lonesome to belong to folks nobody was allowed to go near. No doubt being invited to a preaching was the first thing that had ever been done to make her feel "like folks."

"Betsy! Betsy, lass!" shouted a full, rough voice.

She whispered, "Get out of here! Quick! Scat!" Peter disappeared in the bushes. But he did not leave. He crouched, completely covered with vegetation, peering through a single opening, made by pulling a single small branch a little aside.

"Betsy!" The voice called again. Peter thought, "He's gettin' mad."

"Betsy, you damned little hussy!" With a teasing, coquettish grimace, Betsy picked up the mirror and again began to primp.

Around the corner of the cabin came a large, full-bodied young man. "Must be over six feet," thought Petere. His black hair was rolled back off a heavy-jowled, thick-lipped, rather fresh-colored and clean-shaven face. "Wears gentry clothes, but sure looks like trash," thought Peter, observing the well cut but filthy breeches, the boots rank with horse manure, and the shirt which was of fine linen, but torn and yellowed with perspiration where it clung to his brawny shoulders.

He came over to Betsy and said, "Who was you talkin' to?"

"Nobody."

"You lie!"

She flared. "Nobody calls me a liar, Micajah Harpe, and you know it!"

"I don't know no such thing," he said, and seized her by her thin shoulders and lifted her off the stump. Holding her aloft while she kicked and struggled, he shook her till her teeth chattered. "You lie! You lie! You lie! You little bitch! I don't know why I don't choke you." He closed his big hand over her slender throat. She screamed, "Micajah, don't. Su-san! Su-san!" He stopped the sound. Peter thought in horror, "He's choked her. She's dead." Her head with its pink bow among the curls fell limply against the man's shoulder. He began to blubber. "Betsy! Honey chile! Betsy! Betsy, dear! Oh Betsy, I didn't mean."

She snapped her head up from his shoulder, laughing.

"You were play-acting," he said furiously. "I'll teach you to play-act with me!" He seized a hickory stick that lay near on the ground. "Betsy," he said, "you've been asking for a whaling for a long time." She screamed, "Micajah, don't, don't. I'll be good."

He had never let her slight form out of his bearlike clutch. Now he sat down on the stump where she had sat and turned her over his knee, and began whacking. She yelled, "Susan! Murder! Make him stop! He's killing me!"

He said, "Shut up! You don't feel a damned thing through all these petticoats." She continued to yell. "I'll teach you!" he shouted, and pulled up her skirts, exposing her bare buttocks, of a delicate whiteness and her slim white legs, which she was thrashing madly in a kind of scissors movement. "I'll teach you," he said, striking her bottom till the marks showed pink, and switching at her flashing legs.

"Suu-u-san," she yelled.

There was a loud laugh. A heavy, full-bosomed, wide-hipped girl, with strong heavy features, and bold blue eyes stood in the doorway, shaking, and whooping with merriment. "Give it to her. Micajah!" she cried.

He stopped short. "Shut up, you slut!" he said. He turned Betsy over. "There, there, Honey!" he said and kissed her on the lips.

"Micajah Harpe!" shrieked Susan. "God damn it to Hell, if you ain't goin' to make a whore of my little sister before my very eyes!"

Betsy was now seated on Micajah's knee, cuddling her face against his chest, laughing wickedly at her sister, while Micajah's big hand patted her curls back in place and adjusted the pink bow.

Peter who had been frozen to his observation post for a few moments was now trying to get away. As he neared the horse, his hitherto suspended emotions materialized in intense fright. He made a sudden spring. A dead branch snapped with a noise like a pistol shot. "Who's there?" shouted Micajah. Peter and Jerry were already fleeing at top speed. A bullet whistled over their heads. They bent low to the horse and burst out of the dark path, on to the open trail. But they never stopped galloping till they were a mile down it, under the open sky.

"That was a close shave," said Jerry. "I told you your Mammy wouldn't want us to go near the Roberts."

Peter was too absorbed to realize how unfair this was. He was saying to himself, "Micajah Harpe! Micajah Harpe!" All the talk he had heard about the Harpes boiled up inside him. He couldn't put too much space too fast between him and the Roberts place. He told Jerry to shut up. He'd talk about Micajah Harpe some other time. All he wanted now was to keep going.

3

"Look out, Peter. Where you going to, like a bullet shot out of a gun?"

Peter reined up sharp, face to face with two riders on the trail. Looking into the honest, sunny eyes of Finis Ewing, his whole being sang with relief. Comfort, security, the sense of cleanness after foulness embraced him. He couldn't speak. He could only gaze at Finis, beaming. Just as he began to find his tongue, he was struck dumb again as he turned his eyes to Finis's companion, who wore a wide straw hat set on top of a smooth cushion of brown hair, and tied with a ribbon under her smooth round chin. Pretty young ladies were not yet common in Rogue's Harbor. It was still a world of men—mostly young men. He gazed at the lady with his pleasure so painting his expressive face that she felt flattered and smiled lovingly in return.

"What are you boys doing so far from home?" asked Finis.

Peter found his tongue. "There's a preaching at our house. Preacher Lurton's come."

"I hope you are asking my wife and me," said Finis gravely. His wife. He'd got married!

"Oh yes!" Peter nodded vigorously, quite dazzled by the idea that this young lady might grace his home.

"And don't forget Morton Maulding and his brothers. It will do them good," said Finis. He directed them to Morton Maulding's as he and his wife rode with them a little way. But when they came in sight of the large, well built cabin, he seemed to think the children could do better without him, and they galloped off.

Perhaps Morton Maulding thought it best to ingratiate himself with the son of the veterans' attorney who was taking depositions from all who challenged his right to represent western Kentucky in the legislature. For he came out to meet the boys and refused their invitation in words both eloquent and nobly regretful. Like many illiterate frontiersmen whose parents had been educated persons, Morton had an excellent speech, reasonably grammatical, with a vocabulary which, under other circumstances, would indicate some reading in the classics.

He had a natural grandeur of personality. Standing with the breeze roughing his shaggy mane, like wind in the russet foliage of an oak, his strong legs spread slightly and planted on the ground with the firmness of tree trunks, and his big hand making sweeping gestures at the heavens, he explained his own religion to the boys. His family, he said, had been "straight-back Presbyterians," even though his mother had been reconverted by a Methodist and had named her last son Wesley. But in his youth he himself had wandered where white men's foot had never been, by the clear waters of the Green River and the calm waters of the beautiful Ohio. There he had learned, he said, to look on the streams meandering through the greensward or pouring over the crags as evidence of the Creator and his over-ruling Providence. Alone where no white man had been before, surrounded by ravenous beasts, he had felt a calm reliance on destiny. And he knew no missiles of danger could strike him down until he was ready to leave this beautiful world for a better and brighter world above.

All of which Peter remembered and repeated to his mother and preacher Lurton later. "Humph," said Mary to Lurton. "That must be his fancy way of serving notice that we can't unseat him in the legislature so long as he wants to stay there and protect the wrongdoing of Philip Alston!"

Discomfited by this religious eloquence on the part of one who was suspected of being allied to the powers of evil, Peter and Jerry clattered away and almost collided with two figures on horseback, emerging from the bushes on to the path that led from Morton Maulding's to Cedar House. The younger of the two men looked frightened and raised his gun. But the older one, seeing only two small boys, beamed, "A boy—two beautiful boys. And what, my little men, can I do for you?"

"I just-just-" said Peter, through chattering teeth. "I just am in-vitin' everybody to a preachin' at our cabin. Preacher Lurton's here, and he's goin' to preach to-night." Under the pleasant atten-tion of the handsome, pale face of the older man, he was recover-ing his courage. "So I am askin' you, and you," he said turning to the younger man.

"To Hell you are," said the younger man, looking him over cold-ly.

But the older man said caressingly, "My child, nothing could give me greater pleasure than to be with you, for I have ever been a lover of God and frequenter of His holy places. But unfortunate-ly," and here he made a graceful gesture with his hands, "most ur-gent business calls me to the marts of trade and I fear me the haunts of sin, in places far from here. So make my regrets to your good preacher, and say a prayer for me when you kneel at the holy altar."

With that he and his companion spurred their horses and rode rapidly toward Morton Maulding's. "Let's get out of here," said Peter to Jerry. "It kinda makes me sick to my stummick—the high falutin' way of talkin' they have around here."

They visited Richard Maulding's excellent cabin in Clay Lick woods, where the first court had met, and saw only the boy "Red" Maulding who said he would invite all other Mauldings. He told them not to forget the "niggers" down there in the woods. "If anybody needs to be preached at, they sure do." So they looked for and found the tumbledown cabin where a man named Cobb had lived. In 1790 he had stolen some Negroes and brought them here, whether to sell them or free them, Red didn't know. Near the cabin the boys found three Negro families living, and support-ing themselves by hunting and fishing, and invited them all to the preaching. They then tried to get to Bear Wallow, the hunting ground Bill Stewart had reserved for himself, but were stopped on the way by a young man who told them to make tracks in the other direction. "But we just want to see if there's any bears," said Peter.

"There's one comin' on you right now," said the man. "Run or you'll be dead ones."

Peter and Jerry didn't believe this, but thought it best to run. But Peter called back, "There's a preaching at Cartwright's tonight.

Come and bring the bears."

As they turned back toward Peter's house, in the late afternoon a shadow materialized into flesh from behind the trees. For a minute Peter's heart stood still. It was an Indian! Thus far the settlers in this area had had no quarrels with the Indians, though only a few miles south of the border, at Nashville and beyond, there had been incessant fighting with the Cherokees, who were enraged because they thought the settlers were exceeding their treaty rights and overrunning Indian lands. The Indian beckoned. "Come," he said gently. "No hurt good pale face boys. Kind squaw there by fire. Want to see papoose." He struggled for words. "You help may be big heap. Papoose lose Mammy. You may be help find Mammy." His looks and words were mild.

Jerry said, "He ain't foolin' us, Pete."

Cautiously the boys followed the Indian who walked ahead and stopped and beckoned in a kindly way. Then they heard soft chatter and smelled smoke, and there was an Indian encampment by the stream. As they came near, the Indian called, and a little white girl came toddling. "Pappy. Pappy," she cried. The Indian picked her up lovingly and smoothed back her cornsilk hair. Used to understanding without words, the boys grasped the fact that the Indians had picked up this child, lost and crying in the woods. They had brought it to the fire, and had fed it and made it some little moccasins. Now they wanted to find its parents, who, they thought, must be movers on their way south or west.

Then Peter had an idea. Let the Indians bring the baby to the preaching. Either the Circuit Rider would know to whom it belonged because, in his rounds, he came to know almost everybody, or riding over the country he would be able to spread word about it. With this proposal, the Indians were delighted. They had apparently come in contact with Catholic priests and thought a man of God the very person to bring the child to. The boys rode away, leaving the small, round, pop-eyed, fair-skinned infant laughing and romping amidst a circle of friendly brown Indian faces.

4

The sun was crimson amidst murky rain-clouds, when Peter and Jerry reached the Cartwright cabin. A cluster of families who had come early were having a picnic supper under the trees by the brook. Smelling the broiling venison, the boys levied a contribution of burnt meat to fill the hollows they were suddenly conscious of, before going into the cabin. There they saw that the main room of the house had been cleared, and split log benches had been set up for the expected congregation. The long trestle table had been pushed against the side wall, where it could also serve for seats, as could Justurian and Mary's bed, and the trundle bed on which Polly and Sis slept. The rush-bottom chairs, which were Mary's pride, had been put in the preacher's room, where the overflow could sit on them and on the bed.

At the end of the room, opposite the fireplace end, and under the loft where Peter and his brothers slept, the broad, up-ended, sawed-off trunk of a tree had been set up for the preacher's use, either as reading desk or as preaching stand. On it lay his Bible and hymn book, and next it was one of the rush-bottomed chairs. Near it a tall candle of Brenda's dipping had been inserted in a stand five feet high, newly fashioned by Dutch's skilful knife. This would be the only light for the evening service, except for the red glow of the fireplace.

It was several minutes before Peter could get his family to pause in their last minute preparations, and listen to his account of the day's adventures. Absorbed as he was in what he had to tell, he noticed that John was absent. "He wouldn't chance being around where God or Preacher Lurton might take special notice of him," he reflected, "not with the load of sin he's carrying." But he soon forgot all about his brother in carefully marshaling his report of the day, and making sure by the language of nudges and eyes, that Jerry didn't inadvertently fill any blank he might choose to leave.

For Peter made no mention of Micajah Harpe. He felt uneasily that his mother had never intended he should go near the Roberts. He didn't want to worry her by telling her he had been shot at. But when he and Jerry told about the other incidents of the day, Peter was amazed that the really important matter—the finding of the baby among the Indians—passed almost unnoticed while his father and Lurton put him and Jerry through a cross-examination. This man they met on the path to Morton Maulding's—the older one, did he have a fair skin, like a baby's, and large, soft, blue eyes? Did he have fine, silky black hair, a little frosted with gray? "Yes," said Peter, startled that his elders should know what he had noticed but had not thought to report.

Lurton looked at Jus. "It's Alston all right."

Jus mounted his horse. "This calls for some studying. I'm going over to get Dominie," he said.

When he returned with Dominie, the boys were questioned again. Then Jus said, "Dominie's got the right idea. He says the young-uns can track him to his den a lot easier'n we can, and they're a heap less likely to get shot at." All of which was exciting to Peter, but not intelligible. But he was prevented from putting his mind on it by Jerry's nudging him and pointing out that five Indians were huddling outside, afraid to approach the cabin. He slipped away from Jus and Dominie, and ran eagerly to the Indians, and hugged the tiny girl. But when he tried to get his mother's attention on her, she was, at the last minute, changing the white spread on the preacher's bed for a blue one. And when Jerry tried to interest Brenda, she was too busy making sure that respectable German Baptists should not be seated next to questionable Portyghee Baptists. But when Peter appealed to Barbara, he at last found a woman for whom first things came first. For she not only brought the Indians into the cabin and seated them, but she soon had other women around them, exclaiming over the little white girl, and discussing what to do about her. When the baby, frightened by all this attention, retreated to the arms of her Indian foster mother, Barbara said they'd better let her go back with the Indians, till they could find what would be best for her.

At this point Jus called Peter to act as doorkeeper, and tell the men where to tether their horses and stack their guns. Proudly directing the traffic under the glowering shadow of the approaching storm, he felt himself suddenly frozen in his tracks. For there, dismounting from a handsome gray horse, and walking toward the door, was Micajah Harpe, clean and well dressed in gentry clothes. When he brushed by Peter and walked into the cabin, Peter followed, dodging behind him, among the people now crowding in and trying to find a few inches of seating space somewhere on the puncheon benches.

Lurton had now come in, and was seated on the chair near the preaching stump, his head bowed in prayer. Micajah Harpe walked straight up to him, and clapped him on the shoulder. When the preacher jumped up, startled, Harpe held out his hand, on which flashed a diamond ring. Lurton took the proffered hand uncertainly.

"Mr. Lurton," said Micajah, "I have heard you preach before, and always with pleasure, Sir."

Sneaking close, Peter could see that the preacher mistrusted something. His blue eyes raked the man's face and handsome figure. "I try to remember folks' names and faces," he said, "but yours I don't place."

"I'm Taylor," said Harpe. "John Taylor, Sir. I'm a Presbyterian. I heard you in Knoxville."

"Ah," said Lurton, still scrutinizing him. "Then you belong to the congregation of my good friend, Parson Rice."

"Ah, yes, Parson Rice," said Harpe. "And what a little love that lass, Sally, is, isn't she? There's not a prettier girl this side the mountains than Sally is going to be when she gets a little more grown and filled out. I've got a young brother that's sweet on her —mighty sweet."

For the first time Peter felt that Lurton believed him. Peter jerked violently at the preacher's coat tails. Lurton turned slightly and, out of the side of his eye, caught sight of the boy's face. He put out his big hand quietly, while animatedly engaging Harpe, alias Taylor, in conversation, and gave Peter a re-assuring pat. Peter understood that the preacher knew he had something important to say. He waited patiently while Lurton tapered off the conversation with Taylor and courteously pointed him to a seat near the front. Then Lurton turned, and, putting his arm across Peter's shoulder affectionately, walked with him to the preacher's room, and shut the door, and sat down on the edge of the bed. "Now, Peter," he said, "what's on your mind?"

"That man there—his name ain't Taylor. It's Micajah Harpe."

"Harpe! Micajah Harpe!" Lurton's hand clutched Peters arm, and his eyes blazed into Peter's face. "Do you know for certain?"

Mary knocked at the door. "They're waitin' for you, Preacher Lurton, and there's so many it looks like we'll have to borrow your room for the overflow."

5

In a voice designed to reach the crowds still gathering outside, Lurton rolled out the Bible and lined out the hymn, and then started in on a lesson in the geography of Hell. Hell was a fiery pit, yawning like the red maw of a wild beast to take in the damned. But they needn't think Hell was far away because it wasn't. It was right under their feet, and they'd better look sharp, for there were a lot of cracks where they could fall through. Where were these cracks? Well, one ran through the northwest corner of Cedar House, and one was between Cedar House and Morton Maulding's farm. And another was between James Dromgole's and Morton Maulding's. And one was on the way to Bill Stewart's at Bear Wallow. As Peter heard how near he and Jerry had been to Hell, he felt thrills, half of terror, half of sheer excitement, up and down his spine. He knew this was only a "manner of speaking." But the lurid possibility that the ground might actually have opened today and dropped him and Jerry into Hell fire made his breath come short.

Lurton said one of the worst places was that wolf trap they called Dromgole, Stewart, and Reading. It looked like a stout building. But between it and the lake of fire beneath there was such a thin crust he looked to see it cave in any day. And here in western Kentucky there were springs and streams that didn't run water. They ran blood. Brother William Morris knew where one of them was. It was Straight Creek, flowing into the Cumberland. Here the Portyghees sat forward, their dark faces showing ashen even in the flickering firelight, for this was the source of silver for Alston's counterfeiting. Some springs, said Lurton, fastening his eyes with a fierce hypnotic gaze on John Taylor, where he sat quietly in the third row, some springs bubbled blood right out of the ground, where men were buried who had died in a gouging fight, or were murdered for their horses. One such spring was in Horse's Cave. Lurton dared them to go in there and bring out the skeletons.

There was a bellow as of a hurt buffalo—an indescribable roar, wordless, animal-like, as striking right and left with his big fist, knocking over a woman and trampling her, John Taylor leapt up and burst out of the cabin, and shot through the crowd gathered outside, still strangely roaring and bellowing. Lurton shouted, "Let him go! God will take care of him!" There were shouts outside. Then a clatter of hoofs and the strange, hysterical, mad roar receding.

By this time several woman were shrieking, and there were muffled groans. Lurton continued relentlessly. How could they fight the Devil that rode in broad daylight up and down the traces, stayed overnight at Cedar House, went to county court meetings, bought over the magistrate, the judges, and the jury, sold them goods soaked in blood, and sent Morton Maulding to the legislature? "Say that again, you bastard!" yelled Ambrose Maulding, springing to his feet. "I said the Devil is sending Morton Maulding to the legislature," said Lurton, fixing on him such a burning, hypnotic gaze that, to the utter amazement of the few who still retained some coolness, like Jus, Ambrose suddenly collapsed and sank in a heap to the floor, groaning.

Then his thunders turned to mellow, pleading music. "My brothers and sisters, as a man thinketh in his heart, so he is, and this slack, stinkin', no-account life you're livin' is the fruit of your slack, stinkin', no account souls. You've got to be made over right at the heart. You've got to be born again. For, as you are, there is no hope for you. No hope," he repeated, in a sad, mourning voice, the tears gushing from his eyes. And slowly his voice rose to a crescendo. "You'll die! You'll die in a fight! You'll die of drunkenness! You'll die stark, raving mad!"

At this the whole room resounded with shrieks. Several fell to the floor, some thrashing about violently, some lying stiff, with glassy eyes. "Don't be afraid, let all who have found God in the past gather around our suffering brothers and sisters," said Lurton with such clarion authority that the disorder seemed to take a pattern. Helpers knelt by the most violent sufferers. The uproar sank to muffled sobs. "God, have mercy!" "God, help him!" "God, take her to your mighty arms!" The preacher's voice was clear and musical, as he chanted, "High as the sky and wide as the West, the love of God is here and waiting for you. Come, my friends, kneel at the feet of Jesus. See yourselves for what you are. Then fall on your knees, naked and humble, and the light of God will shine on you. Then you won't want your whisky, for you will find the water of life. You won't want your tobacco, for the airs of heaven will blow sweet in your nostrils. God is waiting, my brothers, my sisters. Keep close to Him, and he will work with you, day by day, to house-clean this land of Kentucky till it ceases to be the back door to Hell, and becomes instead the front yard to Heaven."

They were all kneeling now, and many were sobbing. There was a contagion in the sobs, and a wonderful comfort in human nearness as they pressed body to body, there on the puncheon floor. The desperate longing of the repressed frontier soul to let go found an unutterable sense of release in increasing sobs and cries and groans, "Lord have mercy," which were only the whoops and yells of the West muted into prayers. Lurton jumped down from the broad up-ended piece of tree trunk on which he had been standing and walked among them, stopping here and there to raise his arms to the rafters and pray aloud. But when he called for a hymn, lining out Charles Wesley's words, "Glory be to God on high, God whose glory fills the sky, Peace on earth to man is given, man the well beloved of Heaven," Mary stood up and cried, "Sing it! Sing to the glory and power of God!"

She began a kind of syncopated dance, back and forth like a cheer leader, skipping over the prostrate bodies. In the flaring flames of the pine knots which gave all the light there was in the dark, crowded cabin, she looked strangely unreal. Her eyes shone with a full, starry, "possessed" light. Her face was transfigured. Her light, neat figure, was all one dancing aliveness.

A woman like Mary would never make a show of herself on secular occasions. At parties only loose women would sing and dance like that. But under the power of the spirit all was allowed. Even Jus was caught up by something wild and lovely in Mary's face and gestures, and, seeing only admiration and sympathy in the audience, he felt consternation and shame giving way to a kind of pride. "The Holy Spirit has entered into our sister," cried Lurton. "God speaks through her as he spoke of old through Paul and Peter. Sing, my friends, sing."

High and clear and true Mary's voice soared to the rafters, and suddenly there was another voice from above, so clear and unearthly that it seemed to the startled listeners as if an angel had joined her. But it was only Peter, perched in the loft, singing with his mother, his dark eyes intense, and eager, like the eyes of a bird singing its heart out on a bough. And then Lurton put his fine bass under them, and the whole crowd joined in singing and roaring, shaking the roof.

Lurton put out his hand, "Peace, my friends. God speaks in the thunder. But he speaks in the still small voice. Let us be quiet and listen, and in the quiet will each of you that is ready to lay down your burden of sin, and put yourself into your Father's hands, come up and kneel where I stand? Here comes Brother Goins. Here comes Sister Macfadden. God bless you, brother. God bless you, sister. Kneel together here, brothers by brothers, sisters by sisters. We are all one family in the home of our Father. Don't be ashamed that your sin should be known to your neighbor. In God's sight he is no better than you. Before God we are all sinners together. And if He can forgive us, who are we not to forgive each other?"

Up they came, some slowly, some rushing headlong, some sobbing, some crying aloud for mercy. Throughout the assemblage there was a steady sound of weeping, like the sound of the rain now beating rhythmically on the roof. Peter, swinging himself down from the loft, to be nearer the excitement, saw that Ol Waterburg was expertly helping Lurton. Creeping close, Peter plainly heard the Baptist say to the Methodist, right in the middle of a prayer, "Hear that rain out there? There's no salvation without immersion. God has had mercy on you, you old, baked, double-dried heretic, and is sending you the water!"

Mary was kneeling, utterly still, her pale, chiseled face beautiful with peace. To Peter it was all one great magic. Something marvelous had happened and his mother was a part of it. Only Jus sat quiet and unmoved, struggling with his thoughts. There was sense in the preacher's words, and he admired his courage. Well, if all this rumpus made it a little easier for these ruffians to live decent—

What! God Almighty! Could he believe his eyes? There were Dominie and Barbara, those starched Presbyterians, walking up together and kneeling at the preacher's feet!

CHAPTER 13

Lurton was embarrassed by Dominie's application next day not only to join the Methodist Church but to be made the class leader of the thirteen converts of last evening.

"But you arn't ready to be a member, much less a leader," he said bluntly, "because you're not converted. It isn't enough to accept Jesus Christ with your mind. You've got to be *changed*—plumb to the bottom." The look in Dominie's cold, clear eyes angered him. "Down on your knees and pray, and I will pray with you."

Dominie slipped from under the big, hard hand the preacher laid on him and stopped prayer cold with argument. These Kentucky settlers said Dominie, were something new and remarkable, for they really were democrats, the first in the world, ready to go the whole way with Jefferson in proclaiming that men were born not only free but equal. But they had only one hope of making their democracy prevail or even of surviving as free and decent men. This was to build institutions that suited their way of thinking. To this problem the Methodists had the answer. They got at the innermost core of people whose way of life was much below their native capacity, releasing it from ingrained fears and frustrations. In their circuit system they had the means of pooling experience and covering the whole wilderness with social and educational services. And they had John Wesley, a highly cultured man, whose genius for popular education and whose own soul-change had been shaped by his American experience. In their church organization they had the means of letting his fruitful ideas seep down from level to level.

Lurton was quite taken aback by this discourse. Much of it was over his head, which he shook worriedly. "There's so much advantage in having a man like you take charge of these few ignorant black sheep that I'm afraid the pure common sense of it might lead me astray. But the soul of our gospel is the deep, fundamental change. In every man, bar none, there's something that's got to be broken. It's his inheritance from Adam. It's what stands between him and God. And it's got to be broken so it goes with a crash. No half way measures are possible. Everything one was has got to collapse, and out of the wreck, the new life is born. Brother," and he clapped Dominie on the shoulder so simply and warmly that Dominie, for all his reticence, did not shrink, "brother, you're too much like a reed by the flowing waters of life. You bend but you don't break."

He found himself quietly held at arm's length, while Dominie replied soberly, "There are many paths to God, and I must stumble on in my own way, with what light I have. I did not feel the deeps broken up last night, nor did my wife, Barbara. Yet we knelt together with a deep and solemn sense of dedication and a clear sense of illumination. This Methodist way is right, and we want to follow it."

Lurton rode away toward Nashville without arriving at an answer. Dominie, though not yet accepted as a Methodist, assembled the other converts at his house and explained how the preacher felt, with so much accuracy and quiet eloquence that they all said it was as good as a sermon. "But there's no law of God or man that says we can't come to your house if we like," said Mary, flatly. "And since you're the one of us that can really read, and has the education to explain what Bible words mean, we're comin' to you, preacher or no preacher."

A few weeks later Barnabas McHenry, replacing Lurton on the Cumberland circuit, came riding up with the answer. When Lurton told him his doubts, McHenry reminded him that, when Peter Bohler first unfolded to Wesley the gospel of the inner change, Wesley had accepted it intellectually, as Dominie did, but without a corresponding emotional experience. But Bohler had told Wesley not to worry about that—just go out and preach the need of it for others and pray for it for himself. And so, McHenry said, John Wesley did. "The moral of that," said McHenry, beaming at Dominie from under his shaggy reddish eye-brows, "is that what was good enough for John Wesley is good enough for you."

2

So Dominie and Barbara joined the Methodist Church, and Dominie was formally appointed the class leader. McHenry got around two or three times from the end of August through November. In the intervals, Dominie got the Methodists together twice weekly, once for a service on Sunday, and once in the middle of the week for class meeting. For the Sunday service they combined either with the Baptists for the preaching of Ol Waterbug, who was amusing but not edifying, or with the Presbyterians for the preaching of John Grammer, who was neither amusing nor edifying. For such a union service many traveled ten or fifteen miles, and after the preaching there was a barbecue. Only the steadfast opposition of Dominie, Mary, and a few Baptists, kept those who organized a church service for the morning from organizing a horse race for the afternoon. There was usually plenty of whisky at these affairs, and those who were most loudly repentant of their sins at morning services were most loudly drunk at night. As religious exercises, these preachings left much to be desired. But as a means of getting together and pooling the knowledge and moral power of the more righteous among these far-flung settlers, they were invaluable.

The core of the Methodist system was the class meeting. Instructions to class leaders which McHenry left with Dominie said, "It is the duty of a class leader to inquire carefully how every soul in his class prospers, not only how each person observes the outward rules, but how he grows into the knowledge and love of God." A good class meeting was a form of group therapy. It might be preceded or followed by conferences and confessions corresponding to modern consultations with a psychiatrist. With the patience of a born teacher, Dominie coaxed these rude impulsive souls into accepting discipline, and finally into imposing it on themselves. Under his leadership the class meeting made itself responsible for L'il Papoose, as the white baby among the Indians was now called. Having lived much among Indians, Dominie respected their communal life and thought an Indian community a kindly nest for children. At every meeting he reported on the welfare of the baby and explained how the Indians felt and what they did, forging ties of friendship between the settlers and the Indian encampment, without presuming to change Indian ways. All of which so impressed the Indians that, in a few weeks, they asked that their camp be made one of the regular "preaching places" of the Circuit Rider.

Dominie also made the class into a primary school. Like all Protestant sects since the Reformation, the Methodists required the convert to read the Bible. Where ninety-nine out of one hundred were still illiterate, this meant that they must first learn to read. For this they had no primers, no first readers, no blackboards, no notebooks and pencils, no reading and writing aids of any sort. In the area south of Rogues' Harbor, from which Dominie's class meeting drew—an area about ten miles from south to north and twenty from east to west—there were four English Bibles—Mary's, Dominie's, Dean's, and Ol Waterbug's—and two German Bibles. There were only two other books—a copy of Plutarch's *Lives*, which Dominie had taken out of his father's small but excellent library when he went west, because it offered the most reading in the least compass, and a copy of Locke's *On Human Understanding* on which Ol Waterbug nourished his naturally good but eccentric and undisciplined mind. The only other reading was an occasional copy of *The Kentucky Gazette*, which Jus brought back from court and circulated among his more literate neighbors till it fell to pieces.

The development of an adequate distribution of reading matter —such a distribution as had not yet been attempted anywhere in the world—was the first real concern of the church. But so far the Methodist Book Concern had been able to provide only a handful of books for preachers to carry in their saddlebags. Meanwhile Dominie had to do what he could to focus eyes used to the great open spaces on print so close and so small that it was hard for even an experienced eye to follow. Carefully he would print out a Bible verse, word by word, on a smooth board, with a quill dipped in pokeberry juice. When the words were learned, the verse was marked in the Bible, and the book passed around, while each read it aloud in turn. Usually the verse was memorized long before it was read by the eye. Often frontier folk thus trained appeared to be reading their Bibles when all they were doing was using earmarks on the page to recall what had been stowed away by oral repetition in their retentive memories. But even such reading was the beginning of literacy.

Dominie also made his class the nucleus of an industrial co-operative. At the second meeting it adjourned from his cabin to the saltpeter cave, where it was joined by additional men and boys, including Peter and Jerry and Eddie. There Dominie let them examine scrapings from the cave, and explained that from these they could purify and crystallize saltpeter, which was the principal ingredient of gunpowder, the other ingredients being sulphur and charcoal. To get the best charcoal, they must cut dogwood, strip it of its bark, and season it for three winters. "Three winters!" exclaimed Jus, while Peter calculated that in three winters he would be a grown man of twelve. The patience and long-range vision of science and industry were new to these impulsive people.

Dominie said three years might seem a long time, but with what they had to work with, it would take them all of that to pile up enough saltpeter. Moreover, to get their gunpowder to Fort Massac they would have to build a boat. Not being skilled boat-builders like the Yankees, all they could hope to do would be to cut down one of those huge poplar trees, like the Big Tree near Cedar House, and hollow it into a canoe forty or fifty feet long, to be propelled by paddles. He proposed to start the building of this boat on the banks of the Red River. Since all they had to work with was a knife and an axe, they'd probably be busy on the boat during all their spare hours between cutting the dogwood and turning it into charcoal.

He then proceeded to lay out a schedule. The first experiments would be tried here at his cave, but the major manufacturing plant would be set up at the larger caves on the Cartwright place. They wouldn't try to cut the dogwood till the harvest was all in, nor to start the canoe till next spring when the dogwood was all stacked and drying. But they'd begin at once to learn how to get some clean, properly crystallized saltpeter.

Dancing with excitement, Peter and Jerry helped to carry stones to build an outdoor furnace, with a hole in the lower side of its oblong front through which wood could be thrust, and a sort of grill made of pieces of old iron, on top of which the copper kettles from Fort Massac could be set. They scraped earth from the caves, heated it almost to the boiling point in water drawn from the brook filtered it through layers of linsy, and, in a state verging on awe finally achieved the miracle of the first clean crystals. When this happened, they wanted not only to whoop but quite sincerely to thank God in a song of thanksgiving. They had no hymn book and no one knew all the words and the music of any hymn. But one man had a fiddle and most of them knew some old fiddle tunes. To these they put Bible words and so produced a rude forerunner of the kind of singing that the genius of the Negroes was later to develop into spirituals.

3

The faint stirring of civilized sentiment showed itself in an attempt to outlaw the more brutal forms of frontier fighting. On August 24, 1794, Thomas Pateson came into court at Logan Courthouse and proved by the oaths of Thomas Parker and Web Nants that his ear was bitten off, but there was as yet no effective way of punishing cannibals who bit off ears. Worse even than this was an instrument of battle which began to appear here and there. One day, as Peter and Jerry were riding along Red River, a maniacal face and two hideous claws appeared in the bushes, like those of some huge vulture in human form. Kicking the horse violently, the boys tore down the trail, looking back fearfully every half minute to see if this horror was following them. But evidently he was lying in wait for bigger prey. Not till they were in sight of the Cartwright cabin did their hearts settle down to a beating quiet enough to permit them to compare notes on what they had seen. Then they agreed that the man was Kuykendall, who had run off with Mason's daughter, "Hon," and that he had extended his fingers with long pointed claws of steel.

During the next few weeks several other people saw Kuykendall's claws. They were much admired among the wilder boys, two of whom procured similar instruments from Dromgole and Stewart, but these were promptly confiscated by their parents. One day John Wilcox, who had not been home for two weeks, returned, his face covered with red lines half healed. Peter's eyes sparkled with intelligence and malice. "Looks like he was in a fight with Kuykendall."

Startled, Jus and Mary studied the scratches, blurs, and scribblings that seemed to be all that was left of the once handsome face of John. Finally John said, "What if I was in a fight with him? He's a bastard."

"Son," said Jus, in a mild drawl, "if you fought Kuykendall, it's the first good thing I've heard about your doings."

One day, Ulrich, a German boy, told Dutch and Brenda, who told Dominie, who rode over to discuss it with Jus, that he had come on some youngsters gathered about a gentleman who wore a fine beaver hat, satin breeches, a brocade coat, white silk stockings, shoes with silver buckles, and, over it all, this first frosty day, a handsome fur coat. He was tall and princely looking, and had a clean white face, whiter than a woman's, and great kind, dreamy blue eyes, like a child's. His hair, partly silvered and partly black, was of a light and feathery fineness and was worn loose and curling to his shoulders. He stood amidst the children plucking gold coins out of the air. He spread his shapely white hands to show that he had nothing in them, and then said, "Ah, I see one flying through the air. See it?" He reached into the empty air, and held out his hand with a gold coin in it. In proof of this tale the German boy actually brought home a gold Spanish coin—or at least it appeared to be gold.

Hearing Dominie repeat this to Jus, Peter exercised his budding common sense by saying to Dominie, "I bet Ulrich's lyin'. I bet he just picked up this money somewhere, and he's scared to tell how he got it. So he's makin' up a big story." He was rather crestfallen when Dominie replied, "The lad's telling the truth, Peter. This is no doubt the man you saw near Morton Maulding's. What he was doing is just a magic trick. See!" And to Peter's openmouthed amazement, Dominie plucked a coin out of the air. He held out his hand to show Peter the coin and let him feel it, and then raised his hand and the coin was gone. "I've thought for a long time that the spells Alston works are a combination of magic tricks and Masonic ritual," said Dominie to Jus.

The two men then talked very seriously to Peter. "This man Alston is pretty careless when it comes to showing off in front of boys. You and Jerry look sharp. You're not to run any risk. But if you catch sight of the man, learn all you can about where he can be found, and come back quick and tell us."

This assignment made the boys feel big, the more so as it prevented their mothers from questioning their tendency, now that they had reached the ripe age of nine, to roam farther and farther afield. But autumn froze into winter, and 1794 passed into 1795, and still they found no trace of Alston. One day a new circuit rider appeared at the Cartwright cabin. His name was William Burke, and he had a twinkle in his eye, a slow drawl, and the soul of a diplomat. He had been sent down here for the purpose of overcoming the counterforce of James Haw. He had already had a talk with that truculent renegade whom hitherto no circuit rider had been able to beard in his den.

As usual Peter and Jerry were sent to call the neighbors to a preaching. Snug in their deerskin outfits, Jerry rode behind Peter on Plowboy through the woods, where a light sugaring of snow lay on the crispy leaves underfoot, and out of the woods into the trace between the ice-covered grass which snapped and crackled wherever it was touched. Peter sniffed the thick air. It had a fine fresh taste. "It's a good day for huntin'," he said.

"Yes," said Jerry, "I bet I could go right to where there's ten deer, layin' up the side of the Knob, out'n the wind."

Suddenly their horse stopped, pricked up its ears, and squatted, as he was accustomed to do when danger approached. Peter and Jerry lay low. Then Peter raised himself cautiously and listened. "Hold Plowboy while I shin up that tree and look," he whispered. He climbed the tree, and then slid quietly down, and coming back to Jerry said, "It's a whole gang of Mauldings. They're out hunting."

As the boys rode on, they took council, "It's an awful shame to let those deer be killed by folks like the Mauldings," observed Peter.

"Deer ain't never done the Mauldings no harm," agreed Jerry, thoughtfully.

"If we kinda went ahead of where they'll be goin', we could slip word to them deer, and they'd light out."

"All we have to do is to get where they can smell us," answered Jerry.

"That's a thing I never can get used to," said Peter. "How come we smell so rank to them."

"Why shouldn't we smell rank? We're human, and humans don't mean them no good."

So they started off, knowing well where the deer were because, as Jerry observed, "They're just where you and I would be if it was cold weather and we had to live out in it." In the course of being smelled by the deer, they came on several hunting parties and amused themselves gobbling like turkeys, howling like wolves, and behaving so generally like wild animals that they fooled even expert woodsmen.

Once they came on a wolf pit, and hearing a flouncing down below, they approached cautiously. "There's one down there all right." The pit was about ten feet deep, growing smaller toward the top, and widening on all sides as it descended to the dark depths where the creature, like a great, sharp-nosed dog, was whirling round and round. "Must a pulled his bait in with him," said Peter, looking down and meeting the glaring, almost phosphorescent eyes of the thing below.

"Let's throw stones down on him," suggested Jerry.

"No," said Peter, with sudden pity for the wild thing whirling down there. "It ain't our wolf. Stones would only pester him, and he's got trouble enough."

Altogether it was an interesting day. The Mauldings, though famous hunters, could not figure out what had happened to all the animals. All they saw all day were Peter and Jerry, who rode innocently past them about three o'clock that afternoon, and stopped and politely invited them to the preaching.

4

They had spent so much time spoiling the Mauldings' hunting that they had to hurry to leave their messages. As they went dashing down what looked like a new-made track into some of the Dromgole property, a boy on foot, about eleven years old, blocked their path. "It's one of the Dromgoles," whispered Jerry. His skin and Peter's bristled with antagonism. The boy looked at Peter, and said, "If I had a mug like your'n, I'd hang it on the tree yonder and throw stones at it."

Peter looked over the freckled, snub-nosed face before him and said, "If I had a face like yours, I'd hang it on the side of the Knob up yonder and throw the tree at it."

The boy squared up to him, "Say another word like that, and I'll knock your head clean off your shoulders."

"Well, now, if you want to fight," said Peter, with a good imitation of his father's drawling way of meeting an emergency, "I'd just as soon do it as not. The only trouble is I ain't never had any practice in fightin' fair. The best I know is Rough and Tumble." And suddenly he was crouching on the horse, eyes glaring, hands tense and outstretched like claws. Twisting his face into a snarling mask from which his bright dark eyes gleamed evilly, he rent the air with the combined howls of a wolf and panther, and precipitated himself in a flying leap through the air. He landed where the boy had been but was no longer. He was crashing through the bushes in flight. Peter and Jerry whooped and howled and clattered after him till they lost track of him completely.

They were now in strange territory, and rode along wonderingly through primeval forest. "Must be some of the Dromgole land," said Peter.

"We'd better make tracks out of here," said Jerry, "before we're shot at."

At that moment the boy they had seen before re-appeared on the trail, looking most amiable. "Want to come and see what we got in the cabin?" he said.

Peter sniffed loftily. "Ain't got time. We're expected to the preaching down at the Cartwright place." Then he had an idea. "Better come yourself. Wash the sin clean out of you and leave you so pure your own Mammy won't know you."

This the boy seemed to take as a courtesy, "Sure I'll come," he said, and asked about the time. Then he volunteered, "If you're set to ask folks to your preachin' better go in there."

The dark mass of evergreens he pointed to took shape almost by magic, and lo, there was a cabin there. The boys knew how a place could be concealed by trees and brush. But they didn't know a place could be so arranged that it could stand in plain sight and yet not be visible till it was pointed out to you. "Must a been there all the time and hidden by the summer leaves," thought Peter, worriedly. He thought he knew about where he was, and he was sure nobody had ever heard of a cabin of this size in this place. "But nobody gets in here generally without being shot at," he thought.

They approached a heavy door whose latchstring was in. The Dromgole boy made a noise like the tapping of a red-headed woodpecker, and they waited. Inside Peter could hear a low murmuring. His eyes traveled up and down the door in front of him, and suddenly it appeared to be covered with faces, half human, half animal, some grinning, some scowling at him. He looked closely. "It's just the knots in the wood. Somebody's been foolin' around with a knife," he thought, and began to study the way in which some artist had deftly shaped the natural lines of the wood into pictures. Then the door opened slightly, and somebody was looking out. Peter judged she was young and pretty, for the little he saw was pink and soft. The Dromgole boy whispered, "Just a pair of young-uns. Come to invite you-all to the Methodist preaching."

She turned and appeared to be talking to some one inside. Peter could hear a rich laugh, and his face flushed with anger. Then the door opened a little further, and a mellow voice said, "Welcome, my dear lads, and thanks for your kind invitation. It happens we are holding a school here, but in a few moments we shall have our own religious services. Let us in turn invite you to worship with us." Then he heard a whisper, "Keep them with you. Don't let them roam at large."

The door opened just enough to admit Peter and Jerry and the Dromgole boy. For a moment Peter was overcome by warmth and light. A fire was blazing on the hearth, and in the shuttered darkness four tall candles, in brass holders, gave forth light and a pleasant smell. A sword with a jeweled handle hung on the wall between two stuffed heads of deer. Thick bearskins covered the floor. There was a large plank table, with a bench to sit on running the whole length of it, and on it a china dish full of golden balls—something the boys had never seen and now could not take their eyes off. They were oranges!

As these marvels flashed on Peter's eyes, he was conscious that the cabin was full of people. Seated on stumps and on the thick bearskins were about fifteen men and half a dozen boys from Eddie's to John's age, some of whom Peter recognized. Each held a slate and slate pencil. In front of them stood a man impressively arrayed in something like a judge's robe and white curled wig which Peter had seen at the court in Stanford, and on top of that something he had never seen—an academic mortarboard! This personage was saying, "The letter is A. Write A. A-T—what does that mean?"

"It's the same as when you say, 'He don't know where he's at'," volunteered a bright pupil.

"It is indeed the word *at*. But your example is not grammatical, my friend. A better use of *at* would be to say simply, 'He is not *at* home!'"

Peter was staring at the teacher. This was the man he and Jerry had seen last summer near Morton Maulding's. The man his father wanted to locate. Philip Alston! The thing now was to get out, and send Dominie and his father here. His father said if Alston gave him coins or anything to bring it to him. His eye fell on a small book lying near him on the floor. Peter looked warily at the young woman standing over him and began, like the well-trained frontier boy that he was, to plot a series of small moves. First he sat down on the floor and drew Jerry down with him, at his guardian's feet. Then he edged, inch by inch, toward that book. Finally when the young woman's eyes were turned away a moment, his small brown hand approached the book. The next minute it was safe in the bosom of his deerskin tunic, and no one seemed to notice.

The lesson droned on, through the whole alphabet to Z. Then the teacher closed the book. "The lesson for the day is ended," he said gravely. "But before we part, let us perform our devotions together."

A wind blew out the candles, and in the darkness there appeared a huge distorted face in which glowed two red eyes. For a moment Peter was sick with terror. He could feel Jerry's hand clutching his leg. He steadied himself by gazing steadfastly at the face. Then he saw that it was only a large, twisted tree stump, shaped like an evil face, with a suggestion of horns above its furrowed brow. There was a smell of burning. He sniffed. Were these the fumes of Hell? "Somebody's holding live coals behind it," he decided. "Must be holding them with tongs." In the darkness he could see white hooded figures gathering behind the evil face, like spooks in a graveyard. Intense fear gripped him. He could feel Jerry shaking with horror. His mind was racing madly. "It's a lot of tomfoolery. As if we'd be fools enough to be scared!"

The evil great face, with its burning eyes, appeared to speak in solemn, sepulchral tones, "My brothers, you will now repeat our holy liturgy after me."

He then intoned, and the voices in the room answered in chorus, "We are the only Society that lives by Christian principles. We believe that it is against Nature to let any man fare sumptuously day after day, while his neighbors, who are as good or better than he, go hungry. We believe that the first Christian commandment is to take from the rich and give to the poor. We believe that the poor thus ordained to receive what the rich have usurped are exclusively the members of our Holy Band of Brothers."

The choral response ended. The voice intoned solemnly, "This you believe."

The chorus answered, "We believe."

"You swear?"

"We swear."

"By what do you swear?"

"By the fiery cross."

Suddenly the voice thundered, "There are those in our midst too young and weak to penetrate further into our Holy Mysteries. Remove them."

Struggling, kicking, Peter found himself blind-folded, gagged, and bound hand and foot, while a voice whispered in his ear, "Don't worry, Sonny. We ain't hurtin' you, only settin' you on the straight road back to your Mammy."

He felt himself being carried outdoors and through the cold, snowy air. Then he was set on a horse, and knew, by his sixth sense, that it was his own horse and that Jerry was being placed behind him. While he was still blindfolded, his horse was led some distance. Then his eyes were unbound, and he blinked in the tree-shaded twilight. Two men in coonskin caps stood by them. One said, "Your horse is headed the right way. Git goin' and keep goin', and, if you know what is good for you, don't you turn back or git off this path. And keep your mouth shut about what you saw there. Don't say we didn't warn you! Now git!"

He gave the horse a violent blow. It started to gallop. Breathlessly the children rode, through the dark wood, and out into the open fields where the last light of day gleamed palely on the snow and in the distance they could discern the outline of the Knob. They took their bearings by that outline. "I bet over yonder is the way to our house," said Peter. "And if it turns out that it is, I bet you that cabin is somewheres on Dromgole's land."

When the boys dashed up to the door, they found Brenda and Dutch, and Dominie and Barbara worriedly discussing with the Cartwrights whether to send out a search party. It was not till Peter and Jerry had poured out their story, alternately and in chorus, that Peter remembered the book in the bloused front of his deerskin tunic. Dominie took it and examined it thoughtfully. "It's *The New England Primer*," he said. "Somewhere up above Marietta, one of the river gangs must have captured a boat bringing down, among other things, a batch of supplies for the Yankee school."

"Well, I've heard that Alston's been giving reading lessons for years," said Jus, thoughtfully. "Folks have told me that all the booklearning they have they got from Alston." He discharged a stream of tobacco juice at the fire. "It's a queer story the boys have to tell, but I'm bound to say it fits in with what everybody says about Alston."

"Fits like a glove," answered Dominie. "As I see it, he's an educated man with no morals and a theatrical turn. It seems quite likely that what they told me at Fort Massac is true, and he has an extensive secret organization which seeks to make proselytes, and into which anybody from Peter's and Jerry's age up can be drawn."

But what hasn't been proved is that the criminal gangs are in this organization. Nobody Peter recognized today is under suspicion, except the Mauldings."

"No," said Dominie. "But we can arrest him as a counterfeiter. We have authority for that. And if we take him alive, we may get some of the facts out of him."

5

That night, after the preaching, Dominie found his way to Alston's cabin and verified enough of what Peter and Jerry had seen to warrant what happened next day. Under Dominie's command, the woods quietly filled with the most skilful Indian fighters and sharp shooters among the veterans, men accustomed to be noiseless and invisible in the forests. Meanwhile a delegation of the Methodists and Baptists went to wait upon the Ewings. Robert, Young and Urban Ewing then went with them to see that Wesley Maulding, as sheriff, arrested Alston.

Wesley was amazed to hear that Alston was in the neighborhood. He agreed heartily that he was just the man they wanted. Bring him to trial, and they'd put an end to all this counterfeit money. The troubles he was having at Cedar House with bad money! By God, it was gettin' so a man didn't dare to take anything in exchange except buffalo skins and tobacco. Leave Alston at large long enough and he'd find a way of counterfeitin' them. "Don't you think so, Bill?" asked Wes of Stewart, who had just ridden up, the counterfeit coins jingling along the seams of his deerskin pants. Bill loudly agreed.

But for all this voluble concurrence, Wesley found a dozen reasons for delaying. Dromgole came to see him. Stewart hung around, gossiping cheerfully. Ambrose and Richard Maulding came in. They all had the most trivial pretexts for taking the sheriff's time. Finally Jus took Wesley by the shoulders, "Come on, young feller. You've fooled around long enough. Git goin'. Your horse is saddled and waiting." When Ambrose and Richard Maulding proposed to come, too, as an extra guard for the sheriff, Jus forestalled an objection by the three Ewings. "Better have them where we can look out for them," he whispered.

Finally they started off. As they approached Alston's hide-away, Wesley put spurs to his horse and started to gallop. Jus plunged ahead of him, and the Ewings, Dutch, and the Baptists surrounded him. "Hold on, sheriff," said Jus, pleasantly. "You're on the wrong track."

"Am I?" said Wesley, drawing up. "I thought I knew this country so well I couldn't make a mistake."

"Well, you've made one this time. You get on this path here, and ride with us ahead and behind. We know where you're goin' even if you don't."

As they approached the cabin, Morton Maulding came down the path to the left. He was stopped by Jus. "What do you want?"

Maulding backed. "Nothing. I was just going to visit a friend."

"Better change your mind about that, brother," said Jus. "And I'd be pretty quiet about being his friend or giving him aid and comfort if you want to stay in the legislature."

They had now reached the cabin. The latchstring was in, the shutter closed and evidently barred from the inside. "There ain't nobody here," said Wes.

"Alston's here," replied Jus. "Two hundred of the militia have him in siege, and we don't aim to have any monkey business. Go up to that door and knock. And when there's an answer, you say, 'It's just Wes—Wesley Maulding'."

Wesley Maulding was not a man to show fright. And he had no notion of sacrificing himself for Alston. He wanted to remain sheriff, and to be in with the party in power, which ever it was. And, on the whole, he'd rather be on the side of right than of wrong, if it was convenient. He was part of Alston's network, but his heart had never been in it. He took the measure of these determined men, and his face broke into a smile. "You don't need to force me. I'd as soon trap the old fox as not."

He went up to the door and knocked. A voice said, "Who's there?"

"It's just Wes, Uncle Phil," he whispered through the key-hole. "Lemme in. I got a warning for you."

The door opened. Alston stood there, wrapped in a purple velvet dressing gown, trimmed in fur. For a moment Wesley flinched. Jus put a gun to his back. "Do your duty, man." Wesley said, "In the name of the Commonwealth of Kentucky, I place you under arrest."

"Stand back," roared Alston, whipping a pistol from under his robe. "Or I'll put a bullet through your black heart." Wesley stood back. Jus, Dutch, and the others covered Alston with their guns. Magnificently ignoring them, Alston said, in mournful, musical tones, "I loved you as a son, Wesley. I tried to teach you your letters. I put the countryside up to building you that fine Cedar House. I set you up in funds."

Wesley said, abashed, "There's no help for it, Uncle Phil. The law's caught up with you. You're under arrest. They're going to try you for making fake money."

It may be that Alston was playing for time. It may be that, seeing Ambrose and Richard just behind Wesley, he had some hope that they might rescue him. For continuing to act as if Jus and Dutch and the others were beneath his social notice, he now addressed himself to the Mauldings collectively. "My friends, for though you turn on me in this hour, I still call you friends, what is this that you do? Have I not taught you that money, of itself, is of no more value than the sands of the riverbed? It is only a token of exchange. Anything may serve as money. True, the function of providing money is usually usurped by governments, and I took it upon myself. But, my friends, when I came to this country as a benefactor, there was no government, and there is none now worthy of a free man's obedience. And who was to provide you with money if I didn't? I issued coins, and with coins you were able to obtain goods. With these coins you despoiled the Philistines. In the East men with the same principles we profess, but with a hypocrisy we scorn, set themselves up a bankers, and as bankers they presume to issue paper notes. Is paper any better than real metal? And believe me those bankers will have no more behind their paper than we have behind our gold and silver."

Robert Ewing said sharply, "You'd better shut up, Alston, before your eloquence gives you away. The only charge we have against you is counterfeiting. And if you don't look out, we'll get you on the charge of trading in goods stolen from emigrants, often with murder."

If it was Ewing's intention to make Alston incriminate himself he succeeded, for the man replied grandly, standing out proud as a Roman senator, still pointing his pistol with one hand and clutching his purple furred robe with the other. "The only difference between me and most business men," he said loftily, "is that I am honest. The goods on the marts of trade are everywhere soaked in blood, sir. On the rice of Georgia and South Carolina there is the blood of slaves. I have seen them beaten to death by bruta overseers, dying of fever untended, pining to death because their loved ones had been sold elsewhere. Such barbarities no man can lay at my door. And if goods have come to me from those who have been forced to shoot in their own defense, they shot straight and did their murder clean. Look at the Yankee notions. I have got them wherever I could. But whatever I and mine did in taking them was nothing to the murder behind them—the murder of men on foul ships at sea, the murder of poor sewing women in the back alleys of Boston." He paused, and said with a voice edged with disdain, like a great lord commanding his menials, "And now my advice to you gentlemen is to take that warrant and tear it up. For if you don't,"—He made a lunge forward, his pistol within a foot of Wesley's face. "Tear it!" he thundered.

Jus knocked his arm up. The pistol flew out of his hand into the bush. A dozen guns were covering him. Dominie said sternly, "Be careful. Take him alive." A bullet whizzed through the air, clean and clear, into Alston's temple. He fell. Jus, Dutch, and Dominie roared imprecations against the shooter. But as the militia closed in from all sides, excited and curious, every man of them denied having shot that bullet. "Vielleicht it was one of the Brother-band," observed Dutch. "He feared the man blab would."

Dominie was kneeling by Alston's crumpled body. "He's dead, all right. It was a good shot. Straight into his brain." He rose. Jus walked over and kicked the body, where it lay, sprawling across the door-jamb in its purple robe. "What we might a' learned from him has died with him," he said glumly. "He's no good to us now." He turned to Wesley. "We'll leave you the privilege of burying him. Hurry up and get him out of here. We're takin' over the house and its contents."

Wesley and the other Mauldings carried Alston away. Nobody asked what became of him or worried because the frozen ground was too hard for the digging of a grave. There were wild places where the dead might lie and not disturb the living, and the wolves and the vultures were always hungry.

6

The salutary effect on that wild world of the death of Philip Alston was increased by the death of Kuykendall in a brawl during a dance at the Masons'. Next day a delegation headed by Jus and Dominie called on Sam Mason, and said that it would be inconvenient to have any more goings on, and that the whole countryside would be obliged if he'd go elsewhere. "I advise you to take this under consideration," said Jus, "if you don't want your whole outfit indicted for murder."

Sam Mason laughed in his face. Who did he think he was going to catch on a charge of murder? Better look under his own roof for that.

"If you're implyin' that John Wilcox killed Kuykendall, you-all swear out your statements to this effect, and we'll have it out in court," replied Jus, steadily. "You couldn't find a jury for a hundred miles around that wouldn't acquit John and do it with a vote of thanks, after the maniac way Kuykendall's been sportin' those death-claws of his. Nobody's going to hang anybody for killin' Kuykendall, not even a Mason! But I'd sure admire to see it come up in a trial. The dirty linen in the Mason family that would get washed in public would smell from here to Frankfort."

Sam Mason brazened it out and said he'd sure see that some statements were sworn to. But next morning Dominie rode over with a chill gleam of triumph in his blue eyes, like sunshine on ice. "I give you three guesses as to what's happened to the Masons."

"I need only one guess," said Jus, dryly. "They've cleared out."

In other respects they were less successful. For the day after they took over Alston's cabin, Bill Reading called on Jus, and challenged him to prove that this building or anything in it was other than the legitimate property of James Dromgole. The fact that Dromgole's father-in-law happened to be visiting him neither implicated him nor gave them a claim on his property. Jus read law on the subject till he was dizzy, and even rode to Nashville and consulted Justice McNairy and Andrew Jackson. There seemed nothing to do but turn back the cabin and all its contents to Dromgole. Nothing had been found to incriminate anybody. Even the jewelry, lace, and small objects of art, all bearing the stamp of Paris, could conceivably have been honestly obtained in New Orleans. "I'm afraid there's a whole mess of these vipers left," said Jus to Dominie. "Getting rid of Alston is all to the good. But it only means that we've driven the rest of them underground."

But the settlers were so happy that Alston and Mason were gone that, when Burke came around for the next preaching, they welcomed him with a whooping round of Glory Hallelujahs. The cabin rocked with the groans of the mourners and the shouts of the saved till after midnight, and outside those who could not find room in the cabin knelt praying and sobbing in the snow.

Sneaking out of the crowded cabin, past the worshipers on the ground, Peter kept walking, enjoying the fresh cold air after the closeness inside, and the silence after the noise. He stopped on a little rise of ground and looked out on the whiteness, hiding every unsightly thing, smoothing out all the rough places in the land, idealizing and simplifying all, under the full rolling light of the winter moon. The words of the preacher were still sounding in his ears. "Behold I will make a new heaven and a new earth, for the former things are passed away."

Standing there alone, in this cold, white world, Peter looked up at the luminous sky, and, as had happened before, he went away out of his body and left himself standing there. He returned after an eternity of wandering in far bright space, to find his feet and hands numb, and his moccasins frozen to the snow. As he started on a run back to the cabin, a thought was buzzing in his mind, like a single fly in a shut room, "A new heaven and a new earth! But the preacher said I've got to be made new, too. What would it feel like to be made all over and come out new? Would I still be me? Or would I be somebody else?"

BOOK III

1796 - 1800

John Adams, President

CHAPTER 14

With the death of Philip Alston and the departure of the Masons, life was better in Logan County. For one thing politics was cleaner. Though the election committee of which Jus was a member had not succeeded in challenging the election of Morton Maulding, their inquiries and depositions had educated citizens to their privilege of manhood suffrage—unique, at that time among American states. At the next election, in the spring of 1795, Young Ewing was chosen to replace Morton in the legislature. Young Ewing's brother, Robert, had recently been appointed magistrate, and shortly after the election his brother, Reuben, replaced Wesley Maulding as sheriff. So the respectable Ewings had won, at last, over the dubious Mauldings.

Morton Maulding concurred loudly in his own defeat. He had come back from Frankfort growling like a sick bear. Though the capital city consisted only of a few log cabins scattered through the woods, and the house where the first legislature met was a two storey log structure no better than Cedar House, Morton talked as if he had been imprisoned behind high city walls. He confessed he couldn't make head or tail of politics. All politicians did was to gab, gab, gab, and think of fancy ways of tying their own hands on committees, and snarling themselves in rules and precedents, so that nobody could go ahead and just do what had to be done, and nobody dared to speak right out. Morton never minded telling an outright lie. But it made him itch all over to have to sit and listen to what wasn't either lies or the truth, but just words.

So when Young Ewing was elected, Morton laughed aloud, and said that anybody that wanted to pickle himself in the "pison" of politics was welcome. As for him, he was going where he could draw a free breath. Where was that? Fifty miles west, where the buffalo fleeing the oncoming settlers, had found themselves a great patch of young pea-vines—miles and miles of pea-vines rolling west, untouched by the foot of man. So westward he went, and returned with some Indians dragging on a sledge the 1400 pound carcass of a buffalo, and gave a banquet to all his friends to celebrate his defeat.

Meanwhile the new order at Logan Courthouse was further strengthened by the arrival of Hendley Russell. Hendley was the son of General William Russell, the beloved commander of many of the Virginia veterans. In 1787 General Russell and his wife, who was a sister of Patrick Henry, had become Methodists. Thenceforth their home, near Abingdon, Virginia, had been a headquarters for the circuit riders. Coming out to Logan Courthouse, in 1795, Hendley Russell brought social dignity to the Methodists.

The economic situation was as hopeful as the political. With the opening of the market in New Orleans, they had high hopes of prospering from the growing of cotton, which had been the main agricultural excitement of the summer of 1795. Peter had heard Andrew Jackson tell about the profits to be made in cotton, one day when his father had taken him to court. Jackson had ridden up from Nashville to confer with the veterans' lawyer on a disputed land claim along the Kentucky-Tennessee line. Always a propagandist for something, Jackson took advantage of this to "sell" the farmers lounging around the courthouse on cotton growing. Standing on a stump, trim and taut in his "gentry clothes," his red hair combed straight back and tied in an eel-skin bag, his gray eyes flashing electric sparks, Jackson overwhelmed them with arithmetic.

A man, a woman, and two or three children, he said, could easily cultivate four acres of cotton in addition to feeding themselves and their beasts. They should be able to get 350 pounds per acre or 1400 pounds in all, free from seeds. This, at the current price of cotton, should net them $250, with $40 deducted for expenses. All a thrifty family needed for a year in a country where manufactured and imported goods were still very limited was $250. At this somebody shouted that it was too hard to get the seeds out of cotton. For answer Jackson appealed to the "ladies." Wasn't it as easy to get the seeds out of cotton as to water-rot and break flax? Flattered by being called "ladies," several sun-bonneted women pushed their way forward and lent Jackson an affirmative "Aye, aye."

Afterwards Peter heard Jackson tell his father that he planned to make cotton the principal crop of his new plantation at Hunter's Hill. Peter didn't share this enthusiasm for cotton. The very word made him feel all choked up with fuzz, for there had been more fuzz than snow that winter, as in cabins along the Red River, the Muddy River, the Big Whip-poor-will, and the Little Whip-poor-will fathers, mothers, brothers, and sisters had worked together on the hearth in the firelight, from early supper to the nine o'clock bed-time, picking seeds out of cotton with their fingers. The Cartwright cabin had been white with the flying fuzz. Mary and Brenda and Barbara had experimented with carding, spinning, and weaving. The result was a soft white cloth more beautiful in their eyes than linen. In Nashville, there was talk of getting up a fair to show off the new cloth, with a prize of $10.00 to the woman who produced the best. Peter thought they should give a prize to the fingers that had pulled the most seeds out. If they had, he knew his would have won it.

With politics and economics looking so hopeful, all would have been well had it not been for the Masons and the Harpes. Though the Masons had departed, every attempt to get near the Mason cabins was met by gunfire from an invisible source. Once or twice the Mason Negroes, Pompey and Sambo, were seen at Logan Courthouse. Once Sam Morris was seen coming out of the bushes near the Mason cabins. And there continued to be evidence that the stretch of the Lexington-Nashville road nearest Logan Courthouse was unsafe for travelers. Travelers coming from Nashville were sometimes seen at Cedar House and then they were seen no more. Inquiries seeped in from distracted relatives from as far east as Pittsburgh or Philadelphia, saying that the travelers had never arrived at their destination. Similarly travelers coming from Lexington were last seen near Morton Maulding's. When they first began to hear of the alleged murders, the militia patroled the road and Jus, with the Ewings, Dominie, Hendley Russell, and others, inquired into the matter. But so long a time usually elapsed between the disappearance of a stranger and word from his friends and relatives, and the whole accusation was so vague, that nothing could be done about it.

As usual, suspicion clung to the Harpes, who came and went, mysteriously. The burly figure of Micajah Harpe, and the small, thin body of Wiley, were known to most of the small boys who were taught to flee them at sight. Peter now knew that the sour young man with a cold eye, whom he had first seen with Philip Alston when he was inviting the neighbors to Lurton's preaching, was Wiley Harpe. The Harpes were known to be "sweet" on the Roberts girls—Susan and Betsy. This rumor led some wild young blades to suppose that Susan and Betsy might be easily accessible to other daring spirits. But this conclusion was found to be premature when Susan took deliberate aim with a pistol and broke the leg of one aspirant to her favor, saying, "That'll teach you to step in where you're not wanted," and when Betsy clawed at the eye of one of her admirers, permanently injuring it. This resistance to approach gave the girls a pseudo-respectability, the more so as, when they went abroad, they were guarded by a dirty, wild-haired, sullen young brother who was never heard to utter a sound, except to snarl when any one approached his sisters. Nobody wanted to approach Susan who was large, homely, and fierce-looking. But Betsy was pretty, reasonably clean, and generally "rigged out" in ladylike finery, and, over the barriers that enclosed her, she frequently cast glances half friendly, half challenging out of her blue eyes.

The Harpes and the Roberts were discussed every court-day, but no way was found to bring them up before the court. Logan Courthouse was busy enough those days, without looking for trouble by indicting the Harpes. The court did business for an enormous area. Men rode in from far and near, usually with their wives on their saddles behind them—men in deerskin jackets and coonskin caps, tobacco chewing, drawling men, men from stations on the Red River, the Green River, the Barren River, and from the far off lower Cumberland, near the boundary of the Chickasaws. Disputes about boundaries and land titles were continual. But the crime which was still thought to be sheltered in Rogues' Harbor was left severely alone.

2

On a balmy afternoon in the spring of 1796 Peter and Jerry were riding back from Joshua Gates' mill on the Big Whip-poor-will. The bright green was mantling the pastures, and the new peach trees were pink with their first blossoms. But the forest trees were still leafless above the pools of thick gold water that spread around their roots, and the coppery gold earth was still slippery under foot.

At ten years of age, going on eleven, Peter and Jerry had each risen to the dignity of a horse of his own. Peter's was a medium-sized roan, with large feet, a thick neck, a hard trot, a hard mouth, and a wicked eye. His name was Diablo, and he was one of the brutes on which Dominie had packed sulphur back from Natchez. His ancestors had come with the first Spanish conquistadors, and had escaped to the wilds. This brute had been caught in Louisiana, and had been put up for sale in Natchez. Kentuckians who floated tobacco down the Mississippi bought these pieces of biological dynamite for $50.00 each, and loaded their unwilling backs with whatever they wanted to take up the Chickasaw Road. They were then given to the boys of the family, to ride if they could, and to break in as work-horses. There was no better way of cultivating perseverence and resolution in a boy than to assign him to the task of keeping his seat on one of these things.

Peter was triumphantly riding Diablo bareback, letting him know with every pressure of his lean, hard, rubbery legs, who was master. But Jerry's nag was a poor old thing who looked as if either his father or his mother had been a thoroughbred, and had formed a mesalliance. Dutch, like Jus, had been glad to take some of the Spanish ponies off Dominie's hands, but, after Jerry had been thrown six times, and had broken an arm and a leg, his father, with his usual indulgence for this slight, gentle son, had given him a safer horse.

Both boys carried guns, and each had slung over his horse a bag of meal or flour, from which, as they bounced along, the white dust was diffused like smoke on the balmy April air. This was the last of the wheat. The Germans, more far-sighted, and given more to plowing and planting than their Scotch-Irish neighbors, made their wheat last through the winter and into the lean months of spring. But in Peter's family the wheat had gone long since, and the last of the corn had been consumed two weeks ago. However in return for some legal help, Dutch had divided his wheat with Jus. Since the stuff was too precious for the usual method of pounding it in the mortar and sifting it through a deerskin in which holes had been burnt, the boys had been sent to the new mill lately set up by Joshua Gates to have it properly ground into flour. This flour would be preserved like so much gold dust till the new harvest came in, and made into cake and biscuit only for "company."

When sending their boys on a mission to a strange neighborhood, good mothers like Mary and Brenda wanted them to be well dressed. So both Peter and Jerry were wearing what was as much of a luxury as the wheat flour—white cotton shirts! To show them more plainly, they had taken off their deerskin tunics and hung them across their horses. The shirts had made quite a sensation at the mill among people waiting for meal to be ground. Most of them had heard of the marvelous new cotton cloth but few had seen it.

Riding along, the boys eased the gnawing in the pit of the stomach which beset frontier children at this time of year, by sampling bear's lettuce, sassafras, spicewood, dandelion leaves, winter green leaves, and delicate stems of new grass, and gloating over the fact that a single watermelon hill which Dominie had planted last year had produced enough seeds to promise all his neighbors all the watermelons they could eat this year. Coming out of a stretch of woodland into the open, they saw on the trail that led from Morton Maulding's farm a cavalcade whose dress and accoutrements made even their new shirts look commonplace. It was the Maulding, Dromgole, Cauldwell young people, and the two eldest of William Richardson's famous family of eighteen beautiful girls. Peter rolled out the oath he had borrowed from his hero, Andrew Jackson, "By the Eternal! Do I view the backside of my sainted brother, John? But who is the dame he's riding with?"

Peering around John, who had turned his horse around and was parleying with a lady, Jerry said, "It's Mrs. Dromgole." Peter stared. He had heard his father say that Mrs. Dromgole had come up from Natchez to join her husband. By this time John was riding alongside of Mrs. Dromgole, coming toward Peter and Jerry. Jerry commented, "She must be as old as Mammy, but she sure gets herself up like she was sixteen."

The dark glare in Peter's eyes seemed half anger, half curiosity. Actually his inner feeling was utter confusion. He had heard some nasty scandal to the effect that John's fight with Kuykendall had been over Mason's daughter, Hon. And now John was riding with somebody else's wife! As Mrs. Dromgole approached, she turned her sweet, dazzling eyes on Peter. Like her father, Alston's daughter had fair skin, fine black hair, and baby blue eyes. In him they had seemed womanish. In her they had a natural feminine charm. Educated in all the delicate little ways girls acquired in the convent, clad in a black broadcloth riding habit bought in New Orleans, she looked quite fabulous in the eyes of the frontier boys. Under her blue-eyed gaze, Peter felt an unwonted shyness. Making an effort to overcome this, he cast at her a look so bright and challenging that she stopped, startled.

John made haste to say, "This is my brother, Peter, Mrs. Dromgole."

She cast a languishing, sidelong glance at John, and said under her breath, "The makings of a cabellero there? What?" She turned to Peter, enveloping him in sweetness, "Honey, can you dance?"

"A little," mumbled Peter, embarrassed, and angry that he should be so, for bashfulness was a lowering of pride which Peter refused to tolerate in himself.

"We'll have to give you some lessons, won't we girls?" said Mrs. Dromgole. She smiled at the girls who had clustered around her. They all tittered. Peter blushed but stared at them boldly. Out of the corner of his eye Peter observed that John was ill-pleased with the attention his junior was getting, but was covering the fact handsomely. Three years of association with the Masons, the Alstons, and others whose manners were better than their morals, had spread a veneer of amiability over John's selfishness. Graceful, upright, and easy on his spirited thoroughbred, he listened, smiling, while Mrs. Dromgole chattered to his young brother about shooting matches, quoit throwing, horse-races, dances, and barbecues which she was organizing for the young people. Despite his determination to be neither cowed, embarrassed, nor visibly impressed, Peter listened wistfully. It would be fun to be grown up and in such gay company!

When they finally left Mrs. Dromgole's party and rode on, Peter was vexed to see how enamored Jerry was of his elder brother. Time was when Jerry would join him in fighting John. Now he was so excited by the few kind words John had deigned to direct at him that Peter was quite disgusted. Family loyalty kept Peter from raising, even with Jerry, the questions which, he knew, were troubling his mother. How could John come by all those fine things honestly? But he observed sulkily, "Seems like your Mammy don't think so well of him."

"Oh, Mammy!" said Jerry, kicking his horse in sudden irritation. Jerry was feeling less and less content with the moral and social rigors of life within the high spiked fence of the Baptist denomination. Peter was silent. That laughing Dromgole crowd had soured the sweet spring day.

3

After riding a little way with Jerry on the trail that led west to the Baptist settlement, Peter turned back on a little used trail to his own home. When he came to the point where it turned south, he noticed that it had been entered from the east by a horse whose hoof-prints he did not recognize. He stopped and examined the prints, and finally dismounted and measured them. Must be a gentleman's horse, with slender, light feet. To right and left of the tracks the dried grass of last year rose several feet high, with new green running all through it, close to the ground. Peter sniffed, "If only I was a houn' dawg, I could tell whether it's a new horse somebody's got or a new person riding through here." Fear gripped him. There was so much talk of murders and robbers, of Mason's gang still in hiding, and the Harpes guilty of nameless horrors. The sunshine seemed dead lonely. He heard a rustling in the grass and his heart leaped to his mouth. He dug his heels into his horse and rode back to Jerry's house, with a phantom rider, aiming a pistol at his back, close behind.

Not wishing to frighten Brenda, he entered into round-about negotiations to have Jerry go home with him and sleep in John's bed that night. Brenda finally consented, and the two boys galloped off. On the way Peter unfolded the news of the strange footprints. Both boys dismounted and studied them, and then, leading their horses, cautiously followed them, looking to right and to left. Suddenly Jerry said, "Look here. Somebody's come through the creek." They followed fearfully up this trail which was rarely used because a man was said to have been murdered here, and his bones were still lying white under the leaves. Then they saw horse manure, the grass beaten down, and a pile of leaves. "Somebody's slept out!"

They were sure now that it must be some of "Mason's gang" or "the Harpe gang"—not the Masons themselves nor the Harpes, with whose faces and figures they were well acquainted, and who therefore were known to be only human beings; but somebody who, because he was unknown, had an eerie quality of terror.

Full of their secrets, the boys galloped to the Cartwrights. As they came up to the rail fence enclosing the dooryard and truck garden, they saw a fine horse, with graceful legs, a high arched neck, and an excellent saddle tethered there. And under the big red maple, drinking whisky with Jus, and with Mary sitting quietly by carding wool, a graceful gentleman was elegantly poised on a log. His trim long legs were encased in well cut breeches, and well made leggings and riding boots, and the hand that held the gourd of whisky looked as if it had been clean all its life and had only recently got a few smudges and scratches on it. Peter was used to hands that looked as if they had been dirty all their lives. Even when they were freshly scrubbed, and pink and wrinkled as a new baby from having been soaked in hot water, dirt appeared to be their inalienable property—something which would return when the alien and temporary cleanness had worn off.

Peter had seen men like Burwell Jackson, Cauldwell, and the Ewings, on dress parade. They wore knee-breeches and ruffled shirts like this man. They had a flourish of politeness and some pretense of education. They talked in sonorous phrases, often with a literary turn. He knew Andrew Jackson, whose high bearing, innate style, and clean, sharp, dashing honesty made him unique. But they were all men of the wilds. This man was as different from them as a dove from an eagle. He was rumpled, tired, and dirty.

And yet, Peter thought, "He looks like he'd always slept between sheets, and had carpets to the floor, and drunk coffee outa china cups, and wine outa glasses, and had niggers to do all the dirty work." There was no censure in the thought. Only an enchanted wonder.

As they were talking, Dominie rode up with Eddie who, Peter surmised, had been sent to summon him. Jus said, "This is Mr. Ball." Mr. Ball rose and bowed gracefully, and said gravely, "I don't want to pass under false pretenses. Ball is only a name I am assuming for the time being." Dominie sat down, eyeing him with sidelong looks under his light eyelashes. For a while they discussed politics. The stranger appeared to be an admirer of Mr. Jefferson. Then they talked about the widening of the Boone trail. The stranger said he understood they wouldn't change the original trail but would make a new road following the same general course which they would call Wilderness Road. Dominie's eyes caught Justurian's for a moment. Peter, being used to the intricacies of frontier conversation, guessed that Dominie had thought the stranger might have come up from New Orleans, but that his knowledge of Boone's trail might indicate that he came from the East. Dominie then spoke of two Spaniards who had been at Cedar House, talking about the trade advantages Spain could give the Cumberland people if they'd cut loose from the Union and become a protectorate of Spain. Andrew Jackson had said if he heard any more such nonsense he'd recruit a force to shoot the Dons out of Louisiana. Mr. Ball listened politely but seemed so honestly ignorant of this burning question that it was clear, even to Peter, that he had not come from New Orleans.

Mr. Ball then directed the conversation to Logan County. "I have heard that Rogues' Harbor here is peopled by fugitives from justice."

Peter's elders made haste to explain that this was a military reservation, largely settled by poor and respectable veterans. But the only center of administration for all western Kentucky was Logan Courthouse, nine miles to the north, and unfortunately there was a large outlaw influence there supported by most of the original settlers and big landowners. "They form part of the county government and they have a monopoly of the Exchange business here," said Jus, "but we keep 'em in check and watch over 'em."

Mr. Ball listened, his handsome face deeply troubled. Finally he said, "I am a fugitive from justice, but believe me, Sirs—not because of any connection with your outlaws or with their works. I want to rear a shelter and get a plot of ground where I can raise my humble necessities. I have nothing to offer for it except my watch, my ring, and $25.00. I would gladly exchange my clothes with some one who might want to go to Lexington or New Orleans, and get instead such country costumes as I see you wearing, at once comfortable and picturesque."

"You don't look used to working," said Dominie, eyeing his hands.

"It is true I never cut down a tree or built a house. But I can learn. As for tilling the ground, I understand both tobacco and cotton culture. The only trouble is—" He hesitated.

"The trouble is," hazarded Dominie, "that while you know the business of a plantation, in your experience the actual work on it has always been done by black slaves."

Mr. Ball looked startled. Then he said, "That is true," and added, apologetically, "But I was quite in favor of Jefferson's and George Mason's stand for a clause outlawing slavery in the Federal constitution. I wrote and spoke much on the subject."

Peter saw his father's and mother's eyes meet those of Dominie, and a social warmth, like sun coming out, began to permeate the group. Jus said, "I ought to tell you that, although this land is reserved for veterans, much of it has not been taken up, and therefore it has recently been thrown open for general settlement. You can preempt it at the rate of $30.00 a hundred acres, in plots up to 200 acres. Your $25.00 will be enough to hold 100 acres. We'll trust you for the rest."

Mr. Ball was thunderstruck. "100 acres of such land as this for $25.00." He smiled wistfully. "To be such a landowner. What a rod for a broken spirit."

Dominie was considering whether they should offer to put him up a house. But no. He was trying to maintain an area of respectability around the nucleus of the Methodist classmeeting, and this man was, by his own account, a fugitive from justice. Better go slow. In mild weather he could sleep out or make a lean-to.

By fall, if they decided he would make a good citizen, they could help him build a house. He said, "We can help you burn a field, and furnish you with enough seed to start you. We still depend on hunting and fishing for more than half of our food. I need not ask you if you can hunt, that being a gentleman's avocation in the more genteel parts of the country."

Mr. Ball said, " You are like Christian brothers to me, and I don't know how to thank you. But won't you do one more thing? Help me out of this perfectly useless raiment."

Mary looked up and spoke for the first time. "He's about the size you are, Jus—only a little more slender. You could use some good gentry clothes for going to court. I could let out the seams and make them fit you." Mr. Ball smiled boyishly, and said to Jus, "Come, Sir, what do you say?"

So Jus got a suit of tailored clothes, and Mr. Ball was turned into a bright-looking frontiersman with butternut colored homespun breeches, a crisp, scratchy tow-linen shirt, and neat moccasins laced up around his ankles. He seemed quite pleased with himself, as he carried off a pair of leather breeches, two more shirts, and a handsome deerskin tunic. He particularly admired the way the tunic bloused all around, providing a roomy pouch in which anything could be carried. Thus furnished, he rode out in the April twilight to glimpse before dark the piece of land he might have. Peter rode with him, leaving Jerry to bring in wood for supper—a job Jerry accepted with delight because Polly offered it, and what Polly wanted had suddenly become law to him.

The April dusk vibrated with the delicate music of the peepers, like the ringing of millions of tiny bells. There was magic in the sound, magic in the purling of little rills, magic in the bluebird singing in the sugar maple tree, magic in the breath of a thousand growing things, magic in the first misty stars, because there was magic in Peter's heart. A boy's first romantic love is not a woman. The emotional obliviousness of childhood had passed, and this stranger from another world was filling Peter's heart and his imagination.

4

Late that summer there was an outbreak of "summer sickness", with fever, nausea, and diarrhoea. Dominie's little girl lay near death. Sis was sick. Many children died. Mr. Ball got Dominie to call a meeting of the Methodists and Baptists and all their friends, including the Portyghees, among whom the sickness was most virulent. With quiet authority he explained to them that while no one knew what the cause of this sickness was, it was obvious that it was greatly aggravated by pollution of soil, water, and food. He went around the country looking at springs, pointing out places where sewerage and garbage leaked into drinking water, instructing people in the making of privies and the cleanly disposal of waste. He advised them to make sure that milk and water were kept covered and cold. Though many years were to pass before surgical antisepsis was to be understood, physicians had already observed that there was some connection between cleanliness and health.

A passion for cleanliness is the primary civilized instinct in women. Mary, Barbara, and Brenda took up Mr. Ball's teaching with enthusiasm. With their help he was soon operating throughout the stricken area like a doctor with three district nurses. Once as Ball rode by, in the late summer twilight, gray with weariness and dust, Dominie came out with a pewter mug full of cold metheglin for him. "It is a wonderful thing you are doing for us," he said, "bringing us the blessings of medical science." He hesitated and added, "You will pardon me if I assume that you were educated as a physician?"

"Yes," said Mr. Ball, quietly, "I was."

Doctor Ball, as he was now called, had become the hero of the countryside, which hitherto had had no doctors except mid-wives and old herb-women. Above all, he was Peter's hero. Just to be near him Peter volunteered to go with him everywhere on his sick calls, carrying extra supplies, looking after his horse, and helping to bring water with which to bathe patients or to make stretchers on which to carry them.

Jus was pleased. "It's an education for Peter to be with a man like that," he told Dominie. And so indeed it was. Sometimes Doctor Ball made passing references to far-off times and places and strange persons—to Greece and Rome, to Socrates and Shake-speare. Such names were to Peter like the landscapes and strange faces in the clouds at sunset, forming, fading, and re-forming on far horizons, vague but magnificent. Even about the familiar world of grass and trees, Doctor Ball could teach him something. Peter knew every plant in the fields and the woods and ascribed medicinal properties to many of them. But Doctor Ball taught him how to classify them in families, tracing, under all differences, the fundamental marks of the family and genus. And he opened to him the mystery of cross pollenization.

Riding with this bright boy, day after day, lonely and glad for a receptive young ear into which to pour his thoughts, Doctor Ball communicated to Peter that inspired common sense which in eighteenth century professional men so often supplied the practical guidance later supplied by experimental science. Yet for all his hero worship, there were times when Peter felt older, stronger, and far more knowing than this gentle man. For Ball had no judgment of people, at least not of people in Rogues' Harbor. "I got to look after him," thought Peter. "Else he'll set his foot plumb in a nest o' rattlesnakes."

One day a Negro boy stopped at the Cartwrights' to ask where Doctor Ball was. Peter had never seen the boy before and therefore eyed him with suspicion. But he directed him to Ball's place, and then immediately got his gun, mounted his horse, and followed him. He caught up with the boy just as he was asking the doctor to come and see a sick woman. He wouldn't tell where she was. He would guide the doctor. "I'm coming, too," said Peter.

The doctor smiled. "I love your company, Peter. But you needn't feel so responsible for me. I am of age, even if I don't look it."

"When a strange nigger takes you to a strange place around here, you don't go alone," said Peter. "Not if you know what's healthy."

"If you weren't such a lovable young rascal," observed Ball, "I'd say you were impertinent."

They started off, Peter riding ahead, behind the Negro boy. "Here," said Peter, reining up sharply, as they left the trail and plunged into the bushes. "This here is the way to the Mason place."

The Negro turned. "Mrs. Mason—she say she's powerful sick."

Peter said in an aside to the doctor, "It's John's woman. The Masons were all run out of here as bad characters some time back. But some of them must be here. It don't bode no good. I say we turn back."

Doctor Ball answered with something about the Hippocratic oath. For once Peter felt that the doctor's fine words lacked charm, since they so obviously lacked sense. But, seeing that in matters pertaining to his strange vocation or dedication, the gentle doctor was obdurate, there was nothing for Peter to do but ride along, following the Negro closely, with his gun in his hand.

The Negro led them into a large, untidy, but well furnished cabin, with a polished dresser laden with pewter, and a rose-colored satin bedspread on the bed. Propped up in bed, looking anything but ill, with her bright red cheeks and roving black eyes, was Marguerite Douglas, John's "wife." Her dark hair was curled and neatly arranged in clusters on her neck, her plump, bare arms were covered with jeweled bracelets, and her plump fingers with rings.

"Come here, Doctor," she said softly. He approached the side of the bed. She reached up her arms and drew his head down and whispered something to him.

"Peter, I will see Mrs. Mason alone," said the Doctor gravely. As Peter stubbornly stood his ground in the middle of the floor, the Doctor came over to him and whispered, "You must understand, Peter, the delicacy of a female shrinks from exposure to any eyes but those of a physician bound by the oath and the ethics of his profession."

"Female delicacy! Bah!" thought Peter. However, there was nothing to do but go outside. But neither modesty nor ethics prevented him from quietly climbing up and observing all that went on through the small, high, open window.

He saw the Doctor recoil. "Madam, you are not ill. No one could be in better health."

The woman leaned toward the doctor, her lace shift falling away from her large white breasts. Her voice was caressing and languorous. "I'm not ill. But Honey, I'm powerful lonesome. I'll go crazy if I have to stay here day after day, and never a real gentleman to talk to." Her bare arms went round him. "A real gentleman you are, not like these brutes, the kind a woman dreams of—"

The doctor flung her off, and said sharply, "Unhand me, Madam."

A shriek rent the air. Peter leaped from his perch outside and bounded into the center of the room, almost colliding with a large, handsome, blue-eyed young man whom he instantly recognized as Thomas Mason. Marguerite was shrieking, "Tom! Tom! Protect me! Oh! Oh!" She was sobbing wildly, "He attempted my honor."

"Honor!" The word glared through Peter in a fury of anger. He clenched his fist.

The doctor said angrily, "I did nothing of the sort. If this woman is your wife, take charge of her." Peter observed with relief that the doctor had his pistol in his hand, and, with unexpected presence of mind, was backing out.

Thomas Mason's hearty laugh rang out above Marguerite's sobs. "Shut up, Maggie," he roared, and still laughing, he came toward the doctor. He was obviously unarmed. "Put up your pistol, Sir. I'm not fighting over my brother's whore."

Peter was standing close to the doctor. "Better get out, quick," he whispered, "but watch where you step." He kept his eye on Thomas who, cordially, and with laughing apologies, came to the door and saw them on their horses, calling after them, "Good-bye. No hard feelings. We part friends."

Peter said to Ball, "You keep your eyes front, ready to fire. I'll watch out back." He turned and rode backwards on his horse till they were out in the open fields on the main trail. Then he said, "We all know the ways of the Masons. They don't murder unless they're drunk or right up against trouble. It was just as well to be careful, but I knew they wouldn't want to raise a hue and cry after them, just to suit that trollop."

Ball looked at him in amazement. "How do you know all these things, Peter?"

"All I know is what bears and wild cats know—*keep out of trouble.*"

"It's more than most civilized men know," answered Ball, thoughtfully.

But when he tried to explain how he had been taken unawares, while delicately concealing the real nature of the woman's approaches, Peter cast at him one of his shrewd, brilliant, challenging dark glances. "Doctor, you might as well save your breath when it comes to telling about Maggie Mason. I know her, same as I know a polecat."

At this the Doctor laughed. But he cautioned Peter to say nothing about it all. "It is almost impossible for a gentleman to explain these things. No gentleman wishes to cast aspersions on a woman, whoever she is. And there is always the suspicion that he has invited or at least put himself in the way of her advances."

Peter was silent. The doctor took the silence for a promise to say nothing. But when he reached home, Peter lost no time in telling his father and Dominie all about it, adding a circumstantial description of the cabin and the way to it. On the frontier there was no time for niceties of honor and reticence, where persons like the Masons were concerned.

CHAPTER 15   Logan Courthouse
                             October, 1796 to June, 1797

Peter's report led to the appointment of a committee to keep watch on those who went in and out of the Mason cabins. It worried the veterans that, with the widening of Boone's trace, and the opening of their tract to other settlers, there was renewed bravado among the outlaws. New families were putting up cabins and breaking land on all sides of Logan Courthouse, and kept up a round of social life, with house-raisings, shooting matches, cock fights, weddings, and dances. Most of them looked on the veteran settler as dull and countrified. But John was absorbed into their social affairs, and Jus handled legal business for some of them. Bill Stewart, very smart in a new coat of many colors, with real U. S. dimes for buttons, was a favorite with the new settlers. With this influx Cedar House was very gay. There was a new slave there, who wore a white coat and served guests from a large silver coffee pot.

One night when Dutch was posted to watch the Mason property, he saw something which made him boil into profanity in two languages. It was the sight of two of these newcomers stealthily emerging from behind the thick growth of cedar that screened the Mason cabins. One of these was a new settler named Jacob Leiper whom Dutch had done some favors for, as being a fellow Dutchman. The other was Moses Stegall, a frank and agreeable young man who had joined the militia, and whose pleasing young wife, Trixie, was a Methodist, and as such had been taken under Mary's and Barbara's wings.

Leiper and Stegall had taken up land northwest of Logan Courthouse, where Cherokee Bill had been living in lonely contentment, with his silver blonde French-Chickasaw wife, and two little white haired children with eyes like ripe blackberries. Knowing that the Indians, like the Negroes, were authorities on the doings of the Mystic Band, Jus made it a point to look out for Cherokee next court day. He found him leaning against the Big Tree, calling out advice to some boys practicing tomahawk throwing. "Howdy, Cherokee. Got new neighbors up your way?"

Cherokee spat a charge of tobacco juice like a gun going off. "I have." He was silent a moment. Then he added, darkly, "That man Stegall and his friend Leiper—they're two bad 'uns all right."

"How do you know?"

Cherokee rolled his glittering black eyes and said in a low, confidential tone, "What you all don't know and can't get at is known to every Injun and nigger around here."

"Why don't they come into court and spill it?"

Cherokee spat again. "Ask me another," he said, grimly.

"But what's the matter with Stegall and Leiper? They seemed all right."

"Firstly, they're in with the Harpes. Secondly, they have too much company, too secret, and too late at night. Thirdly, they had a row over there the other night, and murder was done. Gray Wolf—you know he's the Injun that has L'il Papoose, the white child—saw 'em carrying away the body about four in the morning. It was hanging limp over a horse."

"Will the Injuns testify to that effect?"

"Jus, you make me laugh. Why would an Injun testify against a white man in a white man's court? No, Sir. Gray Wolf and his folks are happy. They like being friends with the Methodys, and taking care of L'il Papoose. Why should they risk being burned and murdered out of where they are just to suit the white man's justice? Besides—this one that was killed—he was one of the gang. It's just one varmint the less."

Jus rolled this thought over in his mind, as if it were a quid of tobacco in his cheek. He wondered whether the inherited techniques of the law would ever square with the plain logic of life as lived in these wilds. But when he told Cherokee that Dutch had seen Leiper and Stegall coming out from the Mason's place, and added, "It's lucky we've got you for their neighbor to keep an eye on them," Cherokee's dark face grew darker. "I'd like to help, Jus," he answered, "but I can't do it from where I am now." He paused, and seemed to turn something over in his mind, and said finally, "The fact is I'm sellin' out—land and improvements."

Even under the shock of this announcement, the land-speculator latent in every frontier soul sprang to activity in Jus.

"Well now, it might be quite an idea to dispose of what you've got. You can make a tidy profit on improvements, and there's some mighty good land, dirt cheap, about thirty miles west of here. So many people are moving in that direction, they've cut it off, and beginning January 1, it's to have a court of its own, and be a new county. Young Ewing's land goes with the new county, and he's right pleased. All he can do in Logan is to see-saw in the legislature with Morton Maulding, but over there he'll have politics all to his self."

"I thought Mort was done with politics."

"He was, but he's changed his mind, or may be Sam Mason has changed it for him. Or may be he thinks that now they've got a real mansion for a statehouse in Frankfort they're gettin' so civilized that they'll be worthy of his company."

"Is it true that they're callin' the new county *Christian* County?"

"Yes—I reckon it's to distinguish 'em from the heathen in Logan."

"Well," said Cherokee, thoughtfully, "It all sounds pretty good. But I ain't interested. I'm goin' down to the Injun country—back to the Cherokees."

"Back to the Cherokees!" Jus was aghast. "Look here, Bill. You're as much a white man as any."

"You mean well by that," said Cherokee, "and I take it as meant.

But I want you to understand, Jus, that the more I see of white men, the more I like the Injuns. I wouldn't give all the white folks in my family for my Cherokee Granny. For pure good sense, and a good heart, and downright honesty, she had 'em all beat."

"But you throw away all the white advantages."

"The advantages of them that has the power—yes. But not advantages of living. Jus, you know as well as I do, that the Cherokees arn't wandering wigwam Indians. Name me one art of living in which the mass of Cherokees arn't more civilized than nine out of ten of the whites that come across the mountains. There's several men down in the Indian country, part white like me, that have got a life there nobody's got up here—big, comfortable houses like the Ranger's, blooded horses, fine clothes of broadcloth and silk they put on and off as they please. They send their children to school in Charleston and New Orleans. Look at Alexander McGillivray, Big Chief of the Creeks. Three years ago he died, and do you know how much he was worth?—$100,000.00."

Jus whistled. "$100,000.00—I didn't know there was so much money west of the Alleghanies."

"And do you know what his title was when he died? Major-general in the United States Army."

"And he was Injun, you say?"

"More Injun than I am—half and half. And then there are the Weatherfords. There's a lot of them. They have the choice of two worlds, and those that choose the Injun live just as high, wide, and handsome, and get a sight more out of life than those that choose the white."

Jus was silent. The blooded horses and big estates and children going to school in Charleston and New Orleans put a different face on Cherokee's proposal. Finally he said doubtfully, "Sounds too good to be true."

Cherokee went on earnestly. "There's other reasons I want to go down to the Injun country. Eloise, my wife, is half French, half Chickasaw, as you know. There ain't a woman around here that's had her bringing up except Mrs. Dromgole, or anything equal to it except Barbara, and she don't count because she's Yankee. But Eloise is a Catholic. And that means every low-down heathen around here thinks she's pison."

Jus winced at this. The prejudice against Papists was so deeply ingrained in him and his kind as to be beyond tolerance. Negroes, Indians, Dutch, and Portyghees—the mantle of Jeffersonian equalitarianism could be stretched to cover all these. But not Paptists. He said weakly, "Well, it isn't her fault."

"Her fault! My God, Jus, who talks of fault, except the fault of the ignorant, narrow-minded white savages of which this neighborhood is filled with far too many. But I think it only right I should take her back to where she can go openly to service, and when she sees a priest, he doesn't have to sneak in, in disguise, the way Father John does here now and then, to look after Eloise and Gray Wolf and two or three other Injuns that commit the crime of being Catholics."

Jus looked at him curiously. "I heard there was a Papist priest that got in here—I heard he was one of Alston's gang."

"God Almighty!" exploded Cherokee. "If it was any but you that said that, I'd shoot you where you stand. Father John's a saint. He's my friend. He's the friend of scores that ain't got any other friend on earth. His one and only connection with the Alston-Mason-Harpe outfit is that he knows more about them than is healthy."

Jus was aware of a deep distaste of and distrust for these Catholic connections of Cherokee's. But he was fair-minded enough to try to argue with himself, and reluctantly to admit that a Papist might just happen to be all right. But if Cherokee was going to have a priest coming to his house, he'd better go. They had enough doubtful characters to deal with now. Immediately he regretted the thought. A man didn't have many such friends as Cherokee—tried and true through the years.

Cherokee, observing but not able to interpret the cloud on Justurian's face, said more gently, "There's one more reason why I'm going, Jus. I think it's high time those of us that can should help the Injuns out with their land-troubles. Nobody could have played fairer than the Cherokees have. The United States, under the Articles of Confederation, made a treaty with them in 1785, recognizing that they were a nation, and leaving them to have their own law supreme in the bounds of their territory. They kept inside their land, but whites overran it. And finally to make legal what the whites had took, the Cherokees signed another treaty in 1791. The whites went against it again, before the ink was dry. The Cherokees were mad that time, and they attacked the whites. Well now, I don't need to tell you what happened then. Jack Sevier went on the warpath with his murdering white savages, and the Cherokees have hardly had spirit to raise their heads from that day to this. Now I think it just don't do them any good to let the whites push 'em and push 'em. They go so far a Christian couldn't go further turning the other cheek. I remember when an Indian killed a white man, Chief Hanging Maw of the Cherokees sent John Boggs and ten others to join the whites in hunting down that Indian. I'd like to see you or anybody else in Logan Courthouse do as much if a white man killed an Injun. No, Jus—it's no good. Somebody's got to help the Cherokees." He smiled wryly, with an appealing look at Jus for understanding. "And who's to do it if not ones like me? What else is my name Cherokee Bill for?"

Jus was touched. He held out his hand, and clasped Cherokee's warmly. "Good luck to you, Bill. And anything on earth I can do to help you, I will."

"And I'll help you," said Cherokee. "Out of sight is not out of mind. The Mystic Band's got its net flung wide. The day might come when I'll be more use to you where I am than here."

Again they shook hands and parted.

2

When Mary heard that Trixie Stegall's husband was suspected of being one of Mason's gang, she was aghast. "She doesn't know it—poor girl! She has no idea." Fury possessed her. If she could beat on the doors of Heaven! If she could wake God up and *make* Him pay attention to what was happening here. Sometimes she wondered how long she'd have the patience to be a Christian with God no more interested than He seemed to be in things that would tear any sinful, flesh-and-blood heart with pity. "It could happen to any girl," she thought. "It could happen to Polly." The thought of that made her blood run cold. "She'd meet a taking young man and she'd marry him, all innocent!"

She was despondent for days. Poor Trixie! In no time she'd be having a baby by that young man. And then—if he was caught red-handed—if he was hanged—What if it was Polly!

Her mind whirled in circles. She consulted Brenda and Barbara. At the next preaching, which Trixie attended with her husband, helping with the poor writhing mourners that fell convicted to the ground, whispering how she herself had been "convicted" when she was a vain, flirting, selfish girl, and had found God's love, and the patience to try to deserve a good husband, they watched Trixie narrowly, and were sure she did not know what Moses was. Innocent and clear-eyed, she kept turning to him with a wife's trust and pride, shining in her young eyes. They talked it over in whispers. Should they try to warn her? No. That was not to be thought of. "Never come between wife and husband— whatever the cause"—that was the unwritten law. And all the while Mary was thinking, over and over, "If it was Polly—" "There's no human power that can get us out of it," she told Jus. "It would take an angel of God."

But she did not recognize the angel of God when God sent him, in the gentlemanly person of the latest fugitive of justice to arrive in Rogues' Harbor. Jus rode home full of the news.

"Well, somebody else that has been run out of where he was has come to join us."

He looked around the circle picking seeds out of cotton in the firelight—plain, honest Eddie; Polly with the firelight gleaming on her tangled gold curls, and making her downy smooth pink cheeks, and full red lips, look ripe and lucious; Peter with sudden interest sparkling like a crackling flame in his bright dark face; round-eyed, snub-nosed, freckled little Sis; and Mary, cool and pre-occupied; and all of them white and downy under the flying fuzz of cotton. Sensing a story in their father's tone the children said, in one breath, "Who?" Mary quietly looked the same question.

"Name's James McGready. He's a Presbyterian parson."

"A parson! What ud anybody run a parson out for?" asked Mary.

"He got converted."

"Converted? But you said he was a parson." Mary looked at Jus doubtfully. Then she reflected that Presbyterians could be parsons without being converted. All they had to do was to get crammed full of book knowledge and have a high-toned air. Her interest quickened. "How come—*converted?*" A Presbyterian parson brought low with a real sense of sin would, to her mind, be something really to talk about!

"It all comes of these Methodys," said Jus. "They can't leave even parsons and Presbyterians alone. Here was Mr. McGready, young, educated, a fine upstanding well living man, preaching what everybody was ready to hear, because it was so nice and comfortable and easy to go to sleep to in church. And along comes a Methody woman, and she says, right out, so McGready can hear, that decent living aint enough to get to Heaven on. You got to be changed plumb through and come out new and different. McGready was surprised. But the more he thought about it, the more he began to hanker after whatever it was he'd missed. So he thought, and he prayed, and he read the Bible. And suddenly— it happened. He says like the light of day coming on after dark, like food when you've been hungry—don't ask me to explain it. I'm just telling what he says. These things are too much for the lowdown legal mind to understand."

"I know what it is," said Mary, with quiet fervor.

"Well, all excited with what had happened to him, McGready walks into his pulpit on Sunday and he starts right in to tell them all about it. He said the way they were was no good. The power of God had to enter into them and strike them down and make them over. He preached like all thunder—till those that were comfortable before were mighty uncomfortable, and those that were snoozing were thoroughly waked up, and there wasn't anybody's sin and shame that was private any more. And the upshot of it all was he made everybody in that place so mad that they rose in a body and tore the church down."

"No!" said Mary.

"Fact. They tore it timber from timber, and they'd torn him limb from limb—only he got away. When they couldn't catch him, they sent him a letter written in blood."

"Jus," said Mary, outraged, "You're just making up a story."

"I am not," said Jus, gravely. "What I tell you would stand up in any court. They sent him a letter written in blood."

"Was it real blood?" asked Peter, almost dancing with excitement.

"It was real blood all right—it was the red juice that flows in the body of a red-blooded animal. But if you mean was it human blood—that I can't say. They might a killed a calf."

"Jus, I don't think this is any laughing matter," said Mary severely. "If it's truth you're telling, tell it plain."

"It is truth," said Jus. She looked at him as if her eyes would pierce right through him. "I am telling it plain," he added, soberly. She had to believe him. He went on, "They sent him this letter which said that if he didn't want to fry in Hell that night for his heresy and his evil-speaking against good church members, he'd better make tracks out of there before the rim of the sun touched the mountains. Then he saw they were bent on a real lynching, and he got out and headed for Rogues' Harbor."

"What's he going to do here?" asked Peter.

"I understand that he's taking hold of that congregation on Red River that's been without a preacher since John Grammer gave it up. A lot of Presbyterians are pretty mad about it. They're appealing to Doctor Craighead in Nashville to send them a respectable preacher. But for every Presbyterian that won't listen to him, there's two heathen that'll go to any preaching he holds. He says he don't care what the Presbytery does about him. He don't serve the Presbytery, he says. He serves God. And God has sent him to do something about the bloody sinfulness of Logan County."

"It's high time," said Mary. "The Methodys can't get preachers enough to send us anybody. William Burke's a good man, but he's so busy saving the Cumberland from James Haw that we hardly ever see him. If Mr. McGready is really a man of God—"

"Well, I couldn't say as to that," drawled Jus. "God's ways are a little beyond me. But to my poor sinful sight he's something as good for this place as a man of God. He's a man with guts."

Mary ·pursed her lips and looked supreme disapproval of such language. But she decided to let it pass. "What's he look like?"

she asked.

"Tall, well made, a gentleman every inch of him—you know, polished, like Ball. He's got an awful homely face—he looks something like a possum. But it's a right interesting face at that —you can't take your eyes off it. And his voice is so rich and tuneful that it's good as singing to hear."

Mary looked at him in surprise. "Why Jus, I believe you're in earnest."

"Sure I'm in earnest. I ain't a judge of preachers. But I ain't usually fooled when it comes to men. He's all right. The only thing is I'm scared what will come of it. If they wrote him a letter in blood when he tried to save the civilized Presbyterians of North Carolina what will happen when he tries to saves the heathen of Logan County?"

3

McGready's preaching was the sensation of the winter. Folks that no respectable Presbyterian would want to be seen dead with flocked to the little cabin on Red River. When they couldn't get in, they stood outside, in the snow. One man, listening with his ear to a chink between the logs, so far forgot himself that he never noticed his feet were freezing, till they were "deader than so much ice." Many Presbyterians would have nothing to do with the usurper, and started to form a new congregation. But some stood by the preacher, including several of the Ewings.

Mary longed to hear the preacher, but the need of carrying the domestic chores while all the men went hunting kept her housebound. Hunting was one of the few useful acts that the male of the species performed willingly. Mary observed that they all had a way of glossing over the fact that they were providing much of the winter's food, bed-covering, floor-covering, and warm clothing by a peculiarly ceremonious and indirect approach to the job.

There had been a light snow, dissolving into a gray drizzle of rain. Jus came in, dressed in furs, and sat by the fire, thinking. The house, he said, was too warm. But he did not remove his coat. He watched Mary making up the bed, and said he was tired of feather beds. A man needed to harden himself now and then by sleeping on the bare ground. He went to the door and sniffed the autumn wind, and came back and cast a quick look at the rifle suspended from a joist made of a couple of buck's horns. "Peter," he said, "it's time you learned to hunt."

Afire with a rapture beyond even that which Doctor Ball could inspire, Peter was sent to summon Dean, Dominie, Dutch, and others to the hunting. Dominie thought he'd better not come. He was building a barn. His crops had been large. He had four cows, some pigs, and some sheep. He felt much less dependent than the other on hunting, and thought it a better use of his time to provide for his stock against the winter. "It ud take Dominie less trouble to go hunting wild animals than it does to keep 'em out of his stock," said Jus. But Dominie's fencing and building disgusted Peter with the unkempt looks of the Cartwright place. "Why can't we be all neat and tied up and fenced in against varmints the way he is?" he thought. But these discomforting reflections were dissipated by the race back with Jerry and the preparations for the hunt.

The next day was appointed for the march of the little cavalcade against the beasts. They started out with five horses, besides their mounts, laden with blankets, corn meal, oats for the horses, and salt. The whole business was a series of intrigues. First they wet their fingers and held them up to see which way the wind blew. Then they tried to figure out whether it was stormy enough for the deer to seek a sheltered place on the leeward of the hills, or whether they would stay on the high ground, as they did when it was rainy and quiet and the trees and vines were practically a roof against the wet.

From morning to night they were alert to gain the wind on the deer and approach without being detected. When one was killed, they skinned it and hung it out of reach of wolves and immediately resumed the chase. Peter loved it—all but the killing of the deer. He wished deer weren't such gentle, womanlike creatures, and didn't have such sad, soft eyes. A bear he didn't mind killing. He was smart-looking and even good-natured. But there was something about him that looked mean. And a bear had a short temper. He'd be friendly one minute, and the next minute he'd kill you. But the deer—Peter was seldom aware of possessing a conscience but he felt a distinct disturbance every time one of the creatures died. "It don't seem right," he said to Jerry. "They've never done us no harm. There ain't a mean thought in them."

At night they made a lean-to, with dried leaves for beds, and built a big fire, and, lying on the leaves, they talked over the day's adventures, discussing the spiked buck, the three-pronged buck, and the barren doe, with a kind of rude pedantry. Peter thought of the gangs of deer as if they were gangs of folks. Some deer became characters to him, like the Mauldings and the Dromgoles. The hunters' skill was staked against that of the old bucks the way the skill of his father and the others was staked against the inheritors of Alston.

While the men made the lean-tos, and built up the camp-fires, Peter and Jerry would escape on Diablo, and roam the snowy woods, going nowhere, seeking nothing—just escaping odd jobs, escaping the inferiority of boys to men, escaping talk that was over their heads, and admonitions directed at them. During one of these escapes, they saw a party of four hunters, and making a wide detour, and coming on them diagonally from the front, they saw that they were Micajah and Wiley Harpe, and Leiper and Stegall. Kicking Diablo with their four heels, they dashed back to camp and told their fathers. Jus commented to Dutch, "It's as Cherokee said, they're in with the Harpes as well as the Masons." But he cautioned the boys to say nothing about it to their mothers. "They're fond of Trixie Stegall. It'll only wear them out with worryin."

They hunted all week. But on Sunday they came home. Mary and Brenda had told them that, if they hunted on the Sabbath Day, they'd have bad luck all week, and they didn't want to take chances. Besides, the haul of venison and deerskins was enough to keep them busy for some time. Not a part of the animal would be wasted. The flesh would serve for food, the skin for clothes. Even the bones would be sucked dry of their marrow. They sent half a deer to Dominie, who reciprocated with the first smoked ham and first side of bacon ever seen in these parts, smoked in the smoke-house he had built for himself. Dominie, seeing how they used every part of the deer but the bone, worried about throwing out the bones. "Seems as if there should be something we could make of the bones," he said.

But, true to their promise, Peter and Jerry said nothing about seeing Trixie's Stegall's husband with the Harpes. They did not understand all the reasons for silence, but it made them feel important to have a secret in common with their fathers.

4

1797 came in, bringing much satisfaction with the accomplishments of the year just finished. The territory to the South had been made a state and named Tennessee, and Andrew Jackson had departed for Washington to serve as its one and only congressman. A mail route had been opened from Bardstown, Kentucky, to Nashville, and from Nashville to Natchez. The Nashville-Natchez route was ridden by John Swaney, who made the round trip of 1000 miles in three weeks, changing horses at the Chickasaw Agency. He carried, besides the mail, a bushel of corn for his horse, provisions and blankets for himself, a pistol, a tin trumpet to announce his approach, and a piece of flint and a steel. There were only two things that were wrong with Logan County's share in the progress of 1796. One was that almost nothing of the greatly increased flood of manufactured goods which, now that the Indian menace was ended, was coming down the Ohio to the store kept by Daniel Broadhead in Louisville and distributed through central Kentucky, was allowed by Mason's gang to get through to Logan Courthouse, except by way of Dromgole and Stewart. Either you traded with them or you lived at the old rough primitive level—ate venison, drank out of gourds, dressed in skins and tow-linen, had windows without glass, and almost no access to things made of iron and steel —and were scorned by newcomers in broadcloth and calico and even in silk. Andrew Jackson, with his usual resolution, had tried to open a trading post for the Cumberland in Nashville, ordering goods in Philadelphia, chartering wagons to carry it to Pittsburgh, buying and manning a boat there to bring it down the Ohio, and trying to bring it overland across Kentucky. But the expense and the danger had bankrupted him. He sold his store to Elijah Robertson for 33,000 acres of land, sold this for twenty-five cents an acre to James Stuart of Knoxville, taking in part payment a draft on Senator Blount who was in debt to Stuart, for $4,539.94, and set off for Washington with this draft in his pocket to see him through his political labors.

The other thing that was wrong with the achievements of 1796 was the election of John Adams as president. Many of the veterans had been loyal to Washington, remembering that he had been their general, even if he was a Federalist. But almost nobody was loyal to Adams. The constitution of Tennessee was so radical in its concern for the common man that the Federalists in the Senate objected to recognizing the new state. The Tennesseans said they'd come into the Union on their own terms, or they'd stop being a territory of the United States. Adams and his party found it so hard to handle these wild westerners that they finally gave in. Tennessee came into the Union without changing its constitution and with no intention of going along with Mr. Adams in anything. And there was Andrew Jackson in Washington ready to tell the White House so. Though Jus lived across the line in Kentucky, all his political sympathies were with Jackson, and so were those of the majority of respectable veterans in Logan County.

1797 represented to the little neighborhood just north of the line a hope of new progress because it was the third winter in which the dogwood had been drying for Dominie's gun-powder enterprise, and with the prospect of getting some good charcoal, activity was greatly accelerated. When at last they were ready to manufacture the powder, Dominie announced to his class meeting, "Since this gunpowder manufacture is undertaken in the interest of righteousness, to provide ourselves with a means of getting fabricated goods and foreign luxuries without trading in Dromgole's thieves' market, I proclaim that, in penance for your sins and discipline in good works, the class is to assemble every day except Sunday and work on the saltpeter."

The saltpeter proved so absorbing that even hunting suffered by comparison. Mary thought they were clean forgetting their growth in grace in their concern for gunpowder, hurrying through the religious exercises to go out to the caves. While granting that making gunpowder was a mite more useful than growing tobacco, distilling whisky, or raising racehorses, Mary thought this enterprise another example of the capacity of the male for useless activity. "What a world we might have," she said to Barbara, "if you could ever get menfolks to set their minds on food and comfort and keepin' us out of fights, sickness, and sin. But no—if it's anything useful—a man just don't want to do it."

After one of his mother's tart aspersions on his sex, Peter sometimes carried on a mental argument with her, justifying the human male, but her wet-blanketing by no means reduced his own ardent interest in the saltpeter.

By the beginning of 1797 Dominie had built up a manufacturing plant operating through three branches. The first was a small experiment station, under a log shelter, near his own cave. Here, with the incidental help of the more scientifically minded, he had kept up the experiments in crystallizing the saltpeter till he had got a really good product. The second was a series of larger furnaces at the two large caves on the Cartwright farm, whence the main supply of saltpeter must come. Here were stacks of drying dogwood, the three year old wood about ready to use, the larger supply of two year old wood, and the still larger of one-year old, for Dominie looked forward to an expansion of the enterprise year by year. The third branch was the shipyard on the Red River. Hither they brought a huge poplar tree about seven feet in diameter and fifty feet long, and with patient burning out of the center of it and gouging and chiseling, and using the drawknife, and rubbing and polishing, they were slowly shaping it into a canoe to carry their gunpowder to Fort Massac.

Finally the day came when a sufficient supply of nitrate had been accumulated, the yellow sulphur brought from Louisiana was at hand, and the freight vessel was nearly finished. All that was needed now was to produce the charcoal and to combine it with the sulphur and nitrate. This involved building quite a plant. For three years Dominie had been urging his helpers to bring him any scrap of iron they could lay hands on. Out of this, in the winter of 1797, he got a blacksmith who had lately settled there to make him two great iron disks which would run in a circular bed, and a huge iron kettle with vents in it through which gas could escape. Around the iron kettle a stone furnace was built, with space between the kettle and the outer wall for burning wood. The kettle was then set into this and filled with three year old dogwood and fired all around. The wood was burned for from five to seven hours. The charcoal was then cooled, ground on the circular revolving beds, and sifted.

When at last a sufficiently fine product had been obtained, there was the most ticklish job of all—that of combining it with the nitrate and the sulphur. Each ingredient had to be weighed separately, mixed by passing it through a linsy sieve, moistened with water, and carefully placed under the two heavy iron wheels, which were run for about four hours and kept wet all the time lest the stuff should catch fire. Several times this instrument had to be taken apart and reconstructed. The last time it was fitted with scrapers so that the pasty mass kept coming first under one wheel and then under the other.

Peter brought water untiringly, and stood by with his whole being revolving with the rollers. The first lot was spoiled by the nitrate crystallizing out. They tried again and yet again. At last the pasty mass was pressed. "The tighter it is pressed, the slower it will be to fire," said Dominie. Then the pressed cake was broken and grained and sifted. Many a time Jus thought they should give up. He had not the patience of a scientist. At this suggestion Peter always felt as if the world had collapsed, so completely had he identified himself with it all. But after every defeat Dominie began experimenting anew. Night after night, Peter sat up alone with him till dawn, tending the glowing fire, while the water outside their charmed circle froze solid and the stars overhead seemed to snap with cold.

By early summer the miracle was accomplished. They had actually produced a full cargo of gunpowder which every one who tried it pronounced "Number One." At this point Jus showed what the law could do. For it required detailed investigation and many hearings before a court of arbitration, before it could be determined just how much work each had put into the enterprise, and what share of the profits he was therefore entitled to. When this was finally settled, Jus procured some paper and drew up contracts which each one had to sign with his name or a cross, indicating just what his work had been worth and what he wanted by way of goods in exchange. To determine what goods they wanted, they had to find out what they could get. This meant sending a letter to Fort Massac by way of the new mail route to Bardstown, thence to Louisville, and thence by boat down the Ohio, and getting in return, by the same route, a list of marvels in the Post Exchange. Since the number of participants was so great, nobody could hope for much. The average return on three years of work was a quarter of a pound of coffee, a tin cup, a butcher knife, and a yard of ribbon or of calico.

They launched the craft at sunrise on a June morning. Dominie read aloud the story of Christ and the fishermen and compared their many failures and their final success to the failures and final success of the fishermen that night when they had Christ asleep with them in the boat. Then they all knelt in the grass amidst the wild strawberries and the daisies and prayed for God's blessing on their voyage. Dean recited a recitative of his own composing, "Jesus went in a fishing boat," and they all came in on the chorus, "Lord Jesus, bless our sailing." Then Dominie shouted the words of the Bible lesson, "Launch out into the deep," and with a running push, and a swishing of white spray in the first rays of the sun, the boat slid out into the bright waters brimming with the late spring rains. As they floated down stream, the voice of Dean at the helm, with the orchestration of the other voices behind it, drifted back, clear and melodious, "Dear Lord Jesus, bless our sailing."

Peter stood watching, his whole soul going out of him and moving downstream with the boat. He had begged to be taken along. He thought he had earned it with all the drawing of water and firing of furnaces he had done. But he was judged too young. "Never too young to work!" he thought angrily.

He heard a consoling voice and turned to see that Doctor Ball was watching him. "There will be other years. For lo, we, even we in Kentucky, have discovered navigation!"

CHAPTER 16

Logan Courthouse
July, 1797 to September, 1797

On a Sunday in July, 1797, Peter was escorting his mother to church to hear James McGready preach. The indefatigable Presbyterian was establishing a second congregation on Muddy River, about four miles north of the Cartwrights. In the absence of Dominie, and of most of the Methodist and Baptist men on the gunpowder voyage, the women were joining the new congregation in their half-finished chapel of logs.

Peter enjoyed the manly responsibility of squiring his mother. Slim, straight, ladylike, she was wearing the old "freedom dress" which was still in good condition. With Barbara's help she had rolled her hair up high, with two dark curls on her neck, and framed hair and face in a bonnet of braided straw in which she felt truly "stylish." Peter felt stylish, too. The night before, he had had a scrubbing, by the creek, with a soft soap made of lye from wood-ashes and bear grease, according to Barbara's recipe, and perfumed with a strong decoction of balsam. It smelt like strong medicine, but it felt clean, and it had been fun to suds his body and see the suds roll off. He had never had soap before. It made the skin feel smooth. With the unwonted cleanness, he put on such virtue and morality that he disdained to answer when John, who was honoring his parents with one of his rare visits, made fun of him. The shafts of one like John fell harmless against his new purity.

Peter had even scrubbed his hair with the soap. The suds got into his eyes and stung. Believing that he was blinded for life, he had hopped around and howled and wept a flood, till his mother told him to duck his head under the water. He did so, and came up to find his eyes still intact, the world new washed, and himself, as it were, new born. His mother had then trimmed his hair, which was a trying business, for she had no scissors and sawed it off, lock by lock, with the sharp knife they used for skinning deer. She cut only the ragged ends of the curls. The rest of it still hung to his shoulders, a bright, silken, black mop, girlishly out of keeping with his brown boyish face and stocky boyish body. His mother had given him a complete new suit of tow-linen dyed with butternut bark. It felt crisp but scratchy. On his bare feet he wore soft, new, well made moccasins, trimmed with rows of panther teeth. He was a picturesque figure with his straight back and bright black eyes. His mother's eyes rested on him with pride.

Clean and dressed, all his young body alive with the first excitement of adolescence, Peter felt that this day was not as other days. Something wonderful was happening to the world—here, now, this very day! Indeed something wonderful was happening and not in Peter's live young being alone. Almost unrecorded as it has been, except in dry religious annals, without emphasis or interpretation, it was a day to be mentioned in the same breath with the fourth of July. But all unconscious of the forces which would be set in motion that day, and which, in time to come, would make him their instrument, Peter, though riding on the heights, was not so uplifted that he could not also occupy himself with the usual routines of a frontier boy abroad on a landscape. He heard some turkeys in a cluster of oaks and gobble-gobbled at them. His mother rebuked him. Couldn't he ride like a Christian on the Sabbath morning? Peter accepted the rebuke but his eye kept roving over the landscape. It had changed a good deal since they had settled here four years ago. He saw patches of potatoes—must be almost ready to dig. He saw tobacco plants set out in neat rows, and wheat yellowing, and corn tasseled out. He saw a horse-lot newly fenced. Three cows stuck their mild heads through a wall of grass seven feet high and lowed at him. Must be from over Morris's way, he thought. He read the bright landscape as a modern boy might read the latest comic book.

They heard laughter and yells and passed a crowd of the young Mauldings and their friends gathered around a barrel of whisky. Must be going to have a barbecue. Several horses were tethered to trees. Several dogs ran around yelping. In the distance there

were shots. Must be a shooting match. Peter was not above enjoying such a party. He could out-shoot and out-wrestle every
local boy of his own age. But today he passed on, feeling sorry
for them because they did not know the blessed heights of the Sabbath but stayed down in the stew of whisky and fighting they lived
in all the week. So he rode along, as on a mountain-top, till they
came to the beautiful grove where the log cabin chapel stood, its
walls full height, but as yet without a roof. The log enclosure had
been neatly arranged, with plank benches in two rows, and a wide
aisle between and a high structure almost like a blockhouse tower,
but small and open at the top at the farther end of the aisle. Around
this structure was a log rail. The whole front of it was decorated
with flowers and the entire chapel smelt freshly of new logs, pine
boughs and wild roses. Peter stared. He had never seen a pulpit or any preaching place with a church atmosphere. He responded to it with a thrill of intense pleasure, like that produced
by a hymn well sung or by the open sky and the stars at night.

2

About twenty-six people had gathered—the men on plank benches
on one side of the aisle, the women with their children on the other.
As Peter entered with his mother, a man came over to them and
said, in a stage whisper, "I think Peter is big enough now to go with
the men."

Peter blushed a little as he went to sit with the men, but he felt
proud. At last he was really growing up! The limitless horizons
of manhood opened before him. He looked across the aisle, and
saw that his mother had dropped to her knees. He considered
whether, now that he was a man, he ought to kneel, but decided
against it. It was too much like pretending before God and all
these folks. Then he saw Barbara come in and kneel beside his
mother. And Eddie, the sly fox! He'd said he was staying home,
and here he was, at the door back there with a girl. Eddie came
up the aisle and took a seat two rows ahead of him. Out of the
corner of his eye Peter looked to see who the girl was. He knew

her. Her name was Bonny, and just last year he had a snowball fight with her, and she seemed no bigger than he was. How come she was all growed up so soon, looking so proper in a sunbonnet and long yellow linsy dress like a woman?

Then there was a stir and murmur and craning of necks, for quietly and mysteriously there appeared in that structure at the end of the aisle, a man with powdered hair, in a black robe, just his head and shoulders showing. "Looks like a judge," Peter reflected. The only person he had ever seen in a black robe with his hair powdered, was a judge at the court at Stanford.

The service proceeded with an ordered formality to which Peter was quite unaccustomed. But the lining out of the hymn struck a familiar note. Peter loved hymn singing. He listened attentively to the lines, repeating them in a whisper as the preacher spoke them aloud. Then as McGready began to sing in a rich, baritone voice, Peter picked up the tune, true and clear, his young voice gushing out as freshly as that of a thrush on a leafy bough.

When the preacher came to his sermon, Peter was on familiar ground. For McGready had entirely abandoned the Presbyterian style, close, logical, with wide ranging references to history and literature of which the backwoods had never heard. He followed the Methodist pattern, talking in an intimate, personal way about sins, not repressing but openly inviting ejaculations from his hearers—"Yes Lord!" "Amen!" There was no possibility of talking down to a backwoods assembly of any sort. The audience talked right along with the preacher, approving, disapproving, and answering back. And as the preacher unfolded to them the awful state of their souls, there were all the appropriate responses—groans, tears, and that paralyzing realization which was called being "struck down." Though Peter was not conscious of sin, he wished intensely to be part of this drama. He tried to see why these people groaned. He wondered what it would be like to be struck down, like that woman who had fallen on her face on the floor. Probably she was struck with one of those pains in her innards for something she had done, like Doctor Ball. He heard his mother softly sobbing, and wondered why, for in his eyes his mother was quite pure of sin. If the Doctor could only be "convicted" and fall down and give himself up to weeping and groaning, may be he'd be cured for ever of the hurt inside him. If you had trouble or a sin like that, it must be a mighty comfort to roll it off on the Lord. Peter searched his own mind and could find neither trouble nor sin. True he had blacked two or three eyes this past week, but their owners had deserved it. He had snatched Jerry's slingshot away and still had it, but that was only to pay for one Jerry had taken from him. He had kicked John's shins and put burs under his saddle, but that was in the interest of justice.

The preacher's words caught his wavering attention. "Breeze-hung over Hell." McGready was still Calvinist enough to talk like that. Peter pictured himself swaying in the breeze, hung by a spider's thread, with the fiery waters of Hell rolling and sloshing beneath him, flames darting from the waves, and a smell coming off them like Dominie's sulphur which, he had observed, smelt like rotten eggs. That was what Hell was—one great rotten egg that had been set on fire, yet never burned, just rolled and flamed, rolled and flamed, and never died down to ash. His experience in making gunpowder made him see just what Hell was. If you got into Hell, you burned and burned and kept on burning. Your eyes watered with the stench of those rotten, burning, sulphur waves. Your nostrils choked with the horrid smell. The heat singed your hair and burned off your eyelashes and made each of your eyelids swell up into one big blister.

Peter began to tremble. It sure would be an awful thing to be "breeze-hung" over Hell—to be so bad you could never hope for anything any more except to fall into those foul stinkin' flames. He searched his conscience. He thought of some maple sugar he had snitched. Was this enough to make him burn in Hell? He snapped out of the fear that was raising goose-flesh all over him. "Why in hell should I be afraid of Hell? I ain't done nothin' wicked!"

After this he felt quite aloof from the sermon, armored in righteousness. But he followed the preacher's words and the responses of the congregation with an interest both artistic and scientific. As the preacher thunderously rounded a paragraph, he would think with approval, "That there will bring the Amens." He looked speculatively at a neighbor known as Ol Si—because he was all of forty-two, and that, in this young man's land, was "ol." Si was bleary-eyed and trembling. He had been dead drunk the night before. "I shouldn't wonder if he'll be convicted," Peter reflected and made a bet with himself. "If Si ain't convicted today, I'll fill Eddie's chip-box for him tomorrow." He hated gathering chips. It was the worst punishment he could think of—punishment for bad judgment. Now he had a stake in the sermon and he watched Si anxiously. Sure enough, with a howl and a groan, Si rose and stumbled to the altar and fell on his face there.

"Glory Hallelujah!" shouted Mary. "Glory Hallelujah," shouted Peter. He had never shouted in church before, and he looked around, anxious what the effect might be. He sure didn't want anybody to haul him up as a mourner to the altar. But nobody had noticed. They were all shouting as Ol Si lay groaning and wallowing on the floor.

Then there was a shriek and up came Widow McFadden. "It's high time," thought Peter. Even on the innocent edge of twelve, Peter knew that since her husband died she'd had three men boarding with her. Two of them had had a fight over her, and there had been a "stabbin" with one of them lying half dead right now. Peter eyed her waist speculatively. It was said there was a baby coming. "She'd better get under the good Lord's protection right off," he reflected, "because she's sure goin' to need it." She was kneeling and sobbing audibly. Suddenly his mother and Barbara went up and knelt, one on each side of her. Even into Peter's unregenerate young heart there came a dim perception of what it meant for the two really blameless and most honored matrons of the neighborhood to throw a protecting sense of fellowship in sin and suffering around this frail sister. "Nobody's too low to come to the Lord," thought Peter soberly. "And when a body kneels there, you can't hold yourself above 'em, if you're a good Christian, like Mammy and Aunt Barbara. You're all equal, like brothers and sisters." Here he thought of himself and John. No, not like all brothers. He thought of Eddie and Polly and amended his thought, "Like all brothers and sisters ought to be."

At this minute Peter's roving eye fastened on a good Methodist brother named Jo, and a Methodist sister married to a man named

Maurice. Jo and this sister had been members of Dominie's class for years. But he and Jerry had been in the woods, after the last big Methodist preaching, where they had both sung and shouted and worked themselves up. They were close together and the boys had sneaked up and watched and listened till Peter was seized with compunction. "They're very wicked," he whispered to Jerry. "But I reckon it ain't none of our business." They had gone away rather sobered. Peter had been deeply and uncomfortably stirred with what he had seen. There was shame and curiosity and yet a strange pleasure and excitement in thinking about it. Now Peter watched Jo and the Methodist sister who was another man's wife, observing their reactions to the scene at the altar. They were both very quiet and very tense. Once Jo shot the sister a side-long shamed glance. She looked down. Then suddenly she knelt where she was, with her face in her hands.

As the preacher's mellow voice rolled out, James McGready aloft there against the sky ceased to be an active, enthusiastic, gentle-manly young man. He was a timeless being, neither young nor old, impersonal, not related to anything mundane, a materialization of God himself. To Methodists, used to crude young preachers who insisted on remaining just ordinary men, the traditional, Presby-terian styling of McGready's fiery evangelism was terriby, almost painfully impressive.

3

McGready had come to the climax of his sermon. He was paint-ing the sin not only of the individuals but of the whole community. "The one manufactury you have here, apart from the brave and religious efforts of the gunpowder makers, is a whisky still. We drink our corn instead of eating it. Our only business institution is a thieves' market. The most desperate men openly defy us, send their representative to the legislature and successfully block any attempts of the courts to bring them to justice. But even if they were brought to justice what would be accomplished? They would be punished but the harm would have been done. And nothing would be done to prevent other men just as black-hearted from roaming abroad until they, also, committed a crime that could be proved in court. My friends, everything we pride ourselves on as democrats—our elections, our courts—bad men are taking advantage of to confuse us. I tell you there is only one hope for us— *change the bad men.* Enlist now, with God, to fight to change every soul in Logan County. I ask you now to take the pledge the congregation on Red River has already taken. I will read it aloud to you first, and then I will read it a few words at a time and you will say it after me. Rise," he said in tones that rolled out from his high pulpit like thunder. He looked down where a dozen were lying or kneeling at the rail below him. "Mourners and sinners, rise, I say." They stumbled to their feet, lifting their tear-stained faces. He read, in round rolling tones, like a general before an army, "We bind ourselves to observe the third Saturday of each month for one year, as a day of fasting and prayer for the conversion of sinners in Logan County and throughout the world. We also engage to spend one half hour every Saturday evening, beginning at the setting of the sun, and one half hour every Sabbath morning, beginning with the rising of the sun, pleading with God to change every living soul in Logan County into the image of His righteousness."

Phrase by phrase he repeated this, solemnly, as if he knew that he was initiating something as important in man's social evolution as the Plymouth Compact. Phrase by phrase, not understanding, but nevertheless feeling the greatness of the moment, those twenty six humble, sinful, ignorant people repeated it after him, the hysteria of their recent mourning and weeping subsiding, and a kind of martial resolution coming into them as they spoke. Still standing, he asked them to sing the hymn, "Oh God, our help in ages past," and ended with a benediction. Many had now clustered around the altar. The preacher, shedding his black robe, came down among them, and began to labor with Si and the widow, with the help of Mary and Barbara and others used to the Methodist techniques of dealing with those "convicted." Peter liked to see his mother laboring with a weeping mourner. There was a tenderness in her at such times that he missed in her ordinary behavior, even to him. Her face shone. Her eyes were bright. "She tries to help where help is needed," Peter thought, with a deep pride in her.

4

Waiting for his mother, he stood at the church door and watched Jo mount his horse and ride away, avoiding all talk. He saw the Methodist sister ride off with another woman. Everybody knew her husband was a brute. Folks even said he beat her. Peter thought, "She's right pretty. If you was a woman and your husband was mean to you, and a Christian brother was kind—" The whole situation interested him very much.

Riding home, Peter tried to please his mother by seeming sober and subdued. Being a good actor he managed to look very much under the conviction of sin by keeping his mind on Jo and the erring sister. Mary felt her heart swell with hope, and prayed inwardly, "Bring him to Thee, O Lord. Make him to know Thee before he knows evil." But inwardly while he looked so sad, Peter was reliving the preaching with delight. For a boy who had no other theatre, here was drama—living drama—and as he studied it in retrospect, there was, in his mind, the faint beginnings of theatrical criticism. "The parson let go too soon when he was talking about the sin of fornication," he thought. "If he'd borne down a leetle harder, he'd a had Jo yelling bloody murder, and wouldn't that have been a sight? After all the prayin' and exhortin' he's done in his time!" But his next thought brought real concern into his mobile face. "And her—she'd just have picked up and run out in shame." He could not have told how he knew that young woman would not be one to go up before the altar—not before all those people. She'd run away and hide. She's drown herself or strangle herself, in her shame and misery. "A preacher ud have to be quick and follow her," he thought soberly. "She'd be that scared and that ashamed." On the whole he was relieved, for the sister's sake, that the parson had not gone further with the sin of fornication.

He thought of the pledge they all took so grandly to pray for the sinners of Logan County. It had been a great moment. His whole soul had stretched up to it. But he hadn't repeated the pledge. Peter wasn't ready to pray half an hour after sunset every Saturday—not with all the shooting matches and such fun that might be taking his time at that hour. Sunday morning at sunrise was different. He wouldn't mind slipping out somewhere to pray for sinners in the first pinky light of dawn, especially if Mammy would let him do it instead of bringing in wood and water for breakfast. As for fasting the third Saturday of every month, Peter might try that in March or April when there was seldom anything tasty to eat anyway, but not in late summer, not with Dominie's peaches and watermelon getting ripe.

Still it was a great thing to do. He even sensed a kind of cosmic importance in it. Twenty-six people weren't much—especially the kind of no account folks that were there today. But if Preacher McGready should keep it up, get twenty-six here and twenty-six there—get the whole county praying, get all Kentucky praying, get Tennessee praying—that would be something. All those prayers going up might be a mighty power. Could be even Bill Stewart and the Mauldings could feel it. Well, no—not them. Their hides were tough. Might as well try to pray the hair off an old buffalo hide. But Micajah Harpe—his mind went back to Preacher Lurton's service, and the way Micajah Harpe gave a great bellow, and went plunging out. "Micajah's one that just couldn't stand up to a good blast of prayin'," he reflected. "It 'ud mow him down."

Then, with an interest that was almost professional, he thought how, if he were a preacher, he would handle these powerful instruments of preaching and prayer. For in his experience preaching and prayers were not just words. People didn't sit quiet under them. They yelled. They fell on their faces. They broke down and, weeping, confessed to killing, to adultery, to every kind of sin. A man might look tough but aim at him the right preaching or prayer and it could bring him right down, surer than a bullet! He imagined himself converting Bill Stewart and Morton Maulding and bringing Burwell Jackson to his knees and peering down under the smooth front of Samuel Cauldwell. He even thought how he would bring Sam Morris to conviction. Converting them would be a heap more of a triumph than fighting them. He rode along, a conquering hero, while the myriads fell before him, and then, all meek and pure, streamed up to be baptized.

All the while there was something he could not define in this Sabbath Day. The world looked different. It was like nights when the cabin was hot and smelt of burnt fat and sweat and bodily staleness, and there was the hubbub of Eddie and John scuffling, and Polly teasing Sis, and Sis crying, and Mammy scolding. Then he'd step outdoors, and there would be the moon riding high, clear, and serene, and all the stars. And there would be a brooding quietness in the far-off line of the woods, and a quiet buzzing and delicate ringing sounds in the fields. Just as, on nights like that, he'd walk out of his body as out of a house, and roam, a spirit unshackled, abroad in the moonlit cosmos, so now he left the boy going on twelve, jogging along on Diablo beside his mother, and was lost somewhere in the illimitable sunshine. Little and fretful, sticky and prickly, small and tight is the earthly shell, and when they came in sight of their own cabin, Peter came to, and con· tracted himself, and crawled back into it with regret.

5

For there was his father, dragging in some wood, and Polly lolling half clothed at the door of the cabin, her feet bare, her rich, ripe young breasts showing carelessly through her half open shift. Peter cast a sidelong glance at her. The obvious changes in his pretty and amiable sister had stirred him. But there was an instinctive tenderness in Peter's feeling about women folks, and, as Polly ripened, he felt a great affection for her. Polly's undress was partly due to the fact that she had washed her hair, and it hung a mass of gleaming gold tendrils around her soft, peaches-and-cream face. Her mother said sharply, "Polly! Button up your shift. And when you sit where somebody might see you, don't you dare to sprawl carelesslike. Sit straight and quiet. It isn't for a big girl like you to be lolling around."

Polly pulled her shift together and straightened up but smiled unblushingly, "Hi, Peter. Are all your sins washed away?"

Peter disdained to reply, but in passing he pulled the long golden tangle of her curls. She yelled, "Mammy, make Peter stop pulling my hair!"

"I didn't," lied Peter. "I never thought of such a thing!" He looked the picture of outraged innocence. "Whose fault is it if Polly leaves her hair lying around so that it can't help but be caught in something?"

Little Sis was playing near the brook in a pool of mud. Completely plastered with mud, she was surveying with pride a row of neat mud hoecakes. Her blue eyes shone like bits of slate in her muddy face. Peter looked down on all this from a lofty height, as if he had discovered himself to be of another and more princely species.

But by night a whole crowd of the neighborhood boys had gathered outside and were calling on him to come out and fight. Peter had beaten all the eleven-year olds in the countryside. It was the law that he must now beat the twelve year olds. There was no help for it. He must go. In a few minutes the fierce joy of combat would take hold of him. But for the moment he was supremely bored. Why did people have to fight? Why? But he went.

Two hours later he came limping home, the side of his face torn, his ear bleeding. "Licked em," he said briefly, and painfully crawled up the ladder to bed in the loft.

Every bone ached. It was hot under the roof. Mosquitos settled on his raw face in swarms. Below he could hear his mother arguing and pleading with Polly. Polly was sobbing and crying. He sank into a sore, feverish state between waking and sleeping, in which the stricken face of the Methodist sister and Polly's tangled gold hair and half open shift were all intermingled in a profound sense of the utter sadness of things.

6

In the next few days Peter divined that John was the cause of the trouble about Polly. Polly was the only member of the family that John was fond of. Her amiability and soft, pretty looks had always been a cushion against the wounds to his self-esteem caused by his mother's tart strictures, his step-father's mild but ironic judgments, Eddie's solid virtues, and Peter's alternate defiance of him and triumph over him. He had felt proud when his new boon-companions began teasing him—wanting to know where he hid his pretty sister. But when Mrs. Dromgole invited Polly to come with John to a young people's party at her house, Mary put her foot down. There were too many at these parties of whom nobody knew any good and many suspected the worst.

For the first time in her young life Polly was sulky. Careless, self-indulgent, and not very bright, she had nevertheless been the sunshine of the family circle and humored as such by them all. Now her sudden eclipse made them all miserable. Peter, and even staid and sober Eddie, sympathized with her. It was against all frontier American standards to shut a girl away from young company. A girl must learn to take care of herself. Even Mary thought, betwixt worry and pride, "She's the kind the boys are bound to be after like bees after honey. I'll never hold her back from chances that look half-way decent."

That afternoon following Peter's fight with the twelve year olds, two well dressed young men and a smart looking girl on good horses, stopped at the rail fence. One of them, a good-looking young man with clear, delicately fair skin, large, clear, gray eyes and black hair tied in a queue, swept off his hat and addressed Mary in an educated accent. "Good afternoon, Mrs. Cartwright. My name is John May, and this is my sister." He indicated the girl, slim, straight-backed, with tip-tilted features and a rather haughty stare. "This is my friend, Henry Havard," he added, turning to the other young man who was squat and pudgy and had pursed-up lips. Then, barely pausing for an acknowledgement of the introductions, he asked, "Is Peter anywhere around?"

At that minute he spied Peter, pulling weeds in the truck patch, and called, "Hi, Peter."

Peter came running, his face bright and friendly under the dirt and sweat that streaked it. John May said, "We stopped to tell your Mammy what a hero you are. We saw the fight last night." He turned to Mary. "He took on six of them, one after another, and he pummeled them till they hollered for mercy."

Mary glowed with pride, but said severely, "You can all do better with your time than put on these fights."

Peter sparkled under the flattery. Yet, like a fly buzzing over maple syrup, something was bothering him. He'd brush it away, and then, amidst these sweet praises, back it would come. It might be the name. Henry Harvard—he'd heard it somewhere but he couldn't tell where. Again it might be something about the way John May's eyes were set in his head, and their clear light color.

Meanwhile Mary went into the cabin and said to Polly, "Honey, there's a girl out there with two of Peter's friends. Comb out your hair nice, and put on that new linsy dress—the one I dyed with peach leaves. The color sets off your hair real pretty. And I'll make some metheglin. You can carry it out with the cakes I made for the preacher out of the last of the wheat. He isn't coming. So you might as well have them."

Polly looked out sulkily. But when she saw a girl dressed in calico—which to her was luxury garb—and two well dressed young men, and all of them on fine horses, she suddenly bloomed. A few minutes later she came out, neat and smiling in the green dress, and the young people dismounted. Miss May was set gently down on the ground by her brother, and started with them toward the log seats under the chestnut tree, her brother helping her over rough places. It was obvious that she was lame. One leg appeared to be shortened or withered. Mary going about her work, in and out of the cabin door, listened complacently to their chatter. She was glad when Eddie strayed across the scene and was annexed to the party.

After they left, Polly, looking like a newly opened rose, overwhelmed her mother with sudden helpfulness. But Peter walked back to the brook with Eddie. For a few minutes they were both silent. Then Peter observed, "Don't it strike you there's something a little off-color about these Mays somewhere? Did you see how he took hold of her when she stumbled? She ain't his sister and she ain't lame."

Eddie looked startled by his young brother's perspicacity, but confessed that he had made the same observations.

"How come a smart, stuck-up piece like that wants to spoil her looks playing lame?" asked Peter. "And if she ain't his sister, why does he say she is?"

"As to making believe she's his sister, that's easy enough to see," responded Eddie. He hesitated, and added, "You're old enough now to know, Peter. They just want to live together and no questions asked."

Peter reddened a little under his dark brown tan. Finally he blurted out, "Then why don't they get a parson to splice them?"

Eddie was embarrassed. In his late teens he was a sober lad keeping company with Bonny, the demure Methodist lass Peter had seen him bring to McGready's church. Though nobody but Mary knew it yet, he was going to marry her. He said, "Well, may be she's not the kind to marry. Or may be one of them's married already."

"But I still don't see why she plays lame," insisted Peter. "It don't make sense to me."

It began to make sense when he passed Polly, sitting with his mother, stringing beans and lighting the place where she sat. "He says he knows the Gilberts," she was saying. "You know Mr. Gilbert is the largest landowner here. He has 1200 acres."

"Well," answered Mary, judicially, "Mrs. Gilbert is one there has never been a word said against, even if she is Philip Alston's daughter." She added, "Seems like a young man must be all right when he's so lovin' to a lame sister, and takes her around with him. There's not many who would do that."

For the first time in his life Peter questioned whether his mother's judgment was always infallible.

7

After that people were always riding up and wanting Polly to come to barbecues and dances. Mary objected to these social affairs and with good reason. There was always a bucket of raw whisky, around which the young people milled. There was square dancing with a twirling of the girls' skirts till their legs showed to their waists, and an unseemly "handling" of partners by their gallants. And like all American parents from that day to this, she found the mobility of the young appalling. "The place where they say they're goin' is never the one where they end up," she sighed to Barbara. For they all had good horses, and circled around continually in an area ten miles square.

Mary struggled. She prayed. She held out for days against Polly going to these parties, while Polly sulked and gloom hung over the cabin. Pressure to let his pretty step-daughter get into the social swim was brought on Jus on court days. Mrs. Dromgole herself appealed to him. "Let her go," he said to Mary. "It'll make a lady of her and help her to a good match. The way we're goin' out here, it won't be long till we're all out of log cabins and into brick mansions. I look to see Polly settin' her table with chinaware and havin' carpets on all her floors. But if she's goin' to be able to handle what's comin' to her, she's got to get around and learn nice ways."

Mary made a last stand. "There's one thing flat. She's not goin' with John. There's too much talk about the folks he's been seen with."

Even Jus agreed that John's escort might be unsuitable, though he deprecated the gossip about his stepson. "I'm only a backwoods lawyer, but one point of law I do know, and it's natural justice, too—a man's innocent till he's proved guilty."

Finally Mary decided to consult Barbara, in whose worldly wisdom she had as much faith as in her virtue. Barbara's bright, kind, plain face looked very serious as she listened. "I don't know that there is any place outside meetings of the regular members of the Baptist and the Methodist churches, and Mr. McGready's new Presbyterian churches," she said, "where a girl might not meet outlaws or runaways from justice."

"The churches don't interest the young uns," said Mary sadly. "They've got to have some real experience of life's pains and hazards before they're driven to the knees of God."

Barbara could think of nothing except to warn Polly and to try to keep her confidence, and to divert her as far as possible from the Dromgoles and the Mauldings to some of the newcomers who, though nobody knew much about them, had nothing against them. And why not let Eddie take Polly to these social affairs and stay around and make sure that she got home at a decent hour?

Mary sighed. "It's a good deal to ask of Eddie. He's sweet on Bonny, and it will take time off his courtin'. They'd neither of them want to go out in these fast crowds. They're two that has got good clean taste."

However, there seemed nothing to do but to ask Eddie. But this was too much even for his unselfishness and his real concern for his young sister. "I just can't do it—play nurse to a fool girl," he said to Peter. Finally Mary made a trip to Bonny's house and begged her to let Eddie help out for a while with Polly. "Just till she gets her bearings, and shows that she's steady and can take care of herself."

Bonny comforted Mary gravely. "She'll fall in love," she said, her quiet eyes shining into Mary's. "And if he's the right sort, it'll take the skittishness right out of her, and she'll be thinking of nothing except the day when he and she—" The color came up into her face. Bonny was a plain girl, but she was for a moment beautiful. Mary's heart went out to her. "Well, I have troubles enough with John and Polly," she said, "but there's one trouble I'm spared, and that's worry about Eddie. I thank God every day for him and," she added impulsively, "for you."

So Eddie was finally persuaded to escort Polly to some parties —an arrangement agreeable neither to him nor to her. Even Mary was forced to see that it was an injustice to Polly to have her tagged by her brother as if she "couldn't take care of herself." "Take care of herself"—there was a kind of magic in that phrase on the frontier. A girl's pride and her social standing were involved in it, and so were the good sense and social aplomb of her family.

They had no idea how new all this was in the social history of the world. They did not know that their rude sense of the inherent rights of the individual was striking at the last stronghold of authority in the control of the elders over the budding sex-life of the future mothers of the race. In shifting the responsibility for a girl's safety, in a rough and dangerous society, from a duenna to herself and to the good sense and democratically arrived at co-operation of her brothers and young companions, they were setting a pattern of social life which every American takes for granted but which in all its implications, and in its own set of checks and balances, is unique in the world even today. They were making democracy live where it has to live, if it is to be really vital, in the hearts and social assumptions of the future parents of the race. In these family "ructions" over headstrong teen-agers, absurd as they would have seemed in any established society anywhere in the world, the American democracy was being forged in the white heat of family passions all over the frontier.

And so it happened that Eddie went back to happy and unchaperoned evenings with Bonny in the summer dark and Polly was carried off—Heaven only knew where—by whooping crowds of young people and delivered on her doorstep again late at night. And nothing was left of family control except a lighted candle and Mary grimly "waiting up" for her, determined not to sleep till she saw her safely into her own bed. But no finishing school could have achieved what those few weeks of unhampered social activity achieved in turning a beautiful but unformed child of the frontier into a dazzling young woman. Polly grew neat and trim. She took on many ladylike graces. The whole family was happy in the change. Eddie and Peter basked in the small comforts she introduced into family living. The table was tastefully set. Some green linsy curtains were hung at the windows. The whole household was spruced up now that there was a "young lady" in the family. Even Mary began to relax a little. "Well, I guess it's against nature to hold a girl in," she said grudgingly. "Give her her head, and she'll learn to pick her way."

CHAPTER 17

"Well, McGready's done it. He's prayed the Harpes right out of Logan County," said Jus, returning from court full of his news. "I saw Ol Man Roberts today, and he said being prayed at was more'n Micajah could stand. Come sunset Saturday, and he knew all those prayers were going up, and he'd start drinkin'. And by the time the Sunday sun-up prayers were tapering off, he'd be stark, ravin' crazy. So Wiley and the women have taken him away. So long as there's this pison of prayer in the air here, he just don't care to breathe it."

Mary smiled grimly. "It's more'n I could have hoped for—that prayer of mine would have part in getting Micajah out, but who do you mean—women? Susan and the young un, Betsy?"

"Yes, Micajah's married them both. Roberts tells me that anybody who says they ain't both his wives, proper and married, Micajah will shoot him."

"But a man can't have two wives," protested Mary, scandalized.

"Jacob and Isaac did," teased Jus, "Why not Micajah?"

Mary was silent. She never could understand why God let Old Testament men have extra wives when other men couldn't. Jus drawled on, a flinty smile playing over his round, prematurely seamed brown face, and crinkling the corners of his eyes, "What McGready's prayin' is doing to some of our top citizens here is a scandal. I hear Sam Mason headed this way last month but when he got near here, the blast of all that prayin' struck him full in the face and he turned tail and ran." He winked at Peter, who was following this with the usual flash and sparkle of his listening.

With his quid of tobacco bulging in his cheek, Jus looked at Mary teasingly.

She sniffed, "That's one too much for me to swallow. It'll take more than religion to stop Sam Mason."

"Tain't religion," replied Jus. "It's superstition. They think you-all are hexing them. You and Barbara and Brenda and all are like so many witches, brewing spells against them."

McGready had added a congregation on Gaspar River to his praying bands on Muddy River and Red River. The Methodist class had taken the pledge, as had the two groups of Baptists on Muddy River. All through the Cumberland the new groups of orthodox Asbury Methodists, whom William Burke had built up in opposition to Haw's followers, were praying. Withal, by August 1797, there were probably not more than eighty-six faithful and convinced pray-ers. But rumor magnified them into thousands. That sense of guilt which even civilized man cannot quite live down, was an active misery in most frontier folk, forced to live without religion, education, or social outlets commensurate with the energy of their inner lives. Now the knowledge that somewhere, somebody was praying for sinners was like a wind whipping this latent sense of guilt into raging flame. Tortured with remorse, the people came in droves to McGready's preachings. No cabin could hold the crowds.

Doctor Ball had already noted that most of the paralysis, heart-attacks, sinking spells, fainting spells, chronic nausea, loss of appetite and the like which he was called to cure, had no physical origin. They were forms of hysteria. Now under the impact of the prayers, the hysteria increased. A man hanged himself, and a woman drowned her baby, out of terror of the prayers. More than once, when he was called on to deal with patients in violent foaming fits because of the prayers, he sent for McGready. "You got them into this," he would say. "Now get them out."

These things were a scandal to the more respectable Presbyterians, especially to those who were trying to live in peace with Dromgole and Co. They appealed to Doctor Craighead in Nashville to have McGready read out of the church. Doctor Craighead said he would look into it, but nothing effective was done. Except for the Scribes and the Pharisees, McGready was looked on as one sent from God. Early one morning Mary saw the tall, gentlemanly figure of God's scourge of sinners ride up to the Cartwright fence. When, after a pre-occupied, "Good morning," McGready asked, "Is Peter here. May I see him?" Mary gasped, "I hope Peter ain't done anything wicked." She was relieved when he smiled, and replied, "Oh no. I just want him to do something for me."

Greatly flattered, she called Peter out of the cornpatch, where he was cutting "roasting ears." When Peter came running, he found the preacher sitting with Mary on the bench under the chestnut tree. McGready lost no time in coming to the point, "Doctor Ball tells me you know Wiley Harpe by sight."

Peter answered, "Yes. Jerry and I can pick him out, no matter how he's rigged out. There's a squint to his eye—it ain't ugly, but it's sort of special—that beard nor butternut juice just can't hide."

"Have you seen him around here lately?"

"Well, no. Not lately. But I saw him some days after Big Harpe and the Roberts girls lit out." He paused, and added with a curious look of self-consciousness, "Wiley's got a girl of his own."

The preacher almost jumped out of his seat. "How do you know that?"

"They had a lean-to, up inside of Bear Wallow. Jerry and I saw them. They were cooking trout over a fire—and he was laughin' and playin' with her. We didn't know Wiley could look so pleasant."

"Why, Peter," cried Mary. "Why didn't you tell us? We thought Wiley had gone with Micajah."

Peter answered, "Oh, I would have told—when I got around to it." He couldn't say that he'd been silent out of bashfulness about what he'd seen between Wiley and the girl, mixed with a feeling that even Wiley had a right to his honeymoon. Now, under his mother's eye, he reddened. He was relieved by McGready asking, tensely, "The girl—what did she look like?"

"She was skinny, and white as a daisy—except for her lips—they was real red." He brushed the picture of the red lips out of his mind. "And her hair was kinda like Sis's—you know a whitey brown." He paused, "And—well—she looked like she'd been brung up a lot better than Susan or Betsy Roberts."

"That's the girl. That's Sally," exclaimed McGready. Then he told Mary, in a rush of words, that his friend Parson Rice, the Presbyterian preacher at Knoxville, had lost a daughter. They'd beaten up the woods for her. They'd given her up as dead. They'd held a burial service for her. But the other day a Negro, who had got religion, confessed that he'd helped Wiley Harpe to run off with Sally Rice. "And now you've seen her! I hardly know how to tell her father." He looked at Mary. "One would almost rather know a daughter for dead, than tied up with the Harpes."

"While there's life, there's hope," said Mary, "and the Lord can yet save her." Her quick sympathies embraced the girl and set her in that place in her mind over which her thoughts hovered with mothering wings, alongside Polly and Trixie Stegall. "What kind of girl was she?" she asked.

"Sweet, gentle, refined," said McGready. "You couldn't find a lovelier young girl."

"Whatever makes a girl like that take up with a Harpe?"

McGready replied soberly, "The Harpes have something which, when they want to use it, sets them above the run of frontier gallants. It's temperament—it's feeling. And it's been helped by the Presbyterian preachers who've always tried to do something for these boys, and made them at home under their own roofs. Wiley's worked on her pity. She thinks he's been wronged, that there's no truth in what is said against him. Perhaps she hopes to reform him."

As often happened with Mary, intense sympathy turned to fury. "How long are we to stand it? O Lord, how long! Letting the wolves in to prey on our lambs, like this Sally, like Trixie Stegall, like—" She stopped short. She had almost said, "like my Polly."

"We must renew our prayers," said McGready, "and enlist others to pray—hundreds, thousands, tens of thousands." Mary was silent. She wanted a weapon swifter, sharper, more deadly than prayer.

McGready had risen to go, and had turned to Peter. "If ever you see Wiley, ride at once and tell me. It's a small hope we have to hold out, but it will comfort my friend to know that we are watching."

After he rode away, Mary had a talk with Polly, pointing out the fate awaiting a girl that got tangled with such men. Peter, lounging within ear-shot, was struck by something in Polly's face, and when she escaped from her mother's lecture, he followed. "You wouldn't happen to know Sally Rice yourself," he ventured.

"How should I know her?" Polly snapped.

"Oh could be you'd met her at some barbecue. Wiley might be a friend of John's."

"What if he is? A girl's got a right to her own life. I'm telling no tales."

Peter didn't press the matter further. In his world folks were expected to hold their tongues, but that needn't prevent other folks from finding out what they could. He'd see Jerry, and they'd track the girl down. And all the while he was remembering Sally's delicate pretty face, and her red lips, as they yearned up to her man's, while Wiley's hand went inside her shift, and slid along her white body.

2

The Methodist meetings had outgrown the Cartwright cabin. They had built a log church, Ebenezer, four miles away, in the woods, and thither the praying Christians of all the churches were riding for Thomas Wilkerson's preaching, on the circuit rider's September visit. "You'll come with us, won't you, Doctor?" asked Mary late that afternoon, when Ball stopped by to ask if Peter could accompany him on a trip tomorrow.

"No, thank you," answered the doctor. "I don't want to be put in the way of confessing my sins. What has happened is between me and God."

But he lingered, his eye turned wistfully toward the Bible Mary had laid out where she'd be sure to remember to take it to the meeting. Finally he picked it up. "The hardest thing about life here is having nothing to read," he commented. He seated himself and began turning the pages with a practiced hand. Finally he laid it down, and said, in a low sighing voice, "Wilkerson's preaching, isn't he? Perhaps I'll look in a minute, at the end."

That night, in the middle of the preacher's prayer Peter felt something like an electric shock, and turned and saw that Doctor Ball had come in, and was sitting on a bench at the back, his hand shading his eyes. Peter stealthily slipped out of his place, crept back and knelt by the doctor. The Doctor rested his hand on his head with a grateful caress. But when the preacher started to talk, he seemed to be keeping his eye on Peter and talking straight at him there where he sat with the Doctor. This made Peter survey uneasily his small misdoings of the past month. He was startled out of a long, self-justifying meditation by hearing Wilkerson's climax roaring through the room. "Though your sins be scarlet, He will forgive—yea, even though they be scarlet as Beverley Allen's. Rise, Beverly Allen, and confess yours sins," and then the Doctor's voice, at his side, cool, clear, and incisive. "It's no use, Wilkerson. I know all the tricks of that sort of thing." The doctor had risen and was making his way out of the door.

The room was in an uproar. Oblivious of mourners, Wilkerson leaped down and pushed through the congregation after Ball. Peter tried to follow, extricating himself from the crowds, now milling around inside. William Morris, the Baptist, was shouting for order, and McGready had taken Wilkerson's place in the pulpit. When Peter was at last out in the open, he saw, by the light of the half moon overhead, that the doctor and the preacher were together under a tree, engaged in earnest argument. As he was creeping closer, Mary twitched his sleeve. "Come on, Peter. It's none of our business. Barbara and all of us—we're going home."

They talked about it along the moonlit trail home, comparing notes on what Wilkerson had said, and what the doctor had answered. Barbara stopped with Mary and Peter at the Cartwright cabin, to tell Jus all about it. Jus listened thoughtfully, trying to fit it into something he had given much thought to. For, seeing

Peter's devotion to the Doctor, it had seemed to him that here was the means of giving his boy an education in the dead languages and history of dead people. "Not that it matters in itself," Jus had reflected. "But it's something the high and mighty have in common, like playing the same game of cards. And if you don't have it, you arn't counted one of them when it comes to dishing out favors." Jus would be glad to get his boy a classical education, just as he'd want to get him a good suit of broadcloth and a good horse when the time came. "If I only knew more about Ball," he had often reflected, "I'd send Peter to live with him and take on his fancy ways." But he had not felt that he could put his son under the care of a confessed fugitive from justice, living here under a false name. Hearing what Wilkerson had said, he was more puzzled than ever. "So now we know his real name's Beverley Allen," he commented, and added sarcastically, "That's a big help!"

There was a knock and Beverley Allen himself stood in the door. He broke the embarrassed silence at once, looking at Mary. "I can't sleep tonight without telling you the truth," he said. "You've been so good to me. You've trusted Peter to me."

Jus rose and went to him and spoke with unwonted gentleness. "Every man's a right to be heard." He added, looking toward Mary, who nodded earnestly, "Sit down, Doctor. You're among friends."

Beverley Allen's story was long. But the outline of it was simple. He was one of Asbury's early associates in forming the Methodist Church. As a student of medicine, he had been converted by Asbury, and entered the ministry. He was one of the eighty-seven travelling preachers who, on December 24, 1784, had gathered in Baltimore to form the Methodist Episcopal Church of America, and had been ordained an elder at that time. Sent as presiding elder to Edisto, South Carolina, he had found it hard to comply with the social attitudes expected of a Methodist preacher because he had more a gentleman's background than most of them. He drank an occasional glass of wine with plantation gentlemen, and he married a lovely wife who owned some slaves. Opposed as he was to slavery, he could see no way, in this place, of doing without them.

Sworn to oppose liquor and slavery, his brethren in the ministry censured him. Angrily he left the ministry, set up as a plantation owner and merchant, and in the years following the American Revolution, when almost everybody ran into debt, he became financially embarrassed. Thereupon he started an agitation against imprisonment for debt, advising that it be resisted, if necessary by force. When his friend Major Forsyth, the law enforcement officer, told him quietly that he himself would not be molested, and would even be helped to pay his debts, if he would stop this agitation, he refused to buy immunity at the expense of others. "Then," said Major Forsyth, "I have no choice. I must arrest you." "You know what I advise," replied Allen, steadily. "If you touch me I shall shoot." When a few days later, Major Forsyth came with a force to arrest him, Allen shot and killed the major and escaped, not without some connivance from some of the arresting force who disapproved, as he did, of imprisonment for debt.

When Allen had finished his story, there was silence for a few minutes. Then Jus said, "There's not one of us out here who wouldn't have shot in your place. Imprisonment for debt is one law we won't take."

"It is of all laws the most stupid," commented Barbara. "For it denies a man his one honorable means of getting out of debt, which is to work his way out."

"Take away a man's chance to earn, and you take his life," said Jus. "Life for a life. It's a natural law, if it ain't gospel." He looked at Barbara. Barbara nodded agreement.

Peter could feel a burden large as the world rolling off the Doctor's soul. He rose, and held out his hand, "My friends, I thank you unutterably."

Mary said, "Doctor, you are not far from the Kingdom. If only you could come back to God, humbly."

Before her intense starry gaze, he dropped his eyes. "There's a Bible verse for that, Mary. 'It must needs be that offenses come, but woe unto him through whom they come.' There's still blood on my hands. I haven't the effrontery to face God until I have atoned."

To Jus, hardened revolutionary in a barbarous world, this made no sense, and yet it aroused respect. But in Mary's eyes and Peter's, Allen saw a gleam of understanding. Peter, seeing the Doctor was leaving, ran out and brought his horse to the door. The Doctor mounted it silently, laid his hand for a moment on Peter's head, and rode away. Peter stood for a moment under the stars. He felt deeply moved, and somehow uplifted. But what he was really thinking he could not have told.

3

Mindful of McGready's wish that Peter should keep a sharp eye out for Wiley Harpe, Mary asked Jus to take the boy along when he went up northwest of Logan Courthouse to settle some affairs for Cherokee, who had gone south to the Indian country. Jus was delighted. He loved to have the boy with him, but usually Mary objected for fear he might thereby be exposed to liquor. He was the more pleased when Barbara came over with some peach jam to give Trixie Stegall, for he had long wanted to look into the Stegall cabin to see if it was furnished with such articles as were not honestly come by. So he and Peter started off on the fifteen mile ride on a fresh bright September morning.

Trixie Stegall received them eagerly. She was a girl of the new West, without Polly's glamor or Sally Rice's ladylikeness—plain, frank, comradely. She said she was lonesome so far up here away from folks. She'd wanted Mose to settle where there were more neighbors, but he wouldn't. "Where is Mose?" asked Jus, in an off-hand manner. "He's gone to Louisville," she answered.

Peter knew from his father's look that he was stowing this fact away in his mind, but he couldn't imagine why. As for himself, he was basking, as always, in the comfort some women folk could make. The cabin was clean and well furnished, with a carpet on the floor. One wall was completely covered with swords, pistols, and guns of all makes and designs. "Mose collects them," observed Trixie, "But I don't like them. All they mean to me is murder."

Under pretext of admiring the weapons, Jus took each one down and examined it, pointing out details of workmanship to Peter. Trixie, happy that they would stay for a meal, was setting the table with silver cutlery. 'It's not every bride that can bring her family silver out here," observed Jus.

Trixie laughed. "My family were plain folks who ate with knives and fingers. Mose got me this for a present." She shrugged. "They're no good to me here, where I don't set a chair for a guest from one year's end to the next."

When they started back to Logan Courthouse, with Trixie's venison stew, corn pone, hot tea, and the peach jam under their belts, Peter observed that his father was satisfied with more than food. But never having heard the rumors about Stegall, Peter couldn't figure out why.

At Logan Courthouse a big horse race was just ending, with victory for a horse ridden by Red Maulding. Among the spectators they found Dutch and Jerry. Knowing their wives' objections to the way liquor flowed after a race, the fathers sent the boys home, while they stayed behind to enjoy a drink on the Mauldings, warning them as always to stick together, look sharp, and take no risks. So Jerry mounted behind Peter on Diablo, and they were off, glad to have the wide landscape and ripe afternoon at their disposal.

Thinking what could be the most interesting thing to do, in the blessed liberty of being out from under their elders' eyes, with no errand, and no time set for return, the boys decided to visit the Indian camp and see how L'il Papoose was getting along.

When they rode up, whooping, L'il Papoose heard them and came running out with Gray Wolf and his family and half a dozen Indian youngsters after her. She ran straight to Peter, as he leaped from the horse, and wanted him to pick her up and set her on his shoulder, which he did. Something about the little girl with her soft light hair, warm, creamy skin, and adoring blue eyes always touched Peter profoundly. He didn't know why. Barbara's little girl, Dolly, was just as sweet, and Archie, the little brown boy who now ruled Dean's cabin, was more fun than a bear cub. But L'il Papoose was something special. Though he had now no memory of Sylvia, his playmate of long ago, there was an empty nest in his heart into which this little thing always snuggled. As happened at every visit, Peter, after parading L'il Papoose around on his shoulder, had to set her on her saddle, and ride madly off with her, prodding Diablo to make him leap and snort, till the horse foamed at the mouth, and L'il Papoose was dizzy with delight. When they finally stopped, and he lifted her down, to release her into the arms of her Indian Mammy, he had a sense of loss, as if something of himself were being torn away, and clutched her in a final hug, and kissed her on her soft lips.

Then he turned to Gray Wolf who had been showing Jerry the Indians' "improvements," and wanted Peter to admire them, too. For since the Indians had been tied up with the Methodists they had got the white man's itch for progress. Gray Wolf had moved out of his tent into a neat log cabin. All around the ground was cleared and turned to gardens, with corn and beans in straight rows, and two hills of watermelon from Dominie's seeds. And it wasn't hard to talk to the Indians now, because going to preachings had improved their English. As he walked around with Gray Wolf, Peter asked, "Do you know Wiley Harpe?"

Gray Wolf looked at him sharply, and barely grunted, "Yes."

"Did you know he was layin' up there in Bear Wallow with a girl?"

The Indian grunted more distinctly, "Yes."

Peter came out with it. "Do you know where he's gone?"

"To Louisville," said Gray Wolf distinctly.

It flashed across Peter's mind that Stegall had been going to Louisville which, as he had often heard, was the distribution point for goods coming down the Ohio on rafts. "What are they up to in Louisville?" he asked.

Gray Wolf didn't know. Nor would he tell from whom he had heard this. Respectable Indians, like respectable Negroes, would have no more to do with the Mystic Band than respectable whites. But this didn't mean that they'd betray to the white man any member of their race who did.

Elated with even this meagre news, Peter and Jerry said good-bye to the Indians and galloped to McGready's house. The preacher's re-action was all that Peter's sense of drama demanded—eager and grateful. The only trouble was that he asked the boys a dozen questions about it all which they could not answer. And this was deflating.

The katydids were arguing as Peter, having left Jerry at his cabin, rode home in the clear crispy dark. It had been an exciting day, but he could not know how every detail of it would come back, with a sharp, horrific meaning on a day that was waiting around the bend of the future.

4

Dominie and the gunpowder crew were overdue. The golden October days grew ever darker with worry. The log canoe, paddling back against the current laden with treasures from Fort Massac, would be fair game.

But one morning there was a long-drawn note on a horn beyond the Cartwright house. When Peter and the whole family came running, there was a youngster on horseback, tooting on a shiny new horn. "It's from Fort Massac," he said, flashing his instrument in the morning sun. "They're back. They've beached over on the Cumberland. They want horses." And with that he was off. Peter tore after him on Diablo, for the boy had neglected to tell them where on the Cumberland the canoe was beached. By the time Peter caught up with the lad, he was entangled in a whole troop of horses assembled to bring the wanderers and their booty home. What a ride that was through the summer morning! What a welcome! Back they came to Ebenezer, where the women had barbecue fires going, and hampers of food. The packs were opened and the goods distributed. Ribbons flashed—blue, yellow, and red. There were yards of calico and muslin, plain and sprigged, fine white table salt, cane sugar, tea, tin sauce pans, tin cups, nutmegs, nutmeg graters, crockery, butcher knives. Who cared for Dromgole's old store now? And then they ate and kept on eating till the day died, and the hunter's moon came up, and the katydids started their arguments again.

That evening there was quite a different meeting at Cartwright's house. Present were Jus, Dutch, three Baptists, four Methodists, Dominie, Dr. Allen, McGready, Dean, and some of the more responsible boys, including Eddie, Peter, and Jerry. An atmosphere solemn and ominous hung over them. At the other end of the room, not out of ear-shot, Brenda, Barbara, Mary, and Jassamine were shelling dried beans under a candle which gave all the light there was in the room.

For the long stay up on the Ohio hadn't been for trading alone. As a former member, with some of the Masons, of Clark's expedition, Dominie had gone prepared to ferret out the Mason piracy on the rivers. To this end, he had had several secret conferences with the spies at the fort.

"What did you find out that we don't know?" asked Jus.

"Mainly that Peter Alston is now running the Band with fewer fancy flourishes than his father, but a more deadly skill."

"How do you know that?"

"There was a convention of the Band at Louisville, this summer."

"Louisville!" Peter pricked up his ears. So that's why they were going to Louisville. Stegall was going, and Harpe! A lot of things about Stegall began to take shape in his mind.

"Louisville!" exclaimed McGready, and asked if Dominie had recognized Wiley Harpe there or seen a young woman with him.

"No," replied Dominie. "But he was no doubt well disguised. It was fantastic. The village of Louisville was suddenly full of strangers—many coming down on boats, dressed as speculators or preachers or new settlers with wives and children. By day or early evening they were all over the place, in taverns and houses of entertainment. But I understand that from midnight to dawn they had sessions in a warehouse, and with regular parliamentary procedure they were working out articles of a written constitution under which the Band will henceforth operate."

"Did you get into their meetings?" asked McGready.

"I? Oh no. I'm a trained woods fighter and scout. I can manage disguise in the forest, but I have no command of the kind of disguise required for that company. Nor had any white soldier at the fort. But some of the Indians got in and out—quite educated Indians, able to understand what was going on. They brought in reports every day, which I studied with the officers at the fort, and tried to interpret. One thing we learned. They're going out to get the best lawyers, high class men, respectable men. That will end Bill Reading here."

"He's already ended," smiled Jus, and turning to McGready, added, "Chalk Bill up to the credit of your prayin', Parson. He's giving up the law, says there's getting to be too much controversy in it. I think he's getting out of the path of your prayers."

"Did your prayers reach Cave-in-Rock?" asked Dominie of Mc-Gready. "For that's been swept clean, too. Not a single outlaw there."

"What!" cried Jus. "I thought when they left us that was where they went. I understood they'd holed themselves in there to hold out till the last Judgment."

"So I had understood. But it seems they're giving Cave-in-Rock up, at least till they throw Fort Massac off the scent. I knew the cave. You know it was we, on Clark's expedition, who found it—that's how the Masons knew it. So I volunteered to go up with a force from the fort and see if it really was abandoned." He looked around at the others. "Do any of you know Cave-in-Rock?"

Peter started to answer, but Eddie pulled him back. But in frontier councils, they were always ready to hear what a boy had to say. So Dominie asked kindly, "Peter, what do you know about Cave-in-Rock?"

"Only what Preacher Lurton said. He said it was a hole that you can look through right into Hell. And the devil sits there with a lot of damned men, and they play cards, and drink whisky and chew tobacco, and you can see Hell fire just beyond, and blood on all the walls, and hear the yells of the murdered, and the curses of them that are lost forever."

"A little lurid," replied Dominie gravely, "but strictly true." As he went on to tell how they'd made their way to the cave, Peter could see it all—the Illinois shore where bluffs rose screened by primeval forests, the tortuous channels of the Ohio below, between wooded islands—sixty miles of islands amidst the rush and roar of dangerous waters, and all of them possessed and ruled by the Mason and Alston banditti. "Cave-in-Rock is on the Illinois shore, midway between Shawneetown and Golconda, which are about forty miles apart," said Dominie.

Peter mentally went all the way with Dominie up the Kentucky shore to beautiful Diamond Island, the upper end of the robber's island domain, crossed there and came down, stealthily, through the woods, and found the great rock where, to lure boats to stop, Mason had inscribed a large sign, "Liquor Vault and House of Entertainment," with arrows pointing to the great arched opening of the cave in the limestone bluff. Dominie and the others entered in force, with guns cocked, and found—*nothing*. Incredulous, they explored the vast room 160 feet by forty feet. "All we found was some pieces of their counterfeiting machinery, which they'd evidently dropped when they all moved out. The fort has most of it, but I was able to save out this to show you," said Dominie. "It's a a die for casting a large five dollar gold piece and a silver half dollar which you know are the same size."

At this point he brought out and passed around a double plate of iron, four and three quarters inches long, and two and a half inches in diameter, with a gap in the top, opening into a funnel shaped feeder. "See," he said, "They put clay in the circle here, and in it they make an impression of a genuine half dollar, and on the other the impression of a five dollar gold piece. Another mould is prepared for the other sides of the coins. The two parts of the mould are placed in position and hot metal poured into the cavity through the funnel opening."

Allen looked it over. "Must make a pretty crude imitation."

"Well," said McGready, "all our coins are pretty crude."

"And not enough of them passes our hands for us to learn to know good from bad," said Jus.

Peter handled the instrument, studying the way it worked. Used as he had been all his life to hearing about counterfeiters and robbers, they had always seemed unreal to him. There was something solemn in the way this thing he could hold in his hand—this thing for making false money—made all this wickedness seem real and imminent.

It was now growing very late. The women and children were tired. Brenda and Barbara went home under the escort of some of the Baptist men. Mary went to bed in the preacher's room with Polly. Peter fell asleep on the bearskin. But Dominie, Dutch, Dean, and Jus went on talking.

The neighing of a horse startled Peter awake. A cold wind was blowing on him through the open door. Dominie and the others were mounting their horses. Chagrined that he had slept while matters of great importance were talked about, Peter jumped up and ran out to join them. Dominie was already in the saddle. He spurred his horse, then reined up close to Jus. "We were so busy studying the way the Band has got itself re-organized and figuring what they would do next that I quite forgot to tell you that Peter Alston now goes by the name of John May. He's been recognized traveling with a lame girl he calls his sister."

"God Almighty!" ejaculated Jus.

5

Jus was a brave man, but he hated to have his feelings riled. So he put it up to Eddie and Peter to break the news about the identity of John May to Mary. On the frontier it was humiliating to be caught in an error of judgment. Survival required a surety in observation and deduction not needed by civilized people. To make a fool of one's self was unforgivable; to be made a fool of, an intolerable wrong. Jus couldn't bear to see Mary made a fool of.

Mary re-acted in such a white fury of anger that Eddie thought it no wonder his father had dodged. "I told your father," she cried. "I said the way he and all the men were shilly-shallying, we'd have these varmints right in our own homes, going out with our own daughters."

She stopped. Polly had entered, and was looking at them, her soft peachlike bloom underlaid with a hard, chalky mask. Mary said sharply. "Polly, you know!"

Polly choked and mumbled, "I-I don't know anything!" She looked so wretched that Mary went to her and stroked her hair lightly. "I should have known better, to put you in the way of getting mixed up with such trash! What a fool! I deserve to be struck down!"

"Mammy, don't," murmured Polly desperately. "We were all taken in."

Peter's eyes were sparkling with interest. "Did you see him much? Was he at all those barbecues?"

"I don't know anything about him," sobbed Polly. "I don't want to know. I hate him. And I hate that nasty trollop worse. God damn them both. God damn them to Hell." And she rushed out of the door.

"Well, I reckon that's something God is taking care of," said Mary, answering the swear words. Peter, remembering how many times his mother had washed out his mouth and Polly's with water and wood ashes, after they had said such words, was astonished. Lightning played across the stormy blue of Mary's eyes, as she left Eddie and Peter and followed Polly to talk to her alone.

For the next few months, as the year ripened into autumn and shriveled into winter, Polly carried a visible sense of shock, which Peter knew worried his father and mother, for he had no compunctions about listening to their secret conferences. And he knew that, as the months passed, they were relieved because whatever her emotional involvement with this fellow had been, it was plain she had "known how to take care of herself." "It's a load off my mind," said Mary to Jus. "But she isn't the same girl. When the young folks come whooping around after her, she makes me send them off. It wrings my heart to see her peak and pine like this. If only she'd get religion."

Jus said, "She'll get something better than religion. She'll get a new beau, and let's hope he'll be the right sort. I'm bound to say I'm relieved, too. I'd a stood by her. I don't hold with those who turn a daughter out of her own home just when she needs it most.

But it would have shamed us."

Mary flared. "We'd a been shamed. But I tell you, Jus Cartwright, we and every family here have earned a little shame. It ud serve us all right to be made a scandal till we learn not to let stinkin' evil sit on our own doorsteps where our own children can get into it. I've learned my lesson, being taken in like that because he was so nice to his sister. We ain't none of us smart enough to save our own skins single-handed. We've got to get together and burn the varmints out."

As Peter stole noiselessly away, lest he be caught eavesdropping, he was soberly laying these words in a deep place in his mind.

CHAPTER 18 Russellville, Kentucky
January, 1798 to Midsummer, 1798

1798 came in, bright with hope. Since either the prayers, or the sinking of the outlaws underground, had given political ascendancy to the veterans, they marked their advantage by changing Logan Courthouse to Russellville, in honor of their general, William Russell. A town was now growing up around the court. Windows in some new buildings were to be of glass. A brick house had been started. Some citizens were driving two-wheeled carts.

Meanwhile, the luxuries that had been brought back from Fort Massac had so whetted the appetite that the Methodists were overwhelmed with people claiming to have been members of the church somewhere else. "I don't like these gunpowder Methodists of yours," said Valentine Cook, the new circuit rider, a young man of suavity and polish. "There's no sanctification in making gunpowder. Even the devils can do that." He cleared out the bogus Methodists by requiring that they show him a letter from their former pastor or class leader, or become soundly converted again.

But, though Dominie and the members of his class meeting remained the core of the gunpowder enterprise, they took in as many of the unregenerate as would do a day's work. Dominie had brought some needful machinery from Fort Massac. During the fall they got their working equipment under cover, so that they could go ahead in the stormiest weather, and cut more dogwood. Peter worked unceasingly, cutting wood, watching fires, building up merit till he was finally allowed to learn to crystallize the saltpeter. When he went with his father to court, he was besieged by people who wanted to know about the gunpowder. He met all questions with great reserve. "The first thing you've got to learn about business," Jus had said, "is not to talk about it to Tom, Dick, and Harry." But on the frontier, any group that seemed to be keeping a good thing to themselves instead of opening it to their neighbors was bound to have those they left out ganging-up on them. Peter had to fight several boys and two drunken men who seemed to have a grudge against the gunpowder.

One night he was awakened under his bearskin in the loft by a strong smell of smoke. He heard his father say, "There's a fire. Must be outside." Peter hauled his fur jacket over the woolen underwear in which he slept, thrust his feet into squirrel-lined moccasins, and swung himself down off the loft. The cabin door was open. Smoke was rolling in on a blast of cold wind. Beyond, a red sheet of flame shot into the sky. "God Almighty!" shouted Jus. "It's in the dogwood!" They rushed out to the caves, and in the lurid light they saw desolation. The furnace had been hammered down, the sulphur scattered to the wind. The buildings were crumbling in the red fire. The dogwood was a great glowing heap of charcoal.

Peter was sent through the night to tell Dominie. From every side men came riding, but nothing could be done except to watch the flames bring their hopes and the patient work of years to ash. Tired, discouraged, with chattering teeth, they gathered in the Cartwright cabin at dawn. Laying aside her scruples against alcohol, Mary made them a drink of maple sugar, hot water, and whisky, to warm them up. But it seemed as if they would never get warm. Peter shivered with a sense of doom, even while the whisky fumes went to his head and made his face burn. Their hearts had all been so much in it. How had it happened? Who had done it?

Falling back on their one means of morale, Dominie read to them from the Bible, Psalms VII, 6-17. "Arise, O Lord, in thine anger, lift up thyself because of the rage of mine enemies, and awake for me to the judgment Thou hast commanded . . . His mischief shall return upon his own head, and his violent dealing shall come down on his own pate." There is nothing to do, Dominie told them, when all one's hopes are in ruins, but to kneel, praying and praising God, and collect the pieces, even with bleeding hands, and start building again. As he spoke there gradually emerged out of dispair and rage a sober militancy. Then they sang, in ringing voices, Dean and Dominie leading, "Praise God from Whom all blessings flow."

Out of it emerged a plan. They would make a concerted effort to get this crime investigated and the perpetrators brought to justice. This failing, they would fall back on "other measures." What those measures were they did not say. The glances of their eyes crossed like swords and they were grimly silent. Somewhere in Peter's consciousness a drum had begun to beat, and his nerves were thrilling as to a military marching song.

2

Next day a delegation of them, armed to the teeth, rode in to lay the situation before Wesley Maulding, the sheriff. Wesley's round, pleasant face was clouded. "It's a shame, a mighty shame,'" he said, discharging a shot of tobacco.

Jus said firmly, "We expect those men found and brought to justice. We expect their property to be confiscated and used to pay every penny of this loss. Since dogwood takes three years to ripen, this cannot be got to the point where it was destroyed in one night, under three years. We expect full compensation for what we will lose in these three years."

"Well, now," sighed Wesley, "how are we goin' to find who did it? You didn't see hide nor hair of them. How do you know it was anybody from here? You're only a mile or two from the Tennessee border—might just as well have been folks over the line in Tennessee. In fact," (and here his fair skinned face grew red and moist with eagerness) "I just know it must have been strangers."

"How do you know?" asked Dominie.

"Cause folks around here just wouldn't do such a thing."

"Wouldn't they?" asked Dominie, his cold gray eye fixing Wesley's warm and kind blue eyes till they fell before his piercing glance.

Wesley said he'd ride over and look at "the mess." He got Bill Stewart to come along, large, pleasant, expansive, his string of counterfeit coins clinking as he rode. They both went over the ground expressing great concern, cursing the unknowns who did it, heartily. Jus thought he saw a suspicion of a wink as Stewart looked to Wesley. But Wesley answered with a stony stare, and seemed very much on his dignity thereafter. "We'll look into it," he declared "and if there's any way we can do it, justice will be done."

"What an engaging liar that fellow is!" remarked Dominie, after the representatives of law and justice had clattered off.

Jus answered, "Long as I've known Wes, I can't figure him out. Is he with that gang or not? Or does he just want to save his own skin, whatever happens?"

Yet actually they got little more satisfaction from Robert Ewing. "I'm afraid you made a mistake, trying to build up in opposition to the traders here," he commented. "Stewart and Dromgole are putting themselves to a lot of trouble and taking a financial risk, getting goods down here. And naturally it's hard for them to swallow—the way you all have boycotted their store and tried to start a rival business. It would have been much better if you had traded through them. They would gladly take your powder and give you as good a trade as the army."

"Ewing," replied Jus, "let's not beat about the bush. You know why we won't trade with them. I understand you and your family and the Presbyterians generally do all you can to keep out of that store."

Ewing pursed up his lips and was silent a moment. Finally he said, "Well, that's a matter of private conscience. We don't make a public issue of it. We know it's no use. But I do want to point out that while there's no question about Philip Alston's connection with the robber gangs, and little about the Masons and Peter Alston—"

"Who's been around here under the name of John May," interjected Jus.

Robert nodded silently, and went on, "As I was saying, while there's no question about some, I never saw proof that Dromgole and Stewart are in the Band."

"Do you think it's the Dromgole outfit that's burnt us out?" asked Dominie bluntly.

"Oh, I wouldn't say so," answered Ewing, hastily. "It's only that, in looking for a motive, that naturally occurs to one."

After further discussion Ewing walked with them to where their horses were tied, and bade them a courteous good-bye, saying, "It's bad business. But I don't see what we can do till you enter a formal accusation. And before you do that, you'll have to find out who they are."

A few days later Stewart, Dromgole, John Gilbert, and Burwell Jackson all rode over to call on Jus. They made quite an impressive cavalcade, riding up to the rail fence, for they had excellent thoroughbreds, and were handsome men, dressed handsomely in the frontier style, in broad hats, well-cut riding breeches, Spanish leather boots, and fur-lined jackets. Jus wanted Mary to come out and greet them. But Mary refused, and stayed in the cabin, while Jus talked to them outside in the snow. To Eddie and Peter he said, out of the side of his mouth, "Stick around. It's just as well to have witnesses. But don't look like you're listening." So Peter and Eddie busied themselves clearing out of the dooryard the light snow that had fallen during the night. When they all went down to the saltpeter caves, the boys sneaked like Indians to a place where they could listen unseen.

Burwell Jackson was saying, "It's quite an enterprise, but a good deal for you to swing. And it's going to be hard to rebuild it. You'll need better machinery and something better than a log canoe to carry it in." Finally he came to the point, "We all feel pretty bad about what has happened, and we're more than anxious to make it up to you. A thing like this is something we've got to encourage.

We've talked it over, and we're ready to club together and rebuild and stake you till it can get going again. And we won't ask more than fair interest on the capital. The only thing is that it's got to be practical. And it just isn't practical to build up a manufactury of any size and handle it trading in a log canoe with the fort. We've got experienced traders here, and the thing is to let them handle the trading side. You be the producers and turn it over to Stewart and Dromgole, and let them do your buying and selling. It'll make you a lot more."

"Now that's right white of you," answered Jus, "I'll put it up to the others, and we'll sure give it every consideration."

When it came time to say good-bye, he was effusive in his thanks. Peter listened, frowning, "It aint like Pappy to be taken in. What do you make of it?" he whispered to Eddie.

"It's a game," whispered Eddie. "And two can play at it."

After that, every time his father met Stewart or Jackson on court days, Peter saw that Jus was still promising to think it over. He was frank and friendly. He made a point of hailing his new-found backers, going into Cedar House with them, and buying drinks generously. But negotiations inched forward so slowly that they seemed to stand still.

3

Peter knew that for the first time in his life his father was keeping something from him. Solid log doors had been put over the openings to the saltpeter caves, and they were heavily barred. By day nothing was visible there except ruin. But when the moon shone, these winter nights, Eddie did not come to bed in the loft all night. Peter tried to slip down and go out, but waked Polly. He tried a second time and waked his mother. By that time he had perfected a noiseless exit and slipped out. It was as he thought. There was a crew of men working on the saltpeter in the moonlight. Stealing toward them, Peter found a gun pointed at his chest. Then Otto's voice whispered from the bushes. "Oh, it's you, Peter. Get out of here, young un. Scat!" With the gun he was pushed back the way he had come.

Next day he went out to the horse lot, left the gate open by accident, scared a horse so that he dashed in the direction of the saltpeter caves, and pursued him madly—all to get a look at the place by day. There was nothing to be seen except the barred doors. He guessed that they were working by night to get everything ready, but locked it by day in the caves. He had observed that the Baptists and Methodists were doing a powerful lot of hunting on the other side of the Tennessee line, with mighty few animals to show for it, and guessed that somewhere they were cutting dogwood.

After Peter brought the horse back, his father strolled out and suggested that they go down to the sugar grove and see if the sap was running yet. It was a maple-sugar day. The sunless, soft, thick, mild air hung heavy on the snow which packed down wetly under their boots, and, on the way, they saw the first pussy willows. Jus squirted his tobacco juice on the snow, and said, "Peter, I've always liked to have you part and parcel of what I'm doing. But what I'm doing now I want you to keep out of."

"Eddie's in it," replied Peter.

Jus was taken aback. "Has Eddie shot off his mouth?"

"Not a word of it. But I got eyes."

"Your eyes are shut from now on. Understand?" He added, pleadingly, "It's for your own good, Son. I can't have you risking your neck before you're growed. Besides, if my neck's broke, I want yours to stay where it belongs so you can look after your Mammy." Peter was silent. His eyes were dark, burning questions. "Peter, you don't know anything about anything's that done around here, and you won't know. Give me your word."

Peter hesitated. On the frontier the feudal heritage of honor, including the sacredness of the pledged word, had been largely discarded in favor of elemental cunning. The real obligation was to survive, and help those you had a natural responsibility for to survive, by an efficient use of your wits—promising, breaking promises, lying, deceiving as need be. Peter would have promised anybody else readily, and broken the promise. But where his father was concerned—

Justurian's eyes were shrewd and his voice tender. "I know how it is. You'd lie to anybody else, but not to your ol Pappy. Well, Son, what you don't know won't hurt you. Don't know any more than you can help. And keep your mouth *shut*."

"You don't need to worry." The boy's eyes were pleading. "Wild horses couldn't drag it out of me."

Jus cut another quid of tobacco and turned to a maple tree. "The sap's running all right." Talk of anything but sugaring-off was at an end.

4

But it is hard to keep anything from a boy trained to note a single broken twig in apparently unbroken bush; to take a complex sound to pieces and know who and what made each noise, down to the faintest scratch; to be as sensuously aware as an animal in the woods and yet take a man's pride in "putting two and two together;" to be practiced from babyhood in making his presence invisible and soundless, in lying with a straight face, and weaving a web of deception; to have no scruples about listening in on anything; and to follow a lead with the persistence and cunning of an Indian. So Peter soon knew that other things were going on besides the rebuilding of the gunpowder plant. The veterans were organizing, in secret night meetings, with guards concealed, like Indian fighters, in trees. They had a password. It took Peter a long time to find out what it was. They had a hand-clasp. He figured that out. They had a reserve of horses and guns. Peter knew where they were and how to get at them in a crisis. They had a name. The name was Regulators.

Regulators—he'd heard that name before. Hadn't there been Regulators down in Nashville? He knew better than to ask his father questions. But one day when he'd ridden to Doctor Allen's to get him to call on a sick man a mile north on the Nashville-Russellville road, he asked offhand, "Doctor, was there Regulators back where you came from?"

In no time the Doctor was off on one of his rich surveys of history. He told how when North Carolina was still ruled by the King of England, the men in the mountains didn't like what the royal governors and their officers did. Then a Quaker named Hermann Cousins had the idea of organizing bands of citizens to "regulate" public officers and see that they did their duty. Cousins was a man of peace, and meant the regulation to be peaceful. But when the public officers resisted being regulated with guns, the Regulators fought them with guns, in the bloody battle of Alamance which, said Doctor Allen, was the real beginning of the Revolution. He went on to tell that when the Regulators were outlawed two of them, John Robertson and John Donelson, brought a band of them out here and settled Nashville back in 1780. "John Donelson—that built the big blockhouse south of here," asked Peter, impressed.

"Yes, Mrs. Jackson's father, Mrs. Andrew Jackson." He added, "Such civilization as there is out here the Regulators started."

At this point Peter put on the look a boy wears when a respected elder rambles on about some boring matter. He made no comment, asked no more questions. But mentally he had a sense of rest. Now he knew what it was all about. Pappy and Dominie and Dutch and the other were going to "regulate" Wesley Maulding and others to see that there was an inquiry into the destruction of the gunpowder plant.

Now that he understood what they were up to, Peter managed to keep abreast of the situation by a kind of mental algebra, using what he was allowed to see and hear to solve the mystery of what he was not. There was the time Jus came crashing home, in blacker anger than Peter had ever seen in his easy-going parent. Jus sat at the supper table, eating nothing, sunk deep in a bog of meditation. Then he told Peter to get his horse, mounted, and rode off furiously into the night. "It's something about the new lawyer," said Mary, in answer to Peter's questioning look. But that is all she would say. It was enough to set Peter on the track of the new lawyer. Next day, he offered to go to court with his father and help him. Jus, harassed and tense as he was, was comforted by the way Peter made himself useful there, tending his horse and running errands.

And so Peter got a look at the new lawyer, Ninian Edwards, and soon knew all about him. Edwards was a baby-faced, well spoken young man in his early twenties, the nephew of U. S. Senator Edwards of Kentucky. Even in that raw democracy, there were still some who were looked on as being of a higher species, and U. S. Senators were among them. "I told you," said Dominie to Jus, "that the Band is hiring top-grade lawyers." Nobody admitted that the Band had hired Edwards, but he was representing Dromgole and Stewart, and straightening out details of Alston's estate for John Gilbert, Alston's respectable and wealthy son-in-law, and warning trespassers off the Mason property under threat of the law. Edwards bought a farm south of Russellville in what had been the veterans' settlement, two miles from where McGready lived. This made him McGready's nearest neighbor. The preacher helped him to move in, and became his closest friend.

As the Senator's nephew and McGready's friend, Jus and Dominie couldn't see why Edwards shouldn't be on their side, once he understood the situation here. But when they called on him, and told him about the destruction of their gunpowder plant, they were baffled by his courteous, friendly exposition of what they knew already. They couldn't lodge a complaint before they know who did it. As a lawyer Edwards said he had no political or police power. To start an investigation, they'd have to see the sheriff. "But if we should be able to bring action against Dromgole and Stewart, you'd defend them," said Jus bluntly.

"They have engaged my services," replied Edwards blandly. "You are a lawyer yourself, Mr. Cartwright. You understand one's responsibility to a client."

Most of the veterans had no patience with the niceties of the law. They felt completely sold out. With the nephew of Senator Edwards acting as lawyer for the criminals, and Preacher McGready openly his friend, what hope was there? Some who had been praying turned to cursing. Others, trembling under the growing sense of doom, joined the praying groups. As spring leafed out into summer, the little log churches overflowed into the outdoors, and the numbers of those enlisting to pray for the redemption of all sinners in Logan County grew with every preaching.

Frustrated in the use of gunpowder for exchange Dominie had braved the Dromgole outfit by sending an order for goods to Daniel Broadhead, in Louisville, who had said he'd undertake to get a consignment into Logan County right past Mason. He was doing it all over the West. True, much was lost in transit. But some got through. He sent Dominie's order under the charge of two experienced Negroes. Weeks passed. Neither the Negroes nor the goods were ever heard of. Dominie went with Jus to Wesley Maulding and demanded that the Dromgole Exchange be searched to see if any of the missing items were there. Edwards intervened and prevented the search. He said it was unwarranted.

5

So much Peter had picked up, mainly at second-hand, by seeming not to pay attention to anything that transpired on court days. But there was one conversation which he heard with his own ears. For, one afternoon while he and his father were hoeing the long rows of potatoes, covering the young spuds which kept popping out of the light soil and turning green and bitter under the sun, a horse dashed over the fields, and there was Preacher McGready hailing his father. Though Jus was sour on the preacher these days, for his friendship with Edwards, he greeted him courteously, and settled down under a big tree with him to talk, motioning Peter to take McGready's horse where he couldn't do damage to growing crops. His look told Peter plainly, "And keep out of the way, young un."

But the tree trunk was three feet across, and behind it there was a thick undergrowth. So having tied the horse in the midst of a full grassy meal, Peter wriggled back and lay on the ground under the bushes, with the tree between him and the two men. And so he heard their talk.

It seemed that one of the veterans had broken down in meeting and got religion and confessed to McGready his compunctions about the course they'd embarked on in organizing the Regulators. Jus, while stoutly refusing to admit that they had determined to get redress even by resort to arms, said, "I suppose you'll tell Edwards this, and he'll tell the sheriff and the outlaws."

"I shall not," replied McGready, and added, "if Edwards knows, it will not be through me. Don't misjudge Edwards. He's young, and this is his first legal work. All he's trying to do is be correct according to the principles of his profession. You ought to understand that."

"I understand," said Jus, brutally, "that he's a tame chick in pinfeathers, in a den of wild beasts—the kind that comes from bringing a boy up soft where things are civilized—no sense, no guts, just human mush. However, he's Senator Edwards' nephew, and that gives him weight. And that weight he's throwing against everything decent here, and you know it."

McGready sighed. "Trust him to me. I'll try to educate him." He recurred to the Regulators. "If it comes to guns between you and the law—"

"What law?" said Jus. "It isn't natural law. It isn't the law of God. It isn't even the statutes of Kentucky."

"I know that," replied McGready steadily. "But if you shoot and they shoot, you'll throw the whole West here into armed fighting. With both state and federal government so weak here, it will be an occasion for England or Spain to step in. Some of you may die. Some of you may meet cruel punishment."

"Don't tell me that if we wait, law and politics will right the wrong for us."

"Law and politics will not."

"May be," observed Jus sarcastically, "you think your prayers will do it."

"They will."

"How?"

"We'll get little groups of godly persons, dedicated to God, in every neighborhood, by every trail, on every stream. They'll be like so many fires set in the grass, and we will keep blowing them with the breath of the Lord till these little fires start running together in one mighty roaring flame that will sweep over this land from the mountains to the Mississippi and burn it clean."

As McGready's beautiful voice rolled out, Peter's imagination caught fire. For a moment he'd rather be a preacher than a Regulator, and set holy fires and start the great conflagration! But Jus answered, in a dry, drawling way, "Well, religion's something that's out of my reach. But I can see the sense in organizing like that. Get a lot of these gangs of people hooked together under good leaders, and may be they'd begin to stand fast and show some guts. Then it will be easy enough to smell out these criminals and get warrants sworn out against them and trials in the courts. But when you've saved your sinners, Parson, they've got to do a lot more than cry, 'Glory Hallelujah.' They've got to harness this here piety and put it as a real force behind sinful but honest lawyers like me, and politicians like Ewing, that would do the right thing if anybody would back him in it."

"That's what we mean to do," said McGready. "God help us if we don't."

"To that I can say 'Amen,'" replied Jus. "God help you if you don't."

"Because you veterans will resort to guns?"

"I didn't say that," answered Jus. And that is where the talk ended, with McGready baffled, but Jus a little friendlier to him, and with at least a glimmer of understanding of the preacher's alternative to overthrowing corrupt government by force.

But if Peter thought he could listen in on his father's conferences with impunity, he soon found that he was mistaken. For next day, with a sharp look and an odd, tongue-in-the-cheek kind of smile, his father said to him, "Son, you're going to be educated. I've fixed it up with Doctor Allen to bed you and board you at his house, and larn you all he knows. Pack up your gear. You're off tonight."

For a minute Peter found it hard to draw over his expressive face the mask which the situation required. So his father knew he'd been eavesdropping! At any other time he would have been beside himself with joy. To live with the dear Doctor! To learn to read and write and talk in such a high, eddicated style! At this moment there was added excitement because the Doctor's skill had made him prosperous, and he was building a beautiful house to bring his wife to with two real carpenters working on it. But the Doctor was three miles away from where the Regulators were likely to gather. Anything could happen, and Peter wouldn't know about it! "Might have known that Pappy would find a way to fix me," he thought, between chagrin and proud respect for his astute elder.

6

"Now, Peter, mind your manners and don't give the Doctor any trouble," said Mary, standing in the doorway with Sis, as Peter sprang into the saddle.

"Have you got everything you need, Son?" asked Jus, laying his big hand caressingly on the horse's neck. Peter knew the caress was not for the horse.

"Everything's fine, fine as a fiddle," mumbled Peter, giving his horse a sudden involuntary kick. And so he was off. But after he had ridden a little piece, he slowed down, and wiped the back of his hand across his eyes, and turned and waved. They were all standing in the rays of the late sun, watching him.

He felt sad and alone riding through the empty landscape, as the sun sank to the level of the yellowing fields and lost itself behind dark woods. But the feeling suddenly vanished when he came to the rise of ground from which he should see the smoke from the Doctor's chimney. Instead of smoke he found himself facing a fierce, blinding blaze. "Heavens above? What is that?" he asked himself, reining up sharply, and staring at the unearthly conflagration. It was the Doctor's new house all alight, and yet it wasn't on fire. It wasn't till he was nearly up to it that he could figure it out. It was the new glass windows! The setting sun had caught them in a certain way. This was the first time Peter had had a chance to examine glass windows close at hand. Before going to the door, he went up to them and looked at the glass carefully.

The doctor heard him and opened the door. "Well, well, Peter," he said affectionately, "So you've come to be my boy for a while! Welcome, Son."

The Doctor's cabin was furnished with such pewter, silver, and pictures as Peter had not seen since that day he blundered into Alston's cabin. For people who could not pay the Doctor in cash gave him the treasures they had toted over the mountains. When he protested, they would say, "You'll take care of them better than we could," or "The young uns would break them any way. They're safer with you," or "You can keep them till we're better fixed." The Doctor accepted them on loan, always redeemable with tobacco or a deed of land. Grateful patients had filled the cabin with comforts. A woman whom he had brought back to life after "child-bed fever" had woven his bedspread. A man whose broken leg he had set had made him a long plank table and chairs with woven seats.

Supper was waiting, with china dishes set on a linen cloth. "I got them out in your honor, Peter," said Allen. "Your father wants me to educate you, and drinking tea out of a china cup is a kind of education, isn't it?"

The romance of comfort and kindness on this high civilized level was a dazzle in Peter's eyes, and a thrill in his nerves, and a wellspring of gratitude in his heart as he sat down at the table, and, watching the Doctor carefully, was served by the Doctor's Negro house-boy, Cassius.

"Cassius has sure fattened up," he said, in a low voice to the Doctor, looking after the black boy. Peter had been with the Doctor when he had found the poor black piece of skin and bones, almost naked, under a pile of leaves in the woods, whimpering and whining, dying of hunger. He had helped the Doctor make a simple sledge on which they had laid him, and had walked beside him as he was slowly drawn to the Doctor's house. He had helped the Doctor bathe him and put him to bed.

Peter had also been at the Doctor's house when Bill Stewart, who was then sheriff, had come around to look into the rumor that the Doctor was harboring a runaway slave, for the county court had decided that the privilege of asylum, so freely accorded white **fugitives in Rogues' Harbor**, would no longer extend to black persons. Any Negro who could not show freedom papers or a master would be sold by the county court at auction. In 1797 William Lowry, Negro vagrant, had been knocked down to a master. "But there ain't much of him to sell," said Stewart, standing over the black shadow on the bed, and smiling in a friendly way into the beseeching eyes on the pillow. "Who owns you, Son?"

The boy looked anxiously at Allen, and, meeting a re-assuring look, said, "Nobody owns me. I own myself."

"Let him alone," Allen had said to Stewart. "If you must establish a master for him, I'll buy him."

Stewart had clapped Allen on the shoulder. "Doc, from now on he's yours, and no questions asked. You've come by him fairly, and if anybody says you ain't, send him to me."

Wherever he had come from, Cassius had been trained as a houseboy, and now his gratitude flowed out in domestic service to the Doctor. Having shared in the finding and the tending of the runaway, Peter felt a proprietary interest in Cassius, and during supper they talked about the day Cassius would be helped to get away across the Ohio, where nobody could own him or sell him, with the forward-looking interest of a family planning to send a son to college.

It was all exciting and glamorous, but Peter's spirits flagged. A sense of deprivation, of outrage even, was yawning like a black hole under all this friendliness. He had never spent a night away from home before. He didn't want to stay here. He wanted to go home!

The Doctor noticed his wan face. "You're tired, Peter. You'd better go to bed." Climbing to the loft, Peter's very feet resented every rung of the ladder as alien. When he crawled between the sheets on his cot, they felt cold and slithery. He missed his own bearskin, and the smell of spruce under him. He missed his own stars looking through his own window. His father had said that he wasn't to come home to visit, and the family wouldn't visit him for a long while, till he got used to being with the Doctor. Peter understood what that meant. Till whatever the Regulators were going to do was done! He was out of it. Banished!

Then a thought struck him. He caught at it as a falling man might catch and cling to a rocky ledge. Here at the Doctor's he wasn't far from Jerry. And Jerry's father was in the Regulators! Out of respect for his own father's injunctions, Peter had left Jerry out of his own research into the Regulators. Resenting his exile, he no longer had compunctions. He'd see Jerry tomorrow and tell him. They'd watch where Dutch went and what he did. And whatever was doing, they'd be in it. Weren't he and Jerry almost men grown? It was their right!

CHAPTER 19

Russellville, Kentucky
Midsummer, 1798

The next day was Saturday. After trying to be polite and fall in with the Doctor's ways all morning and much of the afternoon, Peter asked if he might ride over to Jerry's. The Doctor consented gladly. He was bothered by the boy's unwonted listlessness. Young company and Brenda's motherly ministration might do him good!

On the short mile ride through the woods to Jerry's house, Peter thought a good deal about his chum. He hadn't seen much of him for months, not only because of the need of keeping secret his own researches into the Regulators but because of a great change in Jerry. Up to now Jerry had been Peter's shadow, smaller, weaker, dependent—something to care for and think for. Now, maturing ahead of Peter, but without growing in stature, Jerry had developed a disturbing individuality of his own. For one thing when he came to Peter's house, he did nothing but moon over Polly. Peter was wondering what he'd said that evening, some weeks ago that made Polly look so startled. He recalled how she'd thrown her arms around Jerry, and kissed him, and said, "You silly, silly little boy," and then, "Come Honey, sit down at the table with Sis, and I'll give you a nice hot hoecake with maple syrup." Peter had been uncomfortably aware that such behavior was an outrage to Jerry's feelings.

But when he came in sight of Jerry's house, Peter had a sudden sense of comfort. The Germans had more substantial well being in their homes than the Scotch-Irish, mainly because of their greater aptitude for craftsmanship, especially among the men. Nobody was smarter than Mary in weaving and cooking, but menfolk, even at Dominie's house, never made anything unless it was some kind of machine. But in Jerry's house there was a big chest carved with goblins, where things were stored, and a large dresser on whose upper shelves pieces of pottery and pewter could be set out of the way of harm. Among the Germans there was a bigger carry-over of wheat and rye and corn and salt meat, and they had a few pigs— mean, skinny, black brutes who ran wild and fought for survival against wild animals, but which could be rounded up and butchered. Instead of throwing out the pig's head, as even Mary would have done, Brenda boiled it with corn meal and made a marvelous food called scrapple. To Peter going to Jerry's meant scrapple, and that to a boy at the chronically hungry age was a great lure. But Peter had no chance even to smell scrapple that day. For Jerry saw him and came running out. "Come, Pete," he said, springing lightly behind on Diablo, "let's go over to the Baptist meeting. It's a long time since we've given their sins a going over."

Peter had often enjoyed the pre-Sabbath Day confessional of the Baptists. But tonight he had other things on his mind. However he saw that there was diplomacy in joining in Jerry's spying before asking Jerry to join in his. So the boys rode to within a safe distance of the little Baptist log chapel, and then tethered their horse, and crept noiselessly to the place where, with ears to a chink, they could sit like priests hearing a confession while inside some twenty English and German speaking Baptists, both black and white, thoroughly reviewed each others' sins in preparation for service on the Lord's Day.

They heard Brother William lay a complaint against Brother Ely, and the congregation appoint Brothers Jesse and Duren to look into it and cite them to the next meeting. They heard a solemn report that after an examination of the brethren appointed to labor with Brother Elisha, Brother Elisha is "no more of us." They heard this followed with a mournful statement that Black Brother Ben was no more of them, either. They heard Black Sister Fillis complain that Black Brother Jule had drunk three gourds of whisky three parts full, and heard Black Brother Pompey lodge a complaint against himself for being drunk. They determined to look into the report against Black Brother Jule, but to bear with Black Brother Pompey because of his acknowledgement. They heard a white brother complain against another for selling him an unsound horse, and another white brother lodge a complaint against himself for getting out of temper. They listened with careful concern to the report of an injured wife that her husband drank too much, swore profanely, and debarred her from the use of necessities for the accommodation of the many people he brought to the house. The husband was brought before the bar, and after some talking to, agreed that henceforth he would give up to his wife the whole control of the house that belonged to a woman. The refusal of a brother to pay excessive usury was considered, and his brethren determined to sustain him in his refusal.

All this went on in the weekly Methodist class meeting also, but there the atmosphere was more easy, kindly, and informal. Peter enjoyed the sombre, legalistic, and grim dignity of the Baptist performance, very much as a lover of the theatre might enjoy the different theatre techniques of a troupe from some foreign land. Besides he knew all the sins of the Methodists by heart. An inside picture of Baptist sins offered something new!

In the summer dusk it was easier to hear than to see. When it came to the foot-washing, with which these sessions ended, an imitation of Christ washing the feet of the disciples, the chink in the wall and the single candle inside afforded so little that Jerry pulled Peter away. "Come to my lean-to," he said. Pressed against Peter's back, astride Diablo, isolated in their intimacy, as they rode under the dark roof of the forest, Jerry let his opinions of Baptists flow freely. He said they were a nosy lot, always spying and telling on each other, and he resented the effort now being made to bring him to a conviction of sin at the threshold to man's estate—after which he would be immersed and would cross that cold and icy barrier between the sinners that are lost in this world and the saved who are pledged to the next.

Arrived at Jerry's lean-to, and snugged in, side by side on the spruce boughs, Jerry continued. If it wasn't for his father, he'd light out tomorrow. He spoke of his father with a strange sentimentality. It didn't seem right to Peter for Jerry, at his age, to be clinging to the thoughts of his father as to his Mammy's skirts. He only dimly perceived that his big strong parent was all Jerry longed to be, and never could be.

Nor did Peter like it when Jerry brought out from a hiding place under the spruce boughs a quid of tobacco and a jug of whisky which he wanted Peter to share with him. Peter refused the tobacco with loathing but, not wanting to put himself above Jerry in virtue, choked down a swallow of whisky. "Chewin' tobacco and drinkin' liquor is the surest way I know to spite the Baptists," said Jerry. He took a drink of whisky from the jug's mouth, and sputtered, "If Mammy and the Baptists don't stop aggravatin' me, I'll get drunker than a Lord." Peter couldn't see liquor and tobacco as a means of revolt because what he himself was secretly against was associated with liquor and tobacco. Even his love of his father had never reconciled him to his father's habit of squirting tobacco juice in all directions. And he disliked dirty old women, reeking with strong body smells mixed with tobacco, their lips dark brown above their dirty yellow teeth, pulling on corncob pipes.

But Peter didn't argue with Jerry. Having grown suddenly much bigger, he looked down on his chum's greater emotional precocity from the fatherly height of a big boy whose soul is not yet torn with the storms of coming manhood. And when, on a second swig of whisky, Jerry babbled of Polly, Peter's soul sickened with shame and pity. "If I could see myself married to Polly, and settled down with her in a little house—that's all I ask of life," said Jerry. In his mind's eye Peter could see Polly, luscious, golden, with her rich, ripe curves, and rich blonde coloring, and next to her Jerry, skinny, under-sized—he felt intolerably sorry for Jerry and vexed that he should be sorry.

But when he finally got a word in edgewise about the Regulators, Jerry came out of his emotional fevers. "It explains a lot of things," he said, and told of men coming up late at night, and talking to his father in German, always in German. "I know where they might have a meeting place, and it's not two miles from here. I'll look into it, Pete, and let you know." They talked about it a long time, matching the bits and pieces of talk they'd heard about Regulators in the early days at Nashville, trying to figure out just how the Regulators would proceed to make public officers do their duty, and how they themselves might, in time, be allowed to carry guns and ride with them.

But riding back to the Doctor's, Peter wasn't thinking about the Regulators. He was thinking, with something between shame, recoil, and desperate, aching pity, of what Jerry had said about Polly, and of the way he drank whisky. He remembered what his mother had said about John and Polly, "Every young-un's got to climb Fool's Hill to come to the point of being man or woman grown." "Jerry's sure climbing it," he thought. Then he wondered. Does everybody have to climb Fool's Hill? Would he ever climb it? He thought not. "Not till I take leave of the sense I was born with!"

Next day Peter's reading lessons began. They didn't go very far, for while he stowed the letters away efficiently in his head, there was nothing to read except the *Kentucky Gazette*. Allen had not yet obtained a copy of the Bible and he refused to teach from the New England Primer because of its gloomy Calvinism. But he marked passages in the newspaper, and Peter struggled with them not caring what they said. Then Allen had an inspiration. He marked out a square of dirt almost as big as a small room, which Peter was to keep level and clear of weeds. On it Peter was to trace a message with a stick in the dirt, if he went anywhere while the Doctor was out. Excited by this idea he quickly mastered the marks for "Gone to Jerry's. Back by—" This was the beginning of writing.

What Peter knew astonished the Doctor much more than what he didn't know. He had never studied arithmetic, but he figured quite complicated sums in his head. He reasoned from the known to the unknown, almost as if he knew Algebra, and handled measurements in space as if he had been born with the elements of geometry. When Peter had learned this, he could not have told. It was as native to him as his mother tongue, and acquired in the same way.

His knowledge of natural science was scattering, but extraordinarily detailed and quite accurate in spots. Allen enjoyed organizing Peter's knowledge of the world about him—the rocks, the waters, the trees, the stars, and expanding it. This was Peter's favorite subject. He thrilled to it, with a thrill not even religion had been able to send along his nerves.

With history the Doctor had less success, but considerable amusement. The thousand years of Greek and Roman history impressed Peter not at all. The only classical personage that interested him, though momentarily, was Socrates. "He was a kind of circuit rider, wasn't he?" the boy asked. But he lost respect for Socrates when he wouldn't let his disciples help him to escape. "He acted like a fool," Peter commented decisively. The punishment by drinking hemlock fixed his attention. Was it from the same kind of hemlocks as grew in the woods here? He went into that thoroughly. But poisoning a man, especially under the authority of the state, revolted him. "I've heard tell the Harpes have been known to kill," he said shocked, "but not with *poison*. Even Micajah would hold himself above that." The poisoning of Socrates gave him nightmares for a week.

Popes, kings, and Crusaders Peter dismissed along with the Greeks and Romans. Some of the codes of chivalry struck him as idiotic, especially the idea of unconditional loyalty to a leader. You'd follow a leader so long as he led you the right way, and when he didn't, you'd leave him. As for kings and nobles in great stone castles with moats, Peter was briefly concerned for the engineering problems involved. Otherwise castles were just a special kind of house, like an Indian tepee, but not practical for Kentucky. But the Cromwell Revolution really fixed Peter's attention, for most of his own forebears and those of other so-called "Scotch Irish," had fought under Cromwell, and the ideology of that struggle was widely diffused on the Allegheny frontier.

The Puritans, Peter thought, were real Regulators, and tried to act by some kind of law. Even so he was outraged at the idea of beheading the monarch. "Why couldn't they just have shot him?" he asked. "He'd been just as dead." For in a land where men were quick on the trigger, most of the harsher forms of European punishment were regarded with horror, and in all the discussions Peter had heard on court days, they had been vigorously ruled out.

Allen laughed at Peter's remarks, but they startled him into a new perception of what being an American really meant. Here, in this bright boy, was the new American mind, serene on its own base, naked as Adam of inherited culture, but building its own ideas out of its own needs without cavil or apology.

But the most valuable part of his education at the Doctor's house was not the formal lessons, which were sketchy enough. It was the talk that went on between the Doctor and the two or three kindred spirits who formed the intelligentsia of these wilds. Peter was still sitting at the supper table one night, delicately sipping his tea out of a china cup, and trying to be patient and let Cassius serve him, instead of reaching for what he wanted himself, when James McGready came in. He drank a cup of tea, and then propped himself back on his rush-bottomed chair for a talk, in the favorite posture of the long-legged men of the frontier, but remaining, like Allen, incorrigibly the gentleman in his most careless moods. Peter took his favorite place on the floor at the Doctor's feet, his eyes fastened on McGready's vivid, homely face, his ear listening expectantly for the changes in McGready's beautiful voice. The two men liked to have the boy there, and talked the better for it, as men often talk better in the presence of a woman. Peter listened afloat on a flood of ideas.

Allen began by twitting his guest on the arrival from North Carolina of the Reverend James Balch, to establish a decorous Presbyterianism here in opposition to McGready's revivalism. Balch had settled in North Logan, and built a small log church two and a half miles north of Mote's Creek, and about halfway between the Morgantown and Procter roads, and named it Mount Taber. He had started with twelve members who were going to do things decently. "It's dwindled to nine now," said McGready, with a wicked smile. "Three of them have come over to me."

"How did you fare with Doctor Craighead?" asked Allen. The dignified preacher from Nashville, who had been the stronghold of Presbyterianism out here from the first, had ridden up to hear the complaints against McGready and had attended several of his services. "I really worked on Craighead," replied McGready. "How edifying to have seen the good doctor stricken right in the center of his solid conceit of his own rectitude, falling down before our rude Christians, with tears streaming down his face, for once like other men, a poor broken soul, helpless without God's mercy."

Allen smiled. "What a show that would be!"

"My eloquence washed like a stormy sea against a rock. However, I understand he has refused to do anything about me."

"What can he do?"

"Nothing. That's the wonder of this land. The frowns of your betters, the ostracism, the repudiation that can destroy a man in a tight society, back on the sea coast or in Europe, fall helpless here. The sky and the land smile freedom. As I ride, the wind sings in my ears, 'Who cares!'"

Then they talked about Lewis Moore who had come out from North Carolina and organized the Portyghees into a Baptist Church about four miles from the courthouse on the Bowling Green road, near the headsprings of Muddy River. He had a school there and taught the children, black and white, six days a week. "I know," said Peter, "Jerry's little brother Heinie is learning A B C. He knows them better than Jerry."

"It's a good thing," said McGready, "because he's the first Baptist preacher they've had who is fairly well educated and will stay sober. Walt has brains but he was so drunk on last court day it was a scandal."

Walt was the one the boys called "Ol Waterbug." Peter had seen him drunk. It was fun!

"It's wonderful what you're doing for Asbury's church," observed Allen. "Valentine Cook told me their circuit is now 600 miles around, and he's got William Burke and John Cobbler riding it under him, picking up every convicted soul that staggers back to his cabin, drunk with your eloquence."

"I admit," said McGready ruefully, "that Cook is mighty quick to haul my fish into his net. But I couldn't do without him. He holds me up as if I were one of his own."

"Well," said Allen, "for the first time I begin to see what you and Cook and your brethren are up to. You're organizing a mystic band of the saved, stronger and tougher and more widespread than Alston's mystic band of the damned. Instead of his Masonic hocus pocus and burning of fiery crosses, and swearing blood-brotherhood, you are substituting Glory Be, Amen, Hallelujah, the water of baptism, and wine of communion—"

There was a pounding on the door, and the twinkling blue eyes and tobacco stained, iron gray beard of Ol Waterbug, the Baptist preacher, looked in. "Allen," he bumbled, rolling in on a strong blast of nightfog and tobacco smoke, "I've come to take a burden off your mind. You arn't damned. You never will be damned. Nobody's going to Hell."

"Walt," said McGready, "what's this I hear about you standing up in Russellville last court day, waving a gourd of whisky, and calling on everybody to come and drink the health the devil drank to the dead hog? What do your Baptists say to that?"

The big hairy man looked like a child suddenly reminded that it had been in the jam pot. "They quite properly had me up before a meeting of the brethren the night before the Lord's Day," he mumbled. "And though I confessed even with tears, and a broken and contrite heart, and promised to amend, they think they can dispense with my preaching for a season. However," and here he brightened, "I know now that the hand of the merciful God has been leading me. For I am no longer a Baptist, and I see that whole doctrine of Calvin with which my brethren are poisoned and sickened, is false."

"And what leads you to that extraordinary conclusion?" asked Allen.

"These pamphlets. By the grace of God they were delivered to me by one who thought they were heresy and wanted them burned. But I read them, and lo! I see the light. See," he said eagerly, his long, well-formed, but rough fingers, with their broken, blackened nails, turning the pages, first of one pamphlet, then the other, with trembling eagerness, "God is good. God is love. He is the universal soul of love in the universe, and man is His child, made in His own image. How then can man be bad, when he is God's own pure image in the flesh?"

Allen took the pamphlets. "They seem to be sermons," he remarked to McGready. "One on Atonement, and the other on Retribution by—" he looked at the names, "John Murray and Hosea Ballou."

"Murray was a Methodist and Ballou a Baptist," said Ol Waterbug eagerly, "but they've seen the light. And they've started a new church—the Universalist Church, in Boston, dedicated to the supreme truth that God is Love, there is no Hell, all men are really pure and good, and everybody will get to Heaven in the end."

"But obviously men are bad," said McGready. "You arn't too good yourself, Walt. How do you explain that?"

"Men are not bad. They are mistaken. Take me. I don't drink drams because I'm bad. I drink because everybody drinks and I want to be friends with my brother man. If I stick too narrowly to the prohibitions of the stricter Baptist brethren, I am cut off from my brother man. I am sour, censorious, better-than-thou. They don't trust me. They think I don't love them. So I decide to drink a little."

"Then by the spirit of pure brotherhood you are led to drink too much," observed Allen.

"Exactly. But am I bad? No, my motive is good. These writings explain it all. There is salvation for all men. The end of man is perfection. God will guide us. Heaven lies before all mankind."

Allen was leafing through the pamphlets. "There is something in this," he remarked to McGready. "You ought to read it."

McGready took the pamphlets, glancing at them, and threw them on the table, and turned to Ol Waterbug. "Get you behind me, you double-dyed imp of Satan. This doctrine is of the Anti-Christ. Man is not deluded or blinded. What is wrong with man is not his mind but his will. There is no man, however low, who does not know what is good a great deal better than he practices it. In every man, even, and especially, in the man whose outward life is pure and actively righteous, there is the hard core of original sin. It is different in each man. It is his own private bundle of reservations—the point at which he commits the sin of Ananias and holds back part of the price. You've got to get at that hard core. It's got to be smashed or utterly melted down, so that it can't be put together, ever again. All a man is must die, and he must be born again, a newborn babe in grace. Until this happens, he is damned. Hell is just a lurid symbol of the end to which he is inevitably moving *now*."

Against this pronouncement Allen battled. Walt battled. The sturdy rafters of the little cabin rang till after midnight with their arguments. Peter listened, siding sometimes with one, sometimes with the other. As far as he could understand Calvinism, he didn't like it. He quite agreed with McGready that most folks were bad and nothing but a miracle could change them. Still it couldn't be God that had condemned them for ever. "It just don't seem right that God should be so mean," he thought.

Finally, Walt departed saying he was glad the Baptists had thrown him out. For now he had found his true vocation. He was going to form a class to read the Universalist literature, and when he had enough disciples he and they were going out to proclaim salvation to all mankind.

McGready lingered. "Brother," he said to Allen, "may I have the privilege of saying my nightly prayers here by the fireside, with you and the boy?"

Allen put out his hand, as if to ward him off. "No, no, James. Spare me. Really, you converters of souls carry this thing to far. It is a kind of intrusion. I must ask you to leave my soul to God."

"As you wish, Brother," answered McGready, in his rich organ tones, and laying his hand on Peter's head in a priestly gesture of blessing, he went out into the night.

4

The one subject nobody had thought to include in Peter's school curriculum at the Doctor's was the one he made most progress in. This was the study of German. For a few days after Peter had told Jerry about the Regulators, Jerry rode over to the Doctor's, to invite Peter to spy on the meeting of the German Regulators which he had located about a mile and a half away in a clearing amidst century old trees on the edge of his family's property. But they were baffled because the talk there was all in German. If they were to keep up with the Regulators, it was plain they'd have to learn German. Next morning at breakfast, Dutch was amazed and flattered by his son's interest in what had been his mother-tongue, for, since Brenda had refused to learn German, the language of the household had been English. Dutch's own tendency to tangle English by putting words in the German order had been an embarrassment to him, like stammering. The interest of the boys in what was still the language of Dutch's secret thought gave the good-hearted, solid German an extraordinary release. Talking in German to the boys he had a kind of bearish humor, and clumsy bearlike tenderness, quite lacking from his daily English speaking habits. He even revealed a singing voice and rolled out ditties which his mother must have sung to him. Peter basked in the warm, substantial fatherliness that emanated from the big man when he talked German, and began really to love him, almost as Jerry did.

The German lessons made Peter at home at Jerry's house. Brenda fed him lavishly, looked over his clothes with a motherly concern, and blamed him for anything Jerry did amiss. Peter didn't love her, but he felt a certain filial responsibility to her, and never disputed, even in his own mind, her conviction that he was Jerry's keeper. But he adored Jerry's little brother Heinie, who was far more amenable than Sis had ever been to big brother bossing, and who, with his limpid gray eyes and pointed face, and blond hair, had all Jerry's puckish charm, together with droll good nature that made as much fun as a kitten.

Otherwise Jerry's family consisted of two stocky older brothers, Hans and Otto, and a big solid sister, Gretta, married to a man named Obadiah. Obadiah charmed Peter. He was long and limp, and had a pallid flat-nosed, shallow-eyed face and a look in his eyes like that of a beaten dog. But this was just the mask for a humorsome dancing spirit. Obadiah said he was a Methodist, not one of the praying, exhorting, always-confessing-your-sins-at-meeting kind of Methodist; but a singing Methodist. He had a fiddle, which he would strum while he sang, out of key and out of tune, at the top of his voice, a long amusing recitative, deftly including in it the local gossip, the news of the day, and winding up with an appropriate Bible verse and a melodic series of *Amens, Hallelujahs, Glory Bes*, and *God bless you alls*. Obadiah was also a great catcher of fish. Christ was a fisherman, he said, and so were the disciples. Catching fish was one of the ways he made himself like them. Obadiah and Gretta lived miles from Jerry's on the way to Gates' Mill, but he often came home to Brenda's house, and Peter loved to be there when he and his string of fish and his fiddle came through the door, for where he was it was always a holiday.

5

As usual in late summer, the country seemed to have made great strides since this time last year. Hearing that some new artisans had come to Russellville, Dutch rode over there to see if he could trade the surplus of his corn crop for their services and products. He returned, smiling broadly, driving a new wagon, with a new dray horse for which he had traded a saddle horse, and with quite a budget of news. He said a main street had been laid out in Russellville, wide enough for two wagons to pass each other. This had inspired owners of log cabins along it to fence their yards, straighten sagging walls, put on new roofs, and sometimes to add another room. George S. Jones, a potter, had come to town, and was making churns, jars of various sizes, crocks, pitchers, bowls, and even cups and saucers. Josiah Wilcox, a tailor, had set up shop, and was making buckskin breeches and deerskin jackets.

When Peter carried this news home to the Doctor's, Allen bethought himself to give Peter a lesson in politics and geography. On the cleared space of ground which they used as a bulletin board, he drew a map of the country from the Mississippi to the Alleghenies, and showed Peter that the wild forest through which the mailman, Swaney, must pass to Natchez, and through which all who floated goods down to New Orleans must return, was to be made the territory of Mississippi. The wilderness on the other side of the Ohio, into which more and more Kentuckians who wanted to get away from Negro slavery and corrupt members of the legislature were going, had been made the territory of Indiana.

But in September, when the whole rich Mississippi Valley was basking in the comfort of fine weather, increased harvests, increased population, and hope and ambition on all sides, a terror and excitement began at Knoxville, Tennessee, and swept west. In the midst of conversation, one would stop and listen. "Hark. Did you hear shots?" Or, "Didn't you hear horses's hooves?" At night there were unseen presences just outside the door, and a haunting sense of voices in the barn. If a horse neighed suddenly, there was instant apprehension. The sense of smell was alert. "I thought some one was smoking outside. Didn't you smell tobacco?" Or, "Don't you smell powder?" "Don't you smell something burning?" A red glow on the horizon was terrifying, though at this season some one was always burning rubbish or having a barbecue.

Wherever one was, there was a feeling of being caught, and a gnawing desire to see one's fellows, combined with a sense of nameless danger in relation to any stranger, and sometimes between one and one's neighbors. When a friend appeared, one looked at him with a certain apprehension, as if he might be bringing bad news. There were persistent rumors, repeated but never quite proved. It was reported that there was a dead man lying on the road. It was one of the Baptists. It was William Morris. When Morris proved to be alive, it was one of the Mauldings. When the Mauldings were all accounted for, the story moved on to some one else. Sometimes the dead person was a woman. She had been raped, and her dead body found. The dreadful fate was fastened first to one girl, and then, when she proved to be all right, to the next. Through it all there was a sense of utter helplessness, as if the earth were no longer solid under one's feet or the sun sure to rise again tomorrow.

Before the skeptics had a chance to dissipate these stories, the ghoulish truth behind them became known. Dead bodies had been found, in several separate places, cut open, filled with stones, and dropped into rivers. Riverbeds, drying in the rainless days of autumn, revealed them. One who had courage to investigate such a story was Dean. With two Negroes he had ridden to the river and raised the body, which was in a state beyond recognition, and buried it, and picked goldenrod and asters and fringed gentian, and laid them on the grave, and then knelt and said a prayer.

Next day Dean rode over to talk to the Doctor. Peter saw him coming and ran to him, and, as he dismounted, stopped just short of running into his arms, like a child flying to its mother's breast; for seeing Dean was the next thing to seeing his family. Dean beamed through a shine in his eyes that was almost tears. "What a man he's gettin' to be," he said fondly to the Doctor. When Allen and Dean settled down under a tree to talk, and Peter took his place, as if by right, at their feet, Dean described the finding of the body and its condition in some clinical detail. Physician though he was, Allen sickened. Peter sickened, too. Allen wished he had sent the boy off. He could not get used to the frontier idea that life, whatever it was, should not be hidden from the young. He could see that, religious and gentle as he was, Dean was glossing over nothing for Peter's sake.

"It's widespread murder," said Dean, "and likely there's much more of it than we know yet. But what we don't know is who is murdering who, and why."

"Is it the Mystic Band?"

"Without question. Nobody can kill or rob without paying tribute to them and taking orders from them. Else they do away with him. Now, what we don't know is are they murdering each other, or killing the innocent"—he stopped and added soberly, "It looks like it might be both."

"But can't we trace who is missing—in places where unidentified bodies are found?"

Dean shrugged. "Out here folks will be missing for weeks, and then turn up somewhere. So if some one is missing who knows whether they're dead or have just got tired of being where they were?" He paused, and added, lowering his voice a little, "We arn't sure, but among the Negroes, we think we've found out about three that were killed this summer—two of them were Methodists. They found the grace of God, and joined the church. We think that's the whole secret of it."

"The whole secret?" repeated Allen. "I don't understand."

Dean explained. "You see, Doctor, the Band's got along all these years by using people that don't murder or steal. They just do errands for the Band, or make a profit by it, and keep their eyes shut. Or they've found out what's going on and have been scared into keeping their mouths shut. But it's heavy on their conscience. And when Brother McGready or Brother Burke starts preaching, and the power of God takes hold of them, and they come to the altar and kneel and sob before God—don't you see the Band's beside itself with fear of what they might tell. There's been a lot of telling going on—"

"Does Jus know this?"

"He does, and he's figuring right now how to get some of it into court. But he has to go careful, because before he does, there'll be murder."

"God help us!" said Allen. He seemed utterly crushed. There was not in him the toughness that had been bred even in this gentle, noble black man and in the boy Peter by long exposure to this situation.

Dean went on. "And there's the prayers. We've kept at them steady for more than a year now, and there's several hundred of us now, praying and fasting without fail. And I for one, won't stop wherever it leads, for this praying is the power of God speaking out of our poor sinful mouths. But, Doctor, on these wicked men, this prayer drips, drips, drips, like water wearing away a rock. Some of the Band have sworn to outdrink the prayers, and wherever there is grog to sell, they swarm in. Five minutes before prayers begin, they speak a string of profanity in unison, and down a gourd of brandy in one swallow. And they have what they call communion and drink from one cup which they pass along from one to the other, and any one who doesn't keep this up steady till past Sunday services in the churches, gets his throat slit."

"Have you told McGready and Elder Cook this?"

"I have, and they both say it's in God's hands. They say if you start facing up to evil, that's what you get, and not to be afraid, but to go on, for it's a terrible cleansing fire that will burn this land clean, but God will protect the innocent, and hold them in the hollow of His great hand."

"But suppose, among these madmen, some innocent person is killed?"

"It will happen," said Dean humbly, "only where it's God's will to take his own beloved out of this evil, and into the blessedness of His presence."

"True faith is a wonderful thing," observed Allen. "If you have it, you can't lose. Either way it turns out, it is for your good because it is God's will."

Quite unaware of the irony in the Doctor's tone, Dean answered, "Yes, that is true, Doctor."

But like many truly religious people, Dean was intensely practical. He proceeded to tell how, secretly paralleling the Regulators, the Negro members of the Christian churches were organizing, to collect and pass along information, to perform sentry duty, to guard women and children, slaves and free Negroes alike, without stepping out from the subservience society had imposed on them, as a secret, underground force in aid of all white Christians struggling for just government. Allen was touched. When Dean left, he took the big black hand and said gently, "Tell your brethren from me, Dean, that you have in you the mind that was in Christ Jesus."

Peter was touched, too. Through a sick, sinking feeling that followed Dean's visit and all he had told, he felt buoyed up by something in Dean's attitude.

Next day the need to keep talking and consulting in this nightmare of uncertainty and rumor and fear brought Dominie to the Doctor's. What Dean had said, Dominie already knew. But he added his own details obtained from his informants at Fort Massac and Louisville. He thought the plan Mason and Peter Alston had made for a tightly knit Band, bound together by a written constitution and an elaborate ritual, was breaking under the reaction of the less stable members of the Band to the preachings and praying. "Neither Mason nor Alston want murder. They want to live high off a great robbery business, conducted with as respectable a front as possible, under the guidance of lawyers and legislators they are able to buy with the profits. It's reported Mason has threatened to shoot anybody who takes notice of the prayers by getting drunk. It's also said that he's split with the Harpes because Micajah is threatening to go on a crusade of blood to stop the prayers, and to kill all preachers. Harpe says as soon as he can get down here, he's going to come and kill McGready, and then he'll go after every other sneaking, snivelling Christian in Logan County."

Allen was aghast. "Have you told McGready this?"

"Yes, and we offered him a guard day and night. But he refused it. However, we're taking measures for his protection, and we shall have armed guards for the preachings."

"Dean says that a good deal about the Band has come out in the confessions that converted sinners make. Can't you get enough for some indictments?"

"Jus has been trying. But every time he tries, Edwards, representing the Dromgoles and Alstons, comes up with a dozen witnesses proving that the suspected man was somewhere else. No matter how wide we fling our net to catch them, they manage to swear each other out of it. And all the while I don't think Edwards is a bad man or holds by this wickedness. It's only that he's doing what he thinks is his duty by the clients that pay him."

"What are you and the other veterans going to do about it?"

Though Allen said "veterans", Peter knew he meant Regulators. He pricked up his ears. Dominie replied soberly, "We now have three demands to make on the county government: That they investigate the destruction of the gunpowder plant; that they investigate what happened to the goods I ordered from Broadhead in Louisville; and the two Negroes in charge of it, and that they investigate these murders, and bring all perpetrators of all these crimes promptly to trial."

"And if they don't?"

Dominie said gravely, "Then let God be our Judge."

CHAPTER 20
**Russellville, Kentucky
September, 1798 to Mid-December, 1798**

On a warm September afternoon while Peter was conning the sentences Allen had marked in the *Kentucky Gazette,* Jerry clattered up and drew him outside. "Tomorrow's the day. The Regulators are serving notice on Wes Maulding and the whole lot." Then Jerry unfolded his plan. Peter would lie to the doctor and say that Brenda wanted him to help Jerry. Jerry would lie to Brenda and say that the doctor wanted him to go on an errand with Peter. They'd meet at the further side of the woods where two trails crossed, and light out for Russellville.

Listening, Peter kept scuffing the dusty ground with his moccasin. He hated to lie to the Doctor. He hated to go against what his father wanted. He wouldn't mind with others . . . But these two men! They were so good to him. Yet, deeply embedded in his mind was what his father often told his mother, "What he knows will never hurt him like what he don't know." He could hear himself arguing it out with his father on this thesis. He gave a loose rock a kick and sent it flying. "I'll be there," he said.

But he felt mean, and he felt meaner when the doctor said next morning, "By all means, go along to Jerry's. It's too fine a day to be inside." He galloped fiercely all the way. The ripe beauty of everything was oddly irritating like the innocent face of a child in the way of some one bent on wrong. But the feeling disappeared in excitement and curiosity as he started off with Jerry. It was as they had thought. Approaching Russellville, they saw grim groups of men, five or six riding together, heavily armed. They hid in the bush and saw the Baptists go by. They saw William Morris, the Portyghee. They saw McGready, with a set look on his face. They saw the Methodists, led by Dominie.

Tying up their horses in a safe place about three-quarters of a mile from the courthouse, Peter and Jerry sneaked nearer on foot, dodging from one hiding place to another. Amidst the rather squalid collection of log huts that was Russellville, and in the dusty open space around the courthouse, the crowds were milling. But it was not like the usual court day crowd. There were no women selling hot corn cakes. Nobody was holding an auction. Nobody had set up a horse race or a fist fight. There was just a large crowd of men, conspicuous among them a troop of young men, all wearing red plumes in their hats. Peter recognized the Mauldings, Dromgoles, Gilberts, and other rich young blades among them. He thought he recognized his brother John. He wondered vaguely what this new fashion of a red turkey plume was. Who was it wore a red turkey plume? Then he remembered. It was Alston —that time he saw him near Morton Maulding's.

Then somebody shouted, "Here they come!" And there was a solid body of men, at least a hundred, riding up to the courthouse, and in the front ranks there was Peter's father. Peter thrilled. "They're going to fix 'em. They're going to make the county court get down to business."

Then a trumpet sounded. A voice shouted, "Up, Rogues, and at them!" The men with the red plumes charged. The whole mass in front of the courthouse exploded—horseman crashing against horseman, volleys of shots, yells, screams, men in single combat, men fighting everywhere on foot, with dirks, daggers, and knives and clubs, blood spurting, fallen men trampled, men locked together rolling over and over in bloody mud.

The fighting men separated Peter from Jerry. Peter had a hot wish to get right into it and fight the nearest man. But one last remnant of loyalty to his father restrained him. His father didn't want him to. And when in the fight he caught a glimpse of his father's big, substantial form—that dear kind person who had been goodness and security to him all his life—he shrank down behind a tree, divided between an intense desire to be where his father was and fear lest his father, seeing him, should be hurt that he had disobeyed. Then he saw his father reel on his horse. He heard some one shout, "It's Cartwright. He's hurt." John Cobbler, the Circuit Rider, cut in, "Get out of the way. I'll get him out." He and two Methodist brothers dragged Peter's father out of the way of the fighting, and laid him under a tree. Peter could stand it no longer. Dodging in and out amidst bullets and trampling horses, he threw himself down on the ground beside his father. "Pappy! Pappy! Are you much hurt?"

His father turned his eyes on him, and Peter could see his spirit coming back as from a far place. "Peter!" he said sternly. "What are you doing here? Get out of this, young 'un. I say 'Get!' " He raised himself slightly, "Don't tell your mother. Go straight back to the Doctor's and, as you're son of mine, you stay there. Go!"

The Circuit Rider said, "Go, son. He's only hurt in the leg. We'll see to him. Go tell Doctor Allen he's wanted here. Don't tell him why. Go!"

Peter wriggled out and found Jerry. Jerry didn't want to leave. But a fury of determination possessed Peter. Always helpless before greater force than his own, Jerry had to go. He grumbled all the way, but Peter inexorably propelled him. "You shut your big mouth or I'll spill the whole thing, and your father will lock you up," he said furiously. Leaving Jerry at the cross-roads, he galloped to the doctor's house, and there was told by Cassius that the doctor had gone two miles away. Peter pursued him, caught up with him, and sent him to Russellville. "There's trouble there. My father's hurt." He broke down and cried unashamedly. . . .

In the late afternoon, after what seemed a hundred years, Allen came back, looking very tired. "Your father is all right. They put him on a sledge and got him home. It's only a hurt leg." Overflowing with relief and gratitude, Peter knelt by the doctor's chair, pulled off his boots, found his moccasins, brought him hot tea, serving him as gently as a daughter, listening with avidity to details about his home, mixed with casualties of the battle. He could hardly resist jumping on Diablo and going straight home. He heard the doctor say, "Peter, your mother says you can come home for the night, and come back here tomorrow." Home! A whole night at home! Peter was out of the door like a shot.

2

After that it was easier to stay with the doctor. A kind of gnawing, somewhere down deep in him, was eased. He knew his father was all right. He knew that Eddie and Bonnie were looking after the farm, and Sis had got her new teeth, and was beginning to be right helpful around the house, and that Polly was looking radiant and beautiful and was kind and affectionate to every one. "Polly must have a new beau," he thought shrewdly, making a mental note to find out who he was. Above all, he knew that his mother was happy in his association with the Doctor. She so much wanted him to be educated and grow up "useful and mannerly." She would not say "grow up a gentleman," because in her eyes gentlemen were still tyrants and "no-good show-offs," and "folks that live off other folks," to whose class she refused to aspire. Just having seen his folks, and knowing all this about them gave Peter a sense of rest as he settled back into the routine of life with the Doctor.

During the next few days he was absorbed in the post-mortems of the battle in Russellville. The Regulators had not intended to fight. They had come merely to show that there was a disciplined fighting force behind the demand that the sheriff and the county government take action in regard to the saltpeter destruction and the alleged murders. But all the while, unknown to them, another group had been organizing, and had named itself "The Rogues."

Its officers and leaders were the young men of the Maulding-Drom-gole-Gilbert set, the "social set" of this wild world, including John Wilcox. They wore red turkey feathers in their hats, and had some rigamaroles borrowed from the old Cavalier traditions of England. But the bulk of The Rogues were strangers, or comparative new-comers. Who was behind this? Who put them up to a bloody bat-tle in which five sons of five prominent families had been killed?

All this Peter heard discussed again and again. But what fixed his rapt attention was Dominie's report, because it gave word for word a conversation he and Jus, representing the Regulators, had had with Wes Maulding and Urbin Ewing, representing the county government.

Wes Maulding had said, "Folks are pretty mad at you Regulators. There was a big meeting in the woods last night with torches and with that old cross of fire which Alston used to call the Klan. They say you plan the violent overthrow by force of the government. They say you assume the functions of government yourself. You patrol roads and challenge people as if you were police. You have spies."

Ewing said, "I agree with Wes that your way's no good. But I agree, too, that there's got to be a change here. We've got to clean up the county government."

"You never will," said Jus, "so long's we don't challenge the prec-edent of always electing a Maulding to cut the claws of a Ewing, and letting Dromgole and his lot spend so much money and dish out so much whisky that they control the votes."

"Well, bring the matter up before the county court," said Ewing.

"We tried that. You know what happened."

"Try again."

"Would you advise us to come peacefully and unarmed, as private individuals?" asked Dominie.

Ewing looked at him levelly, and said, "I'd rather you'd turn up alive than dead."

Beyond that he refused to answer.

The whole country was in turmoil. Fear stalked the buffalo traces and the new narrow, dusty roads. There were said to be dead bodies here and there. A man was killed over by Rich Pond. Another said it was by Montgomery Pond and somebody saw his body floating. The rattling of the wind in the wooden shutters brought one's heart to one's mouth. Some families were planning to move away. Emigrants were staying near Lexington, or crossing over the Ohio preferring to brave Indians rather than the bad men of Rogues' Harbor. It was said that the goulish murderers lived in a cave, somewhere on the other side of the Big Barren River, and that the bodies of the murdered were hidden away in another cave.

In the mutual security of the thronged churches the people "let go" in an ever-increasing intensity of prayer, in violent weeping, and in frightening attacks of what were called "the jerks." Some day, placid scholars not many miles from here, growing gray in a security which had never felt a tremor of such danger as these people had lived with day and night for years, would write top-loftically, "In the year 1798 a wave of religious hysteria, originating in the Cumberland region, spread throughout the West." These safe scholars would never stop to ask, out of what horrors had these people stumbled to their rude altars; nor how out of "religious hysteria" had come the scholar's own chance to write foolish words in peace.

3

Peter had been told to take only the beaten path to Jerry's house which was now guarded by the German Baptists, stationed as invisible sentries in trees. But the afternoons were shortening these autumn days and once Peter, absorbed in trying to turn Jerry's attention from Polly to something more practical, failed to notice how low the sun was getting. As suddenly he saw it come into full sight, round and coppery and almost near enough to touch, spreading a pool of thick gold light over the gold of the autumn forest, Peter leaped on Diablo, and prodded him into those great flying leaps the wild horse of the conquistadores was capable of.

The sun was now sinking fast. Peter thought desperately, "What will the Docotor say? He'll be worried. He'll have everybody out looking for me." He glanced at the woods to the West, trying to figure how much time there was till the sun would be gone. A thought struck him. There was a short cut through the forest there, right into the Doctor's land. Spring and summer it was a swamp. But it must be dry now. He paused. The Doctor's admonition was in his ears, "Don't get off the beaten track." But that swamp was still on Dutch's land, and the Baptists had all this area guarded. Better take the risk that way than be out alone after dark.

He plunged into the bushes, toward the dried swamp, then reined up sharply. For at the sound of the crash a girl stood in his path. Under the gold leaves, transparent in the late sun, with the gold leaves all over the floor of the forest at her feet, she was an elfin, eerie figure. He saw the fair, light hair, the delicate face, and blue eyes with deep blue hollows under them. Then he saw that she was swelled out under her full blue calico skirt. "Goin' to have a baby!" That was his first thought. His second was a memory. Wiley Harpe and that girl—the lean-to, the fish frying, Wiley's hand under her shift along her white body—Sally Rice, the Parson's daughter!

She looked into his eyes and said in a sweet voice with an "eddicated" accent, like McGready's, like Allen's, "You're the Doctor's boy, arn't you?"

"Yes," said Peter.

She said, questioningly, "The Doctor's a good man? He keeps folks' secrets? What he learns in the way of his profession he keeps sacred, like—like a minister?"

"Yes."

"There's a man hurt in there," indicating the swamp. "He's been shot. Get the Doctor. Bring him quick. There's no time to lose. There are men after him. And Mike—" she closed her lips, "and help that was coming hasn't come. Oh please, please. Get the Doctor—please."

She had taken the neck of the big horse in both her slender hands and was trying to turn him around. "Don't worry," said Peter.

"I'm goin'."

Peter knew that Diablo could go fast if he wanted to, but never so fast as when, with great powerful leaps, he made the horse span the distance back to the Doctor's. The Doctor was standing in the door, anxiously looking out for him. Peter pounded up, gasping, "It's Sally Rice—she wants you. You know the one that ran off with Wiley Harpe. Somebody's hurt there—I don't know who. May be Wiley." An idea had been pounding through his mind with the pounding hooves. "Preacher McGready wanted me to tell if I could find trace of her. I'm going to get him."

"By all means," said Allen, "but see Jerry's family first, and tell them to close in about the place."

It was dark when Peter got back to the edge of the woods with McGready, a thick, starless black. He slowed the horse and went cautiously. "The turn off where I saw her should be here," he whispered. A hand gripped his bridle. With his left hand he drew up sharp, his pistol in his right hand. "It's me, Peter—Hans." Jerry's brother barely breathed the words. "Doctor Allen's in there, and the Regulators have the woods in siege, but we can't find hide nor hair of them."

"Let me try," whispered Peter.

McGready held him back. "No, no, Peter. We can't let you take the risk."

"It's no risk," said Peter confidently. "I'm the one to do it, for I'm the one she aint afraid of."

As he went forward into the forest dark, it was as if he had taken leave of the world and of his body, and was abroad in a lightless infinitude of emptiness. He was not frightened. He only felt a kind of wonder that one could go out of all that was and be here, in this nothingness. He called in a clear voice which he tried to make gentle, "Miss Sally! Miss Sally! I'm here. I've brought help."

There was no answer. Not a stir. He spoke again, and for the first time he was a little frightened. The sound of his voice was strange, here in this blackness. "Miss Sally, it's me, the Doctor's boy. I've brought the Doctor, like you asked."

No answer.

"Miss Sally, he's a good man. We don't mean harm. We mean good. We'll help you."

The silence mocked him. Then he jumped violently, and whirled on his horse, his pistol cocked. But it was only Hans, who had approached noiseless as a shadow. "The Doctor and Preacher McGready say come back, Pete. We'll have to wait till morning."

"Let me make one more try," whispered Peter. He called, "Miss Sally, if you don't speak, we're goin' away. The help you want is goin', Miss Sally, goin' now. It's the last chance, Miss Sally."

Silence. Peter turned his horse around and rode back to where McGready and Allen were waiting. He felt "put upon" by that wilful girl who wanted help and wouldn't take it. And all the while he was worrying, "Suppose something had hurt her. Suppose —" The horror of all that he had heard about the Harpes shook him. Suppose they had heard she had asked for help, and, to shut her mouth, they had killed her. He began to shiver. His teeth chattered. "You're cold, Peter," said Allen. "We must go home."

"Y—ye—yes, it's got chilly," sputtered Peter. But of the cold thought that had gripped him, he did not speak. No use upsetting Preacher McGready. He was disappointed enough.

Peter was sent home not to Allen's but to Jerry's house. McGready went home with Allen, to be present if there was a repetition in the night of the call for him. The German Regulators held the woods in siege till morning. With the first light, Peter and Jerry were out with them to view the place where Peter had met the girl, and the dried swamp. They found the ashes of a camp fire, some horse manure, and a rag soaked in blood. But they found no human beings. The Regulators beat up the woods for miles. No one was found. "So all we've learned from it," said McGready to Allen, "is that she's going to have a baby whose father, by all indications, is a thief and a murderer. How can I tell her father that?"

4

Under the name of Rogues, practically every able-bodied man in the county, outside the veterans and church members, was being organized to put down the "malcontents," as the Regulators were called, with Sam Mason and Peter Alston behind the scenes, and John Wilcox, Peter's half brother, as one of the young leaders out in front.

One afternoon toward dark, Jerry came over. "There's big doings tonight. The Rogues was going to come down on us Regulators to burn us all out, and kill us. And the Regulators have got wind of it, and they're riding tonight. After the doctor and you are in bed, you get away and get through the woods, and I'll be waiting on the other side with two horses."

Peter hesitated. He could see his father's head on the pillow, and his father's dark eyes looking at him, silently exacting a promise that next time there was trouble he'd stay out of it. He hadn't promised exactly, but he'd let his father think that he'd obey. But somehow he couldn't. He must see what was going on. If only because his own father was in it. But he was glad Jerry had thought of bringing two horses. Diablo was that noisy and snorting, he'd never get away without the doctor hearing.

After Allen had gone to bed, Peter sneaked out and made a beeline through the woods. It was a cold night, almost frosty. The cold had a cheerless, alien feeling. Peter's teeth chattered with cold and fear. He wished he'd brought his deerskin jacket.

"Hurry," said Jerry. "There's no time to lose." Peter sprang on the horse and they rode out of the shadows into the open fields lit by stars and a thin moon. "Look," said Jerry. "Yonder!" There was a red glare against the sky. Then one after another five great fires flared, each like an enormous bonfire, orange and red, scattering sparks. "It's the Regulators. They're burning them Rogues out. It's all those new cabins. That's the Rogues' hide-out." They drew nearer. Forms of men aiming guns were silhouetted against the flames, men charging, men falling, men appearing and disappearing. They could hear an animal-like continuous, sound—as of barks, and howls, and roars orchestrated with the shrieks of the hurt and dying and the neighing of wounded horses. Suddenly Jerry said, "They're coming this way."

The boys drew back. A crowd went by with a naked man on a rail—naked on that cold night. Then they heard a wild yelling and hooting, as the man was being rolled in tar and feathers.

The boys' horses were trembling, excited and prancing. It was all they could do to hold the beasts back from making a wild dash, and the need of keeping the animals under control kept the boys at a distance. But they were near enough to tremble under the whizzing of bullets. Each boy was looking out for his father. Once Jerry saw his. Peter thought, "That one's Pappy." But he could not be sure. A man whom he recognized as Dominie kept giving orders which no one obeyed.

Even with the fire so bright in the distance, it still seemed bitterly cold. The boys' spirits began to flag. The horses were shivering. Peter said, "We'd better get back. I'd rather not be found out." They rode back, it seemed, an endless distance, and after Peter left Jerry, he had to walk home alone through the woods. He was so nervous that the shadows were like hordes of evil things all around him. And when he got out into the blessed openness under the sky, the way was still a hundred miles long before him. The dark melted into the green light of dawn. There was a burning silver star above the horizon. And then the sun. And still he was walking. Then at last he saw the cabin, and with a last spurt of energy burst into a run.

When Peter saw Allen, he was so happy he could have rushed into his arms. But he stopped short, with chattering teeth, as Allen said sternly, "Well, young man! Explain yourself!" Peter could not have lied if he had wanted to. He was too tired, too broken up, too nagged with a deep consuming worry. Was his father safe? The whole night experience had been too weirdly out of this world. The comfort of this dear man's presence was like his mother's arms held out to him. He began to blubber and shiver, the tears rolling down his cheeks, his teeth chattering so that he could hardly speak. Allen was all tenderness. He made him sit down close to the blaze on the hearth and put a bearskin around him, and gave him hot water with a little whisky in it, and then some corn cakes and coffee. And Peter broke down and told the whole story.

Allen listened, his handsome, fresh face darkening. Almost to himself, he said: "All the law we have is lynch law! God, what a barbarous society! And to think that we expect to people these vast plains out here with savages — white savages! There is little enough of civilization on our East Coast. But what there is never gets across the Alleghenies."

With the whisky and corn cake inside him, Peter was determined to go over to his own home and see if his father was safe. Allen said, "I'll go with you. I'd rather not have you out alone in the state things are. You're tired, boy. Stretch out on the bearskin here by the fire while I get the horses and guns." Peter thought he should offer to get them, but he was too utterly weary. He lay back on the bearskin . . . . .

The next thing he knew he was staring at a night sky full of stars through the open shutter, and Allen was standing over him in the dim light of a dying fire. "I thought you'd never wake. You've slept around the clock."

Peter started up, and said wildly, "Pappy—is Pappy all right?"

"Your father is unhurt," said Allen gravely. "But I am sorry I must tell you that Jerry's father was killed."

5

For Peter all the outward events of his world passed unheeded because he was so absorbed with the way Jerry had taken his father's death. Peter went to the funeral and saw the big, heavy, good man lying in state under a pall of ground pine which Mary and Barbara had made. He had sobbed all through the service, and went home with Jerry afterwards and slept in the same bunk with him that night, holding the slight form that would not stop trembling against his own solid warm body to quiet it. And he was at Jerry's house often during the next few days, for Brenda leaned on him as if he were her own son, and he got along better with her than did most of her own family. Though she was cold and stony, and her handsome dark face was like a mask, he had, through his deep sympathy with his own mother, an instinctive understanding of the reasons why superior frontier women were likely to be irritable and harsh.

From the day his father died, Jerry seemed cut off from life. Most of the time he was thin, pale, and strangely absent. But about once a week he would be transfigured with a strange inner light which lasted about a day, and then gradually went out, leaving him more languid than before. At such times he told Peter that his father had come back and talked to him. Soon these visits came further and further apart, and between them Jerry grieved and worried lest his father should never come to him again. There were times when Jerry's obsession gave Peter "the creeps". But at other times it set him thinking about death and the whereabouts and fate of the personal self when it drops the worn-out clothing of the body.

The hardest thing these days was to keep whisky from Jerry. One day Peter found him prancing along the path by the river. "Jerry," he said, sternly, "you smell of liquor to high heaven." Jerry began to cry, and then he passed out cold. Peter was so angry that he picked him up bodily and hurled him into the icy water. "That will sober you," he said, hauling him out and giving him a final angry shake. Jerry broke down and wept floods. Peter was divided between anger, disgust, and intolerable pity. At another time, Jerry, instead of passing out, was disgustingly sick. Peter said darkly, "I helped clean you up this time, but never again. Next time I'm goin' to leave you there, sittin' in your own vomit!" But through it all Peter clung to Jerry in the same powerful adhesive way that he loved his own family. And the more trouble Jerry was, the more deeply he was concerned with him. Meanwhile the Regulators, being mostly sober, god-fearing men, were appalled by the turn their well meant efforts had taken. They had started out only to forestall an attack by the Rogues on them, and a group, headed by Dominie, and including Hendley Russell, the jailer, had gone on to Russellville and waited on the sheriff with the names of eleven men—mostly newcomers in the community—who were inciting the Rogues, and who, it was believed, were members of the Mason-Alston gang. What happened then, nobody could tell. Some said that the criminals themselves set fire to their own houses. Some said that one set of them attacked the other set. Then the whole thing had got out of hand. A crowd from South Carolina who weren't Regulators had swept in and lynched and hanged a number of men. Dutch, trying to control his own band and keep them from joining the lynchers, had been shot in the head. Dominie and Jus were profoundly affected by the loss of their old friend and comrade—the more so as they felt that the whole performance was difficult to justify. But they intended to defy punishment for it. They would stand out and force the state authorities to investigate Logan County.

Neither punishment nor rebuke was administered. Instead, people in surrounding areas looked upon the Regulators as heroes. It was said that Governor Garrard was intending to look into the situation in Logan County, with a view to backing up these righteous but long suffering citizens. Wesley Maulding was placating. Morton Maulding said, anything state authorities wanted to do to clean up Logan County he'd co-operate with. Neither Jus nor Dominie believed that much would be done. But they had proved to themselves that armed force would accomplish nothing either. Jus even agreed with Mary, who said, "Gunfire is something two can play at, and those with the blackest hearts can get the most guns and do the most murder. If law and righteousness is what you're on the side of, by law and righteousness you must abide."

Under the urging of McGready and the circuit riders and the new Baptist preacher, there came the Sunday when the Regulators in each congregation marched up the aisle, and laid their guns down at the altar, and bowed their heads while the preacher prayed that God would show them a better way. Peter had been allowed to ride over to Ebenezer to see Dominie and the Methodist class lay down their guns. Usually the Doctor discouraged attendance at any preachings, because he thought the "hysterics" of revivalism unwholesome and unseemly. He was striving to find in the Universalist literature a religion which would allay the peoples' terrors, instead of whipping them into these convulsive soul-changes which McGready and the Methodists and, to some extent, the Baptists thought necessary. Moreover, the Doctor did not like to have Peter brought back in contact with his own family, at Ebenezer, lest the powerful pull of old ties divert him from his schooling. So going to Ebenezer to watch the laying down of the guns had been a special indulgence.

It was a simple act, rather clumsily performed, in that bare little log church, but for Peter it needed neither music nor pageantry. The passions behind it, the moral struggle and intention, were for the sensitive boy high drama. He sat with bowed head, while the benedictory prayer rolled over him, thinking, "Killin' won't do it, but something must. We've got to find a way. We've got to." People were rising and beginning to talk to each other. Peter started to his feet, "Why, that's Pappy. That's Pappy shouting out there!" His father had not taken part in the laying down of the guns, though he had concurred in it, because church just naturally went against his grain. Peter stood up. What had happened to bring Pappy clattering to the church door? He looked across to the women's side of the aisle. Mammy and Sis and Bonny were all enveloped in whirls of hoods and furs and skirts. Then the tall form of his father strode up the aisle, and the people, struggling to get out where he had been shouting, parted to let him through, some sinking back on to the puncheon seats. Jus held a piece of paper in his hands.

"Friends and neighbors," he said, "it's my privilege to give you first before anybody else the word that's been sent to me from the court at Stanford, through my friend Moses Shelby, who, you all know is the brother of our first Governor who helped us veterans to settle here against all who would oppose us. The word is: Micajah and Wiley Harpe were captured on the twelfth day of this month of December, in this year 1798, with three women named Susan, Betsy, and Sally, and are in jail in Stanford, and will be tried there for the murder of Thomas Langford on Wilderness Road."

6

Through the crowds thronging about his father, clamoring for more detail, Peter saw that Jus had caught sight of him and was pushing his way to him. He pushed from his end, and amidst nudging of elbows, and treading of toes, and clamor of talk and question, father and son met two thirds of the way down the narrow aisle. Jus drew Peter down into a seat with him and said, "I want you to get Jerry, and you two go and take this message to Bill Stewart, Wesley Maulding, Sam Cauldwell, and Burwell Jackson. Look sharp how they take it, and tell me. And then you and Jerry ride around to your brother John Wilcox and tell him."

The eagerness in Peter's face clouded over. "Must I go to John's?" he asked.

"Most particularly John," said Jus firmly, adding, "and you might tell us how he's set up and how that fancy wife of his is doing."

Peter had not seen his brother when he returned from a "business trip" to New Orleans with a wife he called "Penny," and took her for a courtesy call on his family. Since then they had seen nothing of him, but had heard that he was living in high style. Peter's deep moral distaste for his brother was intensified by a determination not to be made to feel inferior by John's fancy clothes and manners.

"But what about the Doctor?" demurred Peter. "He says it's understood—"

"That you take orders from him and not from me," said Jus, smiling. "So you do. But I'll see the Doctor and fix it up with him for this once."

Spreading his wings like a wild bird free of the cage, and thrilling to the dramatic import of his mission, Peter dashed around with Jerry over the crusty December fields. Jerry's pale face glowed, and he seemed to be alive for the first time since his father's death, as if charged with Peter's own electric energy. The first to get the news was Wes Maulding, the sheriff, and the next was Bill Stewart, who usually alternated with Wes in the sheriff's office. Both were loud in their protestations that it was a good thing. Likely as not the Harpes were at the bottom of all these murders—at least Micajah was. "It's the drink," said Wesley, soberly. "Micajah just can't stand drink."

Cauldwell and Burwell Jackson received the news with the reserve of statesmen who might be called upon to make some weighty decision in consequence. Jackson said, "So they've been operating on Wilderness Road. I suppose we have the Regulators to thank for that. At least they were run out of here." But Cauldwell observed, "So they were in the East all the time! Then the murders in Logan County can't be set to their account." Peter did not say that he knew Wiley Harpe had been here at the time of the murders, and that he had thought Sally's inadvertent mention of "Mike" as one who was coming to their help meant Micajah was here, too. But he talked it over with Jerry as they rode to his brother John's place. Wiley or whoever it was with Sally had got away. If it was Wiley, he had not been too badly hurt to get into circulation again. Peter's thoughts kept circling around Sally. Something he had seen in Wiley's love-play, and in her swelling figure, had reached down and taken hold on the impulses of coming manhood. He felt deeply concerned about her, but in a blind, almost impersonal way, fusing the idea of Woman with a sense of the irrationality of life and the utter pity of things. "It's likely she'll have to have that baby right there in jail," he said, "and no woman to tend her except Susan and Betsy." He gave Diablo such a vicious kick that the great brute rose with all four feet in the air. "It just don't make sense, a girl like her in jail with those trollops!"

But Jerry thought a parson's daughter would run away with anybody to be rid of religion. "You just don't know how aggravatin' religion can be if it's choked down your throat morning, noon, and night," he told Peter. Peter couldn't understand this. Though in his unregenerate young heart he did not share his mother's religion, there was many a time when she had made it a comfort to him, and it was bound up in his mind with all that, in essence, a mother was. Separated as he now was from his mother, and deeply missing her, there was a kind of romantic, idealizing, golden glow over every memory of his mother's prayers and hymns and Bible readings, and tart philosophizing on good and evil. But he couldn't explain this to Jerry. All he managed to say was, "My Mammy's religious, and it kinda makes me feel good that she is."

CHAPTER 21

The low sun was making sparks on fields lightly powdered with snow, as Peter and Jerry turned down the trail that led to John's house, and were struck dumb by the sight of the two storey structure of logs, with one-storey wings reaching to right and left. All the windows were of glass. The massive doors had iron hinges and locks. All around the cedar trees had been thinned out to make park-like masses of green, flanking the house.

And when they rode up to the door, it opened and a Negro man asked them to come in. At the same time another Negro appeared and took their horses. They entered a kind of miniature baronial hall which to Peter, who had never seen a baronial hall, looked like a large and very much dressed up cabin. At one end a large, shallow fireplace of brick, with brass andirons threw a glowing warmth out into the whole room. The walls were covered with tapestries, the floors with Oriental rugs. The chairs had brocaded satin seats.

An inner door opened, and his brother John came in, handsomely dressed in fawn colored knee-breeches, silk stockings, buckled shoes, and a brown cut-away coat. His fair hair was drawn back and tied in a black silk bag. Peter wondered, "Does he rig himself out like that all the time, or is it put on to make me feel low?"

"Why, Peter," said John, in an accent that sounded odd but somehow high-toned, to Peter who had never heard an "English accent." "This is a surprise, a most agreeable surprise," he added, turning to Jerry, and taking the boy's rough paw in a hand that was white, with well cut finger nails. "It's good to see you, Jerry. Penny will be most

There was a sharp click of heels, and a twitter, and Penny came happy that you have called."

rustling through the door, on a breeze of perfume. Peter's first glance identified her as he would a bird—same species as Hon and Sweetie, Sam Mason's daughters—reddish hair pulled high over what must be a pillow, greenish eyes with a staring, yet droopy look, eye-lashes stiff and black and standing straight out, upper lids touched with silver, and soot smudged under the eyes. Her cheeks were red, and her lips redder, and the rest of her skin a pasty white. She had a tight bust from which her silk skirts sprang out in a big bunch on both sides. She wore white stocking and slippers with heels set up high on what Peter thought must be pegs of wood. She overwhelmed both boys with welcome, in a soft languishing voice with the same accent John had acquired.

A Negro had removed the boys' fur-lined jackets and boots, and now re-entered with wine glasses on a silver tray. Peter was not unfamiliar with wine. The Doctor had a bottle he was keeping for some special occasion. But he had never drunk it. John poured the wine, explaining that it was some special vintage he had got in New Orleans, all of which seemed so much rigamarole to Peter. But he liked the wine, and wondered, as he sipped it, why people burned their insides with whisky when they could have this. However, he did not mean to let all these amenities divert him from his message. As soon as he could get John's attention, he came right out with the announcement that the Harpes were now in jail in Stanford awaiting trial for murder. He saw John blanch and his hand tremble so that he had to set down his glass. "Who are the Harpes?" asked Penny.

John, recovering his composure, unfolded a tale of heroic suffering. The Harpes, he said, were martyrs to the cause of hereditary *noblesse* in a barbarous world. Their father had been a British officer who, remaining true to his king when the rabble revolted, had died a hero's death at the Battle of King's Mountain. As a gentleman's progeny, his two sons were of finer clay than the peasants among whom they were left in the Carolina mountains. And when these crude Americans taunted them and avoided them as sons of a Tory, the high-spirited youths could not abide this insult, and ran away to the Indians.

"They took refuge with the noble red man," breathed Penny. "How romantic!"

When the youths grew up, they returned to society, with a deep and burning sense of wrong. "Wiley takes it like a philosopher," said John, "and, if it were not for Micajah, would settle down somewhere and become a planter. But Micajah is driven by a wild and dark desire for justice, and when he tries to drown the memory of what his father was and what he is forced to be, in drink, it often brings him to a state where Wiley feels bound to save him from himself."

"Lest he plunge a sword into his own bleeding heart," said Penny. "What fraternal devotion!"

Peter looked at her in amazement and disgust. He had never heard of the late eighteenth century cult of "sensibility," nor the maudlin heroics of the new romantic movement. So when Penny dripped with sensibility, in accordance with what was then the latest fashion in polite European circles far from these Kentucky wilds, Peter thought she was just a new and nauseous kind of fool. And as John paused in this masterpiece of narration, Peter remarked bluntly to her, "All John's doing is taking a long and fancy way of saying the Harpes are trash."

Penny blinked her stiff black eyelashes, and the puffs and folds of her stiff silk dress seemed to rise like the feathers of a startled bird. John said loftily, "You can't believe all you hear, Peter, especially among the low-bred yokels out here."

"It's not what I hear but what I see," said Peter. "Micajah Harpe was—" He paused, seeking a word. Two could play at this game of high-toned language. He borrowed a word from his father's legal vocabulary, "er-er *domiciled* with Old Man Roberts. And that's where a pig wouldn't ever be if it had a choice."

Ignoring Peter, John said meaningly to Penny, "Micajah was enamored of Betsy Roberts."

"And a true man will do anything for love," said Penny, rolling up her green eyes, starry with feeling.

Peter could stand it no longer. He set down his glass and stood up. "Jerry and I have got to be going, John," he said. "The dark sets in early, and though we've got the Harpes locked up, there's plenty of your Rogues left that we wouldn't want to meet in the night."

John chose to ignore this. With great courtesy, both he and Penny saw the boys into their fur-lined coats and accompanied them to the door. Penny hung on Peter fawningly, telling him that she was his sister now, while his skin twitched under his deerskin sleeve at her touch. Then she transferred her endearments to Jerry, who, unlike Peter, blushed and beamed under the honeyed caresses with which she pulled his jacket snug around him, and said if he ever needed to confide in an understanding heart to come to her.

All the way back Jerry was in a romantic daze which made Peter furious. He acted as if, in his half brother's wealth, fine manners, fine house, and beautiful bride, Peter had come into a great fortune which he was idiotically spurning. 'There's plenty that would be glad to pick up a piece of what you're ready to kick out," he told Peter. "If I could grow up like a brother in that house, if I could have Penny—to—to talk to—to tell me—"

"You let them alone," said Peter angrily, "or you'll rue the day. They're trash!"

Heading for his parents' house, he forced Jerry to listen to his own description of John, Penny, their accents, their sentiments, in his own language. Against the ironic lights that played on Justurian's face, as his son made his report, and something between horrified recoil and occasional grim amusement in Mary's face, Jerry had no chance to tell what he thought. When Peter had finished, there was silence for a moment. Jus raised one eyebrow and looked at his son quizzically, as if asking a final judgment. Peter looked at his mother questioningly. Mary, looking from father to son, said, with a grim smile, "I think so, too."

That was all they'd say about a member of the family before Jerry. But even Jerry knew that it was enough.

2

The Harpes were to be tried before Hugh Logan, Nathan Huston, and William Montgomery, Judges. This trial made *The Kentucky Gazette* a household necessity, and put the art of reading at a premium. Allen sent Peter to get his copy at Cedar House as soon as it was delivered. If he wasn't there at the moment when the carrier rode up, with packhorses laden with papers, he couldn't get one. For it was impossible to save one of the precious sheets against the demand on them, even for the Doctor. Peter learned more in spelling out the details of the trial than he had learned in all his life before. For once there was a murder for which there were enough witnesses to testify. Five men appeared before the court and gave testimony written down on loose leaves by the clerk, to the effect that Micajah Harpe and Wiley Harpe had heinously and with malice aforethought murdered Thomas Langford on the road through the Wilderness, and they displayed Thomas Langford's clothes and effects which were found on the Harpes, including a greatcoat of gray coating cloth, a short coat, a mixed-color long coat, a pair of breeches, a shaving glass, a whip, a pair of wrappers, and a Free Mason's apron, and they showed that one of the horses which the Harpes had was Langford's horse.

All through the winter, the discussion of the Harpe trial enlivened Peter's trips with the Doctor on his rounds. Everywhere he heard it whispered that Moses Stegall and Jacob Leiper were confederates of the Harpes. There was a saying whispered about—no one knew where it had come from—some said it had been told to the good Portyghee William Morris in a dream—"If murder comes again, look for it from the northwest." And every time he heard this, Peter remembered that nice woman, Trixie Stegall, with concern. Trixie had a baby now. The baby must be company for her where she'd been so lonesome. But it wasn't fitting to bring up a baby in the shadow of the Harpes.

One stormy morning at the end of February, 1799, Moses Stegall came clattering up to the Doctor's door, his open, well-featured face showing bright red amidst the frosting of snow and sleet on his deerskin hood. "I've ridden since before dawn," he gasped. "The baby has the croup—very bad. I'm called from home on business to Stanford. Please, Doctor, go to her, and whatever you can do I'll more than make it up to you."

"It's too bad a day for you to go out, Peter," said the Doctor, after Stegall, refusing even hot coffee, had galloped off. "You stay home and keep the fire burning bright."

"If the day's too bad for me to go, it's too bad for you to go without me," answered Peter. He took down his fur-lined coat and hood from the peg, pulled on his fur-lined moccasins and laced them up around his deerskin pants, and hung his fur-lined mittens, which were attached to a deer-thong around his neck. He opened the door into the sleety blast outside.

"Where are you going?" asked Allen.

"To get our two horses." The boy's black eyes, glancing sidewise, asked forgiveness for disobeying the Doctor's command and, at the same time, dared him to repeat it. Allen met the look with an affectionate smile. "You are growing up to be one of Nature's noblemen, Peter. Nature's noblemen have many virtues, but obedience is not one of them."

With the Doctor's look and words warm in his heart against the wind, Peter brought around the horses, and they were off. For the dozen or more miles to the Stegall's they rode northwest into the sleety wind, which whipped them as with splinters of glass. Peter kept his head low and rode blind, telling the Doctor to do the same and ride closely, nose to tail. He did not ask, "What would a gentleman tenderfoot do without me on a day like this?", but the strong beat of Diablo's big hooves was saying it for him, and the Doctor knew and was grateful.

Stegall's cabin seemed a haven indeed, as they rode up to the door. Peter could already feel the warm and clean snugness within. Trixie had been watching for them through a small glassed insert in the door, and, flinging it open, almost threw herself into the Doctor's arms. "I've prayed and prayed for you," she said. "I've been so scared I couldn't keep the breath in him till you came." The Doctor went straight to the cradle by the fire, where the blue-faced baby lay gasping. A man rose from beside the cradle. Stocky, weather-beaten, he seemed to Peter about his father's age. "We'll have to have a kettle of boiling water," said Allen. The man spoke for the first time. "I thought you might, Doctor. It's here."

"This is Major Love, Doctor," said Trixie. "He's got one of those old military grants, but he's never had a chance to survey for it till now."

"I'm aiming to bring my wife out here, come spring," remarked Major Love, as he lifted the kettle from the hearth to the place on the table which the Doctor indicated. "Mrs. Stegall's been right kind in helping me settle, and letting me sit down to her table with her when I can't stomach my own grub any more."

"I don't know what I'd do without the Major," she said. "He's been so kind bringing wood and water and helping when Mose is away."

"Well, you're in good hands now, and I'm one too many," observed the Major, tramping to the door. "If I'm needed maybe the boy would be good enough to come for me."

Busy as he was with the baby, Allen gave a searching glance at the man who had suddenly appeared in this attractive and lonely young woman's life. Back where he came from, such a situation would be occasion for gossip. He had a chivalrous desire to protect her, but did not know how. Observant, and even suspicious as he usually was, Peter, in his innocence, thought nothing of it. He was absorbed in helping the Doctor make a kind of linen tent over the kettle, and helping to hold the poor little head and chest of the gasping baby in the steamy enclosure. He had often seen the Doctor perform miracles by steaming the croup out of the blocked windpipe and nasal passages.

After the baby was relieved, and had fallen into a moist and delicately flushed sleep, Peter sat on the hearth by the cradle watching him. He loved babies as he loved kittens and puppies and baby raccoons and small downy wild ducks when he could catch them. And this love which he shared with most good-hearted boys, then and since, had never been laughed out of him by schoolmates or neighbors, as happens to boys in more civilized parts of the world.

So he crouched on the hearth, content as a cat, studying the line of the baby's lashes on its flower soft cheek, and noting with concern the occasional convulsive twitching of its delicate tiny hands. And all the while he was drowsily relaxing in the warmth, after his long ride, and sniffing that new-fangled delicacy, hog and hominy, which Trixie had cooking in an iron kettle, suspended inside the fireplace from an iron crane.

The physician of those days was also a kind of trained nurse. Allen felt bound to stay until he was sure that the baby would be all right, and that Trixie had learned just what to do. This meant sharing the noon meal with Trixie who, as usual, was delighted to have guests at her table. Fortunately for the Doctor who never knew what to talk about in these frontier households, her relief that the baby was better flowed out in a steady stream of talk, into which he hardly had to insert even an occasional "yes." She described Major Love's plan for his house and farm in great detail and repeated all that he had told her about his wife. "She's got red hair, and isn't as tall as I, and she's got a loving heart but a terrible temper, and she's right pretty," adding, "I can hardly wait to have a nice woman for a neighbor, after all the time I've had to be alone." She branched off into a description of the last Methodist preaching here. Come spring and a few more settlers, and may be they could form a class. At this point Peter brought up the question of the Harpes. "Well, I don't know," she commented. "May be they're more sinned against than sinning." Then, turning back to the Doctor, "I'm one of those that prays regularly for the redemption of all sinners in Logan County, and I always say a prayer especially for Micajah and Wiley Harpe."

"Why?" asked Peter. She answered evasively, "Oh, because my husband knows Micajah and those Harpe boys have had a hard time and if they were to get converted, it would take a load off everybody's mind."

Peter looked at her keenly. "She isn't as easy about Mose Stegall as she was," he thought. A devastating idea took hold of him. Stegall had gone to Stanford, where the Harpes were in jail. Why?

As they turned homeward, with night lowering over the icy

landscape, neither Peter nor the Doctor was happy about their visit to Trixie, even though the baby was better. "I kinda think something's wrong there," observed Peter when two thirds of the way home. The storm ceased, the stars came out, and the night was suddenly still, so that they could talk as they rode down the last miles on a main traveled way where they could go two abreast.

The Doctor was startled. "What do you think is wrong?" he asked, thinking of Major Love.

Peter answered uncertainly, "I don't know. I feel more wrong there than I can lay my fingers on."

3

One of Peter's pleasantest duties these days was to take L'il Papoose to Dominie's house to play with their little daughter, Dolly. L'il Papoose was now a pretty girl with a mass of golden curls, who prattled sweetly in Indian dialect. Since her own family had never been found, Dominie and Barbara proposed to adopt her as soon as she could be weaned from the Indians. But she clung to the deerskin skirts of her Indian foster-parents, and could be persuaded to leave them only when Peter took her on Diablo. Otherwise she wailed dolefully until restored to the kind brown arms she was used to.

One gray afternoon in March, as Peter was riding home from Dominie's with L'il Papoose, he saw that Gray Wolf and a dozen other Indians were out watching for him by the brimming river. "Something's wrong," he thought, kicking Diablo into one of his great flying leaps. He splashed through a puddle of water to Gray Wolf's side, and, as he handed down the little girl, he looked questioningly into the Indian's eyes.

"Big Harpe and Little Harpe, loose," said Gray Wolf in his soft, plaintive voice. "Got away."

"But they have them chained. Each one is chained by two horse-locks to the ground in the jail in Stanford. They're chained fast, Gray Wolf. How could they get away? It's a jail they're in

—thick walls of big tree trunks, and a man on guard, and they chained inside."

Gray Wolf shook his head. "They break loose. Are free. Get away. Go to Cave-in-Rock." He added, almost in a moan, "Nobody safe any more. They go on a big kill. Kill every praying Christian."

Unable to make sense of the Indians' story, yet knowing that, in such matters, the Indians were usually right, Peter galloped home to the Doctor's. There he found McGready and others already discussing the news. On March 16, 1799, while their trial was still going on, Micajah and Wiley Harpe had broken jail, leaving behind their three women, Betsy and Susan Roberts, and Sally Rice, each with a new-born baby, one boy and two girls. Peter's first thought was: "Somebody must have helped them—may be bribed the jailer." He remembered that Moses Stegall had gone to Stanford. But he didn't speak his thought. His second thought was, "If Wiley has left Sally, may be she can be made to go back to her father." This thought he spoke to McGready.

McGready answered, "That's what we are working on. But even though Sally is my friend's daughter, I think we should not try to help her only. The three girls are sisters in sin, in trouble, in motherhood. We must help all alike."

During the next weeks this kindly thought materialized in a great outpouring of good-will to the Harpe women. Collections of money and goods were taken in all the little log churches between Russellville and Stanford. Three horses and clothes and provisions enough for the trips back to their homes were sent to the jail at Stanford, and the jailer himself escorted them out of town and set them on their way. A bill at the jail for tea, sugar, and ginger for Betsy was paid out of public money.

It was soon known that the Harpe women had traded their horses for a canoe, and were floating down the Green River, then down the Cumberland, and finally that they had joined the Harpes at Cave-in-Rock. "Looks like it had all been a put up game," said Peter, listening wisely to a crowd who had brought the Doctor *The Kentucky Gazette* and lingered to discuss the news. "Looks like the jailer that let the men go was bribed, or else he was part of the whole gang, and the women had got word to their men where to meet them." He pursed up his lips, thinking hard trying to reproduce the thoughts and movements of these people, exactly as he tried, in hunting, to figure out where the deer or the bear would go and what they would do. Just then Jo, the Methodist brother came galloping up, his horse sweating, perspiration streaking through the dust on his own face. "Heard the latest," he gasped. "The Harpes are up along the Ohio River. They took a man, stripped him naked, took him to the edge of a cliff, set him on a horse, and pushed him and the horse over, and there they were dancing and shrieking and pointing to the bloody mess 100 feet below. Folks below saw it. They're out, full cry, after them."

The whole state rocked with anger. Petitions poured in on Governor James Garrard, urging a state-wide hunt. He published a proclamation in the *Frankfort Palladium*, offering $300.00 reward for the capture of Micajah Harpe and Wiley Harpe. Descriptions of the men were broadcast, posted in taverns, carried by circuit riders, passed on by word of mouth. Peter rode over to Jerry's to read him the notice. "The big man is pale, dark, swarthy and has a reddish gun-stock. The little man has a blackish gun-stock, with a silver star with four straight points. They have short sailors' coats very dirty and large greatcoats." Since the machinery for law-enforcement was weak and the criminals' escape into these wide open spaces easy, the people were rapidly developing the characteristic American attitude to crime. It had become everybody's business to get the criminal.

It was no less everybody's business to protect against crime. Hearing that many new settlers hesitated to cross the Green River, because the Barrens had so long been the haunt of outlaws, Jerry's brother-in-law, Obadiah, the singing Methodist, set up a welcome station on the further side of the river. When he saw a group approaching on the opposite bank, he crossed over to meet them, carrying a string of fish as a present, and usually with his fiddle swung across his shoulder. He would guide them across, offer them rest and entertainment, chart their course for them, give them names of

Methodists who might help them, and, if they wished to stay with him for a while, would end up with a program of his own recitatives and spirituals, accompanying his voice with his violin. For this service Obadiah took no money. But when grateful people insisted on paying him in cash or produce, he would set it aside to be used for "movers" who might be in distress.

For the last few months, since Dutch died, Obadiah had had Jerry's little brother Heinie staying with him. When it came time to take the wheat to Gates' Mill to be ground, Obadiah said, send Peter and Jerry and he'd meet them and guard them through the only really bad place—a stretch of tangled woodland now coming into full leaf. So, with great delight, Peter and Jerry made the trip and spent a wonderful day at a fish-fry Obadiah had organized for "movers" out of doors, and came back with the music of his fiddle in their ears.

4

The attempt to get at crime through the Regulators had failed. The attempt to try the Harpes had failed. There was now only one hope. A new young elder, big, radiant John Page, had replaced Valentine Cook on the Methodist big 600 mile circuit. He and his circuit riders were preaching four or five times a day at meetings from five to twenty miles apart. McGready was working intensively around Russellville. Lewis Moore, the Baptist, was gathering in the Portyghees and the Negroes. But it wasn't enough. "We've got to have some place where they can gather, not by little log churchfuls, but by the thousands," said Page to McGready.

Then McGready made a bold stroke. About four miles north of the Cartwright farm there was a noble grove of trees and a spring. There McGready determined to set up an outdoor church, with a stand or pulpit for the preacher, and rows of split log seats—all decent and in order as became a Presbyterian. Everybody helped except Mr. Balch's decent Presbyterians, who by this time were reduced to three. Peter went over there every morning and spent a happy day, cutting trees, splitting logs, and eating a picnic lunch with his mother and Eddie whom he had not had much chance to see. The blue sky, the fresh summer sunshine, the savory smell of the things the women folk were cooking for the men workers, took Peter's mind off the Harpes.

One day as Peter was helping to set up the last log bench his mother came to him. "Quick, Peter! Ride over to Jerry's! A dreadful thing has happened!"

Peter raised his eyes, absently at first, his thoughts still far off. Then he went frozen cold, and began to tremble. Mary's lips were dry. She could hardly speak. "The Harpes. They've killed Heinie." "Heinie!" It was a wail, a protest, a cry of utter unbelief. Heinie rose before Peter's mind—dear little Heinie, with his winsome face. "Heinie! Mammy!"

"They killed him," she said, speaking almost mechanically, "and they killed Obadiah."

Somehow Mary gave the details. Broken, unorganized, out of sequence they reached Peter's stunned and unbelieving consciousness. Obadiah, discounting the tales about the Harpes and trusting to the Lord, had sent Heinie with his dog to a neighbor's to get some flour and seed beans. Then he had seen what he took to be movers on the other side of the river. Clad in shirt and trousers, without shoes and stockings, a turkey over one shoulder and a string of fish over the other, and a fiddle tucked under his arm, Obadiah started to wade across the river. He was butchered, and his body cut open, filled with stones, and thrown into the river. Going on, the "movers" had met Heinie, and had dashed his head against a tree, and taken his flour, but not the seed beans. His dog had returned home wounded. A little further on, the "movers" had been recognized as the Harpes, but had escaped the cry raised after them.

Riding to Jerry's, Peter found Brenda and Jerry and the older brothers gathered in the Baptist church, with the Baptists, white and black, in a close circle around them, weeping together, praying, and singing softly in a moaning way. He tiptoed in and knelt with them. At the sound of weeping he felt his heart break and become all water, and he wept and wept as if he would never stop. They stayed together like that for hours. They could not bear to part, and face the horror of everything outside. When Allen came with an armed guard to get Peter and take him back to his house, and Peter rode away in the drowsy summer afternoon, he could hear through the woods, the sound of their voices, like the dropping of rain, singing the words of Charles Wesley, "Help us to help each other, Lord, each other's cross to bear."

5

Every able-bodied young man was out to hunt the Harpes. The man-hunters went by continually, in squads of a dozen or so. The hot air was choking with their dust, and the leaves of trees and bushes gray with it. Horror stories swirled wherever two or three were gathered together. The Harpes had been seen north of Green River. They killed a little girl and a Negro boy, but left the Negro boy's horse and bag of grain untouched. They split open the heads of a man named Graves and his son with an axe, and threw the bodies into the bushes. About eight miles from Dromgole's station at Adairsville, at a place long associated with murdering bands, they and two Cherokee Indians killed the two Triswold Brothers and many children. So the stories ran, not yet verified, and growing from mouth to mouth.

The women and children were gathered together in the log churches, and in the larger private houses under the armed guard of the older men. Boys of Peter's age were a problem. Some were inclined to keep them with the women and children. Others to use them as spies and messengers under strict orders and precautions. But it was hard enough to make the women and children stay cooped up in the suffocating heat and dark of cabins, barred and shuttered. In the end the boys were anywhere that zeal or curiosity took them.

In Peter both zeal and curiosity, for once, were dead. The thought of Heinie and Obadiah lying side by side with the Baptists weeping around them, was between him and the seething outer world. He stayed indoors the morning after the funeral, going dully through tasks the Doctor set him, such as bottling pills and arranging botanical specimens. A single thought beat like a hammer in his aching head. "Obadiah trusted God, and God let him down."

When, through the open door, he saw a troop of horses crashing by three and four abreast, breaking bushes on each side of the narrow road, he identified them without interest or curiosity. Just the Baptist Regulators, Jerry's brother, Otto, first in command, and Hans second. He barely pricked up his ears when he heard shouts, "No, you don't! You'll have no part nor parcel with us!"

Allen went to the door. "They've stopped somebody on the road."

Peter came and looked out. "It's Moses Stegall. There's two they've stopped." He looked again. The other figure was less familiar. "It's Jacob Leiper."

They all came riding up to the Doctor, Hans and Otto guarding Stegall and Leiper, the others crashing alongside through bushes in a position to surround them. Stegall appealed to the Doctor. "Doctor, you know my wife and baby."

"Yes," said Allen.

"They've been killed," he said, in a strangely toneless voice, his eyes staring out of a face pallid and blank. "Mike Harpe—he killed them. I want to join the hunt. I am going to kill Mike with my own hands." Dropping his reins, his hands clinched convulsively as if he were wringing and squeezing something between them.

It was as if a heavy blow had struck Peter's heart and stopped its beating. Trixie Stegall killed! The baby killed! His heart started beating again with a sensation of unbearable pain, so that he wanted to cry out. But he only stood still, his brown face drained of all its underlying ruddy color, his black eyes staring. Hans spoke coolly, "How do we know you're not lying?"

As Stegall did not answer, Otto followed Hans with, "You're one of Harpe's own gang."

Still Stegall did not speak. "What you want is to lead us astray so the Harpes can get away by one road while we follow you up another," persisted Hans.

"We don't put ourselves in the way of being ambushed by your gang," added Otto. "Better we bind you and lock you up. My young brother lies dead. My sister's heart is broken. We take no chances."

Stegall had found his voice. "My wife lies dead," he said with something that was almost dignity. "It gives me the right—" His dead calm gave way to frenzy. "It gives me the right, by God, to strangle him with my two hands!"

Here the burly German, Jacob Leiper, spoke rapidly in German. There was a snarl of protest among the Regulators. Otto said, "We don't speak Dutch. Talk Amurrican."

"Mein Gott!" spluttered Leiper. "His wife in the ashes of his house lies dead, with three case knives in her, one so deep you can't pull it out. His baby is slit from ear to ear with a butcher knife that lies by it. And you say he shall not the Harpes hunt with you. Mein Gott! Ach lieber Gott! Why? Why?"

Hans appealed to the Doctor. "We can't take chances. We can't trust a word they say. Better lock them up."

The gentle Doctor turned to Stegall. "I'm afraid it's no use, at least till your story's verified. Better yield peaceably. You're outnumbered. It will do you no good to resist."

Stegall said, "But I swear—"

"Don't," said Otto. "Your oath's no good."

"But if I can show she's been killed, and the baby, and Major Love."

There was an ugly look on Otto's face. "May be you killed them yourself, for their carrying on."

With a frenzied howl, Stegall spurred his horse forward and lifted his pistol and shot. The shot went wild. With a brutal roar the Regulators closed around him and Leiper. And almost at the same moment another band of horsemen, five or six in number came charging down the road and seemed to plunge straight at the Regulators, and all was dust and yells and pounding hooves.

The Doctor, unarmed and on foot as he was, but fearing lest Stegall should shoot again, plunged into the melee and seized Stegall's bridle, shouting, "Quiet! Quiet! Stand back."

Peter seized Otto's bridle. "Otto, listen to the Doctor. You know him. He means only good."

"The young un's right," said Otto to Hans. He shouted to his Regulators. "Put up your guns. Rein up your horses. Remember you're Christian men. We're going to do this lawful."

By this time the newcomers had been generally recognized. They were a group of five men from north of Russellville, led by Bill Stewart, the Sheriff. Allen, having re-assured Stegall, was speaking to Stewart, and as the noise quieted he now spoke to them all. "The Sheriff and these men who come with him have something important to tell you."

One of the Regulators shouted, "We don't trust the Sheriff. He's been in with the whole gang of them."

"We don't know these men," said Hans, staring coldly at the Sheriff's companions. "And what we don't know we don't trust."

Peter thought Hans was lying. For he recognized all the men as friends and neighbors of Stegall's. He had often seen them at court.

There was a crashing of brush, a beat of hooves to the North. "Quick!" shouted Hans. "Hold em where they are, dead or alive."

Otto and the mass of the Regulators wheeled around to make a solid wall of horseflesh and bristling guns around Stegall, Leiper, and the Sheriff's band. Hans, with a bodyguard of four, turned to face the oncomers. But before any one else could recognize them Peter's heart leaped to the sight. "It's Pappy," he shouted, running toward them.

Jus and a band of armed Methodists swept by him without greeting and came to a halt in front of Otto. "So you've got him," said Jus, looking at Stegall.

"We heard Mose Stegall had gone to kill Harpe, and we followed," said the Sheriff.

"We can't trust any of them," said Hans to Jus. "We'll lock Stegall up, and let the rest get the Hell out of here. They're all out to divert us till Harpe gets away."

Stegall started to roar—a crazed maddened sound, and was

stopped by the point of a gun at his chest. His eyes were bulging. He was foaming at the mouth in rage and frustration. Stewart said, "Jus, if they'll listen, we can relate what has happened. Don't let them act blind."

"Shut them up," urged Hans.

Stewart said soberly, "I knew Mike and Wiley Harpe in the way of bar room fellowship. But the bloody murder of women and children is something I don't stand for. We've come to testify as to what Harpe did, and to act with you all in bringing him to justice."

"He don't know what justice is, nor them that are with him," shouted Hans. Most of the Regulators with him roared agreement.

But Otto said, "Give them five minutes to speak and no more. Then we act." A minority of the Regulators, mostly devout Baptists, said piously, "Amen."

Peter had come to his father's side and was looking up at him, as he sat his horse, calm amidst the tumult. Jus looked down at him briefly. All the boy's desperate craving for law, for security, in this chaos, was in the look with which he met his father's eyes, and all his faith that his father could do something.

Jus spoke with quiet authority. "It's the right of the Sheriff and those that are with him to speak. And it's the right of those who wish to listen. Let those who are of Hans's mind go back with him to the patrol. Those that are of Otto's mind and those with me are enough to outnumber the Sheriff, and Stegall, and those with them, two to one. And what man of us wants better odds than that? We'll hear them out and act accordingly, and then Otto and his men can join Hans again on the patrol. Hans can then take our decision or not as he thinks fit."

"Fair enough," said Hans, spurring his horse. "Come, Kamerads!" And the main body of the Regulators galloped after him.

While his own body of armed Methodists, and Otto's armed Baptists stood guard, Jus faced the Sheriff. "Very well, Sheriff, you may take the stand."

Stewart spoke mildly. "We only want to tell what happened."

"We all know what happened," said Jus, nodding to his own men.

"We were on the patrol north of Russellville. We saw the house in smoke—and what was in it." He looked at Stegall, who started to speak and broke down in muffled blubbering. Jus turned away from him, with something between disgust and pity on his bronzed face. "Otto and the Baptists don't know. Tell them in order. Who speaks first. James Tompkins, is it you?"

So, one by one, they told their story. Tompkins said that yesterday afternoon two Methodist ministers, one big, the other small and slight, mounted on good horses, had stopped at his house and were invited by him to dinner. The big man said a long grace. When Tompkins apologized for having no venison saying he was out of powder, the big man poured him some in a tea-pot. They rode away with courteous thanks, leaving Tompkins feeling that they were eccentric fellows, but with no suspicion of them.

Here Squire McBee took up the story. Some time in the afternoon, he saw the two ministers come into his road. But before he could go out to welcome them, the pack of dogs he kept for tracking deer and bear rushed at them, and they put spurs to their horses and fled. Squire McBee felt badly to think that men of God had been driven off like that and jumped on his horse and spurred after them to apologize and bring them back. But the faster he went, the faster they fled before him. Finally, he saw them turn in at the Stegalls. Knowing that Mrs. Stegall was a good Methodist, he felt satisfied that they would find entertainment there, and turned back to his own house.

Some time in the night he was aroused by Mathew Christian, who here took up the story. He said a neighbor had told him the Stegall's house was on fire, but before he could go to help, William Grierson and Neville Lindsey rode up. "And they'll tell what happened." Neville Lindsay and William Grierson both said that they had been awakened in the night by two Methodist circuit riders, apparently the Harpes, who told them that Mrs. Stegall and the baby and Major Love had been killed by two men named Hulgend and Gilmore. Each had rushed to the Stegall house and had met the other on the way to it. Fearing an ambush, before visiting the premises, they got Mathew Christian, who got Squire McBee.

The four of them then approached the smoking house in the early summer dawn. One end of it had collapsed, but making their way into the other part, they found Major Love dead with a bullet through his heart, and Mrs. Stegall and the baby, butchered with knives.

Since Stegall had apparently been away, they sent out in all directions and eventually found him about ten miles to the north, riding with Jacob Leiper. He took one look at it all and rushed wildly off with Leiper saying he would kill Mike Harpe. The other men went straight for the Sheriff, and they trailed Stegall and Leiper. "And we've caught up with him here," said Bill Stewart.

When Stewart finished, Jus looked around at the Methodist and Baptist Regulators, and said, with dry satisfaction, "So there's the story. At last we've got testimony that will look mighty good in court." The same grim satisfaction was reflected on all faces except Stegall's and Leiper's. They seemed to shrink at the mention of the word *court*.

A question was going around in Peter's mind? Where had Stegall been, and what had he been doing all night? But it was pushed aside by a second, which he whispered to the Doctor, and which the Doctor immediately asked: "Since the Harpes were seen north of Russellville, how did you happen to come eight miles south of Russellville almost to the Tennessee border to find them?"

Stegall answered frankly, "To head them off from getting down the Chickasaw Road. It's the only way out for them. Everything from Russellville to Lexington and Louisville is patrolled."

"Well, I reckon that makes sense," drawled Jus, looking around for confirmation. The Regulators nodded. Both Otto and Dominie had been trying all day to get a heavier patrol on the south side of Russellville. The atmosphere perceptibly warmed. For the first time they seemed inclined to consider associating Stegall and Leiper with them in the hunt. But the air chilled again, as Jus said, "We arn't holding court here. And for all that's been said, it's by no means certain who committed that murder and why." At this Stegall who had relaxed to the sense of acceptance gave a wild, desperate, animal-like moan. Jus continued, deliberately keeping the man on the rack. "Keep Stegall by you and let him lead you to the Harpes—if he can. And when the time comes, this will be up in court, and we'll make Stegall talk." He paused, and tried to catch Stegall's eye, and added, with mock gentleness, "But even so, Mose, you will have your own lawyer. You might get Ninian Edwards."

Stegall found his voice and his self-control. "You've got the knife in me, and keep turning it," he said quietly. "But do what you will, I tell you I will kill Mike Harpe with my own hands."

"What do you say, Otto?" asked Jus. "Will you let him join you?"

"If the Sheriff, and those with him will go warranty for him and Leiper, and stay down at this end of the county and ride with us, too," said Otto. To this his own men all agreed.

"We'd feel easier about it," said Otto, aside to Jus, 'if you and your men could stay with us, too."

"I'd sure like to," said Jus, "for more reasons than one." His eye rested on his boy. "But we're on guard at the courthouse, and overdue there now."

As, tense with suspicion still, grim, and gloomy, the Regulators with Otto, and the Sheriff and his companions, rode off with Stegall and Leiper, Jus paused only to meet the pride and affection in Peter's eyes. "Reckon we'll soon have you home, Son," he said. With a look of complete understanding between them, he was off with his men.

6

There was no sleep that night. Allen and Peter and Cassius barred doors and windows, and, though it was warm, lighted a little fire on the hearth for comfort. And there they sat, with guns in their hands, going over and over plans for action, in any eventuality—if Allen should be called out to minister to some one hurt or sick, if the Harpes should come by the back door, or crash in the front door, or even slip through a window, if men in any disguise should appear. Peter dozed intermittently, and started awake with his gun in his hand whenever there was a rush of horses' hooves

outside. But always there was some familiar re-assuring voice saying, "It's all right, Doc. We're just patrolling."

By the time the sun was high, groups of weary men, stopping at
the Doctor's for a drink from his spring, were saying that the Harpes
had been too quick for them. By now they were no doubt miles
down the Chickasaw Road, out into the trackless territory of Mississippi. But the Regulators sternly refused to relax the chase, and
were joined by fresh squads of men sporting the red turkey feathers
of the Rogues in their hats. There was much angry discussion
about admitting Rogues to the patrol, instead of fighting them
where they stood, but in the end the Regulators and the Rogues
were riding side by side. There was now not much question that
the Mystic Band and all its associates were as determined to stop
the Harpes as anybody, nor that the murderers had been distribut-
ing their blows about equally between those who had been praying
for the sinners and those of their own confederates who they
feared might break down under preachings and confess.

"But why kill so many children?"

Peter answered shrewdly, "They're easier to kill, and you hurt
folks more through them."

Fortunately for the boy, the necessity of watchfulness and action
had kept horror at bay. But now, as the strain relaxed, it came
upon him. Three times he ate some breakfast, and three times
something he was trying not to think about—Trixie—did they kill
the baby first, before her eyes?—would force its way to consciousness, and he vomited violently. And then suddenly he collapsed
on the bearskin by the hearth. The Doctor, running to him, saw
that he was already asleep. "So Nature takes care of the young,"
he said to Cassius, knowing that, though he also had been awake all
night, there was no sleep for him.

CHAPTER 22

Peter started up violently, struggling out of the grip of something monstrous that was holding him fast in sleep. Allen, standing at the open door and talking quietly to Dominie, turned, "Oh, so you are awake, Peter. I was telling Dominie that I hesitated to rouse you."

Peter came to the door, smiling wanly at Dominie who, he saw, was followed by a troop of the Methodist Regulators. Dominie wasted no time in preliminaries. "Peter, Barbara and I want to get L'il Papoose and keep her at our house. We think she'll be safer there. But you know she won't come without fussing unless you bring her on Diablo."

"I'll come," said Peter, seizing his gun, and not looking to Allen for permission. In that moment nothing could have held him back. He was consumed with sudden anxiety. L'il Papoose! Why hadn't he thought of that himself. The delicate child face, the soft blond hair, Trixie's baby—they formed one ghastly thought in his mind. Hurry! He flew to the place where Diablo was tethered and leaped on him bareback. No time for saddles. Hurry! Hurry!

Dominie and the others had fast horses, but to Peter their feet were lead as they pounded through what seemed a million years to the Indian encampment. But before they rounded the bushes in sight of it, they heard it—the dirge of the women for one that is dead. And there they were in a circle around something that lay under a blanket on the ground, swaying all together and moaning. Clutching a last wild hope that it could not be, Peter crashed ahead, prodding Diablo into his long flying leaps, and drew up sharp.

Under the edge of the blanket he could see the soft, golden curls. His hands went weak, so that he could not hold the reins. His back went weak, so that he could not hold his seat. His legs buckled under him as he slid to the ground. He did not faint. He did not black out. He just gave up and was going down. Down, down, down into bottomless horror!

It seemed a thousand years before he could get up and stagger to where Dominie and the others were talking to some of the Indian men, and stand listening to details each of which stabbed like a knife. That morning, the two Methodist preachers, one big, one little, had come, and the big one had said that at last they had found L'il Papoose's parents and would take her to them. Gray Wolf said he was glad, and called for the little girl and showed her to the preachers, but asked them to wait while he sent for Dominie to make all the arrangements. The little man dismounted and tried to coax the child. Frightened, she clung to her foster Mammy and cried. Whereupon the little one grabbed her, and flung her up to the big one who instantly made off with her. The little one jumped on his horse, and followed. Several Indians leaped on their horses and flew after them. Above the crashing of brush, and pounding of hooves, Gray Wolf could hear the child's shrieks. And then there was silence.

The Indians came back with her poor little body. As they had gained on the abductors, the big one, furious at her shrieking had wrung the child's neck and flung her far into the brush. It had happened this morning, only two hours ago. They had not had time yet to send out word.

Dominie instantly dispatched most of the Regulators to warn all the patrols that the Harpes were still here in the neighborhood. And then he offered to hold a religious service for the little girl. More scientist and teacher than priest, he knew that in this rude world there was only one means of morale or even of spiritual sanity. Peter felt unutterably grateful, as, speaking from memory, Dominie repeated one Bible text after another, "Suffer little children to come unto me, for of such is the Kingdom of Heaven." "She is not dead, but sleepeth." "In my Father's house are many mansions." Praying, Dominie seemed to lift her and lay her in the arms of the Father where she would be safe for ever. There was a strange magic here to ease pain which otherwise could not be borne.

To Peter the ride back to the Doctor's was a blank. He saw nothing, felt nothing, because everything in him was concentrated on not remembering that soft flaxen curl showing under the edge of the blanket. But when he succeeded in keeping this out of his mind, it was only to remember a little girl's fair hair against his breast, her laughing face turned up to him, as holding her tight on the saddle with his left arm, he guided his great shambling Spanish horse through his wild leaps and cavortings. His heart was bleeding, "L'il Papoose! L'il Papoose!" He grasped for relief at the words, "Suffer little children to come unto me, for of such is the Kingdom of Heaven." He said them over and over like an incantation. And they helped a little. But, oh, to go back in time— just two or three days back—when this had not happened!

When they came to the Doctor's house, Peter rushed straight up the ladder to his bed in the loft and flung himself face down on his bunk, while his whole being seemed to heave in utter sick repudiation. It couldn't be! Such things can't happen! He had no memory of a flaxen haired little girl named Sylvia, and a gold curl he had laid in his mother's Bible, and did not know how a long ago hurt was bleeding anew. But he felt sick unto death. He couldn't bear it. He couldn't go on living. But living or not, what did it matter? In the vastness of this horror, time and space had melted away, and he seemed to have entered into eternity. This wretchedness was for ever, and there was no way out.

2

With the Harpes known to be so recently in the area south of Russellville, the question was what to do about the revival meeting McGready had called for that night, in his new outdoor church. The consensus was that it was safer to be gathered together in one large crowd than to remain in small family groups in isolated cabins. So the Regulators spread the word to come to the meeting. Like creatures parched with thirst, rushing to water, they came. All afternoon on the narrow, dusty roads there were the convoys of wagons, filled with women and children, the armed men on horseback riding alongside. By sunset, all the area around was a huge picnic ground, with families visiting back and forth from fire to fire and wagon to wagon. But no one was allowed in the space reserved for the church.

Inasmuch as the Harpes had threatened to kill McGready, and anything religious had a strong, though sinister, pull on them, it was thought that they might appear at this meeting. So long as the light lasted, the face of each newcomer was scrutinized to identify them under any disguise. After dark the techniques of Indian fighting were used to put the whole surrounding area under guard. The awareness that the killers might be in their midst, or might crash in at any moment, or that among the mourners at the altar Micajah Harpe might appear howling, creating an indescribable tension.

Then in the warm dusk they silently took their places; the trees dark around them, the sky above a deep, vibrant green blue, in the afterglow; and one wisp of pink cloud fading like fire into ash. They huddled like creatures barely escaping from a stormy sea to the safe shores of an island. Some dropped immediately on their knees and began to pray. Others were weeping—they could not have told why. And here at last was peace and God to look after them.

Aroused from the nightmarish sleep into which he had fallen, Peter had come, not because he wanted to do this or anything else, but because Allen thought he would be safer here for the night. But now that he had taken his place on one of the split log benches, where he could look across to the women's section and see his mother's face, barely recognizable though it was in the dimness, the load on his heart lightened a little, and he looked around with faint curiosity. In the dusk between the walls of trees, he could just trace the outlines of this strange woodland church. It con-

sisted of a kind of natural room, formed of a depression about
fifteen feet square. Around three sides of it were benches. The
fourth had a rail, and above it a platform from which the preacher
could speak. The seats on three sides were the "mourners'"
benches, to which those who wished to be prayed for could come
up from the audience. The hollow square formed by the benches
and the altar rail was for kneeling, and for those who, under the
burden of sin and shame, could not even kneel but would fall prone
to the ground.

Around three sides of this square, rising with the natural rise of
the ground in an irregular horseshoe shape were seats for the congregation. So much Peter saw, but never had he seen such a
miracle as happened when McGready, his powdered hair and white
neck bands spectacular above his almost invisible black robe, appeared on the platform above the altar, and in rich, rolling tones
called, "Let there be light!"

Up the green walls of trees on each side of the amphitheatre, the
light ran in lengthening lines, as troops of boys and girls, with
flaming "light wood" touched the wicks of one hundred candles in
sheltered sconces in the trees, turning the leaves to emerald trans-
parencies, casting a growing glory on all below. Peter had seldom
seen more than one lighted candle at a time. Now he blinked,
startled, and a thin keen flash of artistic joy pierced the heaviness
of his soul, at this lovely, dynamic flowering of light.

As the night wore on, Peter strove desperately after salvation
till the sweat poured down his face like rain, for it was the only
way out of the horror that engulfed him. For the boy forced, at
every point, to fight it out with other immature male brutes with
taunts, with lies, with fists, with sling-shots, with tomahawks, almost everything joyous and innocent had been associated with those
who had been so hideously snatched away. Trixie, setting trenchers of savory food before him; winsome Heinie, so amusing to
tease; kind Obadiah, with his fiddle and his fish-fries; L'il Papoose,
looking on him as a great God on horseback—through them he had
known not only joy and affection but a self-esteem he did not have
to earn by punching somebody's face for it. There was more than

personal grief in the boy's blind rebellion. There was a kind of cosmic terror. Must it be so? Where was God? Couldn't He stop it?

Mary who, amidst the brutal rush of events, and the restrictions on movement and communication, had had no chance to be near Peter, observed his struggles and braved the rule which separated men from women in the congregation by going to him, and getting the old man next him to move over on the seat and let her sit beside him. Few women except Mary could have done this, even at the dictates of a mother's heart, for it was well known what advantage could be taken of women in this close contact of body against body on the puncheon benches. But Mary was above blame, and, attractive as she was, few men would have cared to brave her armor of inviolability with unseemly touch of foot or hand. Peter recognized his mother's courage in coming to him, and was proud and grateful, and somewhat less desolate because she was there.

Desperately seeking re-assurance, Peter lifted his eyes and concentrated on a single radiant star and thought of God. What was God like? He saw light spread in an immeasureable sea of spotless radiance sucking him up with an irresistible allurement. For a moment, the beatitude of this meditation lighted his face even in the dimness and enveloped his whole being. Then sharply he came to. He was sitting on the hard bench. His legs were cramped. His back ached. His feet felt like boulders. Then the old man, Si, who had moved over to make way for his mother, and whom Peter knew for a notorious sinner, was seized with such compunction that he got a violent case of "the jerks" and staggered and fell over Peter in his effort to get to the aisle up to the altar. Peter had to support him and drag him till he got on his way. As Si went on, his head jerking from side to side, sharply and rhythmically, muttering, "Damn it to Hell! Damn it to Hell!" Peter was momentarily diverted.

Then the memory of all that had happened returned, and this and the agonized pleading on his mother's face, turned on him in the glimmering dark, reminded him to seek again his soul's salvation. He concentrated on Christ—Christ in a long shining white robe like a woman's dress, his long hair like a woman's, his eyes tender, his hands caressing—God in human form, all that one loves in man and women concentrated in a being at once human and divine. He elaborated the image lovingly. His heart went out to it in intense affection. The light shone on his face. His mother fell on her knees and prayed for him convulsively.

Suddenly, coldly, he was aware of an intense, objective pity for his poor mother. She did so want him to be converted. He concentrated on the idea of conversion itself. What was this unique, this transcendent experience, this crossing for ever of the mysterious bar between the lost and the saved?

Just then his mother patted his sleeve. "Peter, look! There's Jerry." The slight boyish form was going blindly up the aisle to the altar, uncertainly, shaken with sobs. "He's going to be prayed for," she whispered. "Go after him, Peter. Let them pray for you."

But Peter could not budge. He felt bound to stay here till he had fought it out. He was getting very tired. He lifted his eyes to the stars, and they swam in a sea of light. The congregation had risen and was singing:

> Guide me, O Thou Great Jehovah,
> Pilgrim through this barren land.
> I am thine and Thou art mighty.
> Hold me with Thy Powerful hand.

He knew he should rise. His mother was tugging at him. But somehow he couldn't . . .

He woke to find himself laid out on the ground under a horse-blanket. The pale light of dawn was all around, and in the thick tree above, a half a hundred birds were twittering. His mother was shaking him. "Get up, Honey. There's a sunrise love feast." Sleepy, cross, every bone protesting, Peter stumbled after his mother into the big church enclosure, which was now two thirds empty, and seemed vacant and solemn and chill under the pale sky. In the hollow square, men and women were kneeling, and something rapt and portentous in that kneeling throng stirred Peter awake. "Stay here, Honey, and pray," whispered his mother. "Before many

THE CIRCUIT PREACHER.—Drawn by A. R. Waud.—[See Next Page.]

Neither rain, nor hail, nor hunger, nor loneliness, nor fear of man or the devil, stayed the footsteps of these riders for God.

From an old print by
Alexander Waud

sunups, I hope you will be with me at the table of the Lord," and she left him and joined the others at the altar. It was as if she had crossed over to another shore, and left him here stranded, alone.

McGready, in his black robe, was standing on the ground among the kneelers, holding aloft a silver platter on which were piled small pieces of wheat bread. Though, along with others of the unregenerate, Peter had always been put out of Ebenezer chapel when communion was held, he had spied on it many times through chinks between the logs, and it had always moved him as with solemn magic. Now, in the dawn, under the open sky, he felt the chills go down his spine, as if he had come inadvertently into the presence of God Himself. McGready stood there, a noble and solemn figure, holding the platter aloft, till out of the swelling light in the sky, one shaft of sunlight fell on the bread and sparkled on the silver platter. "Take, eat. This is My body," said McGready, and the platter passed from hand to hand.

Then he lifted a silver goblet, and held it till the sun, now pouring from the sky, seemed to set it all on fire. McGready continued, "And He gave it to them saying, 'Drink ye all of it!'" The goblet passed from one to the other. The people received it, sipped and murmured, "For this, O Lord, we thank Thee." Keeping the ceremony strictly to the bare words of the gospel narrative, McGready said, in the same quiet, intimate way, "And when they had sung a hymn, they went out into the Mount of Olives."

As they rose to sing, the warm rays of the sun enveloped Peter, and he stood with them and sang, with transfigured face, "Glory be to God on high." A sense of infinite, solemn well-being filled him and then slowly the light faded out of his soul, and he knew, with a dreadful certainty, that he was not redeemed.

3

Sunk in bottomless depression, weighed down with weariness, Peter rode home with the Doctor and Cassius. Just as he was being slightly revived with hot hoe cakes and coffee, Jo, the Methodist Brother, with two Regulators, rode to the door and said the Widow McFadden was in childbed again. Would the Doctor come at once?

"But what can I do with Peter?" asked Allen. "He and Cassius can't stay here alone."

Hesitantly, for at that weary moment the idea did not appeal to him, Peter said, "We could go with Jerry's brothers. There's all those Regulators with them in case of trouble."

Since there seemed nothing else to do, Allen and the others rode with Peter and Cassius to within a mile of McGready's campgrounds, which was the area the Baptist Regulators had been assigned. The Methodist brother, Jo, said, "From here on you're safe enough. There's sentries in trees."

Left to themselves, Peter and Cassius rode cautiously on. Peter's head ached and his limbs were weak as water. He wanted his mother. It had been comfort and relief all the long night to feel her near. Now as they passed the trail which led south four miles to his own home, it was as if a strong rope were tied around his heart and some one down there on the farm were pulling it. He could hardly resist turning off and galloping straight home.

But he pulled himself together and rode on carefully, trying to locate a sentry and finding none. Suddenly he drew up sharp, pointing at the bushes on the side of the narrow path. "Somebody's been through here. It's been since we came this way this morning," he said to Cassius. "Must be Stegall and Leiper, and the five that's with them." Like a practiced reader deciphering a scrawl, Peter studied the hoof prints in the soft ground. "A powerful lot of horses have gone in this way—must be to the spring."

"But the way round by the road is easier. How come they smashed all this brush and swamp and mud and truck?" asked Cassius.

"That's what I'm wondering," answered Peter, still studying the hoof prints. "I bet there's more than seven horses been through here. Wonder who they could be?"

Cautiously he parted the bushes and went in a little way. Then he reined up his horse sharply and backed out. "God Almighty! Run!" Whirling around on Diablo to ride backwards, controlling him only with the grip of his wiry legs, he lifted his gun. Diablo, never loth to be off, was a quarter of a mile away before Cassius was able to draw breath and follow. Peter slowed up, while the Negro boy, who was no mean rider himself, plunged up alongside him. "They were in there! I saw them!" Peter gasped. On his brain was stamped as if with a branding iron that fleeting glimpse of a big man, a small man, three women, three children, and a string of horses.

"If we go that way, we're sure to run into them," said Peter. "But then, if we turn back, we could meet them that way." Cassius looked trustingly at him, sure he would find a way out. "There ought to be somebody on guard here," said Peter desperately.

All patrols seemed to have vanished. But the next minute there were a dozen of them coming on to the road from several sides, and then, in a roll of thunder and dust up came Squire McBee and his men. "They're in there," gasped Peter. "By the spring."

"We know it," shouted McBee as the cavalcade roared on.

By this time the whole landscape was alive with people moving in from all sides to cut off the escape of the Harpes.

Intent on surrounding the spring, no one seemed to hear what Peter heard. It was a baby's squall. It seemed to come not from outside but from somewhere within him—as if Trixie's baby, as if L'il Papoose, were crying out. He listened. It did not come again. It had not come from the direction of the spring, where he had seen the Harpes and their women and babies. But it had come. From where? From somewhere near the altar and the mourners' seats.

He turned and went into the woodland church, now empty. As he rode up cautiously under the big tree that flanked the altar space on one side, Diablo started and quivered and reared aside. Peter had one sickening sight of something on the ground that looked like raw meat and bloody rags and baby's soft light hair. He swerved the horse and rode him into the church between the seats and the altar space.

Then he saw her. She was backed up against the altar rail in a crouching position and in each arm she clutched convulsively a six or seven months old baby. As she saw him, her arms tightened around the children who, strangely, did not cry but seemed contented and secure. Peter knew her at once. It was Sally Rice—Wiley Harpe's girl, the parson's daughter.

A faint gleam of recognition came into her white, staring face. "You are the Doctor's boy." She spoke quickly, in hoarse gasps, "He killed her. Mike Harpe—he killed my baby. She cried, and he took her by the feet and dashed her head against the tree—he—he hit the tree with my baby's head—she—she." She choked and clutched the children closer. "I took his babies. He shan't lay hands on them. He would have killed them, too. Susan and Betsy—they won't stand up to him. But I will. I'll see him dead before he touches another child. I'll see him dead!"

She choked again, and then in a whisper that was a hiss, "You can get him. He's in there by the spring. He brought us to the spring. We thought everybody would have gone home after praying all night. But then we knew there were men in the woods. We were trying to get out this way, but my baby cried. He killed it—so nobody could hear. But I was too quick for him. I grabbed the others. They could have hollered to Heaven and I wouldn't let him touch them. Then we heard somebody coming and it was you, and they all shrunk back to the spring. But I wouldn't go because I didn't want the babies near him. If you hurry, you can get him. Tell somebody, and get him. Quick."

She was speaking not only to Peter and Cassius now, but to Stegall and Leiper and the five men with them, who had ridden up the center aisle. She raised her voice in a shriek. "Get him! He's in there! Get the big one! He's the bad one."

"Nobody kills him but me," shouted Stegall, as he and his men plunged toward the spring.

Peter and Cassius were left alone with the crazed girl. "Miss Sally," said Peter, wondering desperately what he could do for her but not daring to dismount, "don't be afraid. You're safe with us. They only want him." Out of delicacy he did not say that they also wanted her own man, Wiley Harpe.

For the first time she spoke almost normally. "I've got to have some place to put them," hugging the babies, her eyes softening a little as she looked down at them. As Peter was wondering whether he couldn't take her and the babies both on Diablo and dash with them to his mother's house, McGready and several of his church members came in on foot, among them three women.

"Parson," said Peter, "you asked me to tell you if I found Miss Sally—"

But McGready had already recognized her, and had leaped over the mourner's bench, and was bending over her. "Sally, my dear, don't you remember me—your father's friend, Jim McGready—"

At the word *father* she burst into tears, and one of the babies cried and one of the women tried to take it. "No, no," she shrieked, and they all closed around her, trying to soothe and re-assure her.

But at this minute Hans and Otto swept up the aisle on horseback. "Stick by us, young un," said Hans to Peter and swept him along through the space between the mourners' benches and the other seats across the church to the spring, through a line of armed men who had already encircled the spot.

By the spring there were only Susan and Betsy, and Stegall and the men with him. Leiper, struggling with the ramrod of his gun which was stuck, was exchanging it with Tompkins for his gun. Otto explained to Peter, "Big Harpe got away, but we've got him treed up there on the ridge. Our Regulators up there are holding him under their guns to be killed by Stegall!"

"He's there! Hold him! He'll get away!" shrieked Peter. He saw the form of the big man appear almost overhead, on a rock. "Look out. He's got a tomahawk." The tomahawk came hurtling through the air at Stegall but fell harmless by the spring, as Stegall pulled the trigger.

Harpe fell forward down the slope toward the spring, and lay there spouting blood. The armed men around the spring closed in. "Is he dead?" asked Otto, laying hold on Peter's bridle to keep him alongside. For answer they heard Harpe's moan, "Water! Water! Give me a drink, for God's sake."

Leiper said roughly to the others, "Leave him to us. We're finishing him." The others shrank back, but Susan and Betsy, guarded by Tompkins, pressed forward.

"Water," moaned Harpe again. Stegall said to Leiper, "Get him a drink before we do it." Leiper pulled off Harpe's big shoe and filled it at the spring, and brought it dripping, and poured it between Harpe's bearded lips. Stegall stood over him. "I'm going to shoot you, Mike," he said coldly. He turned to Leiper, "Give me your gun, Jake." He held the gun before Harpe's glazing eyes. "Wake up and look at it. It's Tompkins gun, and it's loaded with the powder you gave him when you passed yourself off on him as a Methodist minister." Harpe seemed to come to, and, with a glimmer of surprise, to see Tompkins, where he stood guarding Susan and Betsy.

"Now is the time," said Leiper to Harpe, as Stegall deliberately examined the gun, "when all your chickens come home to roost."

"I'll not shoot you in the head," said Stegall, "I want to save that all nice and pretty, because I'm going to cut it off, and set it up for a remembrance at the crossroads." A strange flicker as of some deep understanding, mixed with enmity, passed between the dying man and his executioner. Susan said sneering, "He's settin' your head up— you know where?" A passionate hatred flashed in Harpe's dark eyes. He started up as if to fly at her throat, and sank back helpless. Susan continued hoarsely, "For a warning to all the Brothers—not to get caught!"

This from a wife was too much even for Stegall. "Damn it, you bitch," he shouted. "For that you'll carry the head yourself!"

He turned back to Leiper. "Hold the butcher knife before his eyes while I shoot."

The life in Harpe which was ebbing fast came back into a wild stare of horror, as Leiper held up the knife, and Stegall spoke slowly, "Yes, it's the same. With this knife you slit my baby's throat. With this knife, I'll cut off your head." And with his gun at Harpe's left side he pulled the trigger.

Peter heard the shot, and was pushed up closer with the mass crowding in behind. The ones in front fell back, some looking sick, some gloating, with a strange half hysterical sound, as of some excited animal—"Stegall's cut off his head." Peter was borne forward, and then pushed back. And there he saw McBee move off with Susan and Betsy, and hanging from Susan's saddle by its long black hair, the head of Harpe dripping blood. It got caught in a bush. Susan drew up, and shrieked, "Damn that head!" They moved off.

Then, for the first time, Peter saw Dominie with some of the Methodist Regulators. Dominie was saying to his men, "Follow Harpe's women. Let them do what's on their minds. But surround them and bring 'em back."

"That's sheriff's business," said Bill Stewart, cutting in. "Nobody gives orders for arrest but me."

"We only want to help," answered Dominie, mildly, "and we want it all to be legal. But you've got enough on your hands. Make one of us your deputy with power to arrest."

While they were in a huddle arranging this, Peter pushed closer, for Dominie was, to him, the next thing to home. When some of the Regulators rode off after the women, Peter came alongside Dominie, "There's Sally, Wiley Harpe's girl. She's in there. She's got Harpe's babies." He dismounted and led Dominie into the church where McGready and two women were still trying to persuade Sally to come with them. She was still clinging to the babies who were whimpering. Bill Stewart had dismounted and followed Dominie and Peter. "We'll have to arrest her," he told McGready, "but you'll have every chance to help her." To the girl he said gently, "Come along with us. We'll make you comfortable. We'll send for your Pappy." He tried to lift her up. She braced herself against the altar rail and tightened her arms around the children. "You can't help yourself," said Stewart. "You'll have to come. So you might as well come peaceable."

McGready said gently, "My dear, let these good women take the babies."

"No, No," she shrieked. "He'll kill them!"

"He's dead," said Stewart.

"Dead?" she asked tonelessly, looking from one to the other, with dawning comprehension. "Mike Harpe dead?"

"Yes," said Stewart, "Stegall killed him."

"Oh," she shuddered. "Oh." Tears streamed from her eyes. Relaxed, helpless, appealing, she turned to McGready and the women, and let them take the children. Then Stewart led her away.

4

In the church and in the woods all around, the people were now churning, excitedly talking, while more and more women from nearby cabins appeared among armed men, now standing at ease, or stretched under trees with guns stacked. Some were saying that Stegall had arranged with Harpe to kill Major Love and Trixie, because he didn't like the Major being so much at the house. Some said he wanted the baby killed because it wasn't his. Others said Harpe had intended to kill Stegall, and Stegall had got a warning and left home. All agreed that Stegall and Leiper were part of the gang, and it was only justice that they had done the killing.

Peter, looking for Cassius whom he had lost in the melee, and circling from one group to another, suddenly remembered what all so far had forgotten. "But where's Wiley Harpe?" With something like consternation, he realized, "He's got away. Sally never breathed a word about him. She turned us all to Big Harpe, and Wiley took the chance and skipped."

He ought to tell somebody. He looked for the sheriff, but he had gone with Sally. He looked for Dominie. He had disappeared. Finally he found Hans, whose stolid face softened as Peter told him, "Well, she's his wife, ain't she? She just stood by him to the end, like a woman should."

Peter wondered. Would his mother stand by his father if his father were like Wiley? "She don't serve Pappy. She serves God," he thought. But nobody seemed inclined to worry about Wiley. Otto shrugged his shoulders, "Good riddance to bad rubbish! He's over the line and down the Chickasaw Road by now. Let the Injuns worry."

Another said, "Wiley ain't the killer. With Micajah gone, it's likely that he'll straighten out."

Still looking for Cassius, Peter circled back into the woodland church, now empty, and sat down on the bench he had sat on aeons ago, during last night's solemn service. The question which had tormented him since that morning, when, in this place under this same over-arching summer sky, Mary had first told him that Big Harpe had killed Heinie, was now answered. Is God without power against the Harpes of the world? Desperate, without immediate hope, but impelled by overwhelming need, the people had gathered here, and had knelt weeping and praying all night under heavens that seemed blind and deaf. And here at dawn, the remnant, still blind in their faith, had drunk the cup.

And lo—in a flash—between dawn and noon, it was now finished. Driven by the inexorable logic of his own mania, the killer had come to the sanctuary, and here he had been shot with his own powder, and beheaded with his own knife. No Christian had to lift his hand to do God's justice. The evil-doer had slain the evil-doer with his own weapons. Peter lifted his eyes to the bright noon sky. He knew now that God was there, and He was all powerful. But He seemed at that moment a terrible God. "I wouldn't want to come up against Him," he thought. He felt very solemn, and, though he did not know why, he was afraid.

A cluster of Baptist women came chattering in with Brenda to look at the scene of the late events. Brenda was looking relaxed and at peace and, now that the danger was past, kindness flowed out of these good church people. It was time now for the Regulators again to disarm and disband—time to forgive and forget. No use carrying vengeance against the Harpe women. "I got half a pound of tea. I could send some to Bill Stewart for Sally," said one. Another spoke of the Roberts girls. "They're trollops, but they're young. They might be brought to grace and mend their ways."

Peter listened as they went down the aisle, and out to the spring, too absorbed to notice the boy wearily hunched over, elbows on knees, on the puncheon seat.

It was now high noon, and growing very hot. Suddenly, Peter was very tired and afraid he might vomit. Twice that morning, his stomach had risen and turned over—once when Harpe's head was cut off, and once when he caught a glimpse of it hanging to Susan's saddle. Now that the crowd had all dispersed, he had an intolerable sense of let-down and a nauseous after taste. His whole being churned up, rasped, torn for days with pity and fear, cried out for the security of home. He wanted to sleep in his own bed, to know that his father and mother were near.

It was with unutterable relief that he saw Eddie coming toward him. He cried out, "Eddie, I'm coming home with you." He did not say, "May I?" or "Does Mammy want me?" or "Will the Doctor mind?" He intended to go.

Eddie looked at him kindly. "Yes, Petey, come along. Pappy sent me. He saw Cassius and sent him to tell Doc I was taking you home."

CHAPTER 23 | Russellville, Kentucky
September, 1799 to November, 1799

On September 1, 1799, Peter was fourteen, and since he was old enough now to take a man's load on the farm, his schooling ended and he returned home. He came back inches taller and many pounds heavier to a cabin which seemed to have shrunk together on all sides. What remained of the doctor's teaching was a rudimentary acquaintance with print, a vague consciousness of many strange and interesting things beyond the faint blue scallop of hills on the horizon, a doubt and insecurity about all the moral and religious ideas which his mother thought immutable, and some little niceties of cleanliness and manners which he laid away like sterling silver, to be brought out only on rare occasions.

There was a deep-seated comfort in being home. It was as if

a gnawing at the pit of his stomach which he had felt subconsciously throughout his exile had ceased. And he enjoyed being able to slouch without the consciousness of the doctor's quizzical eye upon him. But withal he was restless, and spiritually and intellectually at a loss for the first time in his life. Jerry, in whom he had centered his need for some one to do for, had been lost to him ever since he stumbled up the aisle, to be prayed for at McGready's camp meeting, and was now so detached in his holiness that Peter felt quite shut out. When he came to the cabin, it was only to watch Polly, waiting for one of her careless, radiant smiles, or to jump to her bidding when she said, "Jerry, Honey, would you bring a pail of water?" It angered Peter to see Jerry so happy under attentions she shed as lightly as a peach tree sheds its blossoms, when all her thoughts were centered in some unknown man with whom she lived serenely and secretly within herself.

All other relationships seemed to have become as empty as the relationship to Jerry. His mother he now viewed with detachment, which yielded, at times, to a quite new and surprised respect and admiration. He wished to please her. He had a deep tenderness for her, but what she thought and said was, for him, no longer law. At times he could assuage the restlessness by thinking about girls. He went to church willingly because that gave him an hour and a half in which he could contemplate first one girl and then another, tracing their shapes under the long-sleeved, high-necked calico gowns, fixing his eye on a bit of soft white neck under a sunbonnet flap, or a tendril of hair. But there seemed to be no one girl for him.

It was at this point that Cracker took charge of his education. Cracker was a long, limp young man from Georgia who had boarded with the Cartwrights, more or less, when Peter was away, sleeping in John's old bunk and lending a hand with the planting, harvesting, and wood-cutting. He came back to help butcher the hogs and young steer. Cracker's voice was soft and drawling, his manners gentle, and his cunning infinite. Though in appearance he was the precise opposite to what was thought to be proper to a "gentleman," he was quietly adept at all gentlemen's vices. With him he brought his fiddle, his pistol, his dagger, and his playing cards. After supper he tuned up and sang some twenty lugubrious ballads in a drawling nasal recitative, while Peter, Polly, and Sis sat around him enchanted. Mary, listening keenly, found with relief that, in contrast to what brother Peter used to sing, these songs were decent. Among the many importations from Europe which got lost crossing the Alleghenies was the bawdiness of the old songs. Instead there was mournful, eye-streaming sorrow.

Mary didn't mind the songs, but the first time Cracker laid out the cards Mary flew in, all her feathers on end, and swept them up. "Cracker," she said, furiously, "for two cents I'd throw them into the fire. But they're your property. Take them, and don't ever let me see them here again." She turned to Peter. "And if ever I catch cards in your hands, Peter, I'll burn them. I'll not see you burn in Hell on account of them."

As she whirled off, Cracker winked at Peter and whistled softly. The next minute he was flat on the floor, blind with pain and a flood of red blood where Peter's big fist had gone through his face. He rose and pulling his linsy shirt out of his deerskin pants, held it to his bleeding face, and spat the blood out of his mouth into the fire. But when he could speak, he only said coolly, "I reckon I kinda asked for that one," and went out to the stream to wash off. When he came to supper with his bruised and swollen face everybody acted as if nothing had happened.

2

There came a spell of rainy weather. The days dragged. All the indoor chores were exhausted. Peter was overjoyed when Cracker found there was still a saddle to mend and asked him to come out to the barn to help. They mended the saddle, and then sat with their backs against the hay, the rain rat-tat-tatting on the roof, the gray light coming in a single dim shaft through an opening between two large logs up near the roof. For a while they chatted about horses. Peter confessed that he was tired of ugly old Diablo. He wished he had a horse like Cracker's Lightning. "He'd be worth money to you," said Cracker and went on to tell how he had won $50.00 on Lightning at the last race in Russellville. Peter stared. "If I had a horse like that could I put him up and win $50.00 on him." "You could if he run faster than the others," said Cracker. "$50.00 or $500, depending on what you was willing to bet."

Peter contemplated unlimited wealth for a minute and then sadly abandoned it. "What's the use. I ain't got a horse like Lightning."

Cracker took out his violin. Peter admired this, too, and admired it even more when he found that Cracker had won it at cards. He taught Peter how to finger it, and Peter produced a few rusty quavers. Then Cracker sang a ballad about a man who was hanged on a hickory tree, and Peter said he could make a better story than that about the Harpes, and did, yelling away joyously in a tuneless recitative, while Cracker strummed chords.This went so well with the audience which consisted of an invisible cricket, and an inquisitive mouse, that Peter then embarked on the sad tale of Sally Rice who ran away with little Harpe. Mary heard the yelling in the barn, and smiled. Her heart yearned over her boy these days, when he seemed to be growing so rapidly away from her. She thought, "I'm glad he has the fiddle to amuse him. It was a good thing I caught those cards before he had a chance to get into that."

Even as she was thinking this Cracker laid down the violin and took out his pack of cards. Peter was so warmed up with the singing and the intimacy, there alone in the haymow, that he had not been so happy for months. A strong current was pulling him along with Cracker—he could not bear to break this magic excitement. For a minute it was as if a hand were pulling him back from the cards. Then he shook himself free of it, and thought, "What's wrong with cards? They're just painted pieces of pasteboard." He had often seen cards in the hands of the players at Dromgole's and Stewart's. But that was a place which even his easy father discouraged him from entering. But he had never seen these bright magic oblongs close at hand. He spread out the cards and examined them curiously. He had seen only three or four pictures in his life, and never ones so brightly colored as these. King, Queen, Jack, spades, hearts, diamonds, clubs—the pictures were like broken fragments of a fairy-tale.

"Come on. I'll show you a game," said Cracker.

Peter hesitated. Cracker knew better than to cast aspersions a second time on the objection of Peter's mother. So he added quietly, "There ain't no harm in playing. It's only when you gamble on 'em that some folks don't like it."

Peter mentally explained to Mary that he was only going to learn a game to while away the time, and, though he knew what she would say to that, he picked up the cards with a feeling that he had done his duty, and in a few minutes he was utterly engrossed. He learned quickly, and enjoyed it more than anything since the first gunpowder experiments. They played as long as they could catch even the dim outlines of figures on the cards, and then Peter tore himself away as out of a wondrous dream. The rainy landscape looked strange and unreal as he walked back to the house. It was as if he had been away for a long time. He slept that night with the cards dancing before his eyes, forming and reforming like figures in a bright pageant. After that he lived for the moments when he could slip away to the magical retreat in the hay and find the king and the queen, and the jack, the diamonds and the hearts waiting there for him. He rapidly got to the point where he could beat Cracker on an average of one out of three games.

3

It had been a long time since Peter had attended court with his father. But when he did go, he found himself unable to enter whole-heartedly into all the excitements because he was suddenly aware that his clothes were countrified, and his horse a disgrace. He held his head high. He cast bold and challenging glances at the dressy young Dromgoles and Gilberts and Jacksons and Cauldwells, and refused to shrink out of sight when Mrs. Dromgole passed, her hair piled with curls, a bright Paisley shawl draping her slender figure. "Why, Peter," she said, "what a big handsome fellow you've grown to be!" Her eyes passed down over his linsy shirt, deerskin jacket, and butternut jeans a little too small for him, and she hesitated and bit her lips. Peter knew she had been about to invite him to the dance at her house, but had thought better of it because she felt he would not be dressed properly. The red mounted to his forehead, and he kicked Diablo savagely. "I don't want to go to her damned parties," he thought angrily. But he knew in his heart that he did.

Even his father was conscious that there was something wrong with his dress. He had been so busy that he had not noticed till now that boys of Peter's age were beginning to have fine woolen breeches, and well-made tailored coats and greatcoats. He said uneasily, as his eye roved over the young men riding in, "There's a good tailor in Russellville now, and I guess it's high time you had a man's suit of clothes made by a tailor. Just as soon as somebody pays me some of what's owing, I'll see you get fixed out."

But even worse than the clothes was the horse. Jus himself rode a good horse, and raised and sold a fine breed. But he had disposed of all the horses just before Peter came home, and had not been paid for them. As soon as he collected, he intended to buy others. Peter could not resist the horse races which were a regular part of court day. But when, mounted on Diablo, he watched the young men prance up on their slim-legged beauties, and push him to one side, and fling insults at him and his horse, only his size made them edge away and become suddenly agreeable.

Peter tried to tell himself that neither clothes nor horse-flesh makes the man. He wanted to fight everybody that jeered or looked sidewise. He wanted to wring the neck of every hoity toity girl. But his commonsense told him that it was good to be well-dressed, and well-mounted, good to be gay and dashing and sure of yourself. Why should he—Peter Cartwright—accept anything less? His father was an admired citizen and a man of parts. His mother was worth a dozen Mrs. Dromgoles. Hold up his head— yes. But why be stupid and loutish about it?

But there was no use broaching the subject of clothes to his mother. For again there was trouble about Polly. Polly's lovely bloom had vanished. Her mother argued with her nights after Peter went to bed. He often heard the sound of sobbing down there by the fire. For Polly's lover had been identified as a man named Pentacost, who was suspected of being some kind of agent in New Orleans for the Mason gang, and was also said to have a wife in Natchez. He came to Russellville and was seen at Cedar House, and at the barbecues and dances and horse races—a dark, handsome man, with flourishing courtesy, a polished speech, and handsome clothes. In vain Polly protested that all the stories were nasty scandal. Pentacost was in business and besides he had a plantation in Mississippi. People in these savage wilds just didn't know a gentleman when they saw one, or understand how the world was. "And I reckon you understand. You've had so much experience," said Mary dryly. Polly's answer was a flood of tears.

4

One day Jus asked Peter to come to Russellville with him. "There are some papers I want you to deliver for me to a man in Henderson County," he said. "It's a considerable ride, and," he hesitated, "it leads by the forks there." Peter knew what he meant. When he had seen Susan Harpe riding with that head hanging by its hair, he had heard that it was to be placed at the forks of the road leading south from Henderson, and branching off in one direction to Marion and Eddyville and in the other to Madisonville and Russellville. From time to time he had heard references to the head—gloating, fearful, or horror-struck. Peter, like most others, was divided between curiosity to see the head, and a superstitious horror of passing the place where it was. Justurian, seeing him hesitate, said, "Why don't you get Jerry to go with you. It'll do him good to shake some of the Amens and Hallelujahs out of his brain."

When Peter asked Jerry, he looked rather eager, and yet he said,

"I'd be scared."

"Scared of what?" asked Peter loftily.

"Scared of the devil. He'd be sure to be somewheres there."

"The devil's got Harpe now right where he wants him, sizzling and frying the soul of him in Hell. What would the devil be bothering now with some ol' dried bones of a head?"

"But there could be evil hanging about the head there. It could put a spell on you."

"Evil's in live things," answered Peter, sensibly. "When anything's dead, the evil in it is dead, too." He thought of an added argument. "You'd better come. It'll help you be a Christian to see what a man comes to when he ain't." This persuaded Jerry. The errands took the boys longer than Jus had expected, and the harvest moon was just rolling up, huge and round like a yellow copper kettle, when, trembling, starting at every shadow, the boys approached the forks and caught the barest glimpse in the moonlight of the white staring skeleton there, with a few shreds of dried flesh, and a hank of tangled black hair clinging to it. They dug their heels into their horses' flanks, and never stopped galloping till suddenly their hearts turned over, and their horses reared in the air, and there was a big man on a black horse blocking the road. And then, infinitely sweet and re-assuring, they heard Justurian's voice. He had worried about the delay and had come to meet them and take them home. Peter and Jerry both felt like chicks running under a mother's wing.

Riding back with Jus, they suddenly saw a red flare on the landscape, and then a fiery cross, and shadowy troops of armed men. "Good God!" cried Justurian. "Ride! To the jail!"

5

The Harpe women who had been carried first to the log jail at Henderson had been brought to Russellville where they would be tried at the Court of the Quarter Sessions on October 28. This mob had heard about the women being there, and had come to lynch them. It was a wild night. But after about three hours of fighting, the lynchers were driven off. Folks were saying they had been led by Leiper and Stegall who were less concerned about the wickedness of the women than that they might be led at the trial to implicate others.

The Baptists, Methodists and Presbyterians were all trying to care for these women. Stewart also helped to cheer them and find families where the two children could be boarded, collect clothes, and borrow spinning wheels, so that they could be put to useful employment and made to feel self-respecting. Peter's mother gave two linsy woolsy dresses and some cotton for spinning. "They're a bad lot," said Mary. "But there's nobody so low that God can't pardon her and raise her up. And the less folks have to live like wild beasts the more they'll be open to the call of grace."

When Peter escorted his mother and Barbara to the jail to deliver their gifts, Susan, dirty even after the bath that had been forced on her, took the cotton and flung it into the dusty corner. Betsy smiled hypocritically out of her eyes, and said how good the ladies were, and how sweet the linsy woolsy frock was. Sally took the dress dyed with wild indigo softly in her hands, and bowed her head and cried into it. She said, "I don't deserve to have good Christian women like you come to see me," and added timidly, "I was brought up a Christian. My father was a parson."

"Yes," said Mary, "we know. And Mr. McGready has sent for him to come and be with you."

"Father!" and she cried again, her slender shoulders shaking with paroxysm after paroxysm of weeping.

Barbara smoothed her soft light hair gently, and said, "There! There, dear! Wouldn't it help if we knelt with you and said a little prayer?"

Sally seemed to nod assent. But as they knelt there was a volley of shots outside, and a snarling, angry roar. Then George Herndon burst in. "Help em! Pick up their needfuls. Throw their shawls on." He was bundling the women together. To Peter he said, "They're rushing the jail, trying to get at 'em here. Your father says you're to come with me. Take charge of Sally there."

Peter looked at his mother. "But—"

Mary said decisively, "Barbara and I've both got pistols and knives. Don't you bother, Peter. We'll look out for ourselves."

While the log jail rocked with the crashing against it of men fighting in front, and the shots of Stewart and Wes Maulding, Jus and others holding them off, Peter and George Herndon sneaked the women out the back way, and set them on horses, and started off through the yellowing woods on a trail which, Peter knew, led to a large cave about five miles away. Sally rode behind Peter on his horse. As he felt the arms of this slight girl around him, tenderness surged through his body, and he wished she need never let go. He turned once or twice and could glimpse over his shoulder the pretty face, the childlike blue eyes, the soft light hair. Such a tender, gentle thing! A storm of thoughts was going through his mind. "The trouble with women is there's such a power of loving in them—and they'll go to Hell itself for what they love." He thought of Polly. "If she'd set her heart on somebody like Wiley Harpe it could just as well a been her." He thought of Polly sobbing by the fire, and the talk that was going around about Pentacost, and he understood with a sudden and dreadful clarity his mother's terror. "But Polly ain't a bad girl," he told himself. "There ain't a thing bad in her." He felt Sally's arms around him. "They could hang her! They could lay the blame on her for murder." His horror and pity were almost unbearable. Sally must have sensed it, for she snuggled her face against the sturdy broad back in the deerskin jacket, and dissolved in tears. So they rode through the yellowing woods. At the path which led off to the cave, Herndon had drawn up and was waiting for them with the others. "I'll take charge of her from now on," he said. "Go on back, Peter."

Peter unclasped the slender rough hands that were now clinging desperately to him, and springing from the horse lifted her in his arms and set her down. She dried her eyes, and cast a grateful look at him. For a second her eye traveled over the broad round face, the bright black eyes, the broad forehead under the mat of curling hair, the stocky, strong, tall figure. "Don't you ever get into bad company," she said, in a low, muffled voice. "When you get in, you can't get out."

When it was found that the women had disappeared from the jail there were the wildest stories. Some said that Wiley Harpe had come and sneaked them away. Some said they had escaped to Cave-in-Rock. Old man Roberts got roaring drunk and went careering around swearing that Bill Stewart had killed his daughters—until Stewart locked him in the jail to sober him. But all the while Peter knew that the women were being kept safe in the cave and would be produced on court day. And so they were.

6

Peter attended court utterly oblivious of his clothes and horse. He wanted to see Sally again. It seemed to him that if Sally were condemned to hang, he could not bear it. Hanging was not for soft things lilke her whom love had misled. He had wild thoughts of rescuing her and taking her off somewhere.

On October 28 the Grand Jury was empanelled in Russellville. There never had been such a court day in Russellville before. To Peter, riding to court with his father, the whole world looked unreal and this day quite different from other days. And in fact the landscape on the way to Russellville had been transformed since he rode this way a few days before. There had been a frost and a wind. The trees stripped of their yellow leaves looked open and nude, above a floor of dewy gold, and on all the wide gold horizon the air was thick and warm and blue as if the sky had come down and were softly enfolding the naked world. In that balmy, azure haze, common things had a remoteness and unreality, and in the dry yellowing grasses by the roadside the steady low buzz of insects had the quality of stillness.

Against this unreal, painted world, with its look of infinite, sunny quietude, crowds from thirty and forty miles away were converging on Russellville, on horseback, in carts, in big new covered wagons. The tobacco crop had been sold. Many had leisure and money, and new wheeled vehicles which were rapidly replacing the old packhorses. And though there were still less than 150 inhabitants in Russellville, it was the metropolis of western Kentucky. Here, if anywhere, there would be something to buy with the tobacco, something to trade for a fine young horse, something to see over and above the excitement of the trial itself. So people came, prepared to stay till the fate of the three Harpe women was settled, and all around Russellville there were encampments and picnic fires.

Riding Diablo, but wearing neat tailormade breeches and his first pair of real boots, Peter pushed through the crowds in the wake of his big father on his handsome black horse, oblivious of everything except the hope of seeing Sally. His heart ached to re-assure her and tell her not to be afraid. He did not see Sally that day, because it was hopeless to try to get inside the courtroom. But he was relieved to know that her father was with her. He waited patiently for an hour and forty minutes in order to catch sight of Parson Rice coming out of the jail with McGready—a grave slender man, with a round black hat, and a neat, full-skirted clerical suit, and black breeches tucked into high black riding boots.

The trials of the three women were held on the next two days—October 29 and 30, and Peter came back with his father each day. Most of the crowds slept in their wagons or on the ground. Cedar House was full of interested strangers. Some said they were actually members of the Mason gang anxious to see what might leak out, and ready to send word to any who might be implicated, to escape. Most of them were well dressed, well mounted men, with open, gentlemanly manners. They disclaimed special interest in the trial, and said they were here on "business" or on their way to Nashville. But somehow or other they got places in the small courtroom, while most of the local citizens were forced to stay outside. Though the trial was of spectacular importance, Judge Samuel Macdowell and Judge Allen were absent, and the women were tried before Judge James A. Hunter. Judge Felix Grundy appeared for them.

Each of the three women was tried separately. Peter pleaded

so earnestly with his father and his father's legal friends that he finally got a chance to see Sally's trial. When he heard the charge that she was an accomplice in the murder of Mrs. Stegall, infant James Stegall, and Major Love, he was so outraged that he nearly jumped up and shouted a denial. His heart bled for her, cowering there, wrapped in an old black shawl, casting now and then a frightened glance at her father who sat on the rfont row of plank benches, and now and then looking for re-assurance to the big sheriff, Bill Stewart, who always smiled back in a kindly way. But she did not weep, and she answered bravely, though in a voice so low that Peter, in the back of the room, could not hear what she said.

The case was strictly confined to the Love-Stegall murders, and made no reference to the others of the twenty-eight victims of Big Harpe in this neighborhood. The prosecution worked on the theory that Harpe had had accomplices in the neighborhood, and that his women may have been working with these accomplices. But since nothing was produced to show that Sally was an accomplice, she was acquitted. The whole court room rushed up and crowded around her where she stood with her father, the black shawl falling back from her soft light hair, smiling through happy tears. The sheriff stood with them, his broad pleasant face wreathed in smiles. Peter tried to get to her through the mass, but it was hopeless. Finally he slipped out and got a place of vantage by the door where he knew she must eventually come out. There he found Parson Rice's horse, saddled and the good Methodist ladies of the Russell family busily packing saddlebags with food and clothes. Big Bill Stewart came out, pushing back the crowd, clearing the way from the log door to the horse. And then she came, still clinging to her father, wiping her eyes, with a light like March sunshine around her. Bill Stewart picked her up in his strong arms and set her on the saddle. Her father mounted in front of her. She put her arms around her father. Over Peter swept the memory of riding like that with Sally clinging to him, and leaning, sobbing, against his back. He was overjoyed that she was free, but he could not bear it that she should leave without a word to him. He pushed his way to her. "Miss Sally! Miss Sally!" She looked down on him, her blue eyes almost on a level with his black ones. Embarrassment overwhelmed him. He stammered, "I-I only want to say I-I'm glad."

She had never smiled at him before, but she smiled now, tender, palely radiant, and leaning over she patted his curly head. "Thank you, Peter." Then she added, "Remember what I told you. Don't you ever get into—you know what."

The parson nodded absently to Peter, and they rode away. Peter stood watching them till they disappeared around a clump of red sumach and were gone.

Susan and Betsy Roberts were also acquitted. As Peter rode home, he saw his mother and the other Methodist ladies at the tumble-down filthy Roberts cabin, busy burning debris, old rags and bones, sweeping the front yard, getting it ready for the two women and their children. Old man Roberts stood by. He had washed his face, more or less, in honor of the visitors, and the cleaner portion made an odd mask over his nose and mouth. He was fawning and affable, but let the women carry out boxes and furniture without ever offering to lift a hand. About half a mile away, Peter found the Roberts brother, naked except for an old pair of pants, half reclining under a tree. He did not appear to be drunk, but he looked sullen and angry.

Peter thought about these folks all the way home. Could they really be saved, as the Methodists believed, or were they damned from the outset as the Presbyterians believed? But, he reflected, it was a queer thing about Presbyterians. They never stopped hoping that among these dregs there might be one whom God had destined for salvation. So they preached to them and worked on them as earnestly as if they didn't know that, in nine cases out of ten, the effort was useless. But then, he reflected, Presbyterians and God didn't judge people by worldly standards. This poor low down trash that had never had a chance was, in the eternal order of things, no more likely to be destined for Hell fire than some of the smart, sleek, handsome, well-fed folks like Cauldwell and Burwell Jackson, who always saw to it that their own bread was buttered.

BOOK IV

1800 - 1802

Thomas Jefferson, President

CHAPTER 24

Russellville, Kentucky
January, 1800 to April, 1800

Over a landscape tawny with tall dried grasses, white with frost
and snow, rising on all sides to a chill, blue scallop of hills, the new
century dawned. There were now 250,000 people in Kentucky, of
whom 20,000 were Negro slaves. In the woodland capital of Frankfort, legislators, tipped back in their chairs around the blazing, pot-
bellied stove, were figuring that the population of Kentucky was
now about equal to that of Connecticut; only 1/3 less than that of
Maryland; more than 1/2 that of Massachusetts; more than 1/3
that of Pennsylvania; 1/4 that of Virginia and nearly 1/4 that of
the two Carolinas.

Most of these people were concentrated in a single island of settlement in central Kentucky, separated by a 200 mile channel from
the second and smaller island of settlement in the Cumberland
area, which included Nashville, Russellville, and Logan County. In
this second settled region of the West, there were only about 5000
people. But it had a moral vitality out of proportion to its numbers, for here the new soul of the West was being forged in the
white heat of its struggle with evil. All around these two settlements there stretched the wilderness, like a storm-tossed, pirate-
infested sea, with no civilized settlement anywhere, except the tiny
stockade of the Yankee veterans in Ohio. Eastward of central
Kentucky there were still 300 miles of robber-infested forest and
mountain. Westward across the Mississippi rolled the unknown.
To the South there was New Orleans, with 500 miles of Indian-
filled forest between it and Nashville. To the North across the
Ohio lay a primeval tangle of forests, which in spring were all one

great swamp filled with Indians, restless and threatening under the black magic that was wielded over them by British fur forts. Though some progress had been made in breaking the clutch of the Alston-Mason net-work on all this region, there was still no real safety anywhere. The rivers had devious and difficult channels, which shifted every year, and their craggy wooded banks provided hiding places for river pirates which the whole U. S. army in the West was not numerous enough to patrol. The bridle paths, and even the new wagon roads led through long stretches of empty wood which could not be guarded.

The remedy, the legislators thought, was more people. The state of Kentucky was ready to sell parcels of 400 acres at $20.00 a hundred to any male citizen of the United States or any foreigner who would take the oath of allegiance.

The remedy, John Page thought, was not only more people but more Christians. The whole of the settled area of the West was organized as the Kentucky district of the Methodist Church and included Ohio, Kentucky and Tennessee. Methodists in Ohio were still very few. In Kentucky, after the great increase in membership as a result of last summer's revivals, there were still only 1626 white and 115 colored members. In Tennessee, there were 631 white members and 62 colored. The infant church in the West, under William McKendree, the big, raw-boned frontiersman as Presiding Elder, now comprised fourteen preachers on nine circuits.

The new century began for Peter with the baptism of Jerry. The weather was ten degrees below zero. The ice on Muddy River was a foot thick and had been cut through to a distance of from twenty to thirty yards. So intense was the cold that some of the good Baptist brothers had to keep stirring the water with poles and staves to keep it from freezing. Mr. Lewis Moore presided and preached a long sermon so hot with hell-fire that Peter thought it should have had some effect on the temperature, but it didn't. Inside his fur-lined moccasins Peter's feet ached intolerably and then settled into numbness. His nose, protruding from a fur hood, seemed to have congealed to ice.

Through the glittering sharp air there was the sharp high thin sound of triumphant singing and over the snow came the penitents, two by two, their breath like snow clouds on the air. Then the devotees, twelve in number, in gowns like long white nightgowns. Peter, standing congealed against an icy snow bank on the outer edge of the congregation, could not recognize Jerry at first in this angel band. But finally he decided that the littlest one was his erstwhile comrade in ill-doing. At the head of the white clad company was Mr. Moore, alternately praying and singing in honor of John, the Baptist. He plunged into the stream breast high. Hand in hand, the disciples followed. He turned on them, intoning "In the name of the Father, the Son, and the Holy Ghost," and seizing the first one, immersed him completely. Praying, the others followed till all were immersed.

Peter's teeth were chattering. He felt awed, but rebellious. That icy stream was now an impassable gulf running between him and Jerry for ever. He was relieved to see a man moving amidst the crowds with a bucket of whisky. Peter usually detested whisky, but now, between cold and a sense of bereavement, plus a trouble somewhere in his conscience, he drank a whole gourd full of the scalding stuff. He galloped home kicking Diablo madly, the snowy landscape dim, remote, but spinning as on an axle of fire. His mother smelt the whisky on his breath as he stooped through the cabin door. Her cry of despair rang through his fuddled brain. "Peter, must I go through this with you?"

He broke down and cried from cold and excitement, blubbering, the tears scalding his cheeks. His hands were stinging, his feet were stinging, his nose felt as if it would fall off. His head was going round, and his stomach heaving. "I'll promise, Mammy, I'll never get drunk in my life till they make a Baptist of me."

Mary pulled off his fur hood, and rubbed his aching hands and feet, and thrust a bowl of hot corn mush into his hands. "There, eat that! It'll settle your stomach." As she hovered over him, she kept scolding, "Baptists! First they drown them in water and then they drown them in drink."

This was not fair, and Peter knew it. For the dozen or so of sins which were regularly castigated at the Saturday meetings before the Lord's Day, and for which rigorous penance was imposed, included excessive drunkenness. However, the Baptists had much less success in that place and time in combating strong drink than the Methodists. For the harshness of the Baptist discipline often created situations from which the only relief was drink. Whereas the Methodists, with their kindlier and more forward looking social attitudes, were beginning to offer, at all their gatherings, something the average healthy appetite on the frontier craved much more than it craved strong drink and found it much harder to get—that is, new and interesting food, and a chance to enjoy the companionship of the sexes under decent circumstances. Eating the hot corn meal mush, and feeling his head slowly clear, and relaxation and comfort replacing the wild hot torment within, Peter wondered again what anybody wanted drink for when food was so much better!

2

There was plenty of food that day, and the cabin was savory with it, for William Burke, the Circuit Rider, was expected by night fall, and would sleep in the spare room, and be feasted as Methodist sisters always tried to feast the circuit riders.

William Burke delighted Peter by listening without rebuke to his all but profane account of the Baptism, and then telling one story after another about Baptists, all with a solemn and sanctimonious countenance and a twinkle in his gray eye. He told of one baptism where a man was carried under the ice by the current. And the preacher—

"What did he do?" asked Peter, eagerly. He had been wondering this morning what would happen if that black flood should carry Jerry under the ice. What would he, Peter, do? He'd feel bound to jump in and try to help get him out. This possibility had been so vivid that it had been like a reprieve to one condemned to die when he saw Jerry emerge dripping, the white gown clinging to his figure and stiffening.

"What did the preacher do?" repeated Peter, his sparkling black eyes on the circuit rider's weather beaten face.

"Oh," said Burke, in a leisurely drawl, "he said, 'The Lord hath given. The Lord hath taken away. Come on, another one of you, my children'."

Mary said, "Why do they pick a day like this for immersing 'em? Why not a nice hot summer day?"

"If you immersed 'em in Muddy River then, they'd come out all dusty," said Peter. "But a spring day wouldn't be so bad. There'd be water then."

Mary sniffed. "Spring wouldn't suit the Baptists. They won't do a thing without they make it is as hard as possible."

"Well," said Burke, "you've got to look at it through their eyes. This baptism is the great change. It marks the sloughing off of the old man, and the putting on of the new. It is death to earth and its glories and its lures, and birth to Heaven and its hope of everlasting glory. And when you come right down to it, neither death nor birth is without struggle and agony. It's a great day in the life of the Baptist. That black river, deep, icy and mortally dangerous, is so like the river of death between him and all he ever was."

Mary looked at him curiously. "One would think you favored them. Would you as soon be a Baptist as a Methodist?"

"No," said Burke gravely, "because I am a Christian, and that means one who follows in the way of Christ, and you know what Christ said. He said, 'John came neither eating nor drinking, and ye say he has a devil. The son of man came eating and drinking, and ye say, Behold a friend of sinners!' I'd rather eat and drink and be a friend of sinners." He helped himself a third time to the pot-roast of venison, and the cabbage sliced thin in sour cream, and drained his coffee to the dregs, his gray eyes twinkling at Peter over the rim of the cup.

3

Burke had put himself out to entertain the young people because Mary had already opened her heart to him with regard both to Polly and to Peter. She said that, though Polly denied it, she was thought to be in love with a handsome stranger from Natchez, whom the boys called Pentacost.

"He comes from Natchez, you say," observed Burke, thoughtfully. "May be I can find out something about him besides hearsay that'll convince her, or else clear his character."

"Yes, that's what I thought," said Mary eagerly. "I said to Barbara, 'Thank God for circuit riders. Even if they didn't bring us the blessed consolation of religion, they'd still be worth anything any of us could do to feed and lodge and support them, just for the errands they do for us, and the messages they carry, and the knowledge and news they spread from one to the other.' "

It would have been impossible two years before for even the Methodists to trace a man to Natchez. But fortunately, at the conference of 1799, Tobias Gibson of Georgie, a man of considerable wealth, had given up all he possessed to preach the gospel. He rode to the head of the Cumberland River, and there he sold his horse and bought a canoe. On the canoe he floated down the Cumberland into the Ohio, down the Ohio to the Mississippi, and then 700 miles down and established himself in the territory of Mississippi. Four times that first year he had traveled the wilderness, a distance of 600 miles, guided and lodged by friendly Indians, and had built up a church of sixty members. "I will send word by Swaney, the mailman, to Gibson," said Burke. "Gibson can go where no one else can in Natchez, and through all that desperate land for the burning love of God fills his mouth with persuasive arguments."

Hearing this, Mary was greatly relieved. She had been even more relieved when Polly listened with so much interest to the Circuit Rider's stories, laughing more freely and naturally than she had done for months, and when she rose from her knees after prayers she sat down on the stool by the Circuit Rider casting at him a soft, confiding glance. He began talking to her in a low voice while Mary set the long plank table for breakfast, with wooden bowls and trenchers and the new crockery cups and saucers, and poured some cold water into the iron tea kettle, hanging from a crane, which was boiling over into the fire. Meanwhile Jus pulled out from under the big bed in the far corner, where he and Mary slept, the wide, low trundle bed for Sis and Polly. He had taken off his breeches and boots, and stood in his woolen underwear, his feet in furlined moccasins. But because it was cold this bitter night in that far corner, he still wore his fur jacket. This gave him a top-heavy and most undignified appearance, which made Peter feel slightly shamed. He hoped the preacher did not notice. But in accordance with the best frontier etiquette Burke acted as if nothing were going on in the house anywhere, and he and the goldenbright young girl on the stool at his knee were the only two people in the world. In such close quarters, privacy had to be maintained by psychic, rather than physical, means. You not only shut what was none of your business out of your sight, you shut it out of your mind. In accordance with this principle, Peter, as he had been trained to do, turned his back on the corner where thirteen-year-old Sis was removing the outer layer of her garments under a large woolen bedgown held over her head like a tent.

Peter sat on an upended log, at the other end of the hearth from the preacher and Polly, and whittled on a new part he was making for his mother's big wool wheel. He didn't try to listen to what the preacher was saying, but he knew that he was talking to Polly about Sally Rice, and the way girls, through love and pity, can get into situations whose end is shame. Suddenly Polly gave a sharp little cry. "No-no!" Then, "I reckon I'd better help Mammy." As she jumped up she turned over the stool in her agitation. Mary interposed, "Polly can help me while you talk to Peter, Brother Burke."

Peter turned the stool right side up, sat down on it by the preacher, but continued his whittling. He felt the need of something to steady him, to stand between him and the full impact of the Circuit Rider's attention. Ordinarily he would have been happy to pour out his thoughts and even his troubles. He often held imaginary conversations with the circuit riders, planning what he would say when this great Oracle came around. But tonight he was like one hiding a forbidden object under his coat. Burke probed with all his skill, but when Peter said good-night, turning on him what seemed a frank and earnest young face as he climbed the rough ladder to his bunk in the loft, there was a faint smile of triumph playing around his full young lips. He had intended to baffle the preacher, and had done so. He crawled under his bearskin, feeling not at all conscience stricken, and lay awake for an hour thinking about his problem, listening meanwhile to the low voices of Polly and the preacher who were again talking together down there by the fire.

4

Peter's problem was that he had lost the last of his six dollars and his hunting knife to Cracker, and had nothing else to bet. He could not bear to give up those secret sessions in the hay which were the drama and excitement of the dull winter days, for lack of something to gamble with. Besides, he would feel defeated and defeat was something Peter was conditioned not to accept. He resented the way Cracker had taken advantage of his greenness. "Beat your neighbor all you can," Cracker had said. "He'll do the same to you." "I sure will do the same," thought Peter. "It ud serve him right to lose every cent he has, and his cards, and his fiddle—and Lightning." The idea of winning Lightning from Cracker awed him. It was a fantastic idea. And yet why not? Men lost and won more than Lightning at cards.

The question was how. If the game he played with Cracker was a matter of skill, he could practice till his skill was greater. But such playing as they did was punctuated by bets like "I bet a dollar the next card that turns up is a diamond," or, "If clubs are trumps, I bet $2.00 I'll *loo*." Peter considered whether Cracker hadn't been playing some kind of trick on him, leading him to bet, but controlling the fall of cards somehow. This might be so. He'd have to watch. But then again it might be just chance that Cracker won every time. This sent him off into a long meditation on chance, trying to understand how it works, and skirting around the law of probability. It seemed to him that no matter how many times chance goes against you, it is bound sooner or later to fall in your favor. "The main thing then is to hang on till chance turns your way," he thought. "To beat chance you have to take lots of chances." But to take lots of chances you have to have something to take chances with. Peter was frustrated.

Peter knew that there was one thing he had which Cracker wanted so much that he'd probably bet against it the six dollars he had won from Peter, and the ten dollars Peter knew he had, and his fiddle. And this was the new fur-lined jacket Peter's mother had made him. These cold days Cracker never stopped looking at that with greed in his eyes. Peter knew that even if Cracker won his jacket he need not be cold, for his old jacket was just as warm, though not as handsome. Mary's skill and industry provided an inexhaustible surplus of homemade clothes. But he could never explain to his mother how the jacket passed from his back to Cracker's. No, he might bet the jacket, but he wasn't going to do it till he was sure to win.

But how to win? Peter felt sure he could figure that out if he could only lay hands on a pack of cards long enough to study them. He had hoped to win Cracker's cards from him. Failing that, he had intended to save two out of his six dollars and buy a pack of cards secretly at Dromgole and Stewart's. He didn't dare ask his father for cards lest his father tell his mother. Probably his brother John would have an extra pack. Peter considered asking John and decided against it. To be beholden to John for anything would lower his pride.

It occurred to him that Cracker was at work all day, and must leave his cards somewhere in the loft. If so, he could take them out and put them back before Cracker came in. This solved everything. Peter went peacefully to sleep. Next morning, when the preacher rode away, the boy smiled good-bye with a bright, untroubled face, too absorbed in his own plans to notice that the preacher had left Polly silent and sad.

5

During the next few weeks all the cunning and stealth Peter had learned as a forest child were put to use in stealing and restoring Cracker's cards. Spending long absorbed hours in the hay, dealing out the bright spotted oblongs, and carefully studying them, he thought if he willed hard enough he might make the cards fall as he wished. He thought if he stared hard enough at them, he might see through to the other side. So he played with ideas which have crossed men's minds since the first throw of the first rude forerunner of the dice, and which even now are a matter of scientific investigation by learned men in laboratories. One day he sat in the hay in the first mild springlike light that had come through the crack in the shuttered window. The sun was warm on the roof outside, the drip of the icicles was like rain. Peter had laid out the cards face downward in the narrow strip of light, and was staring at them from a distance of about three feet. Suddenly it seemed to him that the fine blue spotted backs of the cards which had hitherto seemed just alike, were utterly different. There were four distinct different patterns among them. In one, the lines ran perpendicularly, the next horizontally, the next transversely, and the next was quartered. Peter made a bet with himself, "If they don't each stand for a different suit, I'll wash the dishes for Mammy to-night." He turned the cards over. It was as he thought. He was beside himself with excitement. "Glory Hallelujah! Wait till we bet on suits next time!" He pondered. Did Cracker know this? He reviewed all the times he had played with Cracker. No, Cracker didn't know. The spotted blue backs of the cards looked just alike to him.

Peter examined the backs of the cards again, wondering what kind of second sight he had discovered. Was it in him or was it in the cards? A minute ago he couldn't have told one of these cards from another. Now their backs were as different as their faces! It was uncanny. He picked up the cards and began scrutinizing them one by one, running his fingers along the edges. He stopped suddenly. God Almighty! The edges were different! Some were convex, some concave. In some the width was convex and the length concave, in some the length convex and the width concave. "If that don't mean that each kind is a different suit, I'll milk the ol cow for Cracker to-night!"

It was as he thought. Diamonds were convex, clubs concave. Only by violent effort could he repress his impulse to whoop the very roof off the barn. "You don't have to look at them. You can tell what suits they are just by shuffling," he thought exultantly. He shuffled and reshuffled the cards, convincing himself that this was so. It would take a lot of practice to get to be quick at telling them. But you could do it. He set himself to practice then and there.

But there was still a problem. He could identify suits. But how about picking out aces, kings, queens, and knaves in a suit? "There's a way to tell them, too," he thought with assurance, and set himself to study the fine speckled pattern again. Sure enough. Each card within a suit was slightly different. He laid them out, backs up, and applied his attention to them earnestly. By the time the soft white shaft of light from the window faded, he could identify every one of the fifty-two cards by a glance at the back.

He started up, appalled to find how dark it was getting. Cracker would be coming in from the woods, where he had been cutting trees. He put the cards in the loosely bloused front of his jacket, and raced to the house, his hand inside his jacket delightedly identifying the suits by feeling them. Cracker had already come in and was standing by the fire in his wet woolen stockings, his boots crusted with melted snow, steaming beside him on the hearth. Fortunately he had not yet gone up to the loft. Peter ran up the ladder like a squirrel, and put the cards in their place, and swung himself down without even touching the rungs of the ladder, summoning all his natural gifts as an actor to draw an appearance of nonchalance over the excitement boiling within him.

What he had discovered was a secret of the card manufacturer of that day which appears to have remained unknown to any one except to those regularly initiated into the fraternity of professional gamblers, until it was revealed, years later, by a member of the Mystic Band of Brothers in the West, who was reformed.

6

Peter had two more days of practice with the cards in the hay until Cracker should be free on Sunday afternoon. After the hearty venison dinner, while Jus was nodding by the fire, and Mary, with a Sunday look on her face, was reading the Bible, Peter passed the high sign to Cracker, and they met in the hay. Peter began at once, "I bet you that if diamonds are trumps, you will *loo.*"

"What will you bet?" asked Cracker, cautiously.

"My new coat."

A gleam came into Cracker's watery blue eye, but he hesitated. "What will your Mammy say?"

"She won't know you have it, if you don't show it off before her eyes. You don't want to be wearin' it around here. You want to be wearin' it when you take Milly out," said Peter shrewdly.

"But what if your Mammy sees you haven't got it?"

"I'll say it was hot, and I took it off and must a left it somewheres, and I'll make a fuss keepin' on looking for it and worrying about it."

Peter felt mean saying this. For a moment his mother's anguished face rose before him. "Peter, must I go through this with you?" He hesitated for just a minute. The strong, exultant knowledge that he wouldn't lose swept him on. He wouldn't have to lie to Mammy. So why worry?

Cracker said, "All right. I'll take you up on it."

"What'll you bet."

"Six dollars."

"Six dollars against a coat like that! Make it twenty."

Twenty was more than Cracker had, and Peter knew it. But he knew he had sixteen dollars, and he held out for that. Finally Cracker laid the sixteen in a nest in the hay, and Peter took off his coat and laid it beside the money. Fifteen minutes later, Peter picked up the sixteen dollars and began to put on his coat again. Sixteen dollars! He had never been so rich in his life. He was giddy with excitement. He wanted to go on for ever, and took a rapid inventory of such possessions as Cracker still had. "I bet two dollars against your pack of cards." He won the cards. "I bet $1.00 against the fiddle." He won the fiddle. "I bet sixteen against Lightning." But here Cracker came to his senses. "Oh no, you don't."

There was a loud guffaw on the far side of the hay, and Justurian's face peered out of the brown dimness, his black eyes like sparks of fire. It was one of those moments when Jus looked all Indian. "He kinda cleaned you out, Cracker."

"Pappy!" exclaimed Peter, drawing back, much embarrassed. He was thinking rapidly. Would his father mind? Would he tell his mother. How stupid he had been to be caught.

"Don't worry, son," said Jus. "I've been enjoying this for a long time. You had me worried when you lost the last of your dollars. But I knew you'd find a way out. And you have." He smiled in triumph.

"But," Peter stammered. He was trying to think how he could ask his father not to tell his mother.

Jus understood. He winked, and said, "It's just between ourselves, Son. There's some things that are just naturally beyond the understanding of women."

7

Next day when he rode home from Russellville, Jus took Peter aside, and with great secrecy and a knowing look, he presented him with a brand new pack of cards. "Just in case Cracker wins his back," he said. Peter glanced at them, divided between delight in their shiny bright newness, and apprehension lest their backs should not be as conveniently marked as Cracker's. But as he ran through them, feeling their edges, he was satisfied that he could tell the suits just as well by these. The markings were a little different but just as plain.

Jus said, "I kinda thought you'd like to ride along with me to court tomorrow, and try your luck with some of the Dromgole and Maulding boys."

Something like an electric current passed between Peter and his father. These would indeed be fair game. He thought of the way they rode up to court, so fine and dashing on their blooded horses, with their hats with red feathers in them. They treated him like a lout because he rode Diablo. He'd show them!

He walked out to the barn with his father and climbed up into the hay, while his father went over the cards with him and showed him several card tricks, and warned him against the various tricks of card-sharpers and professional gamblers. Peter was amazed to see that, though his father had played cards a great deal, he was quite unaware that the cards could be read from the backs. He thought of pointing this out to him. But his father's pride and amazement when he played hand after hand with his son, and Peter beat him every time but one, led Peter to keep his secret. It was so pleasant to be looked on as a person of great skill and judgment by his own father. The years melted away between the two. Jus was a lad again, and Peter a man grown. Both were exhilarated.

It grew too dark to play. They sat in the warm, sweet-smelling, dusty dark, snugly nested in the hay, and Jus opened his heart to Peter. "I don't want you to be a gambler, Peter. But there's lots of friends made over a card table, and lots of things you learn about a man playing with him you couldn't find out that easy in any other way. For that, you've got to learn how to play pretty well, because nobody wants to play with a dumb cluck. But it's dangerous, just like everything else in life that's worth having is dangerous, and you've got to learn what the danger is and keep out of it. Take gambling. It's all right to gamble if you limit your gambling to what I'd call 'risk money.' This is money you'd spend having a good time, in one way or another, or money you can afford to lose and think, even if you lose, the whole play was well worth it. But never gamble with your living, or other people's property, or what would so hurt you to lose it that you'd be in a fever to try to win it back. That's the gambler's fever, and it's fatal. If you lose your shirt, be sure you go bare till you can earn a new one by honest means. If you gamble away your living, be sure you stop and starve till you've earned food and a surplus in an honest way."

"That takes a strong character," said Peter.

"It does," said Justurian. "And if I didn't think you had a strong character, do ye think I'd be risking putting a card in your hand, lad?"

His heart swelling with pride and tenderness, Peter put out his hand and stroked the sleeve of his father's fur jacket. "I'll bear in mind what you say. You won't be disappointed," he said earnestly.

Jus put his arm across the boy's shoulder. "I know I won't," he said.

For a moment they were both silent. Then Jus said, soberly, "Peter, I ain't religious like your mother. But when anything don't seem right to me, I just don't do it. I don't do it because I'm afraid of God or Heaven—they're something I just don't know anything about. And when I ask myself why, I find it's because I've got pride. I just can't see myself as a fool or a brute. I've got to think well of myself, and deserve my own good opinion. And that's the way I think it is with you. You've got sense and you've got pride, and there's nothing soft in your backbone."

Peter reached for his father's hand and clasped it. Preachers had often talked to him, and he had been moved by what they said, but never in his life had he felt so dedicated to a standard as at this moment.

"You needn't never be afraid for me," he said softly. "I ain't one to be afraid for."

8

Wolfing down cold sliced venison, hoe cakes, and hot coffee at the log cabin canteen which served visiting lawyers on court day, Jus was proud to hear a sharp witted colleague from over Bowling Green way remark, "I saw that young un of yours playing cards with the red-haired Maulding lad. He sure has a head on his shoulders."

A few minutes later, as Jus was plodding back on foot to the courthouse, along the single street of Russellville, up to his boot tassels in mud and melting snow, Peter splashed up on Diablo. His eyes were sparkling. His curls under his coonskin cap were like black coiled springs. "I'm going over to Dromgoles'," he said hardly drawing up. "Skinny Dromgole says his mother wants me to dinner." He flashed two five dollar gold pieces at his father. "That's what comes of winning ten dollars off Skinny. He thinks I'm a Big Somebody now."

"I'll come around for you when it's time to go home," said Jus. Peter turned and nodded brightly. He was already half way down the road.

Jus was rather glad for an opportunity to look in at the Dromgoles'. Philip Alston's daughter had several times turned her blue-eyed bewitchment on him and in tones that lingered afterwards like the taste of maple taffy on the tongue, had invited him to come in to see them. But this always happened when the question of the relation of Dromgole's Exchange to Mason's gang threatened to come up in court, and he had thought it best not to rise to that bait. Now he'd go on his own terms, just dropping in to pick up his boy.

The foggy afternoon was dimming into universal opaque when Jus turned through the gate, and ploughed up the hoof-trampled slough that was all the spring thaw had left of the Dromgole road. He passed a number of horses tied to trees and recognized, with a pang, that Diablo was the only one among them that wasn't a fine thoroughbred. He tied his own horse, proud that at least it was one of the best. Balancing himself precariously on some planks which had been laid in the slush as a walk to the house, he approached the big plank door. The house seemed to consist of a whole neighborhood of cabins stuck together, for one room had been added to another to make quite a spacious, one storey residence. Through the glass window, the light twinkled on the misty snow outside, and fell on a row of jonquils thrusting up bravely. "Must be they have a flower garden round the house here," thought Jus. Mary had always wanted a flower bed in the dooryard. He must see that she got it this year. A son that was going to grow up part and parcel of folks that lived in houses like this required that his parents take a little trouble to live up to him.

The door was opened by a Negro, and Mrs. Dromgole was

running to him and twittering and holding out both hands to him, and looking up at him—pretty enough to kiss. He felt a little confused as he stepped into the big room, which wasn't very different from the main room of his own cabin, except that there were no beds in it—the Dromgoles having risen to the dignity of bedrooms—and it was lit not only by the red glow of the fireplace but by candles in candle-sticks, quivering like stars in the sky, making a strange magic and confusion of light; gleaming on pewter and wine glasses on a big polished dresser; and on a real mahogany table, and one Oriental rug, amidst the several bearskin rugs on the floor. The light appeared to be dancing and quivering in a vast, musical noise, made up of the chatter of girls and boys, mixed with the strains of a fiddle. Jus heard a strong, clear voice lining out some ridiculous words about Mary Anne, who was a girl, pert as a sparrow and shy as a squirrel, and there was Peter, beating time, and yelling, "Come on, Brother. Come on, Sister," in absurd imitation of a preacher leading the singing in church. For a minute he saw his boy as if he were a stranger, his eye traveling over the tall form, the broad shoulders, the thick neck holding like a strong column the round head thatched with thick black curls. And then Mrs. Dromgole was introducing him to a pretty lady draped in a blue cashmere shawl, and she was saying, "Peter's father! This is indeed a pleasure, Mr. Cartwright," and she added, "We find your son quite dazzling."

The lady introduced him to a row of young ladies—some of the eighteen beautiful daughters of William Richardson, who lived on the banks of Green River. Then who should come up but John Wilcox, with Penny, his wife. A Negro passed him a glass of peach brandy, and then another.

Altogether Justurian's head was going round and round by the time he and Peter were out in the fresh, damp night and riding home through the fog. As they reached the gate one of Justurian's saddle straps broke loose. He dismounted, and struck a flint. And the light flared for a second on the face of a man on horseback who had drawn up at the gate. In that one brief flash, Peter distinctly remembered the face of John May, and Jus thought of Philip

Alston. Then the foggy dark descended. There was only the sound of hoofs sloshing into the distance. Jus said nothing to Peter about what he had thought, and Peter nothing to Jus. They rode on, slowly and cautiously, for it was very difficult to know the way in this universal obliteration, and they had to trust that the horses knew the way better than they.

In a desultory way, they talked about the people at Dromgole's, their voices coming to each other as if from disembodied spirits in the foggy dark. "I understand the Exchange business is bringing John a tidy income," observed Jus. "He tells me he took ten flat boats of tobacco down the river last fall." Privately he wondered how, at the present price of tobacco, he could really make much. Peter's mind flashed back to the mask and different outlandish riggings John used to have, but he said nothing about them. Instead, he spoke of Penny and the way her reddish hair showed pink through powder. "John says any time I want I can stay with him and Penny," he remarked.

The answer was slow in coming through the fog. "Well, now," said Jus, "that isn't going to please your mother." Whether it would please him or not, he did not say. Then Jus commented that he was surprised to see that tall, lean Spanish looking fellow they called Stuart Walker there. "Last time I saw him he was at Cedar House with Thomas Powers, talking pure treason."

Startled, Peter repeated questioningly, "He was talking treason?"

"Yes, the Spanish Intendent at New Orleans sent Powers up here to confer with Wilkinson and Sebastian, and Innes, and other rascals, to get Kentucky to separate from the United States and join Spain. It's a game Spain has tried several times, but the last time was two or three years ago when Spain broke the Jay treaty, and all our flatboats were jammed up on the river, and they wouldn't let them come into the port of New Orleans. Folks were pretty upset and this man Powers came up, and with him that tall dark fellow with those sad eyes, like a cow, and he said the flatboats could go through if Kentucky would forget about the United States which was too far away to do it much good. And we might have done it, because the Federalists in Washington sure hadn't made us love them, except that tying up with Spain would mean tying up with England. We veterans out here had fought seven years to get shet of England, and we weren't going to walk back into her arms just to unjam those flatboats."

"But if John took boats down, they must have fixed it somehow."

"Yes. Captain Isaac Guyon and some U. S. soldiers occupied Chickasaw Bluffs and Natchez, and the Dons thought they'd better be friends, else we'd go on and take New Orleans."

All this Peter knew already. But it seemed novel and meaningful. Something had happened when he won that money from Skinny. It was as if he had been asleep all his life, and now was suddenly awake, aware of and curious about much that had hitherto passed him by. But with this change had come increased caution and secrecy. He considered whether to tell his father that Polly's beau, Pentacost, and Stuart Walker were the same man, and decided against it. Polly's affairs were her own business. Instead, he remarked that he had been invited to a ball at the Tudor place.

He could feel that his father was impressed. The Tudor place was of much interest, because, though it was only a spacious and comfortable log fort, with a kind of tessellated tower, like the old blockhouses, it was almost the only place that was really landscaped. A handsome grove of trees surrounded the house, and all around it were parklike stretches of green, which were kept nibbled into smooth turf by sheep. Absolom Tudor was reserved, dignified, gentlemanly, and appeared to be rich and to hold himself well above the common run of humanity.

"They say he's a genuine Tudor," observed Peter. "Pappy, what is a Tudor?"

Jus was stumped. "Seems to me they were somebody in history," he answered at last. "But I'm not up on history, son. You'll have to ask the Doctor."

CHAPTER 25

When Peter asked Doctor Allen about the Tudors, he got the story of Henry VIII's disposal of his wives, and the beheading of Mary Stuart by Henry's daughter, Elizabeth. "Why they're worse than the Harpes!" he gasped, unutterably shocked. "Why did they keep that kind of truck for kings?" He was used to hearing aspersions on anybody in high places. "But even so," he said, "we wouldn't have a Harpe as Governor of Kentucky. Folks in Rogues' Harbor are low, but not that low!" What puzzled him was that anybody should respect Absolom Tudor, if a Tudor were just a bigger and fancier Harpe.

Allen was amused. "You'll find crime take on dignity and even splendor if it's far enough back in time," he observed.

"I don't see why," said Peter stubbornly.

"Well, what ails Absolom Tudor is snobbery, not villainy," remarked Allen. "Look, I'll show you something." He pulled down Hume's *History of England* from the small shelf of books he had finally acquired and showed him a picture.

Peter stared. "It looks like Absolom all dressed out in a foolish rig."

"It's a picture of Henry VII of England," said Allen. "All this talk about Tudor is based on this resemblance. I don't think Tudor's his real name. It's a silly pretense."

"If I was pretendin' to be somebody else, I wouldn't pick a Harpe," said Peter.

When he brought the scandalous history of the Tudors up for discussion at the supper table that night, his father observed, "I don't know much history. But when I read back a little in law, it seems like every kind of title, King, Lord, Duke, and Earl, was just a way the big criminals had of marking themselves off as above the law, so nobody could get at em and try em the way regular bad uns are caught."

"Like the Dromgoles and Mauldings," said Mary.

"Oh I wouldn't say that. We don't give them titles and make their loot hereditary."

"We pretty near do. Who's keeping Morton in the legislature? Who's making Ambrose a judge? When anybody starts making a Tudor high and fancy, it's them that wants not only to rob the hide off your back, but to make you bow down and worship them for it."

After supper, while Mary and Polly were washing the dishes, Jus sidled up to his tall son and said in his ear, "I wouldn't say any-- thing to your Mammy about that dance at Tudor's. No use worrying her."

Peter stammered, "But—then it's all right to go?" For all the resemblance of the Tudors to the Harpes, he wanted to go to that dance desperately. The brown-eyed Richardson girl would be there—the next to the youngest. Besides he knew, with youth's infallible instinct, that once he dropped out of some of these social affairs he'd be left out of all of them.

"Why yes—sure I'd go if I was you," said Jus. "The more you find out about life the better. Just so long's you keep your head."

2

But on one subject Jus was downright. Peter was never to play cards with a professional gambler. "Learn to smell 'em like you'd smell a skunk," said Jus, "and then make a wide circle around em. Don't think you're smart enough to get away with anything where they're concerned. You ain't, and if you ever are, you'll no longer be son of mine."

Thus warned, Peter transferred the ingrained caution of one

psychically inoculated from babyhood against wild cats and rattlers to gamblers, whom he thought of as another species of "varmints." But he was learning that there was a way of being different which got you laughed at and snubbed, and another way which gave you status. He loved to hang around Dromgole and Stewart's, watching the faro and rolling faro, the roulette and checkers, the poker and whist which went on there continually. But when asked to play, he would answer loftily, "I'll have to pray over it," or "My Mammy don't let me play with folks that might skin the hide off my backside," or "I don't play except with those that have gold linings to their tobacco pouches." This toploftical attitude, combined with the fact that when he did play he usually won, made even grown men feel that "young Cartwright—he's a deep one."

One evening when his father had to stay late, and Peter waited for him at Dromgole and Stewart's, he observed that two quiet, gentlemenly men were watching him. Two or three times they strolled by him and greeted him pleasantly by name. Peter could not have said why he felt uneasy. But when they went and stood outside in the April dark, he found an excuse to come softly around from the back of the house, and listen unobserved. They were talking about him. "The boy reads the cards all right," said one.

"How did he learn?"

"Search me! May be his brother, John Wilcox, taught him."

"But gambling isn't Wilcox's line. Nobody knows what this lad knows unless they're regularly sworn in."

"May be he figured it out himself."

"Nobody ever does. How come he could be more knowing than anybody ever is?"

"But still he might."

"If he did, he won't ever have to work for a living. He's too smart."

This frightened Peter. He thought they might try to claim him as one of their own. To avoid going to Russellville with his father, and perhaps meeting these men again, Peter played sick until his alleged headache, backache, and dizziness had his mother thoroughly worried. Mary's light, rough hand laid on his forehead and her blue eyes bent on him, full of concern, gave him such a sharp twinge of conscience that he cried out as if in sudden pain, and then was so satisfied with the effect of this in confirming his pretense to illness, that he almost forgot to be conscience-stricken.

The terror passed, and with it the illness that was fast becoming genuine, when his father came back from Dromgole's, and, by devious inquiry, Peter learned that the two gentlemen had gone on to Nashville and Natchez. He was so relieved that next time his father went to Russellville he clattered along with him on Diablo, through the mazy fresh green landscape, and hilariously challenged the young scions of Russellville aristocracy to cards, and ended the day by pulling the drawstrings of his leather pouch tight over thirteen hard dollars.

3

Not many grown men carried so much hard money as Peter had these days, and few came by it so easily. And the possession of these dollars made Peter think what dollars were worth in his world. If you wanted anything your mother or the Circuit Rider thought good for you, you didn't need dollars. Take good wholesome victuals. If you had to pay for them, a dollar went a long way. Butter was eight cents a pound, beef two cents, buffalo meat a cent and a half, and big fat turkeys could be got for twenty cents a piece or a pleasant excursion into the woods with a rifle. Fish could be lifted from any brook or pond. Whisky was given away. Linsy (linen), woolsy (wool) and cotton cloth were produced by the women at home. Leather, furs, buttons and other articles of bone were the fruit of the winter's hunting, and all articles of wood, from churns to houses, could be had for the expense of some labor on timber that usually cost nothing.

In the last few years, skilled labor, and the principle of the division of labor, had invaded Russellville. There was now a carpenter, a joiner, a shoemaker, a tinker, a maker of wooden churns and dishes, and a potter there. They charged $1.50 a day for themselves and \$1.00 for their assistants, and took 100 per cent profit on such glass, broadcloth, fine Spanish leather, nankeens, and calicos as they could lay hands on. But generally they could be paid in produce, and so relieve the surplus which, on the farms of the God-fearing and industrious, was chronic.

Hard money was just something that was passed around by gambling, of use in far-away places to get jewelry and silver and wine glasses, and silver-mounted pistols, all those things the circuit rider, the Baptists, and his mother said were just vanity and "show-off." The only thing purchasable by money Peter's mother could see any good in was glass. She looked forward to the day when the sun would come in, bright and clear, right into the cabin, on a winter's day.

So long as you used what the good Lord provided right here in Kentucky, you could live as high as the Governor, who was rich on \$1000 a year, or get along like a gentleman on two thirds of that, as judges of the Court of Appeals did, or even one third as the Attorney General did. Peter knew about these personages because he had heard his father and other lawyers discuss their salaries, usually with the implication that it was far too much money to spend for what these gentlemen did for their fellow men. Folks who did something useful in the world generally had a surplus of something, and this they exchanged for the surplus of something else that some other industrious person created by useful labor. To get hard money you tricked it out of somebody, which is what Peter was doing, or you robbed it from somebody.

Yet there was something Peter wanted hard money for. He wanted it for a horse—a slim-legged, high-necked, graceful horse, one that had wings on his delicate hooves and looked at you with great melting eyes like the eyes of the second Richardson girl. Such a horse would cost \$150. Peter had some money laid by for the horse of his dreams, but, with all his luck in winning money from anybody who had it, it would take a long time to get enough. Meanwhile the one problem in maintaining social ascendency which he had not solved was his horse. Diablo's clumsy big feet, his broad backside, his low hung, thick neck, his mean eye, his hard mouth, all gave Peter such a sense of inferiority that his quick wit deserted him and he blushed to the roots of his hair when somebody jeered at his horse. Seeing that this was his tender spot, the various young blades who secretly smarted under Peter's ascendency in everything else never lost a chance to make fun of Diablo. Worst of all the boys would make the girls laugh. Peter thought he had seen amusement mixed with pity in the big eyes of the second Richardson girl when she looked at him on his horse. It was more than he could bear.

Riding home alone one night, when his father had had to go to the court at Glasgow, Peter vented his chagrin by violently kicking Diablo. Diablo leaped into the air and tore off like a cannon ball through the upper ether. Peter, clinging to him, wondered how fast Diablo could go anyway. And then he had a devastating idea. Could Diablo go as fast as these race horses? Nobody had ever thought that one of his breed could. But why not? "He's got such a spring in this big backside of his," thought Peter, "that, in one leap, he's where it takes those slim-legged things quite a while to run." All the way home he kept trying out Diablo. The horse didn't have much staying power or discipline. On a mile or two mile stretch, he'd break down or get unruly and stop dead. But at the start! He didn't run. He just lifted his backside and kicked off. And when he came down he was a quarter of a mile away. A quarter of a mile! Here Peter's idea burst into full bloom.

For on the next court day there was a quarter race, in which the competing horses would run a quarter of a mile on a straight stretch. It was a glorious spring day, all ashimmer with fresh green leaves. Everybody for forty miles around seemed to be in Russellville. In a field near Cedar House a wide course had been fenced in with split rails for the quarter race. Red Maulding, Skinny Dromgole, young Cauldwell, and others came up leading their thoroughbreds, each with a long whip, clearing the way before him. Along the fence were ranged a motley crew of children, Negroes, Portyghees, and Germans. Suddenly Peter rode up on Diablo, very dashing in a jacket with bright red sleeves. "I'm betting," he said to the contestants. "I bet my noble steed will win against the whole caboodle of you."

There was a loud guffaw which spread in ripple after ripple. Most people thought it only the boy's crazy play acting. But he went through the motions of taking bets against his horse, with great dignity and sobriety, meanwhile rubbing him off, patting him, picking up his hooves and examining them, going through all the usual proprietary motions. At every move, the crowd roared anew. Peter did not grin. He did not answer the jeers. Absolom Tudor himself could not have had more dignity.

The word that Peter had bet Diablo against any thoroughbred in town, penetrated the court room and brought Jus out, as the signal was given. There were the beautiful horses, sleek, satiny, proud, elegant. And there was Diablo, his monstrous head hung low on his short neck. But his red roan coat was polished to a high shine, and his shaggy mane and tail had been neatly trimmed, and a cluster of red columbine was stuck in his harness. And there was Peter, flashing fire from his dark eyes, spectacular in his red-sleeved jacket. They were off! Diablo seemed neither to spring nor to run. He streaked through the air, his nose erect, as if he smelled on the far horizon a heavenly feed of corn, his mane and tail floating like pirate's pennons. And flashing along on top of him Jus saw the big form and shaggy curls of Peter, riding without whip or spur. And then it was over. The other horses had not had a chance. But they came back, high-stepping, undaunted, and proud, while Diablo, like the plebian he was, dragged his head almost to the ground. "It's his modest disposition," said Peter, patting his red roan side with something like affection. "A hoss that can run can afford to be humble. It's only them that can't that has to show pride." With that he stared hard at Skinny Dromgole and his graceful high-stepper.

It was the rule at these races that the winner must treat the losers with the best imported brandy at Cedar House. Peter went around, large and swaggering, inviting his father's legal brethren, Bill Reading, and Ninian Edwards. He even asked McGready, whose school for young gentlemen—all five of them—had cut class to see Diablo run. He asked all the young swells, and some who were not so swell. All afternoon the guests came and went, adjourning to see a cock fight or a foot race, and returning for a drink on Peter. Even McGready took a glass of port, saying, "I'll pay you for this, young man, later on, with an exposition of the dreadful consequences of gambling." When it was all over, every cent of Peter's winnings had been transferred to the strong box of Wes Maulding.

4

Two days later Peter was working in the cornfield. His new vision of life had opened his eyes to the ragged state of the farm and the unkempt dooryard. For Jus, farming was quite second to law. He raised nothing for sale, except some tobacco to exchange locally for other goods, and some horses which were more of a hobby than a business, but from which he realized a tidy profit. The fields were worked on shares by the ever changing but ever renewed supply furnished by emigrants looking for land and working for a while to earn the wherewithal. The only good sharecropper was Dean, whose thrift and diligence had long since set him up on a good farm of his own. Since Eddie had married and built his own cabin, Peter had been old enough to handle the regular daily chores, with a helping hand from his father now and then. For seasons of heavy work like harvesting, or the winter's hunting, Cracker was hired.

Suddenly aware of what the second Richardson girl would think of the Cartwright farm, Peter directed a furious burst of energy at it, guided by Dominie. Dominie's place was worked without slaves. But no slave plantation could equal his neat barns; the well, snugly framed in stones and operated by a well sweep; the tank for rain water in the loft which gave Barbara running water in the kitchen; the cold spring house; the sanitary privies; the trim fences; the dooryard planted with phlox; and the front porch furnished as an outdoor living room, with a canvas hammock and tables and chairs.

As Methodist class leader, Dominie preached an economic doctrine strange to people who, through the long generations of their past, had known no alternative to the fancy-dressing, hard-drinking, hard-riding, gambling gentry for whom all work was done by serfs or slaves, except a hopeless lack of everything beyond coarse food and shelter. Dominie showed them how to make "contraptions" and systematized work-processes serve instead of slaves. He got them to buy work animals and draft animals instead of race horses. He wanted everybody to have good carriages and agitated for good roads for carriages to run on. He urged a greater variety of food, and especially of nature's delicacies, such as fruit and honey, to take the place of liquor. Barbara, slim and neat, crisp and downright in manner, but radiating kindness which could translate itself at a flash into a practical comfort—a hot drink, a medicament, a linsy bandage—preached the gospel of good housewifery. She saw to it that the weekly class meeting was preceded by a supper at which the women vied in displaying new additions to the still monotonous fare.

From Dominie and Barbara Peter got instructions about the care of the young peach trees, now in full bloom, and some seeds of watermelons, squash, pumpkins, cucumbers, and melons to be planted between the rows of corn, and seeds of nasturtiums and marigolds to plant in the dooryard. And he also got a baby lamb for Sis to bring up.

Delighted, Mary beamed on Peter with a trustful warmth which made him feel quite conscience-stricken. Sis was delighted, too. She was growing up into a slim, plain girl, with none of Polly's biological dazzle, but with a restful likableness and the homespun goodness Eddie had always had. Mary said Sis was beginning to be a real comfort. That bright morning, two days after Diablo won the race, Mary and Sis were planting the marigolds in the dooryard. Polly was inside, having volunteered to take over the indoor work now that the others wanted to be outside digging in the dirt. She had no intention of exposing her fair skin to the freckling sun—not with the Tudor dance coming on!

Up dashed Jus on horseback. "Where's Peter?" he asked. Told

that Peter was in the corn field, he galloped past them. Mary shaded her eyes with her hand and looked at his receding figure. "Isn't that a new horse your father is riding?" she asked. Sis rose from the ground and stared, too. Yes, it was a new horse.

Peter in the cornfield saw a horse he didn't know even before he recognized his father on it. He ran toward him, his eyes caressing the shapely body, the satiny black coat, the high arched neck, the trim legs. "Whose horse is it?" he asked, adding, as the creature's great soft eyes met his, "He sure is a beauty."

"His name is Aladdin, and he's only three years old," said Jus.

"Aladdin," said Peter, softly. The creature turned his beautiful head and nosed him gently. Peter's heart went out to him in love.

"Do you want to try riding him?" asked Jus. Satisfaction beamed inside him like a fire behind a shuttered window.

Before the answer was out of his mouth, Peter was in the saddle and riding up the bridle path that led along the cornfields. All the years with Diablo had prepared him for the ecstacy of this ride, through the blossoming hawthorn, amidst the twittering birds, on that fresh spring morning. Aladdin moved as if on air, with a gait as rhythmical as that of the second Richardson girl when Peter caught her in the dance. He hardly needed spur or rein. He responded to the slightest pull of the bridle. And whereas Diablo had never ceased to resent having anything or anybody on his back, Aladdin seemed to be glad to carry Peter. Love flowed from his body to the beautiful body of the horse and came back to him in a sense of comfort and gladness. So he rode down the path beside the hawthorn, as if he were riding a dream animal along the lanes of Paradise.

And then it was all over, and Peter was bringing the horse back to his father. But Jus said, "Just stay on him, Son, and ride around and show your mother. He's yours."

"Mine!" The tears sprang into Peter's eyes. "You're—you're giving him to me?" Stars and suns had been lighted inside him. He was blubbering with gratitude. His father had understood! His father had known what he wanted so much.

"I've wanted for a long time to see you mounted like a gentleman, Son," said Jus, beaming. "When I saw what you did with Diablo, I thought 'That fixes it. He's earned some real horseflesh.' And now, ride along to your mother. I'll cut across the field on foot."

Sis and Mary were admiring Aladdin when Jus came up. But he noted, with some darkening of his sky, that Mary had reservations. "He's sure a sweet crittur," she said grudgingly, smoothing the satiny black neck. "But he don't look good for much except racing." Her eye traveled suspiciously from her husband to her son. Deep down in Peter, where his conscience should have been, there was a sudden shrinking. But she only said, with unexpected gentleness, "Honey, I like to see you riding a good horse, but promise me you won't race him."

Peter had not reached the point where he could look his mother straight in the eye and make a promise with intent to break it. He was silent. Jus cut in, "He can't promise, Mary. Folks has to do what occasion demands. But you can trust him. He's got a head on his shoulders."

Mary said nothing. But that evening, as the sun was setting in a mist of pink and gold over the newly planted fields, and Peter, who had been riding Aladdin alone up and down the lanes, had gone back to the horse lot to give a last goodnight look, he found his mother standing by him. "He's sure beautiful," she said softly, "but Honey, I won't know an easy hour from this day on till God has seized hold of you, and made you His own."

5

Almost illiterate as they were, with little share in the traditions of 6000 years of civilization on this globe, Peter's folks had their own mental discipline. Peter had been taught to "aim to hit the bull's eye," "keep your eyes open and your mouth shut," "use your head to save your heels," and "look before you leap." He knew that no important act was to be undertaken without "studying"—studying being a mixture of observation, retrospection, introspection, and "putting two and two together," continued through a long process of looking, listening, and keeping his mouth shut.

Now that Peter had Aladdin, he felt called on to study as he had never studied before. For Aladdin was a means to that enlarged state of being which resulted from creating a constant stir and excitement about himself, a chatter about what he had done, a wonder about what he would do. He restrained his impulse to ride to Russellville and show off his horse. That would be like shooting your gun off in the air. It would make a brief noise, and all would be over. He'd be just another lad on a good horse. Peter was feeling for a relation to his fellow beings that would be continually dramatic. He wanted to appear on the scene in such a way as to cause a stir—whether of wonder, amusement, or simple gladness. He wanted to be followed by laughter and acclaim—to have always some unexpected device for discomfiting his enemies and building up the pride of his friends. He had discovered the infinite possibilities in the sensation of living, and wanted to enhance and vary it by every means possible. The sparkle, the real "zip" in this sensation was the element of chance, and the challenge to pit yourself against it and see if you couldn't win.

He had no notion of showing off Aladdin until he had his strategy well worked out. So, instead of rushing off to Russellville, he offered to escort his mother to church. Between church and the next court day, he went on long rides by himself after the day's work was done. When he launched himself into the sunset, on Aladdin, he said goodbye to the world, and was off in a dream, in which Aladdin raced against great dream horses, with laughing, jeering enemies of the human race on their backs, and came in triumphant. Coming back late one night, he found the world blanched and ghostly in the light of the moon. Aladdin started violently. Next to him a tall black horse was riding, and on it an immensely elongated rider. Aladdin began to run. The faster he ran the faster that black horse and rider ran. When Aladdin had raced that ghostly opponent to the cabin and had come in neck and neck with him, Peter, dismounting, kissed the horse's quivering nose, and said, "Good boy, Aladdin. I reckon there's just one thing around here you can't beat, and that's your own shadow."

Mary was sitting on the doorstep with Sis when he came in. "Where you been?" she asked gently, not suspicious or challenging, but with kindly interest.

"Just riding by myself. It sure was fine in the sunset with the birds singing, and fine coming back in the moonlight."

"It's a moon that's like nothin this side Paradise," said Mary. Peter could see that she was in one of her exalted prayerful moods.

"Sure is," he answered softly.

Mary raised her eyes to his. She had been unutterably happy in the way he had taken possession of his horse, riding the beautiful crittur first to church, and then out alone under God's sky. She felt the elation in his tall, vital young body, and saw the sparks in his black eyes. Could it be that this night—under this sky—he had known the great experience? Peter sensed what she was thinking. His whole being was flooded with a burning blush. "Good night," he said hastily, and swung himself up to the loft. It was as if there were something he couldn't get away from fast enough. He felt unutterably mean, knowing what his mother thought he had been thinking, against what had really occupied his mind.

A few days later, Peter rode to court with his father, whose pride and pleasure in him restored his self-esteem. The feature of the day was a mile race. Ignoring, while inwardly enjoying, the stir his new horse was making, Peter rode to the field. There Red Maulding galloped up to him. "Howdy, Pete. Where'd you get that hoss?"

"What hoss?"

"The one you're settin on."

"Get it? Why it's mine. You know I have a horse."

"Yes—but not this hoss."

"No—o?" Peter looked surprised. Then he added, "Well, I guess winnin against that gelding of yours kinda made Diablo spruce up a bit."

"Diablo! This aint Diablo."

"Aint it?"

Peter sat nonchalantly in his saddle while man and boy came up and examined Aladdin. But he refused to enter "Lad" in this or any other race. "I guess that race we won the other day will have to do us for a spell," he said.

"But you didn't win with this hoss."

"Didn't I?"

Peter was seeing everything with new eyes these days. All of the fifteen contestants lined up for the race rode their own horses. Most of them were big men, for the tendency of man in early Kentucky was to grow large, and there was hardly one of these young men who had grown up there who did not overtop and outweigh his own father. "Seems like they're all too big for their horses," reflected Peter. "If I was to run a race I wouldn't want a hunk o' flesh like Red Maulding on my back." Then he had an idea. "If I race Lad, I won't burden him with me. I'll get some one light as Jerry to do it." His idea burst into inspiration. "I'll get Jerry himself."

Next evening, when the long day in the fields was over, Peter rode Lad over to Jerry's in the twittering dusk. He had been happy all day in the prospect of luring Jerry back into partnership. "Havin' Jerry too holy to do anything natural and pleasureful has been kinda like havin' a hole in your mouth where you was used to havin' a tooth," he reflected.

Jerry, hearing Peter's whoop, came rushing out and got a lighted faggot with which to examine the new horse. Brenda lighted a candle and stood in the doorway, the yellow light, flickering on her long, finely modelled dark face, making her look eerie and alien, like a beautiful witch. But her greeting was motherly. Peter must come right in and taste something. Peter did so. "It's strawberries—and something else," he exclaimed, forgetting Lad in sheer gustatory ecstacy. He chewed the delicious stuff slowly and swallowed it reflectively, "It's kinda like wheat bread, and kinda like fine ground hominy mush, and it's softer than cream."

Mixed with the sweet taste was a sweet sensation of gratitude and deep respect. The almost mystical reverence for women, buried deep in the soul of a frontier boy, was dimly associated with the capacity of women to perform miracles like this. Brenda explained that the tinker had come around with some white powder some one had given him, looking for somebody to tell him if it was poison. She had touched it with the tip of her tongue, and recognized saleratus. When she offered to buy it from him, he wouldn't take money. So she gave him a side of bacon. "I put it in sour milk with hog's grease," she told Peter, "and sifted wheat flour through two layers of linsy, and baked it in a closed skillet, and put butter and strawberries soaked in maple syrup and cream on it. You can tell your mother about it. Here, I'll give you some of the saleratus to take to her." She handed him the powder in a small gourd.

Peter peered at the magic stuff. Making food of the angels by putting white powder into hog's grease and sour milk and wheat flour, was a chemical achievement that made Dominie's gunpowder look crude. Rising from the table, and casting a last lingering glance at the remnants of the strawberry shortcake, rosy in the candlelight, he asked, "What shall I say you call it?"

"Shortnin' bread—strawberries on shortnin' bread."

"I'll tell her," he said. "I'll say, 'Mammy, if there's anything on earth that's better than anything else to eat, it's Aunt Brenda's shortnin' bread. And if you don't traipse right over and find out how it's made, I'm goin to move over and board with Aunt Brenda.'"

Leaving Brenda aglow with pleasure in this gallant speech, Peter went out with Jerry. Stretched out on the thick leaf mould, their shoulders propped against the trunk of a great oak tree down by the river, Peter and Jerry fell into confidential talk. Content and relaxed, Peter realized that he had been starved for just plain talk ever since he took up card playing. With Jerry he enjoyed whole ranges of conversation quite lacking in his intercourse with Red Maulding and Skinny Dromgole, for, slight as his body was, Jerry's brains were quite as good as Peter's.

When Peter unfolded his plan for riding Aladdin, Jerry was silent for a long time. Finally he said, "I don't say I'm not tempted, Pete. But I just can't. The brothers and sisters would read me out of church before the next Lord's Day."

"I know," answered Peter. "The Methodys are the same. I'm downright scared about the way Mammy is going to take on if she finds out I've ever bet on a horse or card or roulette wheel. But I just don't see why religion's so set against betting. Life is a chance, and without chance what would livin be—flat and stale like ol ditch water. A little gamblin' just kinda makes life more of what life is."

"That's just a fancy way of talking yourself into what you want to do," said Jerry. "You know well enough the harm of gambling. Look at all those ol soaks and bums that hang around Dromgole's. There's more than one of them had a good property till he staked his all on roulette or a throw of dice."

Peter said loftily, "A man fool enough to gamble that way can't be kept from ruin by stoppin' him from gambling. He'll just turn around and slip on some other slide down to Hell."

"You can talk," responded Jerry, "because you're one of the strong ones of the world. Whatever comes up, you've always got the means of being top dog—either because you're big and strong-bodied, or you're smart, or you're good looking, or you've got a quick tongue."

"Or because," said Peter reflectively, "I don't give a damn."

"Whatever it is, you can take it or leave it. But that's not what most folks can do. They're good if the things they're talked into or helped to be part of are good, and they're bad if they're talked into it, or laughed into it, or pushed into it, or just carried along into it by folks that are stronger than they. Nine hundred and ninety nine out of one thousand folks are like that, and it's for them that Christ died, and for them that there's the congregation of brothers and sisters to be protecting arms around them."

Peter did not dispute this. He merely dodged it, bending all his efforts to get Jerry to come over and ride Aladdin, not for the purpose of racing, but just to see what he could do with a featherlight rider. But Jerry steadfastly refused. Turning his gray eyes on Peter, unearthly in the moonlight, he said, "I ain't like you, Pete. I'm weak. There's only one place where I'm safe, and that's right in under the shadow of God's hand."

Peter argued that life, the way the Baptists and Methodists lived it, was pretty dull. But Jerry said, his clear, thin voice vibrant like a fiddle string, "It will never be dull for me if God lets me have the one blessing I've set my mind on."

"What's that?" Peter asked, but he already knew, and his heart almost stopped beating from sheer pity.

"Polly!" Jerry went on to talk dreamily of the time when he'd be grown enough to go wooing Polly like a man. "I know what Polly is," he said. "She's lovin' in a careless, natural way, like a rose is red and smells sweet and all the bees come to it, and she wants things clean and mannerly, and hates mess, dirt and things ugly. And she'll run after anything fine without using her head much, but following her heart and her sense of what is prideful and pleasurable. She don't mind work, but she wants something in return for it—praise and a kind of handsomeness, and plenty to do with."

To this appraisal of his sister, Peter listened with a sharp, precocious sense of what Polly could be to a man who wasn't her brother. But he made no comment.

Jerry rambled on. "My brother Hans hits the nail on the head. He says there's no use hankerin' after a girl like Polly unless you can afford her. But for one who can, she can sure make life worth livin'. Now I'm goin to grow up mighty soon, to afford Polly. My Pappy left me a sight of good land. And there's one thing about us Dutch, especially when we're Baptists. What other folks put into drink and horse racing and wear on their backs, we put into barns and stock and something that keeps makin more of safety and comfort. So there's nothing Polly can want that I can't give her, and there won't be a debt on my offering, nor the stain of sin and murder on it either—the way that gang she runs with has on their property. There's three black brothers workin' my fields now. I could build Polly a house tomorrow of clapboards painted white, instead of logs, and a carved doorway, and glass windows, and she's only got to say the word to have a pink satin bedspread to our bed."

At the word "bed" Peter felt himself blushing. He sensed in the darkness that Jerry's pallid face was suffused with red. Embarrassed, he changed the subject to something his mother had been wondering about. "How come you have nigger slaves working your land? I thought you Baptists were dead set against slavery, same as we Methodys are."

"We are," said Jerry. "If one man makin a slave of another with an immortal soul and livin off his labor ain't wrong, then there ain't nothin' wrong. But you know how it is. You can't break land and build property without hands to do it. And you can't depend on movers for work. They stop a while and work, and then they light out, and leave your hay cut in the fields to be wet by the first rain storm, and your peaches rottin for hands to pick them. You've got to have labor that stays put and stands by. If we wasn't run here by a cut-throat gang of cheats and robbers, we could have free black labor and pay them wages and help them to get land like white folks."

"That's the Kentucky law, my Pappy says. Dean's done it. Nobody is set up finer."

"A few has that's got strong white friends and has been here from the beginning, and are so settled in some church that it's as much as even Ambrose Maulding's life is worth to meddle with them. But how many are like that? If any new nigger comes in, up pops somebody and says he's a runaway, and whether he is or isn't, so long as Bill Reading and Ambrose Maulding are what passes as law and justice here, they can be carted off. And if Negroes do get land and settle, you know yourself that the first time anybody wants that land, they're picked up as vagrants and sold on the auction block. The black folks are like all the weak ones of this world. They ain't safe except in the arms of the church. So what we do is that the whole Baptist congregation stands as owners of the slaves, and inside the church there's no difference betwixt them and us. We're all brothers and sisters, black and white. And we've got freedom papers made out for each one of them, and we pay fair wages for them into the hands of the committee. That money will help to settle them as free men, or to get away to Ohio."

Jerry's voice trailed off. He didn't want to talk about slavery. He wanted to talk about Polly. On that subject he went on and on, till the thrush in the oak leaves above them stopped singing, and the moon breaking through mists rode high and white, and a panther howled somewhere down the river. Riding home, Peter felt humiliated by Jerry's refusal to ride Aladdin lest he get involved in betting. "Talk about gambling," he thought, in anger and pity. "He's takin the most awful gamble. He's got all he has in him on one throw. And he ain't going to win. It just ain't in the cards."

CHAPTER 26   **Russellville and Glasgow, Kentucky**
June, 1800

It was not till they were all in the saddle—Peter and Jus off for court, Polly to stay a few days with John—that Mary remembered the ball at Tudor's. She didn't like Polly's staying with John. But, as Jus said, what could she do? Polly was a woman grown, and John was her own brother. But Peter! She stared at the black curls, clean, tight, and silky as a girl's. She sniffed the resinous smell of Barbara's best soap. And then she saw his hands. So that was why he had offered to scrub and bleach the puncheon floor with hot lye last night! Bleaching his hands—pretending to help his mother! Her eye traveled down over his fawn colored, tailor-made breeches, to the red boot tassels. "Peter!" she said, and there was heartbreak in her voice, "Are you going to the dance?"

Peter hesitated. He still couldn't lie to his mother. And, besides, what was the use? She was too smart. She'd see through him.

Jus interposed, "There's a barbecue. We're all invited. Don't look for Peter or me to be home till late tonight, if at all."

Mary's face was stony. "Where is the barbecue?"

They were all silent. She said, "You're lyin—every one of you. It's that ball at the Tudor-Harpes you're goin to—oh-oh." The last sound was like no voice human or animal Peter had ever heard. It spoke utter despair. She put her apron to her eyes and rushed back into the house. Jus dismounted and went after her. He returned, ruefully rubbing his cheek. Peter knew that she had slapped him. His most dramatic memories were times when he had seen his mother haul off and strike his father. Each time his sympathy had been with her, as it was for any small animal that went for a big one. Polly slipped from her saddle and went in. She returned bathed in tears. "She won't say a word to me," she choked.

Peter spoke savagely. "Get up in the saddle, Poll. No use humoring her in a sulk." Never in his life had he spoken so of his mother. He kicked Aladdin furiously. The sensitive beast, unused to such handling, bounded forward. Propelled by the contagion of Peter's violent exit, Jus and Polly galloped after him, but did not come up to him till they were half way to Russellville. Jus, for once, was really angry. "Peter, you damn fool! Let me see you do that again and I'll take the horse away from you. You know horseflesh better than to act like that." Of Mary they said nothing. Jus was unwontedly strict and cross. Polly kept sniffing and drying her eyes all the way.

Peter felt so mean all day that he indulged in all the vices he usually detested. He smoked a pipe and made himself sick. He chewed tobacco and made himself vomit. He drank a glassful of white mule, and was so mad at himself for doing it that he threw the glass against the wall and smashed it and had to give Wes Maulding what he had just won at cards to pay for it. He won at cards again, and lost it all on the roulette wheel. By late afternoon he was so sick of it all that he was minded to go home. But some braves came whooping by and rushed him out to the Tudors, where all was splendor.

The shadows of the great oaks lay in long, cool, blue-green shapes on the golden turf, and the sheep rested in their coolness. A string of ducks paraded along the creek. Girls in white and sprigged muslins and poke bonnets strolled with gallants in light buff breeches and top boots, mingled with girls in home-dyed linsy and men in jeans and moccasins. Peter had not seen such "boughten" clothes even at Dromgole's. Seing two young men, resplendent in white satin breeches and white silk stockings and powdered wigs, he wondered, "What have they got those things on their heads for?" When he saw that the wigs hid the places where their ears had been cut off, he smiled grimly. He had heard at court that in Maryland, Pennsylvania, and the Carolinas, the punishment of a horse thief was to cut off his ears. "I guess Mammy ain't so far wrong about these folks," he thought. It eased an ache in his heart to agree with her.

In the field, amidst a tangle of long grass, weeds, and bushes there was a horse race. In a shady, but open, space within a semicircle of forest, there was a wrestling match. Down by the brook there was a big fire, with a whole calf cooking on a green log spit, and turkeys and venison waiting to be roasted. Nearby two Negroes were making hoecake over a heap of burning coals. On the breezeway, which ran around the log castle, plank tables were set for cards. Here and there on the rough, knobby turf near the house stood tubs of whisky with gourds for tumblers. Around the card tables and whisky tubs, the crowds milled continually. A few older women sat together under a tree smoking pipes.

Before nightfall Peter had careered through whist, eucre, poker, and 100, winning at all of them, and enjoying the comments on his luck at cards. Absolom Tudor, pompous in his wig and old-fashioned, full-skirted dress coat, made the comment to end all comments, "The lad has truly remarkable card-sense."

"He don't know that all I've got is eyes in my head," Peter reflected.

There was plenty for his eyes to do, looking at the people for whom this party was given—Tudor's friend, "the Squire" and his family who had just come from Virginia and had taken up 1000 acres. The heavy-jowled Squire wore buckled shoes and white woolen stockings, and carried a gold-headed cane, and walked as if on parade. His "Lady" had her hair dressed high and powdered, and wore a brocaded silk petticoat with panniers. She batted her eyes and pursed her lips as she talked about her mahogany, her spode china, her solid silver, and the brooch set with rubies she had inherited from her great-aunt in England.

But what really took Peter's eye was the daughters, Ivy and Gwen; for, in their persons, the new fashions from Paris had struck

Logan County for the first time. Instead of the over-dress and underdress and laced bodice which had done decent women for fifty years, they wore thin muslin wrappers which Peter's mother would blush to go to bed in, and under these there was only a thin slip between the sun and their limbs as God had made them. Peter made a bet with himself that if they got between the low sun and him, he'd be able to see their legs through their skirts, and he nearly lost a game of cards winning that bet. The thin muslin covering was belted with a bright ribbon, not where an honest woman's waist is, but right up under the breasts, so that the full breasts of the black-eyed one, in whose anatomy Peter took more interest than in her sister's, protruded ripely and plumply under their gauzy covering. Above the hardly veiled breasts there was nothing except downy bare neck. "I bet you could look down her neck and see pretty much everything," thought Peter. But with his curiosity and his inherited moral disapproval, there was mixed a kind of trembling tenderness. Women were such soft things—like breasts of birds or petals of flowers!

The charming undress was enhanced by the way the hair was tied off the face with a ribbon to match the ribbon belt, and fell free in loose waves. "Seems like they're bent on leavin themselves the way God made em," thought Peter. "It would sure feel better to catch one of them in the dance than one that's just a bundle of clothes."

A gaudy cavalcade galloped up, and, slipping down from a smart sidesaddle into the arms of Pentacost, he saw his sister, Polly, dressed like the strange young ladies from Virginia! As she pulled her long pale blue gloves from her dimpled arms, he stared in admiration. Was this dream girl his sister? "Lucky Jerry isn't here," he thought. "She'd sure have him crazy." But he didn't like the way that transparent blue muslin erased everything between Polly's slender, rounded figure and the tall dark man hovering over her.

Then he saw Penny dismounting, dressed in the new fangled way. But what a scarecrow! "Them that ain't got meat on them had better have clothes," he reflected. But that grand young gentleman! Could it be John? John was always dressy, and Peter had seen him in many guises and disguises. But, turned out in one of the new cutaway coats, with a plain but fine white shirt, his blondish hair drawn back plainly and neatly, and his breeeches buckled down below the knees, John had a simple elegance that made old Tudor look a fool. "Just the same he's trash," thought Peter. "And Penny's trash, too. And I bet my bottom dollar there ain't anything Mammy mistrusts about them that ain't so." Again it eased a subconscious ache to agree silently with his mother. He looked at Polly, gleaming and glowing under the compliments of those two horsethieves in wigs. "Trouble is she was made for more than a cabin," he thought. "But John's outfit ain't the way to it. She's too good for them because she's kind. And they're selfish —selfish as Hell."

Between him and his sister in that fancy new rig, a great gulf had opened. He was only her young half brother—awkward and without style. He did not go up to speak to her. He slipped away, too, from several who seemed inclined to favor him when they heard he was John's half brother. He'd be damned before he'd be noticed, not for what he was, but for being kin to John! Even when he saw his father arrive and join John's group, he did not go near them.

2

Stony sober when everybody else was increasingly "lit," Peter stood outside the dance hall in the night, trying to get courage to brave a snubbing by these young ladies from Virginia. Listening to the jumpy repetitions of the fiddles, he thought sourly, "up and down, see saw, hee haw, like a donkey." As the dancers whooped and screamed, he matched the sounds to animals. "There go the wolves," he thought, and "There's the panthers yowling now." He distinguished the squealing of girls, a little tipsy. "There go the little piggies." Finally he strolled in.

Seated like monkeys on the ladder that led to the loft, three near-ly naked Negroes were fiddling, and two were beating on "bangies," and a Chicksaw, painted half red, half indigo, was tootling on a flute. Pentacost, standing on a log turned endwise, was calling the figures. His handsome cutaway coat had been discarded, and his shirttails, pulled out of his breeches, were streaked with dirt and blood. "Looks as if he'd been in a fight," thought Peter. Pentacost's voice rang out, "Chase your sweetie round a tree." Peter's ear caught the accent. "Huh," he thought remembering some recent movers, and the way they spoke. "So that's the Spanish Don —talks for the King of Spain! If he ain't common piney woods South Carolina, I'll—" The rest of his thought was not decent. He passed judgment on it as such but refused to retract it.

The log-walled room was shaking with the thunder of human beings gone mad, whirling, stamping, yowling, barking. The scrape of the fiddles and the occasional high unearthly note of the flute were barely discernible above the human uproar. Amidst the whirling mass, Peter distinguished Ivy's black curls and Polly's golden brown ones, as they circled in and out of men's arms, dodging convulsive bear hugs, skilfully evading hungry lips on their bare necks. Not every girl was so adroit. Now and then one was caught by a man who refused to let her go and screamed aloud. Thereupon, hardly pausing in the dance, the nearest male kicked him, and the nearest girl pulled his victim away, and he was thrown off the dance floor. Once Peter spotted Ivy, he never took his eyes off that little dark head as it bobbed amidst the tumult. In vain the second Richardson girl tried to catch his eye. Each time she passed him her cowlike orbs grew more pleading, but he never saw her.

Then the miracle happened. In one of the pauses of the dance, Ivy saw him standing there. She stopped, walked gracefully to him, and dropping a curtsy, asked him to come and dance with her. Overwhelmed with many emotions, Peter responded as gracefully as he could. The young lady moved to his right side. He grasped her right hand with his right hand while she laid her left in his. Never had he known a sensation so delicious as that of her hand in his, her soft arm against his. In this position they walked out on the floor, where all the dancers made a circle, laughing, shouting, and cheering the young lady who dared thus to choose a gallant for herself. Pentacost shouted, "Swing your sweetie round and round." A Negro fiddler yelled, "Swing her low. Swing her high. Love and kiss her till you die." Peter swung her. Everybody swung her. Round and round he went, seeking her, finding her, losing her. In the search all kinds of girls came into his arms, heavy ones who tramped on his feet, half drunk ones who collapsed in his arms—girls and girls, whirl and whirl, listen for the order and try to follow it, tangle yourself in a mess of other folks' arms and legs and untangle yourself, pick up the music, pick up a girl and go on, like a canoe going helpless in a roar of water over a falls, the noise and madness breaking into pure ecstacy as she comes back into your arms. Each time she was sweeter. Each time he held her closer. Each time he felt more desperately that he could not let her go.

She had come back to him. The music had stopped suddenly. Everybody stood still. She did not move away from him but, instead, laid her head against his breast. He stood radiant with tender, grateful pride. She was so soft and luscious, her waist, under the flimsy dress, so yielding to his arm. Then there was a scuffle and a roar as of ten stuck bulls. He detached her lovely, clinging body, gently but firmly, and said grimly, "You'd better make tracks out of here. The dance is over and the row has begun." She screamed and scurried away. All the girls were screaming and running.

Peter had never heard of a dance that did not end in a brawl. Only mildly curious, he joined the circle of yelling, drunken men to see what the fight was about this time. One big, red-faced man whom Peter recognized as one of the Maulding kin, had another, whom Peter saw was a young scion of the Ewings, by the throat and was threatening to strangle him if he did not "drink damnation to Thomas Jefferson." Peter was about to jump to Ewing's defense when he felt his father's iron hand on his arm. "Keep out of it, Son," he whispered. "A Jefferson man ain't got a chance with this gang." Then he saw Absolom Tudor, cold and stately, behind him. Jus said, "I was tellin my son to keep out of the fight, but if you want order restored, we'll pitch in."

"Your services are not required," answered Tudor loftily. "There are many *gentlemen* here who can deal with followers of Jefferson."

The crowd was yelling, "Out! Out! Whip him out!"

"They'll spot us for the same breed," whispered Jus. "Get out while the going is good."

They got out and found their horses. Then Jus said, "If they've thrown Ewing out, we might sneak around that way and help him off." But they ran into a great press of people trying to find their horses and get away. By the time they reached the door where, supposedly, Ewing had been thrown out, all was dark and silent. Dismounting and walking forward cautiously, Peter stumbled on some men prone on the ground. As he was trying, by the dim light from a single candle in the window, to see if one of these was Ewing, he found Absolom Tudor standing by him. He stammered, "I was wondering, Sir, whether I could do anything for them." He was going on to question whether they were hurt or drunk—or dead. Absolom said curtly, "You can do nothing. They will do very well where they are till morning. Good night," and turned on his heel and strode into the house. Not finding Ewing, Peter and Jus rode home. Dawn was breaking when they reached the cabin.

During the next few days Mary's estrangement from husband and son melted in piteous bereavement. For Polly was gone. She had not returned to John's from the Tudors. No one knew where she was. She had left word for no one. Nor had any one seen Pentacost. Mary's anger turned back on herself. "I pushed her away. She left her own home with bitter weeping. My girl— my foolish poor lamb—if I had only been better to her!"

3

To the neighbors, Mary said Polly had just gone visitin'—might be gone quite a spell. Secretly, from the court in Russellville, Jus searched out every clue and sent Peter and Eddie to follow them, while Bonny stayed with Mary, taking Polly's place at hearth and washtub, and giving her healing companionship in Bible reading, prayer, and talk about the vanished girl.

Peter had always been fond of Polly, and, in the misery that now darkened the house, he realized how much he missed her. "It's kinda like when the frost kills the flowers and you see them all black, or when a cloud comes over the sun," he reflected. He was relieved when Jus told him that, since Pentacost was said to be in the Exchange business, he and Eddie were to make a tour of Hopkinsville and Glasgow, and other cross-roads places, where there were Exchanges to sell needfuls to the movers now pouring into the West on the high tide of the annual summer migration.

At Hopkinsville, which was what Russellville had been seven years before, the center for servicing and at the same time preying on movers and seekers of land, they found no trace of Pentacost and Polly. But Peter played cards with Ben Ogden, the renegade circuit rider, in his groggery, and won a pistol from him, and he and Eddie both examined with interest the glass windows, iron stoves, dishes, kettles, wheeled carts and carriages, on sale. How little they had had compared to these favored children of civilization!

At Glasgow, they went, as Jus had directed, to the courthouse of Barren County and looked for "Black Harry." Harry was a distinguished character. Years before, in the West Virginia lead mines, Sam Bell, a common laborer, wild and thoughtless, had been befriended by a Negro slave named Harry, who reformed him. Under Harry's tutelage, Bell saved his money and bought Harry and his wife Hannah. Together, Sam, Harry, and Hannah came west. Though nominally the Negroes were slaves of the white man, actually theirs was a partnership in which Harry was the senior partner and general manager. Ostensibly for his master, but really for the firm, Harry purchased slaves and hired them out to work for wages, and so made them all a good living. What only he and his Maker knew was that, when a slave's wages amounted to one and a half times what Harry had bought him for, the slave somehow disappeared. Nor was it known that the "commission" Harry claimed, both on the purchase price and the wages, went to set up an ex-slave as a free man in Ohio.

When he was lamed in a contest with a bear, Harry had to retire from his more active pursuits. So he hired himself out as a janitor at the courthouse where, he said, he could "enjoy the society of gentlemen." He was religious, waggish, musical. He kept the courthouse very neat, and was the life of many a party with his guitar and his songs. He liked to advertise young lawyers by going into the court room and calling out their names, in a loud, strong voice, so urgently that they would have to leave. This made it look as if they had lots of business.

When Peter and Eddie asked for him at the courthouse, Harry limped out, the gray hair on his temples most distinguished above his keen, dark, smiling face, wearing one of the new cutaway coats and breeches buckled well down over his knees, and a clean, fine linen shirt. He listened with concern to the boys' story, and promised that no one like Polly or Pentacost would henceforth get through Glasgow without his knowing it and sending word to Jus. He told them all about the Exchange business and the Mystic Band, which, he said, were practically one. Four out of five tavern keepers west of the Alleghenies belonged to the Band, he said, and at least seven out of ten merchants. They not only belonged, but they took turns at the dangerous business of holding up and, if necessary, murdering travelers. Every member of the Band had four aliases. "This is all Mason country," he said, "north of where Harpe's head is, through to Diamond Island. I've known some of Mason's gang to come into the court here and try to pass themselves off as judges."

As Peter listened he began to understand more about the society of Russellville, of which he had been a popular member. When Eddie asked how this organized thievery and murder was to be done away with, Harry, making his points on his four fingers, like paragraphs of a lawyer's brief, answered:

1. When roads and rivers enabled them to get all the fancy items of pride and luxury that people out here had money to pay for. Till then there would be a huge profit in stealing all prideful items. More and more goods were coming in, but people still came faster

than goods.

2. When there was some real Federal supervision to prevent criminals from escaping punishment by skipping over state lines.

3. When there was no more wild land, north, south, or west, and all the valleys of the Alleghenies were as easy to see into and get into as these Barrens.

4. When New Orleans belonged to us, and all our bad men couldn't escape down the Mississippi or the Chickasaw Road and be protected by the Spanish authorities in that wicked port.

Peter sighed. "That's too much to do in my lifetime. I'll have to grow old and die alongside these Rogues."

"Well," said Harry, "these are the only ways of getting rid of them by man and man's law. There's a way that's surer and quicker, but it's the Lord's way."

"What way is that?" asked Peter.

"It's to change man's nature—to make his sinful soul right over from the inside out."

"That's Mr. McGready's way," observed Eddie. "And it's worked some. We prayed off Mason, and prayed down the monopoly of Dromgole, and drove Harpe mad, and got him caught and killed. Mr. McGready don't let up. The number that's prayin grows all the time, and the Methodists and Baptists sign them up at every meeting."

"Prayin scares them and makes them duck," remarked Peter. "But I don't think it gets under their thick hides to change them."

"It doesn't have to change them," said Harry. "It only has to change you and me. What these bad men steal and kill for is truck we don't need for anything but vanity. If we had a true change of heart and gave up our vanity, Mason, Alston, and the whole Band would die of starvation."

Eddie nodded his good round homely head in agreement. All the luxury he wanted he had in Bonny, and the good food she cooked and the comfort she made. But Peter reflected that if he gave up vanity, he'd have to give up Aladdin and Ivy and her fancy undress, the drama and suspense of gambling, and the glory of challenging and beating the Dromgoles and Mauldings on their own not very moral ground. Rather than do this, he'd worry along with the Band for a while, and use his wits to see that they did him and his no harm.

Saying good bye to Harry, the boys explored the rest of the Barrens. They talked to Jacob Kesley, one of the long-bearded sect of Dunkers. They stared at a little boat laden with salt which had come in from St. Genevieve, a French village on the right side of the Mississippi, 100 miles above the mouth of the Ohio, and tried to imagine that far wooded north from which it had come, and listened to the strange accents of the small, quick people on it. They saw Neversink cave, 110 feet from top to bottom, with a stream running through it where many skeletons had been found, and which was thought to have been a headquarters of the Band. Until he saw this cave, Peter had a wild idea that Polly and her lover might be hiding here. But when he saw it, he realized that a girl like Polly—Then he thought of Sally Rice. Woudn't she? Who could tell what a girl would do?

Finally they turned home, with a present from Mother Chapman, a glass bottle full of the strange oily substance which seeped out of the ground near Skegg's Creek. It was called British oil, and was thought to be good for burns and bruises. No other use had been found for that hidden substance which, in time, would make the world's wheels go round and be indispensable to the world's wars.

On the way home Peter puzzled Eddie by making a wide detour into an area where an army of Negroes were clearing land. Peter drew up and stared over this hopeful scene. He did not tell Eddie that the house which would rise here would shelter a beautiful girl named Ivy and her sister Gwen. But it satisfied a vague hankering to come by the place and look.

Reaching home, the boys found that while they were away, Mary's worst fears had been confirmed. For William Burke, the Circuit Rider, had brought the report from Tobias Gibson in Natchez, who said that the man who was often called Stuart Walker had been married to a French girl who, as a Catholic, could not get a divorce. And Swaney, the mail man, had brought her a paper on which was crudely printed, "Mamy, don't wory. I hav gone to th man I luv. Am hapy."

All Mary's energies were now bent on finding Polly and per-
suading her to come home before scandal broke. But what if
she came back with a fatherless child already within her? Mary's
thoughts refused to go beyond that. But William Burke, who, alone
among the Methodists, knew that Polly had not just gone "visitin",
did not hesitate to probe Mary's worst fear by observing, apropos
of something else, "For babes that have no earthly father, there's
still the Heavenly Father. And if an erring woman will but turn
back to God, He will forgive her and hold her up till men and
women forgive her, too."

"It's the man that needs forgivin more than her," said Mary stubbornly.

"Our Heavenly Father knows that," replied Burke. "And in
time we hope that all Christians will know it, too. Whatever blind
mortals say, you can always trust God to put the blame where it
belongs." And he took out the Bible and read how Mary Magda-
lene bathed the feet of Christ with her tears, and Christ's words,
"Much shall be forgiven her because she has loved much."

For the first time Mary knew a little comfort. "It may be," she
said, "that this is God's way of bringing my poor pretty lamb
around to His own blessed fold. May be no other way would serve
for one like her who is so full of the juice of life and all its pride."

"Yes," responded Burke. "One way or another you have to be
broken before you can know God."

4

Believing that John and Penny knew Polly's whereabouts, Peter
rode over to his half brother's place. He found them entertaining
two "noblemen" who were going from Canada to New Orleans, and,
after the watery wilderness they had traversed, expressed themselves as agreeably surprised by the elegance they found in the
Wilcox menage. The visitors, who seemed to Peter so dumb about
all matters of common knowledge as to be half-witted, had the same

strange turn of phrase and intonation that John and Penny had acquired of late. John and Penny were putting forth all their charm —John his ready smile, Penny her wistful coaxing grace. Both were showing how adept they were at light conversation, skipping airily around indecency, tossing off judgments which turned accepted moral standards upside down, gossiping about Mr. Jefferson's alleged children by his slaves, sprinkling sarcasm on all ideals of liberty, justice, and democracy. This impressed the "noblemen" as having "to a remarkable degree the tone of good society."

When the "noblemen" rode off, Peter used all his wits to worm some hint of Polly's whereabouts out of John and Penny. But they disclaimed all knowledge of it, saying that wherever she was, she was probably better off than in drudging in that old cabin all day. They said Pentacost represented a number of Spanish firms in New Orleans, but no use telling Peter the names because he wouldn't know them. They had never heard that he was married. They knew he admired Polly but saw no reason to suppose she had eloped with him. "You damned liars," thought Peter.

When he finally gave up and started for the door which stood open this warm day, he suddenly stopped and turned back. "You have some charming company," he told Penny. She looked out and saw Ivy and Gwen dismounting, and with them five gallants, including the earless ones. Penny ran out and kissed the girls, and the three young women came in, their arms entwined around each other, inviting the reference to the "three graces" which was immediately forthcoming from John.

Peter did his best to imitate John's polished bearing and to thrust one leg forward and bow from the waist to the young ladies. It took him aback that Ivy looked at him, pleasantly but coldly, as if she had never seen him before, and then turned away and acted as if he were not there, till, bitter and miserable, he took refuge at the card table where he was joined by three of the five gallants whom the girls had also snubbed. From there he heard the laughter of the girls, and the toasts and compliments of the two men they were favoring. So might the song of the angels float down to a lost soul in Hell.

He was asking himself, "Why does she act like that? Why does she let that fellow without ears smirk at her?" when there was a warm breath of violets, and for a moment a soft white arm rested on his shoulder, and a curly head was next his, and a soft cheek touching his. Ivy was examining his cards. She put her cherry lips to his ear and said, "Play the Jack of Hearts." Overwhelmed with delight and gratitude, he looked up. For one moment her soft gaze met his, and he seemed to look into the depth of her soul. Then she ran lightly away. But when, as quickly as he could, he left the card table and joined her circle, expecting to be welcomed, she again turned a cold glance on him.

But Peter was learning fast. He sat down coolly next to her, accepted a glass of brandy, and, bowing ironically, toasted her sister Gwen and devoted himself to her till the young ladies took their twittering departure. Then, to the extreme annoyance of the earless gallant, he helped Gwen mount her horse. "Mr. Cartwright," said Ivy, crisply and haughtily, "I forgot my scarf. You may get it for me." He went for the scarf, sauntering to hide his eagerness. When he returned with it, she had slipped down from the saddle. "You may put it around my shoulders," she said. As blushing and feeling very clumsy, he put it around her bare shoulders and arms, her warm flesh seemed to push caressingly against him. He withdrew his hand. Where his fingers had touched her neck, there was a sensation so precious that he wanted to guard it from any rough touch or use. He stood like one holding a little bird in his hand, smiling and glowing, as the girls rode away.

Thus was Peter inducted into the alternate Heaven and Hell which the young lady of a society that aimed to be aristocratic was trained to create in the breast of any likely young man. By every possible appeal she constantly awoke a desire she then sharply rebuked or frustrated. This was called being "cruel," and, for some strange reason, the victims extolled it. Her aim was to make as many young men as possible "sigh" for her, fight duels for her, and even die for her. While much of the dying was purely verbal, the most "cruel" and ambitious girls secretly yearned for at least one real death in a frontier brawl to be chalked up to their irresistible "power." As a sign of power the belle often "commanded" young men to do some errand, in the tone she used in addressing a slave. This was to show that he was already her "slave," or to put him in the way of being "enslaved."

Peter did not know that these were accepted niceties of feminine behavior. But he left John's house that night in a state of delicious torment in which he thirsted to see Ivy again, and wondered how he could exist over the infinitude of time that loomed between now and the moment when that miracle might happen.

5

His fever was somewhat allayed when Jus came home from court saying that he had arranged for the boys to make a search in Tennessee, which was to end with seeing Judge Andrew Jackson and spending a night at his house. On the way they were also to see the Methodist renegade, James Haw, who, McGready said, was the best authority on the Mystic Band and its ties with the Exchange business.

So they set off, and circled through the whole arc of the Cumberland south of the border. On the first night, which was pleasant, they camped out. The second, which was rainy, they spent at a tavern kept by some Creek Indians, and slept little because some seven other guests drank whisky all night, and got whooping drunk, and then fighting drunk, and started a brawl which left two of them dead. So they got up and slipped away in the chill dark before dawn and saw the sun come up over miles of dew-spangled meadows, and the river mirroring tree and sky. They passed the house where the sons of the Duke of Orleans lived. They didn't know who the Duke was and didn't care, there being nothing in their training to put a halo around dukes. The only people who mentioned titles with respect and seemed to know one from the other were the people Peter met at John's house, or at the Tudors' and Dromgoles'—which was not an association to inspire respect.

They found James Haw's small, neat log cabin with well-tilled acres around it and, nearby on the bank of the stream, the little log church. Like all early preachers who "located", Haw earned most of his living by farming. He came in from the fields, mopping the sweat from his wrinkled brow, washed his face and hands at the stone basin outside, into which spring water poured through a trough made by cutting trees in half and hollowing them out, and joining them end to end, and came up to the boys, a stiff, rugged figure with grizzled hair above a leathern face. "Looks like he could bite through iron," thought Peter. But he liked the hidden light in the man's melancholy eyes.

"Sit down," Haw said gruffy. Gratefully they sat on the log bench on the veranda under the sloping eaves of the house. "You're hungry. Hungry and thirsty. At your age you always are." He clumped around the house and returned with a bucket of milk, dripping cold from the spring house, and a slab of maple sugar like yellow rock. "That will hold you," he said. As they took it with thanks, he commented. "So McGready sent you. Is he going to put on that gospel show of his again this summer?"

"I understand he is, Sir," said Eddie politely. "I heard him say there warn't a church that could be made with what we have to build with out here, that could hold all the souls God is ready to gather in. So, he says, we have to use all outdoors for the church, and God's own sky for the rafters."

A smile threatened to break through Haw's grim face. "Mc-Gready's all right," he observed. "He's making of the Methodist idea what we should have made it ourselves, if we'd had the guts to stand up to that sanctified instrument of the devil, Francis Asbury."

To this, honest Eddie felt bound to object. "But I have always heard, Sir, that Bishop Asbury is a very good man."

Haw sniffed. "A king can be a good man, but he's a bad institution." Then he thundered, "Why do you call him Bishop?"

"Why—er—er—that's what he is."

"Who made him Bishop?"

Peter looked at Eddie, unable to answer. Eddie said, "I don't know, Sir, unless it was John Wesley."

"And what right had John Wesley to make him Bishop?"

"I don't know, Sir—unless God gave him the right."

"And how did God give him the right? How did a Tory English-man, sitting over there in a country whose kings and bishops we'd thrown off, have a right to set up a bishop over our free souls?" He looked from Eddie to Peter and said, with harsh finality, "You can't answer that, and nobody else can, either."

There followed an uncomfortable silence which Haw broke by saying, "So your father's a lawyer. Why can't the law catch and hang Mason and Alston and all that gang that's made Russellville its business center?"

"Well," replied Peter, "things have kinda settled down there ever since they caught Harpe. We ain't had a murder or robbery to speak of since."

"You haven't because Mason and Peter Alston and Wiley Harpe are down here doing their murders, and leaving you folks in Rus-sellville to take the profits safe and sound, and Morton Maulding to keep the legislature in tow, and Ambrose Maulding to look after the court, with the smart help of Ninian Edwards, who at least can read when Ambrose can't."

The name Wiley Harpe transfixed Peter. "We've never seen hide nor hair of Wiley since Micajah Harpe was killed," said Peter.

"His name is John Setton now," replied Haw grimly, "and he's got red hair, but he still has a wart over his left breast and seven toes on his feet. Mason's the official head of the Band now, and Alston and Harpe are his deputies. Go back and tell your father that if he wants to know what's making your society in Russellville so high toned, I'll tell him. A clean majority of your best citizens—mean-ing the ones with the best horses, biggest plantations, most high toned dress and manners, and political jobs and influence—are in business with Mason, Harpe, and Alston."

Peter said, "I've heard this all my life, but it's never been proved."

"Catch one of them and bring him to trial and I'll prove it."

"How do you catch them?"

"They're all over the place. I see one or the other of them every now and then."

Peter and Eddie stared. "They swagger around as judges, preachers and doctors—generally something fancy. They grow beards and they cut them off. They wear powdered wigs and queues. They crop their hair. They put walnut juice on their skin. Wiley Harpe was around here for some time, passing as a Creek Indian. More than once I've raised a hue and cry after them. But either they skip out into Mississippi territory, or they get their neighbors so convinced that they laugh me down. So I am resolved to keep my mouth shut till I can do something to good purpose."

But Haw knew nothing of a highwayman of Pentacost's description. "I know all those that operate in the Cumberland," he said. "There's no one like that."

6

The burning day was mellowing into drowsy golden calm when the boys left Haw. Riding toward Nashville, through forests interspersed with new clearings, ragged with burning, they came, just after sunset, to a new cabin in front of which a plank sign, swung from a tree by heavy leather thongs, advertised "refreshment for man and beast." Under a huge oak tree there was a plank table and benches. Peter and Eddie paused, though without dismounting. Why not stop here, and get to Judge Jackson's tomorrow? They had grain for their horses with them, and cold corn cakes and a gourd full of precious peach jam. The side of cold venison Mary had given them had spoiled in the heat. But for 25 cents the landlord might give them the use of his table and sell them some bacon.

Before they had made up their minds to dismount, three horsemen galloped in and took possession of the table. They were handsomely mounted and two of them wore well-cut linen riding suits and large straw hats. Something in the set of the big man's shoulders caught Peter's eye. He said to Eddie, "Back into the shadows here, and look close at the big one." As the man turned his head and showed his face, Peter's eye was trying to pierce his brown beard streaked with gray. "He's covered that tooth that sticks out, with a beard," he thought. He looked at Eddie. Eddie nodded. "It's him all right!"

Peter spurred his horse and rode swiftly away. Eddie followed. They drew up out of sight of the cabin. "Let's leave our horses tied in the bushes here," said Eddie, "and sneak back on foot and make sure."

Noiselessly as Indians, the boys returned and took their station under the huge oak tree, in whose shadow it was now almost dark. Sure that the big man was Mason, Peter studied the smaller man, concentrating on the well modelled alabaster brow. But Alston's hair had been black. This elegant youth's was blond and fell to his shoulders. "It's him," thought Peter. According to Haw the other should be Wiley Harpe. Peter studied the man as well as he could in the dusk. His hair seemed to be red and hung in a tangled mass. He was barefooted, and wore only homespun jeans. In any place but the Cumberland two men who looked like "gentlemen" would not be drinking with a fellow who looked like that. But neither Peter nor Eddie thought it strange. They had never heard that gentlemen drink only with gentlemen.

The boys strained their ears to hear what the three were saying, as they chuckled and toasted the "success of our enterprise," and talked about "bringing in the produce," and laughed when Mason said, "He won't talk any more," and the little one piped, "He can't." It was all a kind of double talk.

There was a clatter of hooves and up dashed two horsemen, one of them an old man with a long beard. Passing the three at the table as if they were strangers, they peremptorily called out the landlord, asked for brandy, and wanted to know, with elaborate apologies, if they might share the table with the others. So long as the landlord was in sight, they appeared to be strangers. But the minute he had gone into the house, the old man leaned over and lifted his glass to toast "the produce," and joined with the others in their double talk, but softly, evidently not wishing the landlord to hear, and with subdued laughter. His ear arrested by the old man's voice, Peter tried to hear what he said. But a thrush was singing in a tree nearby, the water was purling in the brook, and there was a rustling of oak leaves overhead. So all sounds were blurred as the forms of the five men were blurred by the growing dark.

Peter tugged Eddie's sleeve till Eddie understood what he wanted and was led some yards away. Then Peter said, "Who did that old man's voice make you think of?"

Eddie hesitated. "Well, he kinda talks like John." Silence thick as the woodland darkness lay between them. Neither would say more. Finally Eddie observed, "But John don't talk natural ever. He studies to sound eddicated. And may be all the likeness we see is the eddicated kind of speech. Seems like every time I see John he's changed from the talk he had before." This was true. Peter had often noticed John's shifts of accent and thought them affected.

They stole back. The men had risen. In a shaft of light from a candle the landlord was placing in the window, Peter saw the silhouette of the tall, loose-moving man with the old one. The image of Pentacost, as he had called the dance at Tudor's, crossed his mind. The men were mounting their horses. Peter and Eddie watched. They were headed east! The two boys sped back to their own mounts. "We've got to get to Nashville and tell Judge Jackson," said Peter.

It was not till they were well on their way, and had to let their horses slow down to rest, that Peter observed. "Something about that other one put me in mind of Pentacost."

"Shucks," said Eddie. "It's only that we kinda have Pentacost on the brain."

CHAPTER 27

There was no time to lose. Peter and Eddie spurred their horses while the forest dark flew past them. When they had to walk their horses again, Peter spoke the thought that was churning in his mind. "We came to find Pentacost and it might be there he was. I wish I'd walked right up to him and said, 'Howdy, Pentacost.'"

"But what if the one with him had been John?"

"Oh John would have got out of it somehow."

They galloped again. At the next walk Eddie took up the speculation. "Suppose you'd done it? What would have been the gain?"

"None, so far as Polly is concerned. John lied to me about her. Pentacost would have lied. But to keep track of him, we could have gone with them or followed them."

"And put ourselves in the way of being recognized in the company of Mason, Harpe, and Alston? No thank you!"

They put spurs to their horses. When they slowed up again, Peter said, "Still I wish I'd done it. I wasn't smart enough or quick enough."

"Thank God you didn't."

"But what do we say at the Jacksons? Do we say we suspicion that the two men with Mason, Harpe, and Alston were our own brother John and the man that's run off with our sister?"

Eddie answered in a voice that anxiety made sulky. "It's a suspicion with so little to it, and so awful in all it might mean, that we can't be called on to say anything."

Peter's knowledge of court procedure came to the rescue of his conscience. "Well," he said, relaxing a little, "when you're called to testify in court you ain't allowed to say what you suspicion. You just stick to what you saw." He could feel that this was a relief to Eddie, too.

Peter wanted to stay on good terms with John as he had never wanted anything before, for John's house would be a place where he could meet Ivy. "But," he reflected, "I don't want to do anything blind. If I was to handle a snake, I'd find out first if it was poison." He had to find out about John.

Coming to a rise of ground with a wide open view under the starry summer sky, the boys saw a light in the distance which they knew must be Nashville. Stopping at a wayside liquor stand, they asked the way to Hunters' Hill. When they reached the fenced acres of the Jackson plantation, they saw a single light amidst the trees, and approached it, with the consciousness of a two storey house rising enormous above and around the light. They pounded on the door, not perceiving the brass knocker, nor knowing what a knocker is for. A pleasant spoken Negro, holding a candle, opened and led them into a room where two young men, booted and spurred, were playing checkers under a candlestick which held six candles, and to Peter's dazzled eyes gave light as bright as day. The young men greeted them with friendliness, and said Aunt Rachel had been expecting them. "But we didn't think you'd take chances, being out on an unknown road at night," said one of them, a handsome dark eyed lad, with Indian straight black hair brushed smooth off his forehead. "There's not many of us here that would ride the way you've come at night."

Eddie explained that they had intended to stay the night at a station they came to at sunset, "But—"

"But the trouble was," said Peter, cutting in lest his prosaic brother should not make the point dramatically enough, "Sam Mason, Wiley Harpe, and Peter Alston stopped there and might have been our bed fellows for the night."

The other boys gasped. "Mason!" "Harpe!" "Alston!"

They insisted on Eddie and Peter sitting down and going into great detail about what they had seen, but not before the dark eyed boy had called a Negro and told him to make sure the guests' horses were rubbed down and sheltered from a chill, and had a good feed and good stalls for the night. The other boy, a big clumsy fellow with a round freckled face, went out and came back with a Negro carrying mugs full of sweet, warm milk, flavored with nutmeg, maple sugar, and whisky. Peter had never drunk such nectar. It loosened his tongue. He drew full length portraits of Mason, Harpe, and Alston, adding to what he had seen all he had ever known about them. But he did not mention the other two who had talked with these three.

Having heard their tale, the Indian-looking boy said, "Uncle Andy's away, and we don't know when he'll be in. But this is something we can't sleep on." He looked at the other, "What do you say we ride over to Judge McNairy now, and tell him?"

Freckles looked at Peter and Eddie. "I bet five dollars you don't want to go anywhere. All you want is to hit the hay."

Since their guests didn't deny this, the boys called the Negro and consigned Peter and Eddie to his care, and said good-night politely, and dashed out. The Negro took a candle. Peter and Eddie followed and collapsed between clean sheets and knew no more.

2

They were awakened by the Negro bringing a big pitcher of hot water to their room. The sun shone brightly through the open window. Outside the birds were singing. The boys gingerly washed in the bowl on the stand, afraid of breaking such a fancy object. Eddie had drunk tea out of a china bowl only two or three times in his life. To wash in one was beyond the wildest luxury. There had been such a bowl at the Doctor's, but Peter had always washed in the wooden tub set on a bench outside. Scrubbed and shy, the boys were escorted by the Negro to the dining room, where a table was spread with linen, silver, and china, and the air was fragrant with coffee and lively with the voices of a dozen children and young people.

Herself one of a family of eleven children, Rachel Donelson

Jackson filled her childless home with nieces and nephews of all ages. Dazzled with the wonder and pleasantness of it all, Peter found his sense of bright confusion melting into beaming incoherence, as Mrs. Jackson herself came running toward him and kissed him on the cheek. "Welcome to two brave, clever boys," she cried, the words gushing pleasantly and seeming to trip over each other. Then she kissed Eddie who blushed even more vividly than Peter.

"Mr. Jackson came in late, and he won't be down for an hour," she said. "But come now and have breakfast with us, and then you may eat a second breakfast with him!"

Though she looked fresh and young as Ivy, to Peter she seemed almost as mature as his mother. Her face was round, brown, and rosy. Her big brown eyes were kind. She had full red lips and a figure plump but neat. Her dress clung to her figure in the new style, but it was not of flimsy material like Ivy's and Penny's, but of substantial cotton dyed green, and the neck and bosom which Ivy left bare were chastely covered by a crisp white kerchief.

Peter's residence with the Doctor had made him reasonably adept with silver and china and all the tricky instruments with which civilized man complicates the business of eating. But he felt out of practice until the deliciousness of hoecakes swimming in maple syrup, and eggs and bacon and coffee, and the absorbed interest on the bright faces around the table made him forget his self-consciousness. When they had exhausted the reports of last night, and efforts to scour the country for the men Peter and Eddie had seen, the young people were eager to hear more and more gory details about "Rogues' Harbor." As the capital of the Mystic Band, Russellville, as seen from the staid Presbyterian sanctuary of Nashville, had a sinister glamor. They all hung on Peter's dramatic version of the death of Harpe, and his saga of the Mason-Alston clans.

As Peter was mimicking the "high-toned" manners and accents of the Tudors and the two "noblemen" at John's house, he was interrupted by a laugh which had a curious metallic sharpness. Looking around, he saw in the doorway the taut, trim figure and starched linen crispness of Andrew Jackson, ex U. S. Senator and at present a Justice of the Supreme Court of Kentucky. "I'm glad to see you have a proper opinion of these British," said Jackson, as he strode to the breakfast table and took the empty place at its head. "For you boys will have to grow up to look sharp or the British will worm their way back into every place of advantage and take us over again. We'll never be clear of them till we fight them again, and this time we'll knock them flat." He looked at Peter. "Would you enlist to knock the British flat?"

"Yes, Sir," answered Peter promptly.

Actually he didn't know a Briton from a woodchuck. It was only during the last year that Russellville had acquired enough of the "tone of good society" to keep any of His Majesty's subjects from traveling on with all haste to Nashville. But he figured that a Briton was a combination of Absolom Tudor and the two "noblemen," and therefore a high and fancy fool whom he'd be glad to boot out of the Cumberland whenever Andrew Jackson should say the word.

Jackson's long, thin, pock-marked face was so tanned that his keen blue eyes gleamed out of it spectacularly, as he smiled grimly at Peter's prompt reply. "Well, boys," he said, now including Eddie in his lightning glance, "I wish I could tell you that we caught those three scoundrels you saw last night, and hanged them to the top of a hickory tree. We've sent riders to warn all the county courts and get the militia out after them. They won't do anything. Mason and his gang don't disturb the local people. They prey on the wayfarer and the stranger. So the settlers leave them alone in their malefactions."

He poured dark brown New Orleans molasses from a small jug into his steaming coffee, and thoughtfully stirred it. A ray of the morning sun fell across his sandy brown hair, combed straight back, and made it look light and golden, like a casque or helmet above his resolute face. When he spoke again, it was as if he were talking not to the family circle, but to ranks on ranks of his fellow citizens. "It will be impossible, within measurable time, to police from any center of government the vast wilderness over which our people are spreading. Just as, under our free Protestant democracy, a man is his own king and priest, so he must be his own detective and police force, and, on his own responsibility, ferret out the evil-doer in his own neighborhood, and bring him to justice. The people must have themselves the will for good government."

"That's what Elder John Page says," observed Eddie eagerly. "He says the old man in us must die, and the new man be born."

Jackson turned his glittering eyes upon him. "Elder John Page is right," he said. "Men have got to be born again and born good democrats."

"Being democrats isn't enough," put in Rachel Jackson. "There's no hope till the Lord changes the wicked hearts of all men from the Mississippi to the mountains."

Peter was startled to hear so elegant a lady echo sentiments which he had been accustomed to hear only from his mother and those whom John, Penny, Ivy, the Tudors, the Dromgoles, and the Mauldings laughed at as countrified and crude. Could it be that the real substance of fine living, as against a gaudy pretense to it, could be grasped only by a man as honest as his father and a woman as pious as his mother? These glamorous people—Andrew and Rachel—were of his father's and mother's breed! This perception gave him a deep, releasing reassurance.

3

After breakfast, Peter and Eddie were invited into Jackson's study and office to talk privately. Peter looked at the painted wood and plastered ceiling, white and smooth as a china dish; at the picture paper, bright as the faces of cards and at the shelves of legal books, as he might have looked at the pearly courts of Heaven. He recognized that here was that something which set Parson McGready and Doctor Allen apart from ordinary folks. But they still lived in log cabins and had only three or four books apiece. Here the spirit that was in them was made manifest. To see a professional man against his proper background gave him the same thrill he had felt when he had first seen his beautiful sister in the costume of a fine lady.

"I hear," said Jackson, "that this Spanish agent, who's known in Nashville as Stuart Walker, has another name."

"In the select social circles of Rogues' Harbor," replied Peter, "he goes by the name of Pentacost."

"Pentacost! Is he a saint or an apostle?"

"Not so you'd notice it," said Peter dryly.

"You haven't seen any tongues of fire descending from Heaven on him?"

"No, I'd rather expect they'd come from the other place," answered Peter, adding hastily, "not that I know anything against him!"

"Nobody does, except that he wants us all to cut loose from the government in Washington—for which, till we get a new president, I hardly blame him—and tie up with Spain."

"All the high and mighty ones up our way talk like that," observed Peter. "Some want to tie up with Spain, some with England. Being American is too low."

"We'll never be free of that till we get New Orleans," thundered Jackson. "It's intolerable to have that corrupt city at the mouth of the great river system which drains the lands where we're trying to build freedom for man for the first time in the world's history. Our criminals flee to it to be out of reach of our laws. It's a center of intrigue for all nations against us. This fellow Walker talks about having the Spanish come up from New Orleans and the British from Canada and combine to take us over. So I say we've got to get New Orleans. Buy it if we can. If not, take it by force of arms." His eyes flashed. Peter could positively feel the sparks.

"What do you do about a man like Walker?" asked Eddie.

"Nothing. Out here talk is free. We can only watch him."

Cautiously approaching the real point of their visit, Peter then asked if Walker, or Pentacost, was in Nashville at present.

"No, he hasn't been seen since your father spoke to me about him. But I inquired about him. It seems he buys tobacco and cotton for Spanish firms, and ships it down the Cumberland and the Ohio to the Mississippi. It's said he can get goods into New Orleans, and bring goods in turn safely up the Chickasaw Road when nobody else can. He's in with the Spanish, the Indians, and the robbers."

Peter's heart stood still. Now they were coming to the truth! "You don't mean he's one of Mason's gang?"

"Oh no. I think he just pays them something to let him alone."

Peter's eyes met Eddie's. So that was all there was to it! If it really was John and Pentacost they'd seen talking to Mason, Harpe, and Alston, all they were doing was passing them a bribe to leave them alone! That wasn't social righteousness, but with things as they were, it was still a long way from being murderers and horse-thieves themselves!

Eddie's gray eyes challenged Peter to come to the point. Peter took the plunge, "The fact is, Judge Jackson, Pentacost has been making up to a girl up our way, but Circuit Rider Burke's learned that he has a wife in Natchez—a French girl, a Catholic. He wants a divorce and can't get it. And now this girl has left home, and her folks are frantic lest she's gone off with him."

Peter stopped short. His face reddened, and he began to stammer. Under his tan, Jackson's face had suddenly gone gray. His hand which had been playing idly with his quill pen was clenched and braced against the top of the desk. Boy though he was, Peter knew that he had flicked that raw wound that was always behind the pride with which Jackson fronted the world. Every frontier teenager had heard the story. Upon an appeal from Rachel's mother Andrew Jackson had dashed back through the mountains to Virginia, to bring her home to her family, out of the clutches of a jealous husband. The husband had then applied for a divorce on the ground that his wife had "eloped" with Jackson. Jackson, supposing the divorce granted, had instantly protected the lady's honor by marrying her—a knightly deed helped by a strong inclination on both sides. After two years it was found that there had been no divorce, and Rachel and Andrew had been living in "open adultery," on which grounds her jealous sneak of a husband finally got the divorce. The Jacksons then went through a second marriage ceremony. Andrew Jackson swore that this pure and lovely lady had been his wife before God, and any man who took her sacred name in his mouth except to glorify her must answer with his life. He forced everybody in his presence to pay her an elaborate courtesy which she smilingly deprecated, but which everybody else knew he was prepared to enforce with pistol, sword, and horsewhip.

All this Peter had heard, and even his strict mother had said Jackson was quite right. But he did not know how much of shame and confusion there had been under Jackson's brave front, nor how constantly they had to assure themselves and each other that as God was their judge, they had done no wrong, and to steel themselves to hold up their heads and look detractors in the eye. Now he sensed this, as silence, hot and stifling, hung between himself and the Justice of the Supreme Court of Tennessee.

Then Jackson spoke, "A man who lures an innocent girl into a life of dishonor is a scoundrel that hanging's too good for. Nevertheless divorce, elopement—yes, even the sacred institution of marriage —arn't clean, clear propositions in law out here as they might be in long settled communities. We're forced to make our own laws to suit life as we find it to be, and we haven't had time yet to make our own laws good enough. The way it is now there's one law on one side of a border, and another law on the other side, and all around is wilderness where there's no law except God's."

He paused. Andrew Jackson was not a man to be confused, even under the stress of a problem which, for him, remained unresolved and tormenting to the end of his days. But he could see in the gray eyes and black eyes that were earnestly trying to follow him that this line of talk was getting nowhere. He rose abruptly, with a gesture of dismissal, and held out his hand to Eddie, who shook it silently, and to Peter, who looked at him expectantly. "I hope soon to see your father at the court in Russellville. This matter of—the—the lady interests me very much. We have reason to keep a watch on this man, Walker. I will try to find whether a lady is domiciled with him."

"Oh, thank you, Sir," said Peter.

"Thank you, Sir," murmured Eddie, and tried to imitate the way Peter bowed himself out.

4

Rachel Jackson urged the boys to stay for a while and offered various allurements in the shape of barbecues and shooting matches. But Peter and Eddie were anxious to get home by nightfall, and tell their story. So with saddlebags stuffed with goodies to eat by the way, they set off immediately, but, hurried as they felt, they could not resist stopping in Nashville, and surveying the wonders of the only metropolis between Lexington and New Orleans.

Set sixty feet above the Cumberland, on limestone bluffs, with hills rising on all sides, Nashville had seven or eight brick houses, and 120 frame houses, perched on the bare rock, with paths leading down the rock to the river, whence all water for household purposes was carried in buckets. It had a printing office, a weekly paper, a dozen stores displaying goods which had come from Baltimore, Philadelphia, and New Orleans, and a college whose total enrollment was seven or eight young men, and whose faculty consisted of Mr. Fish from New England. Honest goods, as distinct from those which seeped in through the thieves market, had to be drawn by wagon from Baltimore to Pittsburgh, and carried from Pittsburgh 425 miles to Limestone. From Limestone they must come down to the mouth of the Cumberland by boat, past the robbers that infested the shoals and channels and islands of the Ohio River —a distance of 608 miles—and then they must be poled 180 miles up the Cumberland to Nashville—a distance of 1521 miles. Goods from New Orleans were poled up the Mississippi 1000 miles to the mouth of the Ohio, up the Ohio 63 miles to the mouth of the Cumberland, and 180 miles up the Cumberland to Nashville. "Any way you look at it," reflected Peter, "it sure is cheaper to steal from those that have brought goods in, than to go to the expense of being honest and bringing them in yourself."

Approaching the Kentucky border at sunset, they passed the big Donelson blockhouse, built by that notable Regulator, John Donelson, Rachel Jackson's father, in 1781,—the most historic structure in these parts. With its big gates standing open, its cabins, stables, gardens, and farms, it still housed a large village of Donelsons.

Peter looked at it with almost a proprietary interest, now that he knew Mrs. Jackson and had even been kissed by her. Leaving it behind, Peter kept thinking about Rachel and Andrew and what his mother had once said, "Those that can be divorced never was married. Whom God has joined together no man *can* put asunder." Then he thought of Polly. Suppose Pentacost was married. Suppose he wanted to be free and before God he was entitled to it because she that was called his wasn't the wife for him. Yet he couldn't be free because of some French or Spanish or Catholic way of looking at it on the part of his "wife" and her family. He thought soberly, "If a girl ran away with a man like that, she might not be bad. She could be—brave."

It was after dark when they turned on to the trail to their own house. Across the great dome of the moonless summer sky, the milky way trailed its drifts of star stuff, and, below, the fields twinkled with fireflies. And then, like a single star, steady and dominant over all, there shone the candle Mary had put in the window. Peter was drowsing in the saddle. His back was caving in. His thighs ached. Perhaps it was because he was tired, and therefore childish. Perhaps it was that he had so many thoughts and plans which were at war with everything his mother prayed for in his behalf, but, at the sight of the starshine in the window, something inside him seemed to break down and cry, "Mammy! Mammy!" He spurred Aladdin forward, as if he were a child again, rushing to hide in his mother's skirts.

But when they rode up to the door, he couldn't bear to see how Mary would take it when she knew that they had brought back no definite word of Polly. She would be so still, so utterly forlorn. Peter wanted to be out of the way of it. So he offered to put Eddie's horse away with his own and went around to the barn while Eddie went into the house.

As he rode around to the barn leading Eddie's horse, Peter heard a whinneying in the hazel bushes, off toward the spring. "What horse is that?" he wondered. A horse in the bushes was not to be approached lightly. It might even be Sam Mason's. He tied both his horse and Eddie's, and, Indianlike, stole toward that whinney.

There was a dry bough hanging there. He could snap it, as if it snapped naturally. It would fall in the bushes and startle the horse out, if it was untied. If tied there, the horse would show it by his helpless pawing, and the man who tied him might be nearby.

When the branch snapped, the aimal started from the bushes and he saw it dimly outlined against the starshine. "It's Jerry's horse Frosty," he thought. "How come he leaves him untied?" Since Frosty knew Peter as well as his own master, it was easy for Peter to catch and tie him. Then he put his own horses away. As he started back toward the house, his foot struck something prone in his path. "It's a man. It's a boy. It's Jerry. He's hurt—" He knelt by the prone figure. A strong blast of whisky struck him full in the face. "He's drunk!" After long months of abstinence, safe in the Baptist fold! Drunk!

What should he do? He couldn't take Jerry into the cabin. Mary would know and she would tell Brenda. It didn't do for mothers to know too much about the doings of the young male of the species. He shook Jerry. He put his mouth to his ear and said, "Jerry, it's Pete. Wake up!" Jerry stirred enough to emit another hot blast of whisky but otherwise did not respond. "Reckon he's a goner for a long time," thought Peter, and went into the house, carefully composing his face so that his mother would notice nothing amiss.

5

Concern for Jerry had dropped like a curtain between him and all the exciting events of the last few days. Seeing that his father was not at home and that Eddie had already told mother most of their news, he was content, for once, to let his brother do the talking, while Bonny quietly finished Mary's evening chores. Mary had her suffering, praying look, her eyes tragic and burning bright in her white face. She was only slightly re-assured by Jackson's promise to find out whether Pentacost was domiciled with a lady. "If she loves him, she won't leave him," she said miserably. "Even if we do find her, she'll find it in her conscience to stick by him."

She knew that was what she herself would do in a like case.

Torn between his mother's sorrow and his concern for Jerry, Peter walked out with Eddie when he went to get his horse and ride home. Virtuous as Eddie was, he was shock proof. Seeing Jerry, he wasted no time in questions or moral disapproval but proceeded in a businesslike way to do what was necessary. Together he and Peter carried Jerry into the barn loft and dumped him in the fragrant dust of last year's hay. "He'll likely do till morning," observed Eddie. "But no telling how long he has been drinking, and he might wake up and holler and see snakes."

Like kind arms around him Peter sensed the pleasant smells and isolation of the barn, reliving happy winter hours spent playing cards here by himself, thinking, dreaming, in the fairy company of kings, queens, and knaves. "I'd kinda like to sleep here myself," he said.

"I'd do that," answered Eddie. "It would be safer for Jerry. You can sneak out after they're all asleep inside."

And this, in the midnight hours, Peter did. Sunk in the hay near Jerry, Peter slept soundly. There was a comfort in having Jerry there, even in that state. Something that had been a part of life as long as he could remember was restored, and he felt at rest. But in the wan light before dawn, he awoke, frightened by a strange blubbering sound. "Hurt! Something's hurt!" he thought, starting up. Slowly he remembered. His eyes focused on Jerry, sitting up in the hay, his face in his hands, shivering as if he had the ague. When Peter pulled himself over to him, Jerry seemed not to recognize him in the dark or to know where he was, but, aware of a human presence, he whimpered, "Polly's run away. She's run away with a married man," and he threw himself face downward in the hay.

So while the sky beyond the window brightened to a clear green, with a pink wisp of cloud across it, Peter half sat, half reclined next to Jerry, and heard him affirm that there was no God, or, if there was, he was meaner than the Devil himself. Else how could He let this happen? There wasn't anything for him now but to drink himself to death, and, if he was damned for it what did that matter, since damnation couldn't be worse than this. Peter earnestly took the part of God, and finally offered even to pray with Jerry. He was surprised at himself, and rather thrilled, for, despite the urging and example of his mother, the circuit riders, and McGready, with all of whom kneeling and praying was a conventional social gesture, something you did almost anywhere, any time, if you felt sympathetic or wanted to convey good advice, Peter had never achieved more than a wordless petition in moments of emergency. But he was now so conscious of Jerry's desperate situation that he was ready to plunge into prayer with him as he would have plunged into water to save him from drowning. But Jerry resisted Peter's tentative and inexperienced efforts so violently that Peter soon gave them up.

Religion having failed, Peter remembered his idea about having Jerry race Aladdin to victory. In Jerry's present state of mind the proposal he had rejected in better days made an instant appeal. At the center of all his troubles was the inadequacy of his slight frame to the savage world into which he had been born. To contemplate himself in a situation in which his small body gave him an advantage, restored Jerry's bruised ego. "Give me the horse," he said. "I'll ride him plumb to Hell."

"I reckon the goal post will be far enough," said Peter dryly. This talk of going to Hell annoyed him. He stuck to his father's idea that a smart fellow enjoys the pleasures and social triumphs along the road to Hell but cheats the Devil of his soul in the end. But seeing Jerry begin to come to life, he wasted no time in theological argument, but dared him to get rid of that head, and rout the heat coming full blast on the first sunshine by plunging headfirst into the swimming hole.

An hour later Mary was amazed to see the boys walk in, their wet hair plastered to their heads, their horny bare feet measurably clean, breathing the dewy freshness of the woodland pool and carrying a string of fish. "Why, Jerry, where'd you come from at this hour?"

Jerry lied, "I sneaked Peter out while you all were still sleepin. He thought he'd get you some fish for breakfast—for a surprise."

Believing that Peter had put Jerry up to this, and touched that her boy should pay her such attention in her trouble, Mary melted into one of her rare moods of soft radiance and got out the last jar of her cherished peach jam. Peter felt mean. For he knew that the only thing that could make a fool of a woman as smart as his mother was her great desire to believe in his love and loyalty and dedication to all that she thought good.

CHAPTER 28

**Russellville, Kentucky
July 4, 1800**

As June burned into July, Peter was so busy keeping Jerry's mind off Polly by training him to ride Aladdin, that he almost forgot to dream of Ivy, and found no time, between his horse and his farm chores, to ride over to John's on the chance of seeing her. All that Ivy had inflicted so far was a flesh wound. Jerry's wound was mortal.

Jerry was to make his debut as a jockey at the great Fourth of July barbecue which the veterans of the American Revolution were staging in a grove on Muddy River to celebrate the tenth anniversary of their migration west, and to strengthen their determination to elect Thomas Jefferson president of the United States. There would be horse races in the afternoon, but the Baptists and Methodists on the committee would allow no betting. Yet in the interest of good horsemanship Dominie was giving a prize—a handsome saddle obtained from Louisville. Peter told Jerry that if he won the race by riding Aladdin, he could have the saddle. This prospect kept Jerry going without recourse to liquor, which Peter strictly forebade.

Peter and Jerry went to the picnic ground at sunrise, to help start the big fires. Before the dew was dry, pack horses, saddle horses and sledges were converging on the grove. While Dominie and Jus conferred on the program, the women unpacked their baskets and displayed their latest triumphs in overcoming the limitations of their wild meat diet; the boys beat down the brush to clear space for a race course, a wrestling place, and a shooting gallery;

the children gamboled in the water, with shrill admonitions from mothers to the seven-year-olds to be sure the five-year-olds didn't drown, and the new circuit rider, Thomas Wilkerson, trained a choir to sing from John Wesley's hymn book. Wilkerson had studied the literature the Methodist Book Concern in New York was now able to get out here, in small bundles, for the circuit riders' saddlebags, and took seriously Wesley's advice, "Let the people learn to sing, and let them learn our songs first."

Even the race course could not keep Peter from the show Wilkerson was putting on. Waving a baton with the bark and leaves still on it, in a kind of rag time known to Negroes and Indians but not to respectable congregations, he lined out the words, blew a strong, nasal blast up and down the scale, and nineteen hopeful voices produced nineteen variations on it. If there had been a trained European musician present, he would have been startled by the emergence in these wilds of a new kind of music. He might even have perceived that these earnest souls, with ears innocent of any rhythmic sound except the song of the birds, the purling of the brook, and the beat of the tom tom, were trying to make harmony of something out of key and out of time, and, in so doing, were producing a kind of wild new beauty. To the performers it was infinitely satisfying. They had no arts and the new generation, coming into more ease than their forbears had ever known perhaps back to Adam, were starving for them. As they sang, their eyes shone, their hearts beat with a stronger, more serene rhythm, and they felt full of courage and confidence. The mood would last for hours, and, to restore it, they had only to hum the words, "How shall I all to Heaven aspire?" to have it come flooding back.

Meanwhile the birds sang. The dragon-flies floated purple and green over the water and the children chased them. In a quiet cove the great pink pond lilies bloomed, and, in the marsh beyond, the blue flags were in flower. Over it all was the blazing dome of the sky, high and far, without clouds, sending down such a force and power of light that it seemed to be pulling the tobacco, the cotton, the corn, the wheat, the peavines, the canes, and the tall grasses straight up out of the earth. Under the trees it was cooler, but not so cool that the strong, magnetic light did not irradiate everything. In it the people glowed, sweated, expanded in a careless outgoing unknown to chillier climes. Their ancestors—border Scotch, Germans and northern French—had dwelt in misty, cool lands from the beginning of recorded time. They and their immediate forbears had come from the dark valleys of the Alleghenies and from forests unpierced by sun the year around. But ten years in a climate which, even in winter, was bright, and, in summer, overmastering, had made a new species of them—more open, frank, explosive, and reckless, less huddling and ingrown.

So they worked and yelled, heaved logs, cut trees, and baked themselves in barbecue fires, not prostrated by the heat but filled with a fierce energy by the fierce light, and drank gallons of water only slightly tinctured with whisky. For in a land where whisky was cheap as water, they had discovered what their European ancestors never knew, that no drink is better than water if it is only cold enough. It was only ten years since they had come here, but in ten years the sun, the wide open spaces, and the surplus of food had made them new bodies, and McGready and the circuit riders and the Baptists were making them new souls.

Peter loved it all. He had grown up a child of the new land, tempered alike to its fierce cold and fierce heat. His tough brown epidermis glowed like bronze reflecting light. The heat and the sun inspired in him a peculiar regardlessness as if he had escaped his body and were abroad in the light, and would go on and on, vibrant and blazing, and not giving a damn. He was bare to the waist. His curls were tight and shining with sweat. The sweat glistened on his round face as he forged ahead through some thirty boys from the position of cutter of brush on the race course to leaning against a huge gnarled oak and yelling out orders to the others to cut. Beside him was little Jerry, his panting and near fainting lieutenant. Since the sun gave Jerry a headache, Mary and Brenda had made him wear wet grape leaves inside his straw hat, and to keep that cool he wore a second one on top of it. He would gladly have lain under the tree and dreamed mournfully of Polly, but Peter wouldn't let him.

2

The program was ready. The cannon was in place with a crew to fire it. The flag made by Mary, Barbara, and Brenda out of cotton of their own spinning and weaving, the red stripes colored with red madder, the blue with wild indigo, arose fluttering on the breeze—thirteen stripes for the thirteen colonies, and sixteen stars for the sixteen states. A band consisting of Negros dressed as Cherokee Indians, with wooden flutes, and drums, beat out something resembling *Yankee Doodle,* and the program began with a prayer by Wilkerson. He begged that those who had thrown off the yoke of all kings and lords might be saved by the grace of God from letting themselves be saddled with the yoke of the Devil and the rule of the Lord of Hell, who was the worst tyrant of all. Then Jus took charge as chairman. The feeling Peter had of being well-born, and destined of right to leadership against stuck-up trash like the Dromgoles, was enhanced by the sight of the tall lounging figure on the platform. Jus had no formal dignity. The manner which some public men put on and off like powdered wigs was one of those "affected" ways his people were against. In shirt-sleeve ease he presided over the meeting, very much as if he were calling the figures in a country dance.

He began, in a rambling way, to recall the events of that march ten years ago and to congratulate them on what had followed from it. Two states had sprung up around the strong core of the soldiers' settlement—Kentucky and Tennessee—and across the Ohio there'd soon be a third state around the Yankee veterans! The business these states were making was spilling over into the wilderness to the south so that they had had to set up the territory of Mississippi, "just to have some place for Mason and Alston and our more unpopular citizens to go when we kicked them out." Now they were setting up Indiana Territory which was so big that two states could be made out of it. So the veterans had reason to be proud of what they had done in ten years. They'd not only taken quite a hunk of states away from King George, but they'd gone right out and made some more.

Looking around, he was glad to see that individually they had prospered, too. Young uns had grown up into tall strong men, and prettier girls even than those back in old Virginny. He didn't see any mansions hereabouts yet. But most people had bigger, squarer, and better plastered houses, with better hearths and chimneys than their forefathers had ever lived in, and the plenty they had to eat would make their great grandfathers in the old country drool just to hear about it. "There's more than one here whose grandfather shipped out of the old country to escape being jailed for killing a deer, there where there was no place for a deer to run wild except on some land that some Sir Somebody said he owned. Killing a deer!" He paused, looked around, and sniffed the fragrant smoke from the barbecue pits. "Brother, do I smell venison?"

When the applause had died down, he went on, "The deer are kinda getting out of our way of late. But it don't make any difference, for the hogs and the cattle are movin in. And though nobody is going to make me eat chicken instead of wild turkey till the day I die, I see my boy Peter and my girl, Sis, growing up to like it."

Here there was a roar of approval. For there was hardly a mature male there who wasn't keeping up a battle with the women on the subject of that insipid bird, the chicken. At this point, Peter ostentatiously walked across the trampled grass between Jus and the audience carrying to the barbecue pits a load of chickens whose necks he had just wrung.

Jus rolled his eyes at Peter, and then at the audience, and went on, "But whether we elect to chase the deer to the setting sun, or whether, like our educated friend, Dominie, we settle down and raise hens with the women folk, the point is we're free to do it. For no man here has the say so when it comes to hunting in the wild lands, or if he does say so, we don't heed it. And so far as the cussedness of human nature and the forehandedness of speculators allows, we've been getting the land parceled out into fair-sized plots, enough for a family to use and no more. Most of the soldiers were agreed at the outset that 400 acres was enough for any man, and so far as we're true to the principles of the Declaration of Independence which we're gathered here to celebrate, that's what we still think. And it's up to us to see that we carry out the great idea that all men are born free and equal by keeping out laws and conditions that impose a man-made inequality and put bars and fences to opportunity that was meant to be free to all. And that's why we want to make the man who wrote our Declaration of Independence President of these United States."

Peter, strolling back from the barbecue pits, heard the applause explode in a volley of pistol shots and shouts of "Damnation to Thomas Jefferson." Out of the bushes crashed some twenty horsemen, wearing the red plumes of the Rogues, yelling, shooting their pistols into the air, and riding into the midst of the crowd, scattering it in all directions. Among them were Red Maulding, Skinny Dromgole, Gwen's earless beau, and others of Peter's cronies at cards. And then he was caught up in the roar of the army that fell on the intruders. For, with the usual miscalculation of their kind, they thought that only the poor and the chicken-livered and other no account folks would be at the Jefferson barbecue, easy enough for cavaliers on fast horses to terrorize and make fools of. The Jeffersonians surrounded them. They hurled them from their horses. They beat them over the head with their own guns. They whipped the horses and sent them wildly careering off into brush and field, while from one to five took on each invader. Peter had Red Maulding under him and was biting and gouging with the best of the *rough and tumble* technique. Both of Red's eyes were swollen shut. He was torn and bleeding, and his hot body was heaving. Through Peter's red hot madness there penetrated a voice small, mild, and conciliatory: "Lay off, Pete. I give in."

Doctor Allen stood over them with strips of a torn white shirt, and beside him, Barbara with a pail of cold water. But Peter heard his mother's clear voice saying, "Barbara can play nurse if she's a mind to. But I won't. Let them lick their own wounds." As the Doctor leaned over Red from whose mouth the blood was now gushing, Jus interposed, "No you don't, Doctor. These fellows have got just what they asked for. And the only help they're going to get is to be carried 200 yards to yonder brush pile and to be thrown in there. Heave him up, boys."

As Peter started to lift Red Maulding, he felt him float up into the air, and there were Jerry's two brothers lifting him one by the heels, the other by the shoulders. Red spit blood and then vomit. "Damnation! He's spewing his vomit on us to spite us," said Hans, dropping him with a thump. An unfeigned howl of pain broke through Red's bloody, slobbering lips. Peter's anger had vanished, and when he was not red hot with anger there was not a living thing he could not feel sorry for. So he was trying to be moderately considerate as they heaved Red up again. But all the while a voice like his mother's was saying inside him, "He asked for it. It's only justice."

When they had dropped Red into the hazel bushes, Peter walked back, mopping his brow and aware, for the first time, that his own head was aching. "Lord, I hate fighting!" he thought. He was mad at Red for spoiling the day, mad at the sun for beating on his aching head, mad at the mosquitoes for settling on his sweaty face and neck. He threw himself down on the moss under a huge oak. The drummers were beating for attention. Jus was shouting, "Time off to duck yourselves in the river and cool off. Then the meeting goes on."

3

Jerry was shaking Peter out of a deep sleep. "Come down to the water. It'll rest you." Under his two hats his small pointed face was fresh as a sprite's, for he had been deemed too small to be of use in the fight and had been sent back to watch the barbecue pits. "I told you there was uses in being small," said Peter, hauling his aching limbs off the ground. "You're bright as a daisy, and I bet there isn't any one else that'll ride a horse this afternoon that is. Good thing you're doing it instead of me."

Not bothering to remove his only garment, his torn and ragged jeans, Peter ducked in the water, and lay on the grass with the air blowing cool on his wet flesh, while Jerry sat beside him, reviewing plans for the race. The fight they did not speak of. It made Peter sick even to think of it. Then they heard the pipes and drums and knew that the meeting was beginning again. If there had been anybody but his father in charge, Peter would have stayed where he was. But filial loyalty required that he remove to the shade of a tree near the platform where his father stood as casual and easy as if he hadn't put his fist through the face of a man named Havard forty minutes before.

"This little fracas," said Jus, "goes to show what happens when we try to make the Declaration of Independence come true." He reminded them that when Jefferson wrote the Declaration, there was not one set of folks that wanted to get rid of King George, but two. One set was those who wanted to put themselves in place of George, and tax the rest of the people themselves and rule them to the fattening of their own purses. Such were the Boston, New York, and Philadelphia merchants and money-lenders, and some of the big fur traders. The other set was the great mass of folks who wanted to get rid, not only of King George, but of everybody like him, and never have kings or lords or gentry anywhere. "Well, you know what happened. We got rid of King George. But we didn't get rid of all that were waitin to step into his shoes."

Then he recalled how, after eight years of marching, fighting, and going hungry and barefoot through winter snows, they'd been paid off in Kentucky lands. But what with the confusion of every kind of interest asserting every kind of special privilege, it was seven years before they got to Kentucky and three more before they could take their land. "Three added to seven is ten," he said, "and the ten years we've been here added to that is twenty. And that's what we've spent getting where we can even begin to make the Declaration come true. Twenty years is the best part of a man's manhood. That's what we've invested. And isn't it high time we got a return on our investment same as men who put money into a thing instead of life, expect to get a return on *that?*"

Here Peter, still aching and slumped against the tree, dozed off. Through a red hot haze he was staring again at the blood and vomit on the lips of Maulding. He jerked himself away from that and tried to fasten his mind on what his father was saying. As long as he concentrated hard, images and ideas conjured up by his father appeared dimly through the tides of sleep, like reflections wavering in water. Jus was talking about Mac and Dutch, and how each had died a victim to those who claimed special privilege. "For though it was Indians that killed Mac, you and I who grew up in the old Indian fighting days know that there was most always something behind an Indian raid that wasn't just Indian. No. What killed Mac was getting mixed up with folks who claimed special privilege, and yet couldn't carry their own weight. They wanted to call the tune and let somebody else pay the piper, and that other was Mac and his poor family. And it was the same with Dutch. Behind these Rogues who are half of them just young show-offs that will shoot and fight and ride anybody down for anything, there's the Mystic Band and special privilege in thievery and murder; and, for standing up to them, poor Dutch paid with his life."

Peter dozed again, and this time he was completely gone. He struggled out of a nightmare in which he was fighting a dozen Indians single-handed, to find that the war whoops he had heard in his dream were all around him. A line of Indians led by a chief in feathered head dress, his face painted blue, black and red, was between him and his father on the platform. He felt himself up-borne again on the whole body of veterans rising to fight, and then the infernal howls and low ominous roars broke in laughter. The Indians laughed through their paint. The Indian chief removed the feathers and mounted to the platform. It was Cherokee Bill.

While his braves mopped their painted faces in the water, and came back and sat in a semi-circle below him, Cherokee told how he and Eloise had made a home in that fine plateau country south of the Tennessee line, which is cut through by rivers that run into the Tennessee river, and descends on its southern side into gentle, low hill-lands, where summer is long and the winter short, and cotton will grow like weeds. Everybody claimed that land. South Carolina said the northern parts were theirs, and Georgia said all land west of them to the Mississippi was theirs. And meanwhile it was set up as Mississippi Territory reaching from the mountains in the east to the Mississippi in the West. French, British, and

Spanish fur traders were all through there, with daughters of Indian chiefs for wives, and villages which they ruled. Cherokee was evidently a big man among the Indians called "Hillbillies" who had good farms, and had gone to Washington to get seeds and tools for them, and was acting as Indian agent for the Federal government.

It was all very interesting, but the sun was getting so high and stomachs so empty that there was undisguised relief when Cherokee jumped down from the platform and joined his old friends among the veterans. But alas! There was still the Circuit Rider to hear from! Wilkerson had the tact to hold the remnant of the audience only long enough to remind them that if all the fine things he'd heard tell about were to come to pass, they'd have to put off the old man and be born again. And, to help put off the old Adam, Brother McGready was holding a big meeting from Friday to Monday in his outdoor sanctuary, to which he urged them to come and bring their friends. Then, still tactful, he omitted the closing prayers and called on his nineteen singers instead.

Peter had rushed up to speak to Cherokee Bill. The burly Indian had to raise his head slightly to look into the boy's sparkling eyes. Jus stood proudly by, a big man, but a shade shorter than his son. During the singing they stood silent, looking at each other with affection and satisfaction, the three pairs of eyes so alike in their opaque blackness and inscrutable gleam. As the chorus finished with "Sing my Great Deliverer's praise," Cherokee lifted his heavy brown hand and laid it lightly on the tangle atop Peter's tall head. "L'il ol Indian boy," he said in his mellow voice, "you're a big Injun now. And yore ol Injun Pappy is shore proud to see you."

4

Peter stood in the cluster of hazel bushes, where a trickle of water cut through the fine-grained powdery gold earth and went to join Muddy River. Here the mile-long race course ceased to swerve around clumps of bushes and tangles of tree roots and ran straight for 300 yards to the goal, which consisted of two saplings set up on each side of the road with a long white thread of Barbara's spinning tied from one to the other. The horse that broke that string would be the winner. Sweat was pouring down Peter's face and 200 mosquitoes were chewing at his bare feet and legs. But he was too anxiously absorbed to feel them. If only he could be at the starting point and here at the beginning of the home stretch at the same time!

He worried lest Jerry should forget what he had told him. "Take off those crazy hats. They'll fly off in the first wind. Tie your head up in this kerchief—it's red so I can see you easy, comin down the road, from where I stand. And keep a sharp lookout for me alongside the road and hold back till I give the sign." And he was to keep clear of Ben who carried a rawhide whip and, when he saw an opponent's horse pass, would strike at it. Nobody could take that whip away from Ben. They hadn't been able to make rules about things like that. Men just got on their horses and went, over ditch and fence and through brush, to some agreed-on goal. The only way to handle men like Ben was to know what they'd do and get around them. Only one who could do that could be a leader in this wild world.

Troubled that he could not be everywhere along the course at once, Peter was thinking, "If you curved it around, kinda like the shape of an egg, and made the finish where they started, you could stand on something and overlook it all." And he wished the course was hard under foot and polished off smooth. "The hooves sink in the dirt like it was snow. They can't make speed that way."

There was a distant shot. "They're off!" Peter's heart leaped into his mouth and stayed there, choking him, cutting off his breathing. A hundred years passed. Then he saw a whirling cloud of dust coming toward him and growing bigger and longer across the golden grassy meadow. His eyes strained. Out of the dust emerged the big figure of Ben on his big brown horse, in the lead. Then Sam on his roan. Peter counted nine of them. Where was Jerry? A spot of red burned through the yellow core of the dust. Jerry much behind the others! Peter exploded. "Damnation!" He had told Jerry to hold Aladdin in, but not so far in as that! Jerry was scanning the side of the road. That was delaying him. "The damn fool! Can't he keeping going and look for me at the same time?" The other horses were coming abreast of Peter. Peter shinned up a young ash and lay out on a limb, waving his hand, wrapped round and round with a piece of white linsy. That was the agreed on signal, at the sight of which Jerry was to speed up. Every horse had passed him. He could see by the bobbing of the red bandanna that Jerry had seen him. Relieved, Peter swung back and the whole top of the young tree broke, precipitating him in the fine red dust of the course below.

Scrambling out, his face bleeding where the branch had scratched him, Peter saw a beautiful sight. It was Jerry on Aladdin, taking off like a bird on a wing, in a long smooth swoop forward, past the last horse, past the next, past the next. He seemed not to run but only to glide forward in long, billowy leaps, Jerry's head bobbing like a red flower in the wind, somewhere above. He was abreast of Sam. Then, smooth and clean, he was pulling ahead of Ben. Ben raised his whip. A howl pierced the air. Startled, Peter perceived that the howl had come from his own lips. Ben's whip came down in the dust where Aladdin's hooves had been, and tangled with Sam's horse. Sam raised his whip and struck Ben's horse, which bounded ahead and came up almost abreast of Aladdin. But smooth and sure, Aladdin soared ahead and came in with the nose of Ben's horse hard on his tail.

Peter started on a dead run and came up panting just as Dominie lifted Jerry out of the saddle on to the shoulders of admiring watchers. He stood for a moment to one side, unnoticed. Then his father's voice spoke in his ear. "You used your head, Son." Peter felt a rush of gratitude to his father, coloring and enriching the high happiness of that moment. As usual, his father understood. A triumph like this was something to live for, to suffer for, to sweat for. He had pitted his brains against both chance and the ornery meanness of some men, and won. Chance and men's cussedness—those were the two great threats in life. It gave Peter a cosmic sense of security that he could beat them by using his brains. For though Aladdin was a good horse, he was not a sure winner, and Ben had prevented many a better one from passing him. What made the difference was management and forethought.

Jus said, with a knowing wink, "Bring him along next court day. Your brother John's going to race a new nag he brought up from New Orleans. It would be kinda good to beat John." His eyes twinkled into his son's.

Mary was proud of Peter, too. For when Dominie made a speech and presented him the saddle, Peter replied with a flashing, deprecating smile, "Thank you kindly. But the winning was in the riding, and it wan't I that rode him. So won't you say all those handsome things all over again and give the saddle to Jerry?"

With that everybody roared applause, and Brenda beamed and whispered, "I declare, Pete has right good manners. And ain't he getting handsome?"

Mary approached Peter in a glow of pride and affection. "It was smart the way you managed, Honey. But never race him against John and his crowd, Honey. It will ruin you, and my heart will break."

As she turned on him her full clear gaze, it was as if a hand had reached out and clutched Peter's heart and wrung it. The glow went out of his face and the swaggering ease from his big body. He spied Cherokee Bill talking to his father, and with mumbling excuse, rushed blindly toward him. But not before he saw his mother turn away, with a look on her face as if he had struck her.

CHAPTER 29   Russellville, Kentucky
                                        Midsummer, 1800

It was like fires in the grass, running together into one irresistible, advancing wall—the way the people gathered for preachings that summer of 1800.

The few humble souls who had faced the crime of Logan County with prayers in the summer of 1797 had, in three years, grown and multiplied in all directions. As Russellville grew respectable and the Mason-Alston-Harpe Band retreated to newer and wilder places, the pledge to pray for social redemption went with them. Wherever there was prayer and preaching, the people flocked, for this had become a magic against all that threatened them. Social leaders who were looking for new bottles to hold the heady new wine of frontier emotionalism and spiritual desire were fired with what McGready had achieved. To carry on what he started, Methodist, Presbyterian, and Baptist preachers linked hands in a way hitherto unknown to Protestant sects. The fraternal effort of Methodists and Presbyterians was dramatized, in the spring of 1800, by the McGee brothers, traveling preachers. John was a Methodist, and William a Presbyterian. They rode together. They preached together. They prayed together. They slept side by side, rolled up in their blankets on the ground or on the dirt floors of remote cabins. They ate together, breaking each hoe cake in two, one piece for John, one for William. Stalwart, bulky men, they cultivated all the arts of movement and gesture, prancing down amidst the mourners, sitting down on the floor and clasping their hands around their knees, and talking in an intimate way as if in a camp fire circle.

These brothers were stage managers for the series of great religious mass meetings planned for the summer of 1800, John Page and most ministers for miles around assisting, except the outraged Mr. Balch. The first of these new camp meetings was to be held in McGready's outdoor church from Friday to Monday. People were planning to come to it for forty miles around.

2

It was a hot summer morning, bright and heady, with a dry, exhilarating freshness in the air. Peter was helping to put the camp grounds in order, and taking a showman's interest in the improvement in lighting, with more candles better placed, while working his way around in the direction of a demure, red-haired Methodist miss, with a merry eye, called "Peaches." He hadn't met Peaches yet, but he was thinking of a natural way to begin a conversation.

Jerry was to have joined him on the camp ground, but Hans and Otto had come without him and were clearing the brush on the north side. Looking for Jerry, while keeping an eye on Peaches, Peter saw a troop of horses advancing up the center aisle, dirtying the path to the altar with manure. At the head was Red Maulding, very smart in the new long breeches and short boots, and Gwen, with her earless one. And there was Jerry, on his new saddle on Frosty, riding on Gwen's other side, his face all alight as he talked to her. "Pee—ter. Pee—ter," they sang out. Peter heard his mother's suppressed exclamation. He saw eyes turned on his in horrified disapproval. His gorge rose. Damn it! They couldn't boss him with their narrow ideas! He turned and walked toward the cavalcade. And then he saw the bright dark eyes of Ivy smiling down on him. He had started in defiance, but he went on eagerly, drawn like a trout on a silken line.

As Peter came up, Red Maulding said heartily, "Pete, you devil, you nearly killed me the other day."

"Well, you asked for it," answered Peter, a little sullenly.

"It's all a matter of luck," said Red. "The one that gets pushed down first takes the beating. No hard feelings, Pete. We came around to say that there's a big house raising over to Ivy's. They could sure use that brawn of yours."

"And there's a dance to-night," said Ivy, leaning over and speaking softly. Her eyes held Peter's with a meaning, languishing glance, as if she were secretly remembering that dance at Tudors and how she came in and out of his arms. "You'll come, won't you?" she whispered, as if her happiness hung on the answer.

"It's sure kind of you, Miss Ivy," said Peter, flushed, delighted, a little embarrassed. "But I'd have no clothes for a dance."

"A lot will dance in the clothes they've been working in," said Gwen, in her clear, supercilious voice. "But your brother, John, sent word that he had clothes of your size at his house, and you and Jerry could come back there and spend the night."

Peter saw Peaches whispering to some Methodist girls who were pointing to him, and, he thought, warning her against him. He looked around. Perhaps it was his fancy, but it seemed to him that he had become a moral leper just by talking to these people. "Damn it!" he thought angrily. "I'll teach them to look like seven days in January when my friends come around!" He smiled at Ivy and felt a delicious radiance envelop him as she smiled back. "All right, Miss Ivy. Just wait till I get my horse. I'm pleased pink to come."

He did not say good-bye to his mother or explain where he had gone. He didn't intend to have a scene or an argument, even such a restrained and silent one as Mary's dignity might impose, not with all those sanctimonious, sour mugs turned on him. He mounted his horse and went without a backward glance.

3

It was Sunday night when, drooping in his saddle, his head aching with the after effects of a gourd of whisky he had downed in his fury, Peter rode through the dark toward the camp ground, and saw it twinkling like an army of great fireflies, and heard the music of a hymn borne softly on the warm air. The five feverish days he had been away seemed like five million ages. He had been one boy when he rode out of the camp ground. He was another now. For the last two days he had roamed a deserted world, from John's to Ivy's, and over to the Tudors', and almost to Glasgow, and back to Russellville. Everywhere he'd seen houses empty, and horses and cattle left to feed on pasture, while their folks went to camp meeting. Even the milch cows had gone to meeting. Folks had driven them along with pack horses laden with provisions, and milked them at the camp ground, morning and evening.

Among the people he'd been with there had been constant jeering at the camp meeting. But under the jeering, Peter could detect worry. "They don't like this coming together and speaking into each others' ears among folks that might want to run them out," he thought. Angry as he had been when he had left the camp ground, he had fought three different men who had opened their mouths against the Methodys, and stood ready to fight anyone else who did so.

A sketch of Peter Cartwright as he must have looked in youth, drawn by Mildred Casgrain from an old daguerreotype.

This seemed to arouse respect rather than resentment among the Rogues, and Ivy had smiled on him for it, a wistful curiosity breaking through her calculated charm. Peter longed to detach Ivy from this crowd and force her to a sincere and exclusive regard for himself. Yet when he had a chance to take her away, he couldn't do it. For on Saturday afternoon Ivy had said, "I've never been to a preaching. Peter, take me to the meeting." Believing this to be one of those traps in which she was always catching him and then leaving him to be laughed at by her other gallants, Peter answered warily. But she seemed quite in earnest. For a moment he was tempted. But when he imagined himself walking into meeting with this girl, and saw his mother's eyes, and Barbara's and Brenda's, turned on her, he knew that he couldn't do it. If he could only trust her to behave! But she'd be ogling, and letting her short puffed muslin sleeve slip from her bare shoulder, and she'd swing her hips under her light muslin gown going down the aisle. All these performances charmed Peter and dominated his senses when she was near, and his thoughts, when she was away. Seeing her as his mother and her friends and all men would see her, he knew he couldn't take her. He wouldn't have her called a trollop. There was a protective tenderness, a latent chivalry, in his perception that this was just what she was, and he liked it!

Ivy had such faith in her power to charm Peter into anything that she was quite taken aback by his refusal. The more stubbornly he held off, the more she really wanted to go. Finally she broke down and cried in honest chagrin, and went off into fainting fits and sobbing. Peter put a pillow under her head. He fanned her. He wrung out a fine linen handerchief in eau de cologne and put it over her eyes. But still he wouldn't take her to camp meeting. Finally, in response to her helpless, childish turning to him, he took her in his arms and laid his cheek fumblingly against hers. Whereupon she slapped him and screamed, and flounced up, and ran into the Tudor's back room which served as the girls' bedroom. Peter was left to suffer for an hour. Ultimately, Gwen came out and said coldly and gravely that Ivy had a terrible sick headache.

But he couldn't stay to suffer because he was due on the race course. The day before he had beaten Red Maulding's Black Prince, and had been tempted by John's quiet boast to put his winnings against John's horse. He had a hard time keeping Jerry sober enough to ride Aladdin because Penny had been talking to Jerry about Polly, and had brought him to such a state of "sensibility" that he had wept, and had been comforted by a glass of brandy, which was the end of him. But Jerry rode Aladdin, and Aladdin was thoroughly beaten. Saturday night Peter went to bed in the cabin John had turned over to him and Jerry, with Jerry sobbing drunkenly, and himself shorn of money and pride. Next morning he spent the sweltering Sabbath hours playing cards at Dromgole's and winning enough to put on his horse tomorrow.

In the afternoon he went over to John's and found Ivy and Gwen there, Ivy rosy, pretty, and gay in a pink gown, with a rose in her dark hair, being squired by a new gallant. His name was Rodriguez. Peter looked at him sourly, "Spanish—they call him. Most likely half Cherokee, half nigger." There was no derogation in this, only analysis of fact, for in Peter's eyes both Cherokees and Negroes were socially as good as Spaniards, and morally they were better. "But," Peter thought, observing his manners and speech, "he's been eddicated somewhere. Most likely in one of the convents the Circuit Rider tells of." He had been impressed by Burke's description of convents that had little doors open day and night, inside which you could put a baby nobody wanted, and the folks inside would take care of it and bring it up.

When Rodriguez had first come in, dressed in a fine suit of clothes from New Orleans, Peter had eyed, with friendly curiosity, his long brown bony face, his slim hips like a panther's, and the black brows which met like smudges of smoke above his smouldering black eyes. But when he saw Ivy leaning on his arm, impersonal friendliness vanished in blind enmity. But he played one game of cards with Rodriguez and won his watch from him, while Ivy stood over them, enveloping him in the fragrance of eau de cologne, of which this new gallant had brought her a bottle. All of which seemed a calculated prelude to the moment when he found Ivy in Rodriguez's arms, and his lips glued to hers.

Thereupon Peter went out, drank a gourd of whisky from a tub of it on the porch, mounted his horse, and rode off in the direction of the camp meeting. The sun beat on his head, throbbing with pain, as he spurred Aladdin on. He was about fifteen miles from home when he started, and it was already dark when he overtopped a low hill and saw the camp ground.

There must have been 1500 people there, an inconceivably large number for a frontier boy to see in one place. The church enclosure was a pattern of white candlelight. Over it hung smoke like a light mist, and through the smoke, out of a deep ultramarine sky, shone a red quarter moon, sharp, rosy, and so near the camp ground that it looked as if one could touch it with a long pole. From the church enclosure rose moans, groans, and shouts of "Hallelujah," too far away to be distinguishable, but mingled in a sounding agitation against which the singing of a great chorus rose thrilling and strange.

As Peter dashed down the slope and spurred Aladdin to a gallop, he felt as he often felt when he had been away and the cabin came into sight. He was coming home! Then he heard a man's voice shouting the old ditty about a maid who went in a maid, from a leafy booth alongside the road, open in front and lighted by candles. There were several men in there and two girls, one of them Betsy Roberts, who was apparently doing the soliciting, for she ran out and with an impudent glance said, "Evenin, Pete. Come in and have a drink."

Peter was so angry to see Betsy plying her trade so near the camp ground that he could have struck her. But he only said, "No, thank you. You've got more'n enough company," and rode on. But not before he saw that one of the men inside was Rodriguez, who must have come by a short cut through the woods.

A little further on, he came to another lighted booth where Ol Patchcoat, the bar tender at Dromgole's, was ladling out whisky from a tub set up on a rack of fresh cut wood, with bark and leaves still on it. "Come and have a drink, Pete," said Patchcoat.

"Don't care if I do," said Peter, jumping off his horse. Approaching the tub, he gave a sudden jerk to its underpinnings, spilling all the whisky. Peter leaped on his horse and sped away. Spilling the whisky made him feel better. He drew up sharp. A man was lying across the road. Peter dismounted and looked at him. He was one of the Baptist brothers dead drunk. Peter dragged him out of the road and left him in the bushes. Finally he was called to a halt, and there was Hans standing as one of an armed guard at the entrance to the sanctuary. "A nice lot you've got out there!" growled Peter. "Why don't you run them out?"

"Because it takes every Christian fist and gun to keep a guard around the congregation here," said Hans. "If any sinner, however low, wants to come in singly, we let him in, for there's room at God's feet for all. But we don't let them gang up and come more than one or two together."

Otto came up. "Where's Jerry?"

Peter lied. "Oh he's coming along." He couldn't say that Jerry was dead drunk. Evading further question, Peter moved up the aisle, looking for a place to squeeze himself in. William McGee was sitting on the floor of the platform, swinging his legs over the edge, talking intimately and informally at the mass of heaving bodies piled on top of one another below him. Barbara sat on the ground, a young girl sobbing on her breast. Mary was kneeling by one who had been an associate of Susan and Betsy Roberts in their sinful enterprises. Men of all ages were like children in violent tantrums while Methodist, Baptist, and Presbyterian brothers talked to them steadily and firmly. Each sinner had one saved brother or sister in attendance. As Peter approached, a woman screamed, "O Lord, my Lord, I've got the blessing. Glory! Glory!" She continued to cry out for some time, her voice sharp, unreal, and yet convincing in its strange ecstacy. Throughout the congregation there was weeping, like the steady falling of rain.

As Peter squeezed himself into a warm, dark place, amidst palpitant but unknown human bodies, the misery of the last days, and a delayed reaction to whisky, overwhelmed him. Somewhere out of the depths his tears gushed. He felt as if wall after wall were collapsing, and his innermost self were lying wide open, exposed, and there was a wild and reckless joy in the release and a kind of shamelessness. The tears came as if they would never stop. It was as if the emotions of hundreds of lives had been dammed up in him, and now they were flowing away, like matter from a boil that has burst. He wept for Ivy because she was so beautiful and so false. He wept for Jerry because life had been so mean to him. The feverish attraction to these card playing, horse racing Rogues, and his underlying scorn for them, flowed out of him. He didn't feel sinful, but he was heart breakingly sorry for himself and sorry for everything in the world, and he burrowed down among the weeping unknowns in the semi-darkness, and wept with constant wordless imprecations to God looking down out of the night sky, as a child in tantrums might call on its mother, not knowing what it wants.

He was just getting over it when his mother found him. As he stood up, a gleam from the candles massed by the altar fell on his tear-stained face, and he saw that hers was warm and moist and quivering with emotion. Then, with a stab of pity, he saw that she thought he had been convicted of sin, and her eyes, already full and bright with feeling, lit up as with a burst of sunrise inside her. She laid her small, tight, rough hand on his arm. "Peter, Honey, come to the mourner's bench. Mr. McGee will pray with you."

He was so sorry for her that, if he could have made himself go, he would have done it. But, though he felt relieved and rested, he had not rolled off a burden nor attained to a blessing, and he knew it. Whatever it was the saved had found, he was farther from it than ever, because he had had his chance and had muffed it. He put his big hand over hers, and unclasped her clinging fingers. "Not now, Mammy," he said gently. "Let me go and be by myself." He went out and mounted his horse, and went home to bed, and did not return to the camp meeting.

In the days that followed he was like the room from which the devil had been cast out. His life was swept of evil and garnished with good behavior that filled his mother with hope. But it was bleak and lonely. Ivy and the Rogues had been given up, but there was nothing in their place. He listened politely while his mother read the Bible to him, and pleased her by spelling out sentences to her. He liked the Bible. The strange, but magic, words sent his mind on far journeys. He did not resist his mother or feel embarrassed when, catching him alone, in the cabin, the barn, or the garden, she begged him to kneel with her and pray. He liked the jumble of Bible verses, shot through with the lyric poetry of her own thinking, which was Mary's prayer. His mother interested him as she interested many intelligent men—McGready, Allen, even at times her own husband. There was something uncanny in the way her sudden sharp observations hit the mark. However you lied or pretended, she could unmask you with a wave of her hand. And her rare moments of softness were very moving. The only thing that made the dull days following the camp meeting tolerable was the beginning of mature companionship with his mother, a companionship which had nothing to do with the fact that they were mother and son, but rested in certain mental attributes they shared with each other and with almost no one else they met in their daily round.

Meanwhile Peter also had his hands full looking after Jerry, who had come home with a temperature of 102, and suffered for days from fever, headache, backache, and sore throat. Peter repentantly stayed with him, acting as nurse under Doctor Allen's direction. This brought him in daily touch with the Doctor again, and with the gentle rather frightened flower of southern womanhood who had finally come out from Georgia to join her husband in his exile. He liked to renew old memories and spruce up his manners in an occasional call on the Doctor, but he felt no more at ease with the new mistress of the Doctor's home than she felt with him. He was mildly pleased that Brenda and Mary both beamed approval on him now. He was indeed being good, but he was thoroughly bored by it!

4

From July to November there were ten great camp meetings in the Green river and Cumberland region, beginning Friday night and ending Monday. Some people attended all of them, journeying as much as one hundred miles. In the middle of the week, during the long summer days, they rose early and worked late, so that on Friday they might be off with their babies, their beds, their food, and their milch cows. The roads were alive with people, singing the newly learned hymns as they trudged on foot or rode horseback, or bumped along in a cart; for, with religion, they were finding new ways of life which, to the sensitive and ambitious among these eager, untaught people, were very exciting—new friends, new contraptions for living, new recipes, new arts, new techniques of co-operation.

Sometimes it seemed to James McGready that he could not cope with what he himself had started. He was trying to find wisdom and courage to handle it one August morning in 1800, as he hoed his bean and squash patch. He wanted to see that there were no weeds left to suck up the scant moisture still in the powdery yellow soil before the sun rose to the broiling point. And he needed the exercise to clear his head and stabilize his judgment after a camp meeting which had reached at dawn the proportions of an orgy. Two people had been stricken with foaming fits. One was still paralyzed. One was in a trance, and several had the jerks. But a score had been transformed into new beings. An hour after he had been saved, Old Patchcoat had walked back from the pond where he had taken the first bath he had ever had. He had shed ten years from his wrinkled, dirty, bearded face, and, instead of looking sidewise down his nose, he had smiled frankly and pleasantly. He was a man now, a very personable man, instead of a dirty tramp.

Worn out with this religious drama, McGready had sent for Doctor Allen to take care of the dire physical results and had turned the meeting over to Jesse Walker, and had come home to rest. He was only slightly re-assured by the Doctor's assurance that abnormal behavior at camp meeting was only the crisis of emotional disease which had been developing for a long time. When the crisis passed, the disease would be cured. "The Doctor means," John Page had explained, "that there's something in them that has to bust out somehow. What we do is like picking up a loaded gun and shooting it off in the air, before another picks it up and kills somebody." McGready envied these Methodists their imperturbability. "Brother," Page had said, "we've been at this for forty years. We're tough as jerked venison."

Hoeing up a row, McGready mentally argued with the Methodists, and when he got to the end of the row, he bowed his head and prayed for guidance. He was standing so, his graceful, limber figure drooping a little, his dark head bowed, when Finis Ewing clattered up and dismounted with a leap that cleared the rail fence, and came running toward him. McGready's flat, homely, vivid face lighted up, for this convert was his greatest triumph. Though good Presbyterians, in practice and church attendance, the Ewings had so far resisted all appeals to their deeper natures. Disturbed as he had always been by the idea of such useful citizens being among the damned, McGready had been deeply happy to see Finis and his young wife kneeling last night at the altar.

Now Ewing said eagerly, with no preliminary greeting, "Parson, I come to offer myself for the Presbyterian ministry. I thought,"—Here he hesitated slightly, his level gray eyes bright with feeling—"I thought you might use an exhorter."

An exhorter, among Methodists and Baptists, was a converted layman, licensed to preach "so long as his preaching and practice are conformable to the gospel." Thomas Wilkerson was looking for exhorters to be trained for the Methodist ministry. Things like that were so simple for the Methodists! If he refused this lad, the Methodists would take him over. He looked at the bright face before him. God had sent him Finis Ewing as a disciple to carry on. He would not lose him to Francis Asbury!

To gain time, he said, "Walk over with me to the spring. I want a drink, and it's cool there." At the spring they sat down on a fallen tree trunk, spongy with moss and decay and fringed with ferns. McGready said, "We have no exhorters. Our church feels that its strength lies in its learned clergy who, alone among Christians, have transmitted the learning of the past and developed schools over large areas of the American wilds."

While Ewing answered this, pleading, promising, arguing, he mentally reviewed the educational resources at his command. Elementary schools there were none in all these hundreds of square miles. There were only classes to teach new converts to read the Bible, which formed and dissolved around the literate, and were kept alive, more or less, in connection with the Methodist class meetings and the pre-Sabbath meetings of the Baptists. Beyond the primary grade there were only two institutions of learning. One was the school of languages he himself had conducted off and on in Russellville for two years to teach scions of the Alstons the rudiments of Latin. The other was the new college at Nashville where seven boys were enrolled under Mr. Fish from New England. The only place west of the Alleghenies where a man might learn something—McGready didn't know how much—was Transylvania University at Lexington which boasted the only library in the West. It was also said that the Yankees at Marietta were upholding the dignity of learning, but he didn't know what they could offer. At none of these places could Ewing get adequate preparation for the theological school at Princeton. And suppose he sent Ewing east? Would he not return out of touch with the people here, and incapable of appealing to them with his learning, as vividly as he could do now without it?

Thinking of all this, McGready appeared to yield to Ewing's arguments, and, sitting with him on the log, alternately sipping cold water from the spring and swatting mosquitoes, he gave the youth a comprehensive entrance examination for a non-existent college of Presbyterian exhorters.

But when he had finished, he was in despair. These Ewings were the most able family here. Robert was already aiming to be elected United States Senator, and would no doubt succeed. Of natural ability this boy had plenty. Of inherited learning he was naked as the day he was born. He could barely read and write. The only historical events he had even heard of were the Protestant Reformation, the American Revolution, and the rise of Napoleon;

and only of Napoleon did he know more than the name, for the proximity of New Orleans kept news of the little Corsican afloat on the rivers. The only book he even knew about was the Bible. But he could talk! The social status and ambition of his family was shown by their grammatical, well modulated speech and their intelligence, by its readiness and eloquence. And the structure and technique of political democracy, and the postulates of the Common Law and the Bill of Rights, were to him absolutely inherent in the scheme of things. That any society could subsist without them was to him unthinkable.

But McGready reflected wrily that whatever he himself had learned in his youth in addition to or contradiction of what Finis Ewing knew seemed of less and less importance with each passing month of his ministry in Logan County. So he told Finis that he would map out a course of training for him, and would give him some duties in connection with the camp meeting. But he did not tell him that he would have to consult John Page about the details. It irked him to have to run to the Methodists with his problems, but in the absence of help from his own church he had to do it.

John Page laughed heartily at McGready's perplexities. "You do have a hard time keeping the last rags and tags of your Presbyterianism from being torn clean off you by the briars out here." As for exhorters, "Call em what you will. Train em and use em, and trust to fighting out the question of pushing them up into the ranks of ordained ministers later on. It may be that God has foreordained and predestined that the Presbyterian Synod should in time see wisdom," he said. "But I doubt it." As for education, what he advised was "Saddlebag College." The main trouble out here was getting books. "Give a man books, and to the extent of his capacity he will educate himself."

John Wesley had been the father of cheap mass publishing. His well-selected list of 478 titles was being put in circulation as fast as limited resources would allow, by the Methodist Book Concern, established in New York City in 1789. Of these, a few books were coming into the West, and were circulated from circuit rider to circuit rider. The Methodists were training their own preachers up from the ranks of "exhorters" by well selected courses of reading, covering biography, general literature, natural science, and devotional Christian writings. It was the business of the Presiding Elder to oversee this reading among the men under his charge, and to examine them from time to time on the contents of the books.

"But above all," said Page, "we teach them what is the true and Christian use of language, out of the words of John Wesley, which sooner or later we get them to know by heart. It's what Wesley says about church hymns, but it applies just as well to preaching. Out of the ample blouse of his linen hunting shirt, he took a small solid book, bound in leather, and read from the Preface to the *Hymns for the People called Methodists*, by John Wesley, 1779. 'In these hymns there is no doggerel, no botches, nothing put in to patch up the rhyme, no feeble expletives. Here is nothing turgid or bombast on the one hand or low and creeping on the other. Here are no cant expressions—no words without sense. We talk common sense whether they understand it or not, and use no word but in a fixed and determinate sense. Here are (allow me to say) the purity, the strength, and the elegance of the English language, and at the same time the utmost simplicity and plainness suited to every capacity.'"

McGready took the book from John Page's hands. He had admired the simple beauty of the Methodist hymns, but he had not read the preface. Now he re-read the words Page had read to him, and said, as he handed the book back, "I quite agree that that is the whole truth about literary style, so far as effective sermons are concerned."

The upshot was that Page promised to share their few books, whenever they could, though "Of course," he said, "we can't offer you any exposition of the devil's doctrine of Calvin. For that you Presbyterians will have to dig into your own dark past." The kind glance of his sunny blue eyes quite belied these teasing words, and McGready gratefully answered the smile rather than the taunt. The conference ended with the two men kneeling and praying for guidance in directing Finis Ewing and all others whom separately or jointly they might bring to God.

CHAPTER 30

The camp meetings, and the enterprises which grew out of them, were so interesting that Peter would gladly have shared in them, that summer of 1800, if only he had not had to cross the mysterious barrier which separated the saved from the unsaved. There was something about those who were saved which stirred him to wonder and envy. Eddie and Sis were both converted that summer. Eddie had always been so good that Peter wondered what sins he could have been convicted of in that awful moment which must precede salvation when one knows one's self to be utterly vile. But some miracle was wrought in Eddie—something more even than the brief bright glow on his colorless personality when he knew himself beloved by Bonny. Self-effacing but unselfish and reliable as he had always been, he now came forward to take responsibility in connection with the growing business of the church, and to speak up in meeting with a plain earnestness that was almost eloquent. "It's made him alive all over," thought Peter.

When Wilkerson, stopping for a cold drink and wheat bread sandwich, explained that "converted" meant changed or turned around, Peter looked at Sis and thought, "That's what she is—changed." Sis was just at the age when a girl blossoms, and the moment in which, without sobbing or crying aloud, but with a still, inward sense of self-giving, she had dedicated herself to God, was like the bursting of bud into flower. Her features were still formless. She still had freckles. But her blue eyes were so full and frank and warm, and she looked so much as if she were hugging a delicious secret to herself, that she was quite lovely. And in the social stir and mutual criticism among the Methodist girls, under the leadership of Barbara, she quickly acquired a style which pe-culiarly suited her.

For, having preached for forty years against the eighteenth century powdered hair and lace ruffles which set off those who lived on other peoples' work, from those who carried their own weight, the Methodists seized on the simple new styles from France but made them decent and modest. Instead of the thin muslin dress, they wore plain straight gowns of linsy or cotton, belted in snugly at the waist, with a folded kerchief covering the neck, and sleeves to the elbow. The costume Ivy made so provocative was, with a few changes, thus made demurely sweet. Inasmuch as some of the girl converts had never worn much but a dirty, flapping sack, and had gone barefoot, with tangled, dirty locks, the Christian maids in their fresh, simple dresses, modestly form-fitting, and their demure faces and bright earnest eyes hiding under little home-made scoop bonnets of braided straw, were quite fetching. Many a young man went to camp meeting just to look at them. Among these was Peter.

But even more startling to Peter than the change in Eddie and Sis, was the change in his mother, who had been the gospel made flesh to him all his life. Despite a look in her eyes, and a deep sad cadence in her voice which seemed to say that, at all times, she was praying for Polly, Mary had somehow come into her own. Peter could not know that Eddie's conversion was a release from a fear which had remained alive, all these years, under the threshold of consciousness—the fear that, in marrying Jus while John might be lying unburied, she had laid a curse on John's children, a fear which the behavior of John and Polly had confirmed. But here at last was Eddie, John and Polly's own brother, saved for God. Not knowing this, Peter did perceive that Eddie was making up for what she had suffered from John, and Sis, helpful and quietly gay about the house, was partly filling the place left vacant by Polly.

But, apart from this subconscious relief, Mary bloomed into happy activity in connection with the women's chores for the camp meetings involving provision for the sale or gift of food to those whose food might run out, for cleanliness, for the care of those taken sick, for the sisterly after-guidance of those brought to Christ. In a world in which women had hitherto been housebound drudges or self-flaunting trollops, the emergence of a new kind of womanliness in the camp meeting had considerable interest for men, especially the young men. There was a frank and affectionate relation between "sister" and "brother," which, outside the church, would have caused gossip. Though the gossip was not lacking, the new spirit rapidly prevailed and was one of the greatest lures of the church. When Barbara called for Mary in a new light wagon drawn by two smart carriage horses, and Mary came running out in one of the new dresses, snugly belted to her slim, smart figure, with a scoop bonnet framing her dark hair, and they drove off together on some Christian mission, laughing and chattering, Peter was proud of his mother. "It's like her whole self has been dusted off," he reflected.

But the most dramatic moment in the summer's revivals came when, among the drunks, the gamblers, and other low down sinners, howling and moaning at the mourners' bench, there appeared a figure whose sturdy outlines electrified every one who saw it. It was James Haw, kneeling on the ground, his head in his hands, sobbing brokenly, "God be merciful to me, a sinner." That proud and stubborn ex-circuit rider, who had defied Asbury and his Methodist brethren for six years, who had preached and administered the sacraments strictly according to his own ideas—James Haw was brought to his knees at last.

But even so he was unwilling to ask the Methodists to forgive him and take him back. He wished to ally himself with McGready and his young associate, Barton Stone, to build up societies which should be to the Presbyterians what the first Methodist societies had been to the Episcopalians. But John Page said that no man could come to God sincerely if, like Ananias, he held back part of the price. "If Haw is in earnest," said Page, "let him stand up on the Sabbath Day and publicly state that what he has said about Asbury is a lie."

And this Haw did, on Sunday morning, in McGready's outdoor church, before hundreds who gathered from all over western Tennessee and Kentucky to hear him. On the platform behind him McGready and Stone and several visiting Presbyterian preachers sat on one side, and John Page and several circuit riders on the other. John McGee sat with the Presbyterians, William McGee with the Methodists. People crowded close on the plank benches; they stood in the aisles; they filled all the woods roundabout. Peter was moved, as he had never been before, by a sense of what real manliness is when Haw stood up and described how he had been led from what was, at the outset, a legitimate difference on the details of church government, into unwarranted assertions, and un-Christian refusals to co-operate with others who were sincerely trying to do the Lord's work. He had been, he said, such a stumbling block in the Cumberland for years that only the perseverence and fortitude of his Methodist brethren, whom he had so grievously wronged, had been able to overcome it, and bring them all to this glorious revival. He humbly begged them to forgive him, and pray with him that God might forgive him, too.

Then the Methodists and Presbyterians took the Lord's supper together and the Methodist and Presbyterian choirs answered each other in a hymn of benediction. Peter had often been moved by religious services, but never so deeply and grandly moved as by this. There was no lingering suspicion this time that the experience of conviction of sin was all too soft and slobbering. The whole magnificent performance called to his spirit like banners flung to the sky.

2

Alas—with all this change in others, there was no change in Peter. He earnestly wanted to be part of the greatest social excitement Logan County had ever seen. But he remained inwardly detached. Sometimes he wondered if the Presbyterians were right—that some people were damned and there was nothing to do about it. He talked it over with Jerry, who confessed his own inability to recover the high conviction that had sustained him after his baptism. The two boys looked at each other, with dawning horror in the black eyes and the gray. Were they both damned, and no end to anything for them except Hell? Without Peter, Jerry would have taken refuge from this thought in drink. But Peter shook him out of his depression roughly, and made him get out and ride Aladdin instead. Damned or not, Peter had no notion of losing possession of himself. He intended to know what was happening to him every minute, and to deal with the Devil on his own terms. "I can't get the blessing," he said to Jerry, "and I have a hankerin for what I know ain't good for me or anybody else. And there don't seem to be any flavor in religion for me. But still, I believe in God because there ain't any sense to anything without Him. And I can't believe in God and believe in predestination, because if God was as mean as that to His critturs, He wouldn't be God, He'd be the Devil."

Jus, thinking that Peter had had enough of camp meetings, asked him to go with him to a big rally for Thomas Jefferson over Hopkinsville way, which was to be followed by horse racing. He thought Peter might bring Jerry along and try out Aladdin against some of the horses the new settlers were bringing in. So, by way of the Jefferson rallies, Peter was soon drawn back into horse racing, card playing, wrestling and shooting matches, harvest feasts, and country dances, and so into the company of the young Mauldings, Dromgoles, Tudors, John and Penny, Ivy and Gwen. Though they professed to be Federalists because Federalists stood for the "aristocratical principle," the Rogues couldn't bear to be absent from the cock fights, horse races, and barbecues that followed the Jefferson rallies.

Though Peter ignored Ivy, she maneuvered to be thrown with him. In the all-inclusive embraces of the country dances, she could not avoid coming into his arms, and those moments she made the most of. She even made up to Jus, and for a time quite charmed him. In the end she had Peter securely hooked. But she never let him believe himself her only gallant, and kept him alternating between hope and despair, tenderness and anger, proud expectation and nagging worry.

Egged on by his father, Peter held his own socially, and flourished by his strange luck in gambling. Through careful management he won with Aladdin a little more than he lost. His "system" at roulette kept him slightly ahead, and he was never tempted by a run of bad luck to plunge. And whenever he was cleaned out at horse racing or roulette, he could make it up at the card table. What he made he spent on clothes, which he left at John's, and on treats for the crowd. His canniness made his father encourage him. He told himself that, so long as Peter was not one to be hurt by it, this was the way to become a leader of men.

However, though Jus was somewhat be-glamored by the society in which Peter shone, he soon had it sized up. He didn't like a rumor that Ivy was already married, and was just "playing around," "collecting scalps." But he thought, "The boy's got a level head, and he's got to get his experience somehow. If the girl's married and the kind she looks to be, that makes it simpler—in a way." Still he warned Peter. "They're a fly-by-night lot. I wouldn't get too thick with them." He was a little troubled by Dominie's statement that the Band was out to involve boys like Peter, so they'd have to sign up and become one of them or run the risk that some evidence of crime would be fastened on them. He told Peter that some of these young blades who called themselves Rogues might be worse than they looked. "Understand," he said. "There's no certain evidence against particular ones, and, if you shoot your mouth off against one of them and can't bring in the evidence, he can bring action against you for slander. But even so—" As he went on, Peter listened quietly. Everything his father said he knew already, and a great deal more.

Jus drew a line between sins which, in a frontiersman's code were venal and those which weren't. "Whisky and cards a man ought to be able to take or not, as he thinks best, and women when they know what they're at and can hold their own. But disgracing an innocent girl, or misleading a good girl, through pure love—"

Peter flushed. "You don't need to tell me that, Pappy."

Jus answered by moving to the higher levels of Jeffersonianism. "I believe it, Son. But what I want to say is that, while I ain't religious, I'm honest, and honest is what I expect you to be. Honesty, public and private, is what security among human beings is built on. And I mean *real* honest—giving the other man his just dues, and not wanting more than you can fairly earn, and paying your own way, fair and square, and respecting a man's, woman's or child's right to life, liberty, and the pursuit of happiness, the same as you want them to respect yours. But—" (and here he smiled knowingly) "when it comes to telling a white lie so Mammy won't worry, and to letting a Dromgole or a Maulding wander up a wrong track on a false scent—"

Peter laughed. He profoundly appreciated his father!

Still Peter did not like the way Jerry was getting involved with John and Penny who offered him a compensation for his small size even more potent than jockeying. For they flattered him into the belief that he was destined to win his way by brains against brawn. Since he had an acute intelligence, and knew it, this was balm to his soul. In September, he went with John to New Orleans on a flat boat, and rode back up the Chickasaw Road. Jerry returned, eager, alight, full of descriptions of the little French city; the unfinished cathedral; the few houses of the gentry with their dainty appointments and manners both sensible and elegant; the Negro women bearing great baskets of oranges on their heads; the waterfront; the dives and the bars where the "Kaintucks" congregated; and the square outlines of their houses on rafts reaching out into the muddy floods of the Mississippi.

But Peter was horrified when Jerry described a meeting with three men. "Jerry, didn't you know who they were? You ought to know Sam Mason and Alston and Little Harpe anywhere!" When Jerry argued that these men weren't so bad themselves—they'd been tarred by those they'd been with, Peter said sternly, "You'd better keep clear of them before you're tarred."

Jerry listened imperturbably. "I saw Polly."

"Polly!"

"I ain't free to tell where. But she was beautiful, and she had a beautiful dress on." Then he added, "She ain't married to him. If she wanted to leave him, there's no law that could stop her."

Beyond this he would say nothing. Peter hesitated to tell his mother. But he spoke to his father, who said thoughtfully, "Keep it under your hat, Son, till I can make inquiries. I gather they're down in Mississippi Territory, and trackin anybody there is like looking for one special tadpole in a whole bog of them."

3

Mary was so busy with the committee meetings, friendly consultations, and private visitations growing out of the camp meetings that she was unaware of Peter's social activities. He often came to revival meetings, as did most of the young Rogues, because these meetings were the most exciting public entertainment they had. Betting on who would be struck down was the latest form of gambling. Peter placed many a bet for or against the preacher's power to bring in some stubborn soul and made money out of these psychic appraisals.

When Peter didn't come to meeting, Mary understood that he was with his father at a Jefferson rally, and was satisfied, for she approved of Mr. Jefferson as one who was out to give a come-uppance to the Federalists, the gentry, and the Rogues, and all the other "high-toned trash that wants somebody else to feed them and dress them fine and fancy, and then to take a kick in the teeth for it."

She looked fondly at Peter riding away with Jus, a chip off the old block, with his broad shoulders, thick neck, and curly black hair. And she was glad when Jerry went with them, for she was proud that Brenda felt safe about Jerry if Peter was with him. It was only slowly that she began to hear hints of Peter's goings on, first from McGready, then from Wilkerson, and finally from Barbara. Then Brenda burst in on her one day and wept and upbraided her for letting Jerry get mixed up with John and Penny.

That night Peter and Jus rode home late, in the mellow light of the harvest moon. As Peter entered, the cabin was dark save for the red remnants of the supper fire falling apart on the hearth, and the darkness was pierced by a single ray of moonlight from one open window. And in that shaft he saw his mother's face—cold, sharp, set, as if every line were carved in marble. Only her blue eyes seemed alight, with a fierce fanatic flame.

"Peter, where've you been?"

"Oh—er—um—there was a political meeting."

"You lie. You've been dancing in McFadden's barn, and cuddlin that trollop, Ivy, up in the hay in the loft."

Peter was thunderstruck. This was where he had been.

She came close to him. He started back—she seemed so eerie and so fierce. She sniffed. "Humph! Not much likker on you! Thank God for that."

By this time Jus appeared in the doorway and she swung on him. What did he have to say for himself, telling her he was taking Peter to a Jefferson meeting, and going to Dromgole's and Tudor's and such places instead? Jus replied that Peter must get his training as a man among men. Mary sniffed, "Man among men! Man among fornicators and card sharpers and thieves and murderers!"

Jus replied mildly that he didn't hold with everything men did or recommend it to Peter. But a man couldn't get anywhere in life by being too good. He had to go along with other men a little ways.

"A little ways on the road to Hell," said Mary. "And then one day his foot slips and he starts sliding down. Who's going to stop him then? Not you, Justurian Cartwright. Not you!"

Her voice broke on a sob. She put her hands over her face, and threw herself down on the bed in the shadows, weeping and praying. Peter wanted to put his arms around her and comfort her and tell her not to be afraid for him. But when he made a slight move toward her, his father said, in a harsh, thundering tone like that of an old buffalo, "Go to bed!" Jus had seated himself on a stump in the red glow of the fire, and in that faint glow his face looked stubborn and ugly. Peter climbed silently into the loft.

4

Mary and Jus were at war. The chill was thick between them at breakfast. Riding home late, Jus would come in bright and cheerful, as if he expected a welcome. There was no welcome. For the first time in Peter's life he saw his father's easy way of carrying all before him stopped dead by his mother's stony silence. Coming down early one morning, Peter saw that, instead of sleeping up against her husband, Mary had rolled over to the farthest edge of the big bed. Next night she went to bed in the circuit riders' room. And there she slept all winter. She had arranged that Barbara should entertain the circuit rider on his rounds.

Jus was daunted. He drooped. He looked suddenly old. He was often harsh and irritable. And he drank too heavily and too often.

But neither would yield. Both explained their stand to Peter again and again. "Peter, no matter what your father says, I want you to understand this," said Mary. "Right is Right, and Wrong is Wrong, and Right Wrong is nobody." Jus gave Peter a lecture on human freedom. Freedom is not only being free in your body to go and come. It is being free in your soul. Nobody has a right to assert a rule over another's soul. "Your mother thinks there's only one soul and conscience in this house and that's hers. And you and I are just to be copies of hers." And he added, half in appeal, half in apology, "Now I don't want to assert lordship over your soul and your will, Son. I just want to give you a chance to find tricks for the mastery of men that it is in you to make good use of."

Sometimes, when Peter was alone with his mother and she looked at him heart-breakingly, he was ready to throw Ivy, his cards, and Aladdin all to the winds. Then, if Mary asked to pray with him, he dropped to his knees and earnestly begged God to help him. More than once he left a card game to steal in among the crowds weeping and groaning at a revival service. Tormented and torn in two as he was, he felt a strange relief in losing himself in the flood of that collective emotion, and sobbing and crying out with them. But it was all unreal. He knew bleakly that it was no different from letting off steam by cussing and whooping.

Yet he could not resist his father when he asked him to come to court or to a political meeting or assumed, with such proud expectation, that he'd be putting Aladdin up in the race. Even though he vowed to change his ways at some future date, there seemed always to be a good reason for going back just once for a card game at Dromgole's, or to a dance at Richardson's or to John's house or Ivy's. Sometimes it was because he had a score to pay.

He said to himself that he'd pay it and then be done. Sometimes it was only to let Ivy know that he could get along without her. Then she'd come to him, sweet as maple taffy, and before he knew it he had promised to take her to a dance. And then he had to go to the dance because he had promised.

Meanwhile he had passed his fifteenth birthday, and election day had come and gone, and, after a long struggle in the House of Representatives, Mr. Jefferson had become President. On election day, Peter fought four bloody bouts with detractors of Jefferson, and won $35.00 in election bets. He was one of the organizers of the torchlight parade for Jefferson that snaked its way all around Russellville and was barely stopped from setting a prairie fire that would have run for miles. He had some good wholesome moments in early winter, laying in the winter's stock of venison and making all snug around the house and barn. Then came Christmas and he was away from home a week, for the Tudors put on an imitation of an old English baronial Christmas—or what they said was such—and roasted a whole ox out of doors in the snow, and there was dancing, gambling, wrestling, and drinking deep for a week.

5

Then the preparations for Gwen's wedding to her earless one began. She was to be married in March, which was, of all months, the worst for a frontier wedding—chill, slushy, muddy, wretched traveling by horseback. All the traditional outdoor ceremonies of a frontier wedding would be very difficult in March. But March it was to be. Mary said she had heard from Barbara that there was good reason why. Gwen had been "too free," and she wanted to get married before the results showed.

On the wedding day there was a thick, cold fog hanging low over the poisonous stew of melting snow and yellow mud. Peter dressed at John's. He dared not let his mother know that he had a fine new suit from New Orleans lest she ask him how he paid for it. By the time he had ridden to the bride's house, he was caked from head to foot with mud, and as the others emerged like ghosts out of the fog, their eyes peered weirdly out of faces masked with mud. But the red glow of the fires bloomed cheerfully through the new glass windows of the big new double cabin. In front of it, in the slush, Red Maulding was lining up the young men for the "race for the bottle" which was a feature of every Scotch Irish frontier wedding. He yelled at Peter to take his place. There was a pistol shot, and they were off—over rocks and stumps, through mud to the horses' knees, through the river, through the brush, straight as the crow flies, toward the home of the Reverend Mr. Balch. There, at that moment, Gwen was being married, as the custom was, with only the family in attendance. Mr. Balch, the inveterate opponent of revivalism, was the only local clergyman the Rogues thought "hightoned" enough to perform the marriage ceremony for their daughters.

The fog was so thick that the young men could see no landmarks, and more than once Peter thought they were lost. He was easing Aladdin along, trying to conserve his strength without falling too far behind the others, and listening keenly for the voices and hoof beats of the returning wedding party in the mist. Suddenly he heard Ivy's voice. The others, galloping ahead of him, seemed not to have heard it, for no one quickened his pace. Peter put spurs to Aladdin and in a few flying leaps passed the others and almost crashed into Gwen's father, riding ahead of the returning bride and bridegroom, as was the custom, and holding aloft a bottle of brandy tied with white satin ribbons. Peter grasped the bottle, leaped from his horse, and, with his most graceful bow, presented it to the bride. This was the coveted honor for which they had been recklessly racing. The young man who seized the bottle first and presented it to the bride was the cavalier of the day.

Radiant with his triumph, Peter held the bottle to the bride's lips, and she, in turn, held it to his. Peter had never liked Gwen, but he felt an unexpected sweetness and tenderness in her nearness, as she leaned down to him from her horse and her white fur mantle fell over him. He saw Ivy flash a jealous look at her sister, and he smiled to himself with something of his father's humorous way of biding his time. Darting a sidelong glance at Ivy from under his curling dark eyelashes, he mounted his horse and rode over to pay his respects to the bride's mother.

By the time they reached the bride's house, Ivy, as Peter expected, had come alongside him and was bringing the full battery of lingering glances and pouting lips to bear upon him. He let her bring them in vain. There was a nagging question like a thorn imbedded in his mind. Was Ivy married? At first she had denied it, and he denied it in her behalf, chivalrously fighting anyone who said she was, till he saw she was manufacturing occasions for fight. One day, Ivy asked, "Arn't you going to fight for me?" pouting and ready to turn on the tears.

"No," Peter had answered coolly. "I don't think you're worth getting my head busted for." She had been taken aback, but before she could produce a sufficiently devastating response, he added, "The fact is I think it's true."

She met his accusing gaze coyly. "Suppose it is? You wouldn't marry me if you had the chance."

"I don't know as I would," he had answered shortly, and left her. He had not seen her till today. Now he said nothing while Ivy rode all the way to her house with him. During the rest of that tumultuous day and night, he paid so much attention to the bride that the earless one, getting drunker and drunker, first wanted to fight him and then fell to sobbing over his bride's faithlessness—an embarrassing situation which caused his best friends to take him out and roll him in the muddy snow till he could "sober up and act like a man."

Meanwhile there was a colossal feast of roast turkey, venison, and squirrel, of wheat cakes made with honey and topped with maple sugar, of chestnuts, hickory nuts, and dried peaches, which went on and on in one room, while a dance went on and on in the other. The fiddles ground out a tune which sounded like a lopsided wheel going round and round on a creaking iron axle. The air was thick with strong tobacco smoke, whisky fumes, sweat and steaming wool and leather clothes. The liquor poured in floods, and nobody was even remotely sober, except Peter. His instinct for ascendancy kept him sober. He had never felt the need of being in possession of his wits among these drunken fools more than he did today. For he had reached the end of being kept in Hell's torment by Ivy. He was going to conquer her or he was never going to see her again.

6

Late at night, with much giggling and twittering, the women and girls cleared out the side of the double cabin where the dance had been held, and stripped the bride of her outer finery, and replaced it with a fine white cambric night-gown ruffled and trimmed with lace, made in the convent at New Orleans. Then they tied a ruffled white night cap under her chin and set her up under a new home made feather bed and a pink satin bedspread which had also been imported from New Orleans. Then the men brought in the bridegroom on whom they had been working for an hour—to make sure that he was fit for what was happening to him—even to the extent of making him vomit up his last two gourdfuls of whisky. They washed the mud off him and set his wig in place to cover his minus ears. In all this Peter was expected to be the leader, since he had won the bride's bottle. But he broke all the precedents of chivalry by saying flatly that he wouldn't wash the fellow and he could vomit all over Gwen for all her cavalier cared. This so outraged the knightly souls of the others that they threatened to fight Peter for it. But after he punched a couple of them, they gave up and began fighting the bridegroom instead, while Peter stood by, making from time to time an unpleasantly truthful remark—a rising young democrat, thumbing his nose at chivalry in its decay.

But when he entered the bridal chamber, now crowded with guests, Peter did not wish to insult the bride by refusing, in her presence, the duties of cavalier. So he lifted the bridegroom by the shoulders, while Skinny lifted him by the heels, and they heaved him into bed, Peter feeling as if he were handling a poisonous toad, while the bride tittered and uttered little protesting screams. Then Peter yelled, "Lights out!" and the guests rushed to be the first to blow out the candles. "And get out," roared Peter. Giggling and squealing and haw-hawing, they piled over each other in the darkness, while Peter and the other young men pushed and even kicked them out. And so they left the bride to the arms of the bridegroom—all except a few of the more drunken ones who gathered under the shuttered window in the snow and the drizzle, and yelled and whooped bawdy songs to the beating of copper kettles and wooden trenchers. Peter had been expected to lead this concert, but he refused.

The older and more sober guests were now leaving. The bride's mother had gone home with the Tudors in order to leave the house to the young couple. She would be followed by her husband and Ivy. But many of the young people crowded into the other half of the double cabin where there was a room with a bed and a trundle bed, newly built, so that the family could live in this half of the cabin while the young couple set up housekeeping in the other. Here the air was thick with the smell of supper, and of cooking grease smoking unheeded on the hearth, mingled with the fumes of whisky and strong tobacco smoke. The table had been pushed back against the wall. By it sat Jus and the bride's father and others of the older men, nodding over their hot toddy. The fire was crumbling to ashes, and the room was getting cold. Peter looked at it and thought sourly, "Seems like I'm the only one that's sober enough to tote wood." He knew that, as cavalier of the day, it was his duty to do this. But he thought, "Damned if I will. Let em freeze."

Tired and doped with liquor, the younger guests lay around on the floor on bearskins, with other skins piled over them, boys and girls packed close together. From under the bearskins came the girls' squeals, "Now you stop! Ain't you ashamed?" Several of them asked Peter to join them, but he was too cross and tired. Suddenly two dimpled arms went around him, and Ivy whispered, "Honey, let's get out of this disgusting crowd. Come back here. I want to talk to you alone. Please, Pete."

As usual, when she seemed sincere, Peter's resentment melted into tenderness. Suddenly comforted, he allowed himself to be drawn into the back room. It was damp and bitterly cold. The bed was piled high with wedding gifts and female flummery. On a split log table against the log wall, littered with pomade and combings of girls' hair, a single candle guttered before a small mirror. Ivy said, "There's a trundle bed under there. Pull it out, Pete. I'm so tired. I've got to lie down."

Peter pulled it out. The thought of the bed where they had put Gwen and the earless one crossed his mind. The rude noise was still going on under the bridal window. For a moment he stopped and straightened himself up. A deep blush burned in his face. Ivy kicked off her buckled pumps and flung herself on the bed. As she did so her skirts flew up, showing the flesh of her thighs and her frilled under drawers above her white silk stocking. Knees and thighs were not so freely displayed in those days as they are today. Peter was embarrassed but he felt a sharp thrill of excitement. She pulled her skirt down carelessly, barely covering her knees, and said, "Put the bearskin over me, Honey." She added gently, as she reached out to pat his arm, "You've got to wait on us. You're the cavalier of the day."

He covered her with the bearskin, his hands trembling, his heart beating wildly. The candle was smoking and sputtering. "Blow it out," she said. "It stinks."

He blew it out and felt his way back to the trundle bed, and sat down on the edge of it. She reached out her warm, soft arms. "Come in under the bearskin. You'll freeze." She moved over and put her head on his shoulder and began to cry. He knew now that she had been drinking, and this was a crying jag. But she was sweet, and the scent of cologne in her hair enveloped him . . .

CHAPTER 31

Russellville, Kentucky
Spring, 1801

There was a furious banging outdoors. Ivy started up. "My Heavens, Peter. See what that is."

Peter stumbled out. In the other room stood Rodriguez, booted and spurred and splashed with mud from head to foot. He was swearing violently. They hadn't ought to have done it, he said. They ought to have waited the wedding for him. John Wilcox was trying to quiet him. Ivy appeared in the door. "Rodriguez!" she cried, and flew into his arms. Peter stood uncertainly. Ivy turned to him and from Rodriguez's arms said, "Peter, meet my husband." Her black eyes flashed triumph and malice.

Peter stumbled out into the wet night. It was black with fog but a deeper blackness was on him. He felt drained of life and weighed down as if tons of wet black earth were pressing on him. John's cool voice spoke in his ears. "We'd better see father home. The old man's a little under the weather. I'll come with you. I'm on my way to Nashville to-night."

Peter did not answer him. John shook him. "Peter!" Peter hauled off and struck John. "Leave me alone," he said savagely.

John replied coldly, "Have some pride, Peter. She's not worth it. And she is his wife. Or so he says."

"He can have her," said Peter, brutally.

Jus came out. He was fumbling a little and putting one foot ahead of the other cautiously but was quite able to manage. John came around with the horses. When they were all in the saddle, Rodriguez came to the lighted door, his arm around Ivy's waist. "I want to talk to you, John," he said.

"We'll talk in Nashville," said John, shortly, and started off.

The five-mile ride to the cabin cleared Justurian's head, and he and John kept up a desultory comment all the way on the details of the wedding. Peter said nothing. Their voices came to him like the gibbering of ghosts through the blackness that surrounded him. When they came to the cabin, John helped them put the horses away and then rode off.

Peter and Jus entered the cabin. It was snug and smelled pleasantly of hog and hominy cooking on the hearth. There was still a good fire. Mary was lying with Sis on the trundle bed. A Bible lay open on a stool by the fire. Peter guessed that Mary had sat up for him, and Sis had stayed to keep her company, reading the Bible and praying together. Praying for him! Finally Sis must have persuaded Mary to lie down with her, for comfort, instead of going alone into the cold back room.

Jus sat down by the fire and pulled off his boots and held his feet in their thick wool stockings to the blaze. He seemed quite inclined to talk, but Peter answered only in monosyllables. He was still like one buried in deep dark mud. He could not think. He could not speak. He could not even feel. Finally his father threw himself on the bed. "Better go to bed, Son."

"I will," said Peter, and continued to sit dully by the dying fire.

Under the apparent stupor of every faculty, he was thinking with a terrible, mature clarity. He had intended not only to command himself. He had believed he could command others. And he had found himself ruthlessly, helplessly and vulgarly used! He bowed his head in his hands while wave after wave of moral nausea went over him. He thought he was going to vomit, and with the effort to choke it back the blood rushed to his head, and his heart palpitated wildly. Then the fire on the hearth seemed to spin round and round in a searing flame and there was darkness. He had gone blind! He was dying. He was so unprepared to die! He sank on his knees with a sound that was half shriek, half bellow. "God have mercy!"

Like rain on the fire, like a thin ray of light in the darkness, he was aware of his mother kneeling by him. "Honey, Honey," she whispered. "Whatever you've done, don't be afraid. You don't have to tote your burden alone. He'll take it. Just drop it at His feet." And then she spoke to Some One there in the room. "Reach out your big warm hand to him, dear Jesus." So she kept talking alternately to Peter, and to That Other who was there with them. When she paused, Peter snatched at her arm convulsively, wanting her to go on. Through all his pain and horror he knew that his mother had never flinched nor compromised in her repudiation of all that had now sickened him. At this moment when he respected nobody, least of all himself, he deeply respected his mother. Everything had vanished, except his monstrous doom. But against that, her voice was lifted like a bird singing in the dark.

2

He started up from sleep that had been one long horror, to see Mary cooking breakfast. He rose listlessly and helped her feebly. But when he started out of the door for a bucket of water, Jus took the bucket from his hand. "I'll take it, Son. You'd better lie down. Looks to me like you're sick."

With a sensation of relief too negative to be gratitude, Peter sank back on the bearskin. He refused all breakfast. When Mary made him a cup of the coffee which was usually reserved for the preacher, sweetened with maple sugar and golden with cream, he drank it and murmured, "Thank you, Mammy." Jus sat down on a stool beside him and stroked his tangled black curls. Peter shrank a little from the touch. His father was too closely associated in his mind with all that had sickened him. Jus was deeply worried. So far as that girl was concerned, a boy had to get burnt once or twice before he learned how to handle fire. No use worrying about that. But there was more than a girl behind this. It looked to him like a serious bodily illness. He thought in unwonted terror. "He's all the son I've got. If I was to lose him—" He gave orders that Peter was to do no work of any kind. He would see that Cracker did all the chores. He himself was going to ride over and get Doctor Allen.

But Mary thought grimly, "All he's sick of is sin."

Sis looked on, her blue eyes soft with concern and quietly took over all household tasks while her mother sat by Peter. After Jus left, Mary asked him if he would like to have her read in the New Testament. He came to life a little. "Yes, Mammy. Please." She read the story of the Prodigal Son. "You see what he said, Honey. He said, 'I will arise and go to my father'. That's what you've got to do. Arise and go to your Heavenly Father!"

Then Peter spoke the first coherent sentence he had uttered since he came home. "There's a lot I've got to do first." He leaped up with furious energy. Mary was frightened. Was he going mad? Before she could protest, he was half way up the ladder to the loft. "Peter," she cried sharply. "Peter, come back and lie down!" He disappeared into the loft. She ran to the foot of the ladder. She was about to climb after him when he re-appeared and swung himself down. "Take them," he said, putting a pack of cards into her hands. "Take them and burn them!"

With a smile in which a certain grimness gave way to pure satisfaction she flung them, with one clean, swift throw, into the heart of the glowing logs. They scattered—kings, queens, knaves, diamonds, hearts, spades, some melting around the edges, some turning slowly black and crumbling. When the last one was nothing, Peter sank back on the bearskin. The sensation of nausea was eased for the first time. "Well, that's off my stomach," he said.

After that he seemed much better, but wanted his mother to go on with the Bible reading, the praying, and the hymn singing. About noon his father returned, saying that the doctor would be over that afternoon. Looking as if nausea had again gripped him, Peter jumped up and burst out of the door. A moment later they heard horse's hooves. Peter came hurtling around the corner of the house from the horselot, riding Aladdin bareback. Mary and Jus rushed toward him, thinking him demented. He leaped from the horse and seizing the bridle placed it in his father's hand. "Take him," he said, "and sell him. I never want to ride him again." Jus protested. He temporized. A fierce gleam came into Peter's dull black eyes. "I'll take him myself right now, and sell him to Red Maulding." He was about to leap on his horse.

Jus interposed. "All right, Son. Take it easy. He's yours, and it's up to you to say whether he will be sold. I can get you a good mount instead of him—not so fast but better suited to your size."

Assured on this point, Peter let himself be coaxed into the cabin and sank down on the bearskin. He looked exhausted. His face was a pallid and sickly yellow, but a grim light flickered in his dull eyes. "Another load off my stomach," he said.

In the afternoon Doctor Allen came, and found that his tongue was coated and, while he had no fever, his pulse was weak and irregular. He was puzzled. The boy was plainly sick. But what was the matter with him? All he could prescribe was rest, a light diet of broth and milk, and a purgative which he proceeded to prepare. But Mary said, "Take care of the soul, Doctor, and the body will take care of itself."

The doctor's blue eyes met hers quizzically. "That's first class doctrine, Mary. But what do you advise I do for the soul?"

"Read the New Testament to him. It comforts him."

The Doctor looked at Peter in some surprise. "Is that so, Peter?"

Peter nodded. Allen took Mary's Bible, reading a verse here and there like a musician trying out his instrument. Then, warming to his task, he ranged through the pages, finding passages Mary had never heard, reading them in his rolling melodious voice. Peter lapsed into semi-consciousness in which the words washed over him soothingly, and the images they invoked formed and reformed in a kind of dark glory against the sombre background of his suffering.

Next afternoon, after another wretched twenty-four hours, Peter was lying on the bearskin by the hearth, while Jus was writing out a brief for a case coming up in court next week. There was a clatter of hooves outside and a chorus of voices. Peter was startled into life. "Damnation! I don't want to see them."

Mary hastily retired with Sis into the preacher's room. Jus asked, "What shall I tell them, Son?"

Peter groaned. "Tell them to get the Hell out of here."

Whatever he might have intended to say, Jus, opening the door, was overborne by the rush into the room. There was Red Maulding, Skinny Dromgole, two Richardson girls, and a dozen others. Ivy fluttered forward. "Peter, Honey. The idea of your sulkin' like that, you silly l'il ol boy."

She dropped her fur coat from her bare shoulders, and knelt by him, spraying him with ribbons and the fragrance of cologne. His father thought, "She'll bring him around." But, to his surprise, the face Peter had turned from her was green with horrified distaste. Jus took her by the arm and, lifting her up, said firmly, "He's in no state to talk. Come over here and talk to me, my dear." And he propelled her firmly to the other side of the fireplace. She covered her confusion with a laugh. "Oh la, la, and you an ol married man! I declare, you make me blush, Sir."

Red Maulding was saying, in his booming, off-hand way, to Peter, "We heard they was driving you crazy over here with prayers and hymn singing. So we came to get you out of it."

Peter made no reply. He had rolled over so that his back was to them all. Skinny Dromgole shook him good-naturedly. "What's the matter, Pete?"

Peter twitched his shoulder out from under his touch, whirled around, and sat up. For the first time since the wedding night words poured from him. "I want prayers and the Bible reading and hymn singing. I want them the same as I'd want clean water if I'd just ducked my head in cow manure. There's no use talkin. I've done with it, and you know what. And if you know what's good for it, you'll be done with it, too, for there's but a step from where you are to the rope's end, and from the rope's end there ain't a flea jump to everlasting fire. It ain't been pure boyish fun that we've been into. Somebody pulls the strings and we all jump. Dromgole and Stewart run the gambling joint, and it's to profit them that we all gamble. Wes Maulding sells the liquor, and we souse away our souls into his till. And when it comes to girls—" Here he looked at Ivy fiercely, "I say there's some planted here for no other purpose than to get you and me into Mason's gang."

At this Ivy made a suppressed sound which only Jus heard. She covered it by smiling into his face and leaning confidingly against him. "Listen to him. Is he crazy?"

This Peter heard. A dull burning red came into his face. It receded, leaving a greenish pallor. He said wearily, "If I'm damned, I want you all to know I ain't goin to Hell in your company. I keep to myself the privilege of goin down into the fiery furnace alone." He turned away, suddenly retching.

Jus shepherded the callers out. The fury of Peter's reaction had been a revelation to his tolerant soul. When he turned back, after courteously, but coldly, bidding the guests good-day, he saw that Mary and Sis had rushed to Peter's side and were anxiously tending him. When the paroxysm passed, Peter fell into a deep sleep. In sleep his color and the charm of his boyish face returned.

3

When Peter woke next morning, the nausea had passed. But he felt depressed and interested only in one consuming problem—how to find peace, which, after the pattern of the day, translated into "How do I find God?" As the days went by and his darkness did not lift, he thought savagely, "I'm doing my best to come to God, but He just ain't interested." Were the Presbyterians and Baptists right after all? Was he damned for ever by the arbitrary decree God had made at the beginning of the world?

This then was damnation—to sleep with a load like the wet earth of the grave upon you, and to start awake at midnight to hear the gibbering of the lost upon the night winds and to see the outlines of the devils in the night shadows. And, when you raised your eyes to the Heavens for re-assurance, to see the stars, which had always seemed like the friendly eyes of angels, looking down on you, remote and cynical. To struggle awake in the morning like a man fighting his way out of a coffin. You wished you need never get up but you dared not die. All day, your head ached and your feet dragged. Your food had no savor, the sunshine no warmth, your wonted occupations no meaning and no hope. And the kindness of those who loved you, if it succeeded in stabbing through your lethargy, was like the piercing of a knife.

But against Calvin and all his brood, Mary set her untutored judgment. "Believin such terrible wickedness of God—that He'd damn you when you're tryin so hard—that's the sin against the Holy Ghost," she told him solemnly, and called on Dominie to fortify her. When Dominie set Peter a course of reading in the Bible, Peter spent all his waking hours on the cramped print, stowing verses away in his memory as a charm against night horrors, ranging though the old Book with something of the sureness and awareness with which he had been wont to range the woods.

Dean came to see him almost daily and expounded his own version of the doctrine of John Wesley. "I don't say I *believe*. I say I *know*. I know it by feeling it, same as I feel the sun. At the center of all, there's a heart like my heart. And my heart leans on that great heart day and night in trust, and I don't grieve that heart ever if I can help it. But if I can't help it and grieve it, not intending to, but out of my weakness and natural sinfulness, I know that He will understand and forgive, if I'll only come back to Him, in true sorrow, and rest again on Him, for whatever happens, He and I are friends."

He said this slowly and haltingly, feeling his way from word to word. When he had said it, he was not satisfied. "That's something like what I mean, and yet it isn't all of it, either. What I mean is there's something you feel and have faith in without really knowing it's so, but once you feel it and have faith, it proves itself as you live by faith—you learn it by living it, so that in the end you really do know." Here he gave up. "I'm afraid I don't know how to tell you, Petey lad. But open your heart to Him, and He will tell you."

Yet, for all Dean's efforts, Peter remained in mortal torment. As the days went by and the gracious reconciliation with God did not come, he was filled with a desperate rage. One day he retired to his old retreat in the loft above the stables, and was walking to and fro in great anguish, wringing his hands, trying to pray, on the borders of despair. It was a warm spring day, and the shutter had been opened. Suddenly, as he turned around and faced it, he found himself looking into the square of sunny sky. A voice said, "Peter, look at me." The blue sky became two kind and understanding eyes. Relief flashed over him like an electric shock. He rushed into the house and caught his mother by the arm. "He spoke to me! I saw Him! He said, 'Peter, look at me,' and then I saw His eyes, and Mammy, they looked at me so lovin'!"

"Honey, Honey. God has spoken to you at last," she said, throwing her arms around him and hugging him. "Don't stop now. Keep on. It won't be easy. He may try you for many a day yet. But in the end,"—she drew away from him and he looked into her eyes, shining with triumphant faith, "in the end you just can't help finding Him."

But hard on this great hope came despair. One day he started out of the house to walk off or work off the stifling depression. It was a misty emerald and azure day in April. The woods and hedges were all a soft cloud of new green, and the shimmering, milky air was alive with bird calls and fresh with the scent of growing things. Peter followed the path that led down to the caves, past the wreckage of the old gunpowder enterprise, now covered with bushes and vines just coming into leaf. Memories of the high excitement of those days of scientific experiment and industrial enterprise assailed him. "Damn them!" he thought violently, "It seems like there's nothing I like to remember that they don't befoul and bring to nothing." They were Evil, and he had come to hate Evil with a consuming fury.

He stumbled over a piece of old iron, and was for a moment released into impersonal speculation. "Must a been used in the furnaces we built. Must be a lot of kettles and things there in the cave."

He unfastened the door which barred the cave and looked in. It was chill and dark and there was the sound of a stream gushing in its lightless depths. "Kinda like a deep cellar under the whole house of the world," he thought. He walked forward a little way into the dark. "There's nobody here but me and God," he reflected. "And right here I wrastle it out with Him, and make Him answer me."

He fell on his knees. His soul was in agony. The tears were pouring down his face. He prayed, "Now Lord, if there is any mercy for me, let me find it," and it seemed to him that there and then he could lay hold on his Savior and realize a reconciled God.

But suddenly he started up in horror. Somebody was there with him in the dark. But it was not God. It was the Devil. He could feel him within touch of his body, coming on a dark, damp blast from the innermost depths, to seize him and drag him down, body and soul to Hell. He sprang to his feet and never stopped running till, blubbering like a baby, he fell at his mother's feet, clutching at her skirts. But when she at last understood what he had seen and felt, she patted him on the head, lightly and soothingly, "There ain't a thing to it, Honey. It's just that mean ol devil, tryin' to scare the guts out of you, because he knows he's licked and you're on your way straight home to God."

4

So in alternation of hope and despair, March passed into April, and April into May. Only when Jerry came to see him, did Peter forget himself in his rooted sense of responsibility for his weaker playmate. Earnestly he pleaded with Jerry to abandon his dangerous companions. Vividly he pictured the perils not only to soul but to body—a stab in the dark, a shot from behind, a rope over the limb of a tree, and Hell for ever beyond. But Jerry pooh poohed his fears and laughed at the suspicion that John might be one of the inner circle of Mason's gang. Again he repeated that it was all hearsay—the talk against Mason. Folks were robbed, sure enough; and now and again one was found murdered. But who ever proved that Mason had done it? Peter said Swaney, the mail man, had sworn out testimony against Mason as the one who robbed him. "But it's only Swaney's word against Mason's. Swaney might have taken the money himself," said Jerry.

Peter woke out of his self-absorption to look at Jerry shrewdly. "Jerry," he said, "it ain't like you to say wrong is right, and it ain't like you to be made a fool of. Something special's got you." Then he asked abruptly, "Do you see Polly regular?"

Jerry answered evasively, "I see her sometimes."

"That explains it. You'll believe what she says because being sweet on her is part of your very life and breathing, and she will lie because a woman will lie to protect a man she loves and not feel it wrong. At least," Peter hesitated. He was thinking of his mother. Would she lie to protect even him, Peter? He knew that she would not, and pride in her for it burned in him like a clear flame. He continued, in careful reverence for his mother, "That is to say some women will, without being all bad."

Something in this observation seemed to pierce to Jerry's heart. His delicate pale face was suffused with a dull blush. He kicked a stone out of the way. "Well, I must be goin', Pete," he said, and leaped on his horse. Peter stood looking after him, feeling miserably that a breach was widening between him and Jerry. But what did it matter in the face of the possibility that an arbitrary God had damned them both since the beginning of the world?

Meanwhile, with the coming of the warm weather, the Baptists, Presbyterians, and Methodists were planning to unite again in camp meetings bigger and better even than the ones they had put on last year. The extraordinary exhilaration of last summer had lasted well into the winter. Out of it had grown innumerable neighborhood meetings for prayer and mutual help. But as the winter dragged on, the enthusiasm waned. It was hard to get to meetings. The meeting places were cold. People retired like ground hogs to their holes, and the bitter isolation and frustration froze over them. But when the sap ran up the maple trees, and the first violets bloomed, circuit riders proclaimed to all local congregations of all faiths which they encountered in their rounds, that the first big camp meeting would be held in May, in McGready's outdoor church on Muddy River, John Page, the Methodist Presiding Elder, in charge.

Then bands of young men were sent riding from cabin to cabin to advertize it further. And finally all good praying Christians combined to dig, out of swamps and caves and forest lairs, creatures that seemed only half human—movers who had fallen by the wayside, tramps and drunks, the mentally and physically sick, the runaways from justice. If the wildest and most wolfish would promise to come to camp meeting, he would get a new shirt, and she a new dress, and all of them would be sure of good meals from everflowing picnic baskets. Mary and Barbara went to see the Roberts girls. Susan glowered, but Betsy promised, with a false little smile, that she would be there. As they were leaving, the loutish brother came up with Big Harpe's little girl on his shoulder. Her bright dark eyes peered through a dirty mat of hair. Her body was covered with scabs and sores. He said, "I can't come. I ain't got clothes that are fit. But if it ain't too much to ask, would you-all kinda keep your eye on the young un here, I wish she wouldn't have to grow up—you know, like them."

He spoke haltingly, pawing the earth with his dirty bare feet, in intense embarrassment, mumbling his words, his eyes downcast. Mary was touched. "We'll furnish clean clothes for you to come to camp meetin in."

"Oh no—no—no," he said. "I dasn't. I ain't fit."

Riding back, Mary said to Barbara, "Mark my words. That man will be saved to the kingdom yet."

Peter heard the story with a sinking heart. It might be as Mr. McGready said. Under his vile disguise, this Roberts fellow might be one of the saved, predestined from all eternity to come home to God. But he, Peter, was damned.

Before the camp meeting, John Page came to dinner at the Cartwrights'. Peter had looked forward to Page's coming for days, expecting to center the great man's attention on his dark state as he had been centering all clerical attention locally for two months. But when John Page arrived, big and booming, with his bright blue eyes and hearty laugh, he merely asked casually, "How are you, Pete? Feelin' better?" Before Peter could answer, Page strolled over to Jus and was laughing with him and slapping him on the back. Peter was outraged. He was more outraged when Page kept up an uproarious report on local politics throughout the dinner and departed without once offering to lead in prayer for Peter's soul. The only reference he made to the boy's troubles was once when he spoke of Ivy. "She's a good-looking gal, but pretty much like pisoned honey—liable to make you sick to your stomach." With that he actually turned and winked at Peter. An angry blush rose to the boy's face.

Still angry, and utterly miserable, knowing now that he was surely damned, Peter went to the camp meeting which began just at sunset on Saturday. The stand was bowered in pink azaleas, and in the fresh green woods all about, the birds were twittering and singing, and a delicious odor of flowers and growing plants and running brooks came on the soft wind off the meadows. Overhead, above the circular wall of the trees, the sky was blue and radiant, with piles of pink-edged clouds showing above the feathery line of the timber on one side. When, with a sound like the voices of angels, the singing began, the Methodist and Presbyterian choirs responding to each other across the great congregation, Peter sang with them. He repressed himself once or twice, feeling that song was unsuitable to the damned. But the next moment he forgot himself, and his voice rose, and he floated away on the strong, beautiful billows of sound. It was so lovely here. Everything caressed the senses. Pleasure and exhilaration began to possess him. He thought in terror, "Suppose I should begin to be happy again and still not be saved. I'd be right back where I was!"

John Page rose to pray. Peter hoped that he would especially pray for him, but among those recognizably listed for God's special notice, he could not find his name. John Page lined out another hymn

> Wretched, helpless, and distressed, O whither shall I fly?
> Ever gasping after rest, I cannot find it nigh.
> Naked, sick, and poor, and blind, fast bound in misery,
> Friend of sinners, let me find, my help, my all in Thee.

Between his old misery and his new realization that John Page had paid no attention to him, Peter sang this with a breaking heart and ended with tears running down his face and his knees collapsing under him. He fell down and covered his face with his hands.

John Page began to preach, starting in an easy anecdotal style, telling them about a man who had fallen into bad ways. He raced horses and he cheated at cards, and he took up with women no better than they should be, until at last he was stricken with the conviction of sin. Then he fell down in the muck and the mire and he wallowed there in utter despair. But one day he heard a voice saying to him, "My grace is sufficient for thee."

"And do you know what that man did?" asked Page, pausing and looking over the congregation. Several voices answered, "No."

Page said, "He stood right up and looked at the sky, and he laughed right out loud in God's face, and he said, 'My Gawd, Lord, if your grace ain't sufficient, I don't know whose is'."

At this there was a roar of laughter, and Peter found himself laughing with the rest. Only McGready, seated on the platform behind Page, frowned. He never could get used to the liberties these Methodists took with the art of preaching.

John Page was off on another tack. In a voice tender and gentle he was telling them about a little bird. He didn't know what kind of bird—a blue bird, may be, or a thrush. This little bird always spent its summers up here in Kentucky. But when the winter came howling down out of Indiana territory, it picked itself up and it flew and flew till it came to a nice warm place in a sugar field in Louisiana, and there it settled down in solid comfort for the winter. But once this little bird, flying away from winter, came smack into a tropical hurricane, and it was picked up and swept out over the Gulf of Mexico. And when it saw the dark waters, lashed into mountains of purple green on all sides, and felt the wind howling along at 100 miles an hour, it knew that there was no use in flying any more. So, with wings still outspread, the little bird just gave up. It stopped trying to save itself, and it stopped trying to fly. It just rested where it was on its wings and let the wind take it. Here John Page stopped and looked around. "And do you know what happened then?"

Peter was sitting on the edge of his plank bench, his dark eyes on the preacher's face. "What?" He just stopped himself from saying it out loud. John Page looked down into the boy's earnest face, and when he spoke again Peter knew he was speaking to him.

"Why! The next thing that little bird knew he was sitting warm and snug in a sugar field in Florida, which was every bit as good as the sugar field in Louisiana! And he hadn't had to do a thing about it. All he had done was to let go, and that big, dark, howling wind had done the rest."

The preacher smiled at Peter so winningly that the boy could feel himself smiling in return. Still smiling, Peter lifted his eyes to the sky. Warm and soft and blue, it shone above him, and as he looked, he knew that he was looking into unutterably kind eyes. The eyes of God. Slowly the impression faded. But something that had been hard and painful deep inside of him was beginning to give way. John Page was saying, "When the conviction takes you, when you know you've been wrong and want to be right, don't tighten and harden yourself and struggle. You needn't battle for salvation. All you've got to do is to let go of what has been keeping you from it. Let go—every bit of you. Let go like you were dying, and say, 'Lord, you're bigger than I am. I don't have will or wish any more. I just give up to you'."

After that Peter honestly tried to give up. He gave up to the music and was washed away on great tides of song. He gave up to the darkening night and to the sky where the stars were coming out, and went away from his body and was abroad in the infinity of space. And when the sermon reached its height, and the weeping multitudes rose and pressed forward with tears streaming down their faces, he went forward with them and fell upon his knees. Then, in the midst of a solemn struggle of soul, he seemed to hear a voice saying quietly, deep within him, "Thy sins are all forgiven."

His eyes were closed. His face was buried in his hands. But, trembling deliciously, he felt divine light flash all around him. He rose and opened his eyes on the glimmering, candle-lit well of darkness, walled in by the velvety black of the trees, and domed by the star-spangled sky. It seemed to him that he was in Heaven, and the trees, and the leaves on them delicately frescoed in darkness against the silvery starlight above, and everything beneath and beyond them were praising God. As he stood in a radiant daze, his mother ran to his side. "He is saved. Thank God. Glory to God! Glory! Glory! Glory!" Her clear voice trilled out in a weirdly beautiful cadence, like a single flute. Her eyes in the candlelight were shining, as she stood by her tall, transfigured boy, hand in hand, their faces uplifted.

The sobbing throughout the congregation died into silence. Then there was a sudden roar, and the congregation and the mourners near by, all sprang to their feet and came crowding around Peter and his mother, congratulating them and praising God. After that the prayers and the singing went on without intermission all night. Eighty people went through the same experience as Peter's. As the rest of the crowd faded away in the chill dawn, the saved were kneeling together around the preacher's stand, in an ecstasy still undiminished. Then, in the bright, chill sunrise, Peter and his mother went home together, rejoicing.

As they pushed the heavy plank door back on its sagging leather hinges and looked into the dark cabin, Peter saw his father kneeling in his underdrawers on the stone hearth, blowing up the breakfast fire. As they came in, he straightened up. The months of estrangement from his wife had aged and coarsened Jus, substituting too much drink for what he had been able to find in her. He looked dull and heavy, and the glance he cast at Mary and Peter was wavering and uncertain.

But Mary went straight to him, with that impulsive gesture that had always moved him in other crises of their life together—as if she were being borne straight into his heart. Stopping so close to him that her head rested on his breast, she raised her face, all alight as it was, and said eagerly and confidingly, "Jus, Peter is saved."

The years dropped off Justurian. The heaviness fell away. He folded his arms around her. "You don't say so," he said, softly and huskily, and pressed his lips on hers.

CHAPTER 32

Russellville, Kentucky
June, 1801 to March, 1802

Early in June, when John Page returned to this district, he took Peter into the Methodist Church in the little chapel of Ebenezer. With a heart too full for praise or song, Peter knelt at the rough log railing around the small plank communion table, which was the only altar, and tremblingly sipped from the pewter cup the juice of the wild grape. He was being born again, transmuted in God's sight, and the boy that had been Peter was gone for ever.

Immediately he was absorbed into preparations for the stupendous camp meeting to be held that summer in Bourbon County, where McGready's young associate, Barton Stone, had worked up two congregations, and where he proposed to gather people in by thousands and tens of thousands. And to that end, he was laying out a kind of outdoor city large enough to hold all the inhabitants of all the cities west of the Alleghenies—Lexington, Frankfort, Russellville, Nashville—; laying out streets along which tents and temporary shelters could be put up; laying out areas for wagons and horses and providing, not one out door church but seven. All the people who could be persuaded to seek their souls' salvation west of the Alleghenies, and all the preachers of all faiths, were to gather here. The fire which had been lighted by McGready in 1797, had been fanned by the rude, itinerating Methodists into a conflagration that was spreading irresistibly north, south, east, and west into what is still known as "The Great Revival."

For the first time the Rogues were really shaken. "We're comin on you now, you spawn of Satan," shouted John Page, at the first big camp meeting in June. "The militia of the Lord is mustering, and you can hear the tramp, tramp, tramp from the Alleghenies to the Mississippi, and the borders of Canada to the hell-hole of Natchez. You thought you could tie up the courts. But you can't tie up the everlasting justice of God. You've been hamstringing and hobbling the elected authorities from the governor down. But there's one you can't hamstring, for we're nominating God to run things for us, and the election rally we're holding at Cane Ridge will make hash of your grand masters and constitutions and oaths signed in blood."

At this there was consternation among some in the congregation. Who could have given away their secrets? Page let his words sink in, and then he went on. "From now on, every camp ground is a battle ground, and there are going to be camp grounds from end to end of this land, and camp meetings, one beginning where the other ends, without let or stopping, till the last of you gives up. From now on we open our meetings with the call of the trumpet. Listen well, you Rogues, for it is the trump of your doom."

Everywhere the Rogues organized to storm the camp meetings, the Christian young men to repel them. The drill meeting of the guards Peter joined began with prayer that God would save his soldiers from doing bodily injury to their enemies, and would make them instruments in bringing those enemies to Him. But the prayer ended with the words, "Nevertheless, O God, we will defend Thy sanctuary." And when they stood and sang "A mighty fortress is our God," the grand old fighting hymn of Luther rolled out like thunder, not the less impressive because they ended it with a kind of Indian war whoop in which the word "Hallelujah" was only barely recognizable.

Every known trick to confuse an opponent was then demonstrated and tried. Ingenious and experienced as he was in all the wiles of frontier combat, Peter found in these exhibitions full satisfaction for his need of drama and instinct for personal ascendency. What could be a greater challenge than the call to beat the Rogues, yet never to descend to their level?

Peter also joined a class to study the Bible, in which he had an advantage over most of the others because, in the long struggle of his mental illness, he had really learned to read. So he quickly made himself the center of the reading class, rolling out the sonorous phrases with dramatic effect, improvising dramatic characterizations of Bible persons, and translating Bible words into spicy phrases of his own. He did not shine so brightly in the singing class, because his voice was still quavering between boyhood and mankind. But he could carry a tune true and clear, and would in time have a fine baritone.

With all this activity, an immense excitement possessed him. He went to bed impatient for the night to be gone and the next day's adventures to begin. Yet he was usually so tired with all he had been doing that he fell asleep while saying his prayers, with a dreamy consciousness of a far off chorus singing, "Hallelujah." The problem, Thomas Wilkerson and Dominie thought, was to bind and shackle this young enthusiast with routines which should become pleasant and comforting habits. Otherwise, when the dramatic possibilities of the new faith were exhausted, and the excitement of the summer camp meetings past, he might look elsewhere for means of keeping himself on the heights.

To this end, Wilkerson set him the traditional routine of the Methodist preacher. This meant rising at four and reading for an hour, preferably in some retired spot out of doors, the reading to be followed by an hour of meditation and prayer, during which the conscience was examined, the doings of the previous day reviewed and criticized, and the plans for the new day organized under God's scrutinizing eye, and His blessing invoked upon them. This routine Peter accepted eagerly but never managed to carry it out the first summer. He could not roll out at four in the morning, because he had gone so hard and so fast the day before and had stayed up so late that once he went to sleep the trump of Gabriel could not wake him. But when he confessed his inability to organize his waking and sleeping hours, Dominie told him not to be discouraged but to keep on trying, and spurred him gently, inexorably, to renewed effort. So Peter found himself being steadily organized despite himself. If he did not wake at four, he was to get up at five, and go though the reading, meditation, and prayer till seven. If he overslept till nearly noon, he was immediately to go away by himself in the woods, read a few Bible verses, review his own acts and thoughts, ask God's forgiveness for what he had done amiss, and organize his day and ask God's blessing on it—all before eating or letting himself be drawn into any general activity.

When, grumbling, heavy with sleep, and feeling himself definitely under the power of the Anti-Christ, he would stumble out, the effort he had to make in so doing would bring a moment of fine rapture. And through all the tumults of the succeeding day, the memory of his morning aloneness with God would be like the soothing, far off sound of music. In the evening he was similarly to read a little in the Bible or to repeat Bible verses he had memorized, and to review the affairs of the day, criticizing himself and asking God's forgiveness for what he had done amiss, soberly approving in God's own presence what he had managed to do well. And then he was to wash his soul clean of worry and resentment by kneeling and praying, rolling all his burdens off on the Lord and resting serene in the sufficiency of His grace. The first six months of Peter's life as a Christian was a schooling he never forgot. It schooled him where he needed to be schooled, in his impulses and emotions. And what was true of Peter was true of most of the frontiersmen whom the western evangelists were beginning to educate. For a frontier boy like Peter needed training of the emotions far more than he needed training of his mind. The early western frontiersman used his mind more intelligently than most contemporary graduates of Yale, Harvard and Princeton. Having few books, he had to carry what he needed to know in his head. To carry it easily he had to organize it as it came to him, eliminating non-essentials and classifying the rest. His observation of man and nature was keen beyond anything known to civilized circles. It had to be. The unobservant were likely to be eliminated. He had a few pet superstitions, but they seldom controlled his actions in anything that really mattered. His attitude to most propositions was the one which has been crystallized as that of the man from Missouri, "Show me."

But what the frontiersman of the first generation in the West needed desperately was a way of orienting himself emotionally to his changed circumstances. Two generations of forest life, in constant fear of Indians, added to ignorance and savagery going back to the dark beginnings of Europe, had filled the subconscious with blood and horror, and created repressions so harsh that they often broke in madness or extreme violence. Peter had lived all his life among people who whooped when they were happy, bawled when they were unhappy, and saw red and murdered when angry.

In 1798 when the great revival began, the sunny world of the West was largely free from fear of the Indians and from the frustrations which had made the frontiersman what he was emotionally. Except for the battle with the criminal Band or with local Rogues, which after the death of Big Harpe was out in the open and relatively free from undefined fears and horrors, life was beginning to be hopeful and easy in Kentucky. People had better houses, better food, and more prideful personal possessions than the ancestors of most of them had had back to the beginning of time. The problem was to see that the people were no longer hag-ridden by the ghosts of horrors now past.

Children of their age, as they were, the early preachers solved the emotional problem for their converts as they had learned to solve their own. They made no effort to suppress the violent emotionalism. It seemed quite normal to them. But in some converts they channeled it and in others they exploded it, and gradually they quieted it at its source by substituting a sense of security and trust in God for the insecurity which had been its cause.

2

Jus made a tolerant adjustment to Peter's conversion supposing that he would get over religion as he had got over horse racing and gambling. Seeing the boy looking so handsome, well, and full of magnetism, he had to admit that a little religion "kinda refined" the personality. And he was proud of the way people were always riding up to the gate and shouting for Peter to come and help them with this or take charge of that. He was particularly impressed when Mrs. Gilbert, the one of Alston's daughters who was held in high repute—a repute enhanced by the fact that her husband was also the largest landowner—bore down upon him beaming and said, "James McGready tells me there are two youths here who are destined to go far in the service of God. One is Finis Ewing and the other is Peter Cartwright."

"Trust the boy to fall on his feet," thought Jus proudly. "Mrs. Dromgole's given him up as a bad job, but that only makes her sister, who is much more a person of quality, take him up!"

But mainly Jus was too happy in his restored status as a husband to bother with the worries of fatherhood. For Mary, the final salvation of her boy had done wonders. She was now free with those charming looks and ways of which he had had only grudging glimpses through eighteen years of marriage, and looked so pretty and fresh and friendly at breakfast that he hated to leave her. All day, amidst conferences with clients, and drinks with brother lawyers, and long lonely rides on horseback, he thought about her. Sometimes he tore himself away from smoky, whisky drenched male social sessions and galloped home to her with the avid anticipation of long ago.

The happiness of his home life after the miserable winter of estrangement would have made Jus tolerant of religion in any case. But he was also impressed with the way these preachers were organizing the whole country, and their immense and enthusiastic following. Though he did not intend to be interfered with, in his temperate enjoyment of sin, religion was evidently the "coming thing," and the coming thing was what Jus was always going to be on the side of.

So, Jus went along with Mary, Peter, Eddie and Sis to the great camp meeting at Cane Ridge in August, slowly making his way with them through great masses of people on foot, on horseback, and in carts, who were going there, too, and making a continuous traffic jam on the narrow rutted roads and paths. It was a show he wouldn't have missed. Besides, it gave him a chance to do some business with some brother lawyers, for all the lawyers of western Kentucky were there, like everybody else. Once there, and established in one of the neat white tents which provided bachelor quarters for men, Jus roamed through the vast concourse of people, expertly dodging any special attention to his soul and collecting statistics. Never, even in the army, even at Crab Orchard, had he seen so many people, and never such organization of everybody for everybody's good. In a land in which, till three years ago, a wheeled vehicle was unknown, Jus counted 143 carriages and wagons, 500 carts, and 500 sleighs and sledges—1,443 vehicles in all. In a land in which the usual domestic light was still only firelight, and to burn more than one candle at a time was the wildest extravagance, he counted 500 candles lighting a camp ground at night, and it "sure was a pretty sight." He saw, to his amazement, that there was not one camp ground. There were half a dozen of them, like the various quarters of a large city, with streets and squares lined with tents and log shelters between. There were clean-up squads, there were garbage collectors, there were water distributors, there were privy arrangements. "This is to make Nashville look like nothing but a collection of wigwams by comparison," he thought. "Turn these tents and shacks into brick buildings, and you'd have a city—a sight more of a city than—" his mind went back to the very few places that called themselves cities which he had ever seen. "More of a city than Richmond." Then he laughed. Richmond, as he remembered it after the war, had only 1800 people in it, half of them Negroes! There were many times that number in this city of God the preachers had raised over night!

He strolled from one camp ground to the other in the forest, where preachers of the different denominations had assembled their flocks. Services went on continually all day and all night, from two to seven preachers officiating from as many different stands. Jus looked in on and appraised them all, lounging at the back of the congregation, an interested twinkle in his eye, his quid of tobacco bulging in his bearded cheek. He saw the convicted falling, jerking, rolling, dancing, and barking. He saw them lying stiff in trances, and noted that most who fell were men. Some fell as if struck with a bullet. Some were seized with a trembling and then fell. Some shrieked and continued to shriek. Some lay motionless as if dead. The uproar was indescribable—several hymns being sung at the same time—shrieks, whoops, Glory Hallelujahs, and hysterical laughter. At one time he saw 1000 people rise to their feet with one shout, and he believed a brother lawyer who said he had heard that shout a mile away.

The "whoopin and hollerin" didn't bother him, as it did some sedate observers from across the Alleghenies. He was too used to that sort of thing. In his opinion folks that got hysterics because they got religion were the same as those who got hysterics because they'd had some liquor, or their girl had jilted em, or they'd seen a ghost, or had a pain in their guts or their conscience. "I wouldn't be surprised if life in their own houses and neighborhoods might be a lot quieter from now on, just on account of the way the preachers have busted all the noise out of em," he reflected.

He left his family at Cane Ridge and rode back to Russellville, first circling the camp ground to observe, with a cynical eye, the liquor stands, the gambling joints, and the shelters for prostitutes which were doing business for miles around. He thought, "We've sure got it right out in the open now—Heaven and Hell drawn up fair and square against each other." Then he thought, "That's what comes of livin in a new country. What's hidden, like a pison in the vitals, in an old country, is right out in front in a new one, and it becomes everybody's business to deal with it."

Riding back against the steady stream of people still coming to the meetings, Jus thought, with a thrill, "This thing is big." Obscurely he was sensing something unknown to his ancestors in Europe or east of the mountains, unknown to himself even in his youth—the conception of bigness, so native now to the American, so foreign and even repugnant to the European. "When you get out from where mountains wall you in and shut you off, and fogs hide heaven from your eyes," he thought, "and from places where one country or state is so different from the next one, so set in its own cussed ways that if you ride twenty-five miles you feel like you was among enemies—it sure is like being new-made." To organize not for tens or for hundreds but for tens of thousands as those preachers had done—how grand and how simple life might be, how lavish in material comfort, how free from the nagging irritations and corroding mental discomforts that come from being stuck for generations in little places, with never a wide open horizon to lift your eyes to, never another place that can be yours by just getting on your horse and going!

Big! Big! That is what bigness is, thought Jus, riding under the great, high, wide August sky, through the sun-beaten golden land.

It was honest-to-God-living-breathing-and-not-giving-a-damn free-dom, such as men before had only dreamed of, but such as his children should miraculously inherit. "Let em get used to being religious on a big scale," he thought, "and they'll get organized to do everything else in a big way." Though he had never once been moved by prayer or preaching or hymn, the exhilaration of it all was singing in his blood. "We're on our way to big things," he thought, as he galloped along. "You've got to hand it to the preach-ers. They've made the start and we're on our way."

3

The meeting went on for weeks. From 12,000 to 25,000 people were present for longer or shorter periods, which was just about the whole number of inhabitants of that country within a radius of 100 miles. Of these between 1000 and 2000 were "happily and powerfully converted to God."

Peter went through it all on the wings of an immense exhilara-tion. When he wasn't busy standing guard or fighting off intruders, he operated as a member of a boy's "praying circle." He and his comrades went from meeting to meeting, and wherever they saw boys of their own ages kneeling among the mourners, they sent one of their number in to ask the lad to come into the woods and pray. All those long summer days the forests were full of bands of boys, praying with boys, and of girls praying with girls.

Peter's praying circle was plagued by a smart, argumentative gentleman whom Peter later referred to as "Mr. D." Mr. D. used to look in on the boys and remonstrate with them for their idolatry of Jesus. The whole idea of salvation by the blood and through the person of Jesus was heathenish, he said. There was only one God, and Jesus had been but a man or, at most, a prophet.

Peter took on the argumentative Mr. D. "So you do believe in God?"

"Yes."

"And if we prayed to God, He would hear us."

"Yes, prayer to God is proper but not to Jesus."

"Then why don't you show us. Do some praying on your own. Get down on your knee here and pray God to stop this work, if it is bad. For you know," he added, "if it isn't bad, all Hell can't stop it."

"Pray! Pray!" yelled the boys, surrounding the rash Mr. D. and forcing him to his knees. Embarrassed, trembling, Mr. D. began, "Oh Lord, God Almighty—" Here he coughed, stopped, and started again. "Oh Lord, God Almighty—" He stopped, coughing.

The boys roared with laughter and began to pray at the top of their voices. The man jumped up and ran. The boys whooped after him, dragging their mourners with them. The mourners began to shout and pray, and yell hymns. When they came to, and they found that Mr. D. was gone, the mourners realized that in the process their sins had rolled away and they were converted. So they raised a Hallelujah all together and started back to camp at top speed, having, they believed, obtained a signal victory over the devil!

There were many "professors," as they were called—that is Christians long set in their habits and their virtues—who were outraged by this dynamic Christianity. But that made no difference to Peter, nor to the thousand and one who found their souls in the violent eruptions of Cane Ridge, and all the meetings that followed.

4

Brenda looked at Peter these days as if he had betrayed a trust in finding salvation while leaving Jerry among the lost. She seemed to blame him for Jerry's drinking, the horse racing, and the intimacy with John and Penny. The truth is Peter blamed himself. And he felt so unhappy about it all that he could not deal with his deep-seated moral discomfort, in accordance with the Circuit Rider's rude principles of psychiatry. "Whatever it is," Wilkerson had said, "lay it out before God and look at it fair and square. And if something keeps bothering you, like a flea biting you but you don't know where the crittur is, just keep at it till you find it. No matter how bad it is, God will forgive, if you do all you can to make amends, and make sure you don't repeat the wrong. And then just let God take care of it. But once God forgives you, forgive yourself. Don't let what's done and past and confessed and made amends for and forgiven, nag you any more."

So Peter had been told. Again and again in his morning and evening exercises, he laid out his sense of responsibility for Jerry before God. But Brenda's burning midnight eyes, looking reproach from under her plumy black brows, continued to haunt him. Desperately he prayed, "If I am forgiven, let me save Jerry. Don't let me fail to make amends when I want to so much."

Coming back from Cane Ridge, Peter learned from his father that Jerry had gone down the Mississippi on the flat-boats which, at this time of year, were carrying the overflowing harvests of Tennessee and Western Kentucky to market in New Orleans. Then for weeks he heard no more of Jerry, till one chilly October night, after he had snugged himself into bed under the eaves, he heard a screech owl outside—Jerry's old signal! He threw on his fur jacket, and climbed down the ladder and tip-toed out past the sleeping family. There, his slight form outlined against the full golden sphere of the harvest moon, sat Jerry on his horse Smoky. In the moonlight, Peter could see that his face looked half starved and haunted, and that the hand which held the horse's rein was shaking helplessly. "Jerry, where'd you come from?" said Peter.

"She's gone! Polly's gone! Nobody knows where. She's lit out! Rodriguez, too!" Jerry began to blubber.

"You've been on a long jag," said Peter severely.

Jerry made some effort to control himself. His teeth were chattering and he was shaking all over. "It's c—c—cussed cold," he said apologetically.

"I got to get you in by a fire," said Peter. "Then we can talk." He considered. If they went into his own cabin here, Jus and Mary and Sis might hear Jerry blubbering about Polly. Peter couldn't let his friend be shamed by exposing him that way. If they went to Jerry's house, Brenda might hear about Polly. Finally he took Jerry down by the caves. The boys crawled into one of the half wrecked buildings there and built a fire in front of it. There they spent the night.

Jerry had gone to the simple little tropical frame house in Natchez where Polly had been living in some comfort, waited on by a colored slave girl. He found the door stove in, as if by somebody who had raided it or robbed it, one end collapsing where a sill had given away, and the whole overgrown with vines and shrubbery. "Couldn't have been there since last spring," was Peter's deduction. Jerry had asked all the neighbors. Nobody knew when she had left or why. He poked into the house, and saw one of her dresses hanging there. It was so desolate that it scared him. "Like everybody there had been dead a long time."

"Did you tell John?"

"Yes, and he said he didn't know anything about it. It seemed like he wasn't interested which is mighty queer, seeing she's his own sister."

However, when he had got back to Russellville, Penny had been most sympathetic, expertly rubbing salt into his wounds by suggesting various horrible possibilities. "When you've been on a long jag, I know who's at the bottom of it," said Peter furiously, forgetting that he was a Christian and burning with sinful rage.

"You mustn't say anything about P—Penny," blubbered Jerry. "She's the only f—friend I—I have."

This so outraged Peter that he said, roughly, "Stop that bawling, or I'll give you something to bawl for." He was still far from Christian meekness. However, his roughness seemed to do Jerry good. And when Peter finally suggested that they go to sleep, and said he must repeat his Bible verses and say a prayer before sleeping Jerry surprised him by asking him to say the verses to him and by listening reverently while he prayed. So they slept, two tired boys wrapped in one horse blanket, the red glow of the coals in front of their open-faced shelter mingling with the light of the high white solemn moon, on the round dark face, all rude power and health even in sleep, and the delicate, fine, white face, which seemed already old and etched with unendurable pain.

5

Through the circuit riders and the circuit lawyers they looked for Polly all winter in vain. One afternoon when winter was thawing into spring, there was a hesitant knocking on the big plank door, and a soft voice said weakly, "Mammy, it's Polly. Let me in."

With a wild rush, Peter and Mary and Sis flung open the door. There she stood. Her blue eyes seemed to fill all the face from which the bloom and roundness had gone. She looked taller than of old and very thin, and her gaunt length was wrapped in a brown velvet cloak trimmed with fur, from the depths of which came a faint mewing like that of a kitten. As her mother sprang toward her she collapsed in the dooryard slush. Peter picked her up in his arms—shocked to feel her so frail and light. She gasped, "Mammy, the baby!" Mary opened the velvet cloak and found the little mewing thing. Peter laid Polly on the big bed. She dissolved into tears, crying as if she would never stop. "I g—guess it took my last strength just to get here," she murmured apologetically.

Mary had the baby in her arms and was unwinding the woolsy in which it was wound round and round like a papoose. It kept squawling faintly, its small face pinched and blue. "Peter, hold it, while I get some fresh linsy," said Mary. Sis was already occupied with trying to make Polly drink some warmed milk and brandy. Peter took the baby awkwardly, weighed down with the immense responsibility of it, and uncovering its tiny wrinkled feet, he held them to the fire, chafing them gently. They felt like the cold claws of a little bird. "It seems kinda blue," he said anxiously.

Polly raised herself a little on the bed and said weakly, "My milk's gone. Try feeding it some pap."

Sis said, "Mammy, we got to get Polly more comfortable." Mary, distracted between the baby and Polly, turned to help Sis but threw a roll of clean linsy at Peter. Wet a piece of the clean rag in milk," she directed, "and give it to the babe to suck."

The baby died that night, Peter holding it in his arms as the last flicker of life went out. Polly died two days later. Mary knelt on one side of the bed and Peter on the other, and together they prayed her home to God. Most of these two days she had been conscious but only in a dim, dreamy way. They tried to find out what had happened to Pentacost. She didn't know. She had come north with him into Tennessee. "I never had no call to doubt him. He was good to me," she murmured, dreamily. "But the day came went he didn't come back. And the winter came, and I had the baby alone. I kept thinking he'd come, but he didn't. It was cold. I had nothing to eat." She had done the best she could. She had brought the baby home to her mother through one hundred miles of slush and snow and rain.

She felt too tuckered out to come to God now. "But I ain't against Him," she murmured. "I never was. I just didn't have much sense, I guess." Her voice trailed off. But she seemed to feel happy in their prayers. They were a charm, a magic to ward off a nameless dread. So she died.

Peter, Eddie, Jus, and Dean made the coffin of rough pine boards. Sis and Mary stripped her wasted young body of its worn finery and burned everything—the fur-trimmed velvet mantle, the convent made, torn, soiled underwear of fine cambric. Then they re-clothed her neatly and honestly in new cotton and purple-dyed wool of their own spinning and weaving. The baby they bathed and re-clothed in fine, white cotton and laid it in its mother's arms in the coffin.

Mary wanted no one to be present at the burial except Eddie and Bonny, Sis and Peter, Dominie and Barbara, and Dean and Jassamine, and, of course, herself and Jus. She refused to send word to John. "If I thought the sight of what they've ruined would soften him or Pen, or bring them to God—" She hesitated a little. Peter said harshly, "They could have helped her, but they didn't. She could have gone to them, but she didn't. They've earned being kept away." But he begged earnestly to be permitted to call Jerry. When Mary grudgingly agreed, he galloped to Jerry's house, dreading to tell him, yet feeling that he could never look him in the face again if he did not make every effort to let him look his last on her. Brenda met him at the door. She had been weeping, and her eyes burned dark and desperate through tears. "He's not here," she said, and added, with bitter sarcasm, "Where he is you ought to know. Who else but you blazed the trail there?"

Peter thought that nothing on earth except the need of being fair to Jerry could drive him to go near John's house. But there was no help for it. Riding up to the house, hating every memory associated with it, he thought there was just a chance of avoiding John and Penny. So he rode around first to the little cabin which he and Jerry had been wont to occupy together. There he found Jerry, lying in a drunken stupor. Peter shook him. He could not bring him to! He lifted him by both shoulders, and stood him on his feet. Jerry crumpled to the floor. "Leave me alone," he whimpered.

"That's just what I'm going to do," said Peter, furiously. A great, crashing wave of anger seemed to lift him up and carry him out and deposit him in the saddle. He kicked the horse furiously and never stopped galloping till he came in sight of his own cabin. Then his anger flagged, and unutterable misery succeeded it. He wondered if he had done the right thing in leaving Jerry like that. Whatever he did about Jerry he always felt haunted with a sense of wrong-doing. Not till he was almost up to the gate did he remember to pray. He stopped and bowed his head, and murmured, "Dear God—help me—help Jerry, help everything. It's all so bad."

"Where's Jerry?" asked Mary, in a whisper, when Peter came in.

Peter hesitated. One of the sins which he was trying to avoid was the ready lying of his unregenerate days. "Tell the truth. Always tell the truth," his Christian conscience was now murmuring. But somewhere inside him another voice was arguing. "The truth, yes. But must it be *all* the truth?" He couldn't let Jerry down by describing the state in which he had found him. Mary might have guessed that Jerry drank too much, but she had never seen him like that. He replied with careful evasiveness, "Jerry wasn't at home, and Aunt Brenda didn't know where he'd gone."

"Well, it's just as well," whispered Mary, looking relieved. She wanted to protect Polly from the moral analysis of the Baptists.

Inside the cabin they knelt in a circle around the coffin where Polly lay looking so fair and sweet and at peace. Dominie read how the women came to the garden to find where they had laid Jesus, and found the stone rolled away. And then he prayed, pausing for the low sobbing answers, "Yes, Lord." "Lord, take her to your own kind arms," and they sang Charles Wesley's hymn, "Help us to help each other, Lord."

Then Peter and Eddie, Dean and Jus lifted the coffin and carried it out of doors and down the long path through the woods to the sheltered place where they had dug her grave—Dominie, Mary, Sis, Barbara, and Jassamine following. At the grave Dominie read the burial service, and then took the shovel and helped Jus, Eddie, and Peter and Dean to shovel the deep red earth over her and set up the cross of wood with the bark still on it which they had made to mark her grave.

Mary stood dry-eyed, her lips moving continually in prayer. The spring sunshine straggled through flying gusty clouds and burned on the red mud. As they turned and walked slowly back to the cabin Mary said to Barbara bitterly, "I'm going to move away. I'm goin to a place where the dirt ain't red. It's like there was blood soaking all through it. I want to die with my eyes on earth that's got no stain of blood on it."

But Barbara said gently, "Think of the blood of the Lamb, dear, like a healing flood, washing all things clean."

As they tramped back, their boots slushing and sloshing in the red, slippery mud, Peter bled inwardly with a passionate, futile pity. The dead face of Polly, still so sweet and pure in all its lineaments, and the little blue, pinched, blurred face of the baby were etched on his memory. He kept trying to push them away, but in every pause of his thinking they would come back. It was as if he would not really see anything else from now on for ever. He thought desperately, "She was soft and weak. But she wasn't bad. And the baby! It ain't fair. There's no justice in it."

If only they'd been able to have the baby baptized! But Dominie was not ordained and could not administer the sacraments. It was such a poor little scrap of a thing! If Peter could only be sure God had taken it. Then he thought, "A sparrow can't fall to his ground without His noticin." That comforted him. If God would look after a sparrow surely He could be trusted to look after the baby. However, the question continued to bother him. He would never feel easy till he had asked the Circuit Rider if a baby had to be baptized to go home to God.

And still, whatever else he thought about, the image of Polly in the coffin, with the baby at her breast, would keep coming back. The thought was like the wound they made when they put a branding iron to a young calf. He thought, "It's branded on me. I can never look anywhere again without seein her."

He tried to divert himself by looking around for signs of spring. But his eyes only fell on the red earth. He repeated to himself what he had heard Barbara say, "It looks bloody. But think of the blood of the Lamb." In their brutal world where so much blood was shed, the best that could be done was to hallow the image of blood itself, and see beyond the death of the innocent, the image of Supreme Innocence dying, of its own will, for the redemption of man.

6

Peter made no move to see Jerry. He dreaded the moment when he would have to tell him that Polly was gone more than he had ever dreaded anything in his life. Three days after the burial, Jerry rode up to the gate. He was neatly dressed. His horse had been carefully curried. He had that look of being spruced up, regenerated, and apologetically virtuous which he often wore after he had finally come out from a spree. Pity for what was to come made Peter lowering and ungracious. "Get down," he said, "I've something to tell you."

Jerry dismounted, and picked his way after Peter down the wet path to the plank bench under the chestnut tree. Jerry sat down. Peter stood over him.

"Jerry, I don't know how to say it easy. I've just got to blurt it out and pray God you'll bear up. Polly's dead. She came home. She died, and her little bit of a baby died, and we buried them Monday, yonder in the woods, by the old oak tree."

All the blood was drained from Jerry's face. His gray eyes had narrowed to sharpness and bitterness. He said harshly, through dry lips, "You might a invited me for —" he choked, but finished, with a kind of venomous intensity, "the buryin."

"I went for you," answered Peter, and the pity and anger in his dark face gave it a strange, glaring, animal savagery, "and I found you in the cabin at John's. You was dead drunk. I shook you. I tried to stand you up. It was no use. You was too drunk."

Jerry said nothing. He was shaking as if in a cold wind. Then he moaned a little and buried his face in his hands.

Peter continued relentlessly, "I was so mad at you I could a kicked you."

Jerry lifted his face. His trembling had ceased. He spoke clearly and sharply. "Kickin would have been too good for me!"

Peter was taken aback, and so suddenly softened that a big lump came into his throat. "Oh Jerry," he choked.

Jerry put out his hand as if to ward him off. "Don't, Pete. I can't stand it. I got to handle it alone." He jumped up and ran as swiftly as if he had spread wings down the path—so swiftly that Peter, running after him, could not catch up with him. He had leaped on his horse and was off at a gallop when Peter came up to the gate. Peter shouted, "Jerry. Jerry. Hold on!" But Jerry did not stop or turn. Peter stood looking after him, feeling all broken up, knowing he should do something. But what? In the distance Jerry turned, and made a motion as if he were waving good-bye. Eagerly Peter shouted and waved. That little gesture of Jerry's brought a strange sense of relief.

Next day Hans brought him a note on torn, soiled paper, written in a brownish fluid that looked like blood. "Dere Pete I hav gon away to start lif agen, and mak a betr job of it. Tel Mamy not to wory. Dont yu wory about drink. I am don with al that. Jerry."

Slightly relieved, dreading to see Brenda, but knowing he must do it, Peter rode over to Jerry's house. Brenda fiercely upbraided Peter for everything, talking as if Jerry had been a young saint before Peter enticed him away to ride Aladdin, while Peter stood dumb and helpless under her abuse. But on the way home he kept up a fierce mental argument with her, explaining and excusing himself. "All I did was to try to keep bad from getting worse," he kept saying to himself. He felt sore and scratched all over, as if wild beasts had been clawing him, and weighed down with a burden as large as the world. "Cast thy burdens on the Lord." The verse came to him like a thin strain of music amidst yells and curses. All the rest of the day he spent reading the Bible, trying to find out how to roll off the burden. When he went to sleep at last that night, he was still far from happy but somewhat at peace. "Seems like if I didn't have the Bible, I couldn't stand life the way it is," he thought. "I'd do like Jerry did. I'd take to drink."

CHAPTER 33

**Russellville, Kentucky
to Sumner County, Tennessee
March, 1802 to August, 1802**

Jesse Walker had succeeded Thomas Wilkerson on the circuit. He was a plain, rough, vigorous man, always in a hurry, never daunted by anything, less charming than Wilkerson, but with a solid manly piety that won Peter's respect. Peter had never been more glad to see a circuit rider than he was when, in April, Walker's rough homely face showed up above the Cartwright fence.

Walker set Peter's mind at ease about baptism, explaining that baptism is not for the sake of the child, for every child is safe in God's care so long as it has not reached the age where it can exercise its own free will and intelligence. Baptism, he said, is only a means of pledging the parents and the church to care for the soul of the child and to bring it to full knowledge of God by the time it reaches the age to take charge of its own life. "So don't you worry, Pete," said Walker. "God has the baby in His mighty arms. And I'll wager that right now it's laughing and crowing and lookin up in His face as happy as can be."

"And Polly?"

Walker looked worried. "Did she come to God before she died?"

"She was too sick. She didn't hold out against Him when we prayed. She didn't have strength or heart left, one way or the other."

Walker was silent. He pursed his lips and blew his breath out with a hissing sound and frowned worriedly. Finally he relaxed, and, laying his square rough hand on Peter's shoulder, he said, "Well, I wouldn't worry about it. God's got it all in His charge, and He'll take care of it. It just wouldn't be like God not to be kinder than you or me. And I guess you know what you or I would do in the circumstances."

With this ambiguous theology Peter was strangely content.

He was comforted, too, by a passage from John Wesley's writings which Walker let him copy, slowly and painfully on a piece of legal paper he got from his father. It was a warning against what, in modern times, would be called perfectionism. "Perfect Christians are not free from ignorance nor from mistakes. I want you to be all love. This is the perfection I believe and teach, and this perfection is consistent with a thousand nervous disorders, as a high-strained perfection is not ... Man can no more attain Adamic than angelic perfection. The perfection of which man is capable while he dwells in a corruptible body is the complying with that kind command, 'Son, give me thy heart.' It is the loving of the Lord, his God, with all his heart, and with all his soul, and with all his mind."

Where they had so little to read, Peter's paper served for a month of class meetings, and when it was worn to pieces and had been memorized by everybody, Finis Ewing borrowed it for the Presbyterian converts for whom, in imitation of the Methodists, he had set up a class. Doctor Craighead rebuked McGready for letting him do it, and the synod ordered that such unorthodox proceedings be stopped. But Finis went on holding the class in his own cabin, and feeding it from the Methodist bread basket.

But even among Methodists there was a limit to amateur theology. At a meeting at Ebenezer, Peter was earnestly exhorting the others to keep time in the day for putting your soul in order, just as you ought to have times to wash and to clean your teeth. "Sometimes when I get up late or go to bed late, I say to myself, 'Well, I can skip it this time.' But if I do I begin to get all mixed up. Things worry me that shouldn't and scare me that shouldn't." He paused and looked around appealingly, "I reckon if you let God out of your mind, it's not only the devils that come in but hobgoblins and spooks."

He stopped suddenly, the blood mounting to his tight dark curls. Jesse Walker was standing by the door listening. Embarrassed, Peter said no more. He was still more embarrassed when a few days later Walker handed him a paper which read: "Peter

Cartwright is hereby permitted to exercise his gifts as an exhorter in the Methodist Episcopal Church so long as his practice is agreeable to the Gospel. Signed in behalf of the Society at Ebenezer. May 1802. Jesse Walker, A.P."

"I—I—can't," said Peter, desperately, thrusting the paper back at Walker. "I can't exhort. I've no trainin. I try to think things out—for—my own peace of mind. I've just got to. And then, when peace comes, and I begin to feel happy—well, I tell about it. I tell it just to encourage other folks—there's so many that's low in their minds. That's all I can do—and I don't need a license for that. Seems as if God gives the license to anybody to say what's helped him and might help somebody else."

But Jesse Walker said, "For all that, Peter, we think there's got to be some order and discipline in all the talking about God and the soul, and sin and salvation, that's going on everywhere, since this country started coming back to God. You'd better keep that paper. You're all right, my boy, and what you say's all right. Don't worry. Just go ahead and say it." He clapped Peter on the shoulder with a kind, friendly smile. Unable to argue further, but feeling not at all comfortable about it, Peter finally tucked the paper away in the pouch of his linsy shirt.

2

The results of four years of the attack on the sins of Logan County, since McGready first started them all praying, began to show, in the summer of 1802, in regeneration where regeneration had been least expected. It was first noticed when Jacob Young, an assistant preacher on the circuit here, saw young Roberts, the Harpe brother-in-law, standing at the back of the congregation at a camp meeting in McGready's camp ground. He was hatless, with open shirt, his breast bare, his feet bare. The tears were rolling down his rough, dirty face. One month later Jesse Walker took Roberts into the congregation at Ebenezer. Peter could not believe his eyes when he saw him walk up and kneel at the preacher's feet. He had shaved, and cut his hair. He wore a neat new suit and new shoes. He carried a new hat in his hand. Nobody could have looked more quietly respectable. Two months after that Young appointed Roberts the class leader of a small group of new converts in his neighborhood.

From Roberts regeneration seemed to spread to his sisters. Betsy Roberts married John Husstetter. She and her husband set up as tenants on Colonel Anthony Buller's place, six miles south of Russellville. Betsy's little son, Big Harpe's boy, was growing into a sturdy little fellow. He was called Joe Roberts, and by common consent his father's name, and his connection with that death's head still at the forks of the road north of Russellville, was to be forgotten. Susan Roberts also occupied a cabin on the Buller place, and now appeared to earn an honest living by spinning. Her little girl, Big Harpe's other child, was an exquisite little creature, with delicately rounded, pretty features, a graceful figure, and a dark, devilish bright eye. It seemed a great triumph to the praying Christians of Logan County that they bade fair even to knit Big Harpe's children into the fabric of a civilized society.

Despite improvement all around them, for Peter and his family the beautiful land had been poisoned by all that they had gone through. Mary felt the cabin haunted by the memories of Polly. Peter's efforts at self-discipline, all the fellowship of his church and the excitements of camp meetings, could not fill the empty place which Jerry had left, nor bring him a girl on whom he could lavish, with self-respect, the tenderness Ivy had constantly aroused and betrayed. There were charming girls at camp meetings. Peter attended all gatherings with ever renewed hope. But somehow there was no girl for him.

Seeing his family's state of mind, Jus began to talk about a fine piece of land he could get in the new country that was opening up nearer the mouth of the Cumberland, in Livingston County. At this the pioneer blood began to stir in them all. To leave behind all that had hurt so much! To build again and build better! Their dreams had failed but there was a new dream on the horizon. For Peter there was here neither friend nor sweetheart. But over the rim of the hills to the north—who could tell? For Sis there was not a man here to marry. But perhaps—in the new country. And meanwhile Jus calculated that the difference between the price he could get for this land with "improvements" and the price he would have to pay for the new land would almost make him rich! And so it was decided that when the last harvests were in, late in the fall, they would move. The prospect brought a strange relief—like the sudden cessation of a pain that had been hurting as long as they could remember. Even Jus agreed that it had been worse than he had realized to live among Rogues.

Even with the prospect of moving, Peter was so restless that he thought of signing on with a crew to take a flat-boat of flour down to New Orleans. A boat costing $100 stored from 200 to 300 barrels of flour and required five men to navigate it. The man in charge of the crew received $100.00 for the voyage. The others received $50.00 each. At this price, western Kentucky was being stripped of all its likely young men. Back in Peter's mind was the thought that, if he went over this route which he believed Jerry had followed, he might possibly find Jerry. He could not rid himself of his old sense of responsibility for his lifelong playmate, and he had not ceased to miss him.

But there were watchful eyes which had no desire to see the most promising of all the converts of the great revival go down that path to New Orleans which had been the ruin of so many. So in August, Walker turned up with a counter proposal. How would Peter like to be one of the guard of young men with rifles who were to be sent east across the mountains to meet Bishop Asbury and escort him to our Cumberland country for the Annual Conference?

Peter's eyes sparkled. To escort Bishop Asbury! There was something so fabulous about the idea that he was struck dumb. Walker, misunderstanding his silence, said, "Don't worry. You won't be the only one from here. I spoke to your brother, Eddie, and says he'll go if you will. And going east across Tennessee you will be able to pick up others at our regular preaching places till by the time you hit the big mountains, there'll be thirty of you. I'll go with you myself a hundred miles or so and put you in charge of the preacher on the Knoxville circuit."

"Oh," said Peter, able to speak at last. "I'd go if I had to go alone and on foot and nobody anywhere to show the way!"

3

It was not the first time Asbury had visited the Cumberland, on his annual trip to the West. That summer two years before, when the camp meetings were just beginning, he had been a solemn spectator of a service initiated by Presbyterians at Drake's Creek meeting house near Nashville. "The stand," he wrote in his diary, "was in the open air, embosomed in a wood of lofty beech trees, and the ministers of God, Presbyterian and Methodist, united their labors, and mingled with the childlike simplicity of primitive times."

This formalizing of the out-door preaching place into a magnificent natural cathedral by the Presbyterians was something he never would have thought of, for, no matter how he roamed the wilderness, he was mentally an exile there, homesick for snug roofs and close gardens. But he was quick to see the enormous possibilities of the new institution. The eloquence and imagination of the half dozen local Presbyterian preachers to whose souls McGready had set fire were opening an opportunity of which their own church was not ready to take advantage. Dryly Asbury recorded his rejoicing that "God is visiting the souls of the Puritans who are candid enough to acknowledge their obligations to the Methodists."

Hence the plan to hold the Annual Conference in the Cumberland, in the autumn of 1802, was part of a well calculated design to follow up where the Presbyterians had opened the way. The conference here would give all Methodist ministers west of the mountains a chance to see at first hand the wonders God and McGready had wrought in the Cumberland, and to master the technique of the camp meeting. At the same time it would advertise the Methodist Church to the many whom the preaching of the Presbyterians were bringing home to God, but who were repelled by the "soul-searing doctrines" of Calvin, and the lack of machinery in the Presbyterian Church, as hitherto constituted and dominated in these parts by Doctor Craighead at Nashville, to meet the rather primitive needs of unlettered and inwardly hag-ridden converts.

The conference was to be held at Strothers Meeting House, a neat, substantial little building of squared timbers, well plastered, built two years before in Sumner County, Tennessee, the area so long

dominated by James Haw, who had now joined McGready, Stone
and others in the Limbo between Methodism and Presbyterianism.
If, after Haw's public recantation two years before, anything were
still needed to show that Asbury as "Bishop" was not the advocate
and inheritor of the ancient tyrannies of ecclesiasticism, the holding
of the Annual Conference by Asbury here, in Haw's own country,
ought to do it.

4

Peter and Eddie set off on a dry, blazing day in August, with
saddlebags packed with all the food Mary, Bonny, and Sis could
think of—cold boiled venison, sliced bacon, corn cakes, wheat cakes,
green roasting ears, and ripe peaches. They travelled east on the
narrow rutted road known as the Cumberland Road, which ran
from Nashville to Knoxville. About half way to Knoxville they
overtook a man of clerical appearance on foot. He said that last
evening, as he was riding this way, Sam Mason and two others had
blocked the road. Mason had said, "If you have anything to say
to your Maker, I give you five minutes to do it." Trembling, the
preacher knelt and consigned his soul to God. Bowing low, with
closed eyes, he shuddered under a violent and painful blow, and
thought, "This is it. My God, I come home to Thee." Slowly he
realized that he was still alive. All that had happened was that
he had been brutally kicked. He opened his eyes. The broad
bronzed ruddy face of Sam Mason was looking down on him. His
mouth stretched over his protruding tooth with a harsh sneering
expression. "Get up you, fool. Your miserable life isn't worth taking." And with that he caught the preacher's horse by the bridle
and crashed into the bushes.

Peter said, "They're always telling stories like that about Mason
but nobody will swear to it." "I'll swear to it," said the preacher
grimly. The boys shared their food with him and took turns walking
while he rode first one and then another of their horses. As the high
mountains began to close around him, Peter felt a deep formless
terror rising from the depths of his boyhood memories. The first

night they spent east of Knoxville, camping out-of-doors, in a valley by a rushing stream, he could not sleep. He steadied himself by alternately praying and recognizing and defining the night sounds. "That's only a wolf," he would say to himself. "That's a wildcat. That's just a tree cracking." Finally he began to repeat to himself every Scripture passage that he knew. In the midst of this he fell asleep. When he woke the sun was looking over the shaggy brow of a mountain, in solemn and sumptuous splendor.

The first sight of Bishop Asbury was an experience he was never to forget. He came toward them—a lean, aging, sickly looking man, in a black woolen suit, with black woolen stockings, black buckled shoes, a round hat, and, under the hat a wig, its queue tied in a black silk bag. Such a figure was common enough in the old states or in England. But to Peter's Kentucky eye he was inconceivably strange. In his world, if you wanted to be plain you wore almost anything that came to hand, as most of the Methodist circuit riders did. But if you dressed up, you wanted some color and ornament. It seemed an odd kind of affectation—to dress so fancy, with wig and all—and yet be so very plain. But, in a lifetime on the frontier, Asbury had never made the least concession to its ideas or its tastes. He remained incorrigibly the provincial Englishman, than whom no race or style of being could be more contrary to the trans-Allegheny picture of what it is that makes a man.

And yet this strangeness of the thin, indomitable, unbendable, and unbreakable being had an almost supernatural effect on the imaginations of simple folk. A man without wife or kin or earthly habitation, a frail sick man, who looked as if a feather would knock him over, going up and down the earth preaching salvation! He was coolly indifferent to the frontiersman's skills, superstitions, fears, and concrete knowledge. Yet he was utterly invincible. Robbers could not scare him. Fever could not kill him. An unearthly kind of creature, a true messenger from above!

But his preachers were not all so susceptible to Asbury's charm. As he rode back with the cavalcade, day after day, through the dangerous passes of the wilderness, and then out across the fair open acres of Kentucky, Peter was aware of stormy under-currents of discussion among the stalwart men who kept adding themselves to the company. They resisted Asbury's steelly will. They raged against his mental limitations. But he was conscious, too, that when Asbury got them all together and began to read and pray and talk about God, as he did whenever and wherever he could, sometimes four or five times in one of those hurrying, hard-riding days, his utter other-worldliness brought a solemn quieting of all the storms.

5

There were only twenty-seven traveling preachers, including probationers, in the Western Conference, which included all the territory west of the Alleghenies. And of the 350,000 people in all that area, there were only 7,738 white and 464 colored Methodists. Of church property there was nothing, except a few one-room log chapels, reared and owned by the local societies, and the Academy at Bethel which struggled to convey a few elements of education beyond the barest literacy. $80.00 a year was all a travelling preacher was allowed to keep out of his collections from his humble and scattered parishioners. And the presiding elders and bishops got no more.

Yet as they gathered at Strothers Meeting House, Peter had the feeling that he was part of a great moving fellowship across thousands of miles of forests, barrens, and floods. Many of the circuit riders he knew. They had stayed at his home and had been revered household figures. He beamed and glowed as one after another hailed him—Burke, Lurton, Northcutt, Wilkerson, Page, Walker—throwing both arms around him and clasping him in a manly hug, or tousling his hair or clapping him on the back, each according to his own style of demonstrativeness. Of many whom he had not seen or did not clearly remember he had heard. They were like heroes of well-beloved stories, and seeing them in the flesh, he stared at them with a feeling that to see them with his own eyes was strange and wonderful. There was Francis Poythress, haggard, with staring eyes, always with another solicitously at his elbow. After the long years in which he had battled as the first Elder of Kentucky, it was said that he was losing his mind. He believed that there was a malignancy emanating from the mass of mankind which was poisoning him. Peter looked at him, anxiously, a kind of cold horror in his heart. Why should God let this happen to one who had served Him so well? But somewhere within him a tonic voice spoke. "God didn't let it happen. Elder Poythress let it happen to himself. The grace of God is sufficient. But a man must lay hold on it." Man is free and God is good. Peter had to believe that. The best of his generation in the new West had to believe it. But how many had believed it before them?

Peter looked with equal interest on William McKendree, the new presiding elder of the Kentucky district—a big, raw-boned man still on the young side of middle age, with a round, firm face, strong features, blue eyes, high and arched eyebrows, smooth fine light brown hair, curling a little at the ends, getting a little sparse on top. He had heard how McKendree had been ready to secede, with those who wanted a democratic church and the repudiation of all that was Tory and English, and how Asbury had won him over. And now, they said, it was McKendree who was keeping the rest of the Kentucky preachers in line.

Peter and the other boys who had acted as guards, and the hundred or so class leaders and leading laymen who had come from the conference, attended the open meetings, and heard Asbury recommend diligence and faithfulness in dealing with the multitudes who were ready to come to God. He heard some discussions of the problem which had so exercised the quarterly conference in May— the need of developing means of education for all and special training for the many new young leaders who must be raised up. He heard that the Academy at Bethel was to be recommended to the special attention of the Kentucky legislature, and that in every circuit the circuit rider was to do what he could to see that books were made available and that schools were started—whether with public or private funds, by any group or any denomination. They must cooperate with all.

But he had to remain outside when the great climax of the Conference came, and the circuit riders gathered in the chapel to hear them read the assignments for the next year. Westerners as they were, they would have liked to bargain among themselves, and pull wires and make exchanges, and so parcel out the circuits by common agreement. But under Asbury's rule, they did nothing of the sort. They went where they were sent. Why they did it—God only knew. He had no means of compelling them. He offered them only hardships, persecution, starvation, and rags. And when they did it, they inwardly refused to show him what, as an Englishman, Asbury thought only proper—the reverence due to the authority of God in him vested. Nobody represented God to these Kentucky preachers. They obeyed Asbury because he never spared himself, and was getting so frail the least they could do was not to add to his burdens; and because, though he lacked horse sense, his arrangements were proved by experience to be uncannily right. All of which Asbury could not understand in his preachers. Only God could bridge the gulf between them. And this God continually did.

While the momentous business of assigning circuits was going on, Peter and Eddie sat outside on a log, exchanging bits of gossip and surmise. Finally Eddie said, "Pete, I'm goin' to be a circuit rider."

Peter stared at him open-mouthed. If he had said, "I am going to be the angel Gabriel," it would have been less startling. His own half brother! An ordinary young man, with whom he had tussled and eaten and slept, to become one of that exalted species! Till that moment he had thought circuit riders were born, not made. Or at least called by a special act of God. He gasped, "How do you do it?"

"Brother Walker explained it. First they give you a license to exhort. Brother Walker has listened to me at class meetings. He's heard how when I read the Bible and pray in my turn, I try to do the best I can. And he says I should be licensed as an exhorter. So first John Page and then Brother McKendree spoke to me about it. I don't feel good enough, but if I'm called through no will and thought of my own, I don't see how I can say 'No'."

Peter was thinking uneasily of the license to exhort he had in his pouch. He had told no one about it, not even his mother. "But an exhorter ain't a circuit rider," he said.

"No, that's only the beginning. Many are called to be exhorters, but there ain't many of them that stick it out to be made circuit riders. I'll have to have a course of reading, and the circuit rider, whoever is put on our circuit, will examine me every month, and the presiding elder will examine me every three months when he comes around regular, and at other times if he happens to come special. And I'll have particular jobs given me like looking out for Roberts, and seeing how he makes out with his class. It's not only exhorting that counts; you've got to show that you're a real soul doctor."

"But when do you get to be a circuit rider?"

"When they're satisfied I'm fit, I'll be sent to new territory for three months to form my own circuit and come back and report at quarterly meeting."

"What do you report?" Peter was now thoroughly interested.

"I make a map of the territory, and a list of every living soul in it, and where they are and who they are. And if anybody has started anything—a school or a mill or a church, I report that. And I say what folks raise and whether it's good land or not, and whether there's any road or trail yet, and if not what's the best way of getting around. And of course I say how many times I've preached and whether I brought any into the church."

"All alone in a strange country! It would be lonesome."

"God would be there," answered Eddie, solemnly.

"And what about Bonny?"

Eddie looked troubled. "That's the one thing that's hard. Bishop Asbury and Brother McKendree haven't got wives, and they think no circuit rider should have either. But Brother Page is married, and he says, 'Look at it this way. You enlist as a circuit rider, and she enlists as a circuit rider's wife—and you both do what you can, from one time to the next, for the service of God.' And he says, 'It isn't all bad, if she's the same stuff a circuit rider's got to be made of. It has things about it that snug-abed, stay-put spouses don't have.' That's what he says, and I think Bonny will want me to go wherever it's my call to go."

Peter turned this over in his mind thoughtfully. A girl of the same stuff a circuit rider would have to be! The idea had a wonderful charm. He shook himself out of his reverie, laying the thought aside for contemplation when he should be alone, and said, "Well, then, when you break your circuit, you're a circuit rider."

"Oh no, you don't stay in the circuit you've broken. I'll be placed as an assistant circuit rider on one of the old circuits. They haven't had enough probationers so far to have assistant circuit riders, but as fast as they can train them up from out of the ranks of the ex-horters they will. You see some of the older circuits are getting pretty well settled up now, and they need something the first wild ones don't—somebody to start real schools, not just reading classes, and take a hand in building up town and country. And the circuit riders that have been active a long time have learned a lot they didn't know at first. So after you've shown that you've got what you ought to have to go it alone in wild territory, you're put back in a more settled area, with an experienced circuit rider."

"Kinda to learn the refinements of it," said Peter shrewdly.

Eddie looked at him a moment thoughtfully. Then he said, "Pete, why don't you aim to be a circuit rider? You've got gifts."

"Oh no," said Peter, shrinking back. "Oh no. I'd be scared. I just ain't fit."

At that moment the doors of the chapel opened, and the circuit riders poured out, some looking resolute and exalted, some worried. They broke up into groups, earnestly talking. Black Harry Hosier, Asbury's assistant, touched Peter on the shoulder. "Bishop Asbury wants to see you."

Peter's knees knocked together. He gave Eddie a push. "He means you."

"No, Peter," said Black Harry gravely. "You're the one Father Asbury calls for."

Peter felt as if he were walking on legs of snow that might melt away any moment as, with pounding heart, he followed Harry along the woodland path to a sheltered place where he found Bishop Asbury seated on a rock. Asbury looked at him with a mild benignity on his pale, regularly featured face, and said, "God bless you, my son. Sit down here on this moss at my feet."

Peter sat down and lifted his eyes to the great man throned above him, against the sun-pierced green and gold background of the forest leaves. Asbury was looking down on him, his gray eyes in his ascetic face, full of a still, remote kindness. "I want you to tell me all that you know about Brother Haw," he said.

Amazement and relief filled Peter. This simple question had nothing to do with himself. His relief showed in the ready vivacity with which he described his visit to Haw, and the man's crusty personality. When he came to the drama of Haw's confession, before all those multitudes that summer morning, with the Presbyterian and Methodist preachers shoulder to shoulder in a solid phalanx behind him, he completely forgot himself, building up the scene, gesturing, even imitating the tones of Haw's voice. A faint gleam, like the ghost of a smile, kept lighting up Asbury's face as he listened, and he kept concentrating his attention on the boy with sudden sparks of almost human interest. But after a second or two, he would again draw the pale mask over his face and his eyes would resume their look of remote, impersonal watchfulness.

"And now, Peter," he said gravely, "seeing that you are observant and have a good memory I want you to repeat exactly what it was that Haw had said against me, and that our good Presbyterian brethren made him unsay."

Peter was painfully embarrassed. Excellent as his memory was, he had never really understood the objections to Asbury. They dated back to pre-Revolutionary and trans-Allegheny conflicts of opinions and personality which were quite beyond his ken. But he did his best to explain. "As I see it, Brother Haw thought you wanted to rule like you was God himself." He stopped, and added quaintly, with a disarming smile, "I reckon he was thinking of a Presbyterian God, who makes up His mind before any body's even been created and there's nobody anywhere to raise any objection— He makes up His mind beforehand who's to be damned and who's to be saved, and where all they'll go, and what they'll do, and nothing they ever do after He's created 'em, can ever change His mind."

This version of Presbyterianism almost cracked the porcelain glaze of Asbury's face, but he composed himself and listened with a sharpened gleam in his gray eye, as Peter went on. "Brother Haw said that you wanted to get yourself up like a king and lord over God's ministers' wills, and their consciences and the whole way the church was fixed was no different from having King and House of Lords, and all that truck we here had got rid of."

Peter stopped, blushing painfully. "I've no business to be repeating this to you, Sir. It's all been unsaid."

"I asked for it," said Asbury with the grim flicker of a smile. "And what I ask for I expect to get, as even Brother Haw 'knows." A faint flush had suffused his marble face. He was silent for a moment, and when he spoke again, his eyes looked quite human, almost as if there were tears of vexation just behind them. "As for those who rail against church government," he said, his smooth baritone voice growing ever more sharp and rough as he went on, "I pity those who cannot distinguish between the bishops and lords of the Church of England, and a worn old man of sixty, who has the power given him of riding 5,000 miles a year at a salary of $80.00 a year, through summer's heat and winter's cold, traveling in all weathers, preaching in all places, his best covering from rain often a blanket, the surest sharpener of his wit, hunger from fasts voluntary and involuntary; his best fare for six months of the twelve, coarse kindness, and his reward, from too many, suspicion, envy, and murmuring all the year around."

There was a slight throb in his voice as he finished. Peter had an extraordinary feeling that this was a child, unjustly hurt. Intense concern and pure hero worship shone in his eyes. Asbury looked down into those glowing dark depths. If there were a son or a woman somewhere to look at him like that! He said gently, "I understand that you have had a true experience of conversion, my son. Tell me about it." Peter told him.

Asbury laid his hand on the boy's head. "You are called to be one of God's ministers, dear son, and will be a mighty one."

Peter started so abruptly that he jerked his head away from Asbury's hand, which caught for a moment in one of the tangled curls and pulled it sharply. "Oh no, Sir. I'm not fit."

"Nonsense!" said Asbury, coldly. And without another word, he rose and walked away.

Peter sat where he was on the moss, feeling like a child that has been slapped, so excited and so frustrated that he wanted to cry. He watched the tall, gaunt, black clothed figure as it went down the woodland path without casting a backward glance. He wanted to run after him and clutch at his long black coat-tails and say, "I will be a minister. I'll do anything you want." But he only sat dumbly, watching Asbury go. He felt as if God Himself were walking away from him.

CHAPTER 34 Livingston County, Kentucky
Autumn, 1802

As Peter and Eddie were preparing to leave the conference, John Page came up to them, beaming, and said, "Have you heard the news? The Cumberland area is to be cut off and made a district by itself, called the Red River district, and I'm to be its Elder. So tell your good mother to keep that comfortable bed for me."

Politely Peter explained that their farm had been sold and that he and his family, with the exception of Eddie and John, were moving up to Livingston county. Taken aback for a moment, Page smiled brightly. "Good, Peter. All that country's reckoned to be in my district, but I've never been up that way. We haven't got any rider up there, either. But now you'll be able to tell me all about it." Then he added, tentatively, "You and your family are going to miss the church. Where you're going it's eighty miles from any circuit."

"Well," said Peter, hesitantly, "I thought there might be Methodists moving in, the same as we're doing, and may be we could get together. Could you give us a letter for my mother and sister and me to introduce us to other Methodists there?"

Page's face was sparkling, as if an idea had suddenly occurred to him. He said, heartily, "Surely. Surely. Wait. I'll go write it at once."

He strode off, rapidly. A few minutes later Peter saw him walking back and forth under the trees in earnest conversation with Asbury. He felt disappointed. No doubt the elder had forgotten all about his request. He was just discussing with Eddie the question whether he should ask for the letter again when Page came back to him, and handed him a folded paper. "There you are, Peter," he said.

Peter started to thrust it into the blouse of his shirt, for he and

Eddie were anxious to be off. But Page said, "Better read it, Peter. In case you want to ask any questions."

Peter's practice in Bible reading had not involved any corresponding practice in reading script. He began slowly to spell out the words. Suddenly he stopped, appalled. "Oh no, Sir. There must be a mistake. I meant just a letter of membership. Oh, please," he pushed the paper back at Page, while Eddie looked on surprised.

For the paper not only stated that Peter Cartwright was a member of the Church with authority to exhort, but that he also had authority to travel through Livingston County, hold meetings, organize classes, and, in a word, form a circuit. It further stated that he would come to the fourth quarterly meeting of the Red River Circuit with a plan for the new circuit, a list of church members, number and size of classes, etc., and that all Methodists were called on to assist him in every way. The idea filled Peter with distress. "I can't," he said to Page. "I—I—I want to be a Christian, but I ain't ready to show anybody else. I've got all I can do to make tracks for myself to the waters of salvation."

"But what are your plans, Peter? You've got too much in you to go on plowing and rafting."

"The first thing I got to do is to get educated. I went to school to Doctor Allen but I didn't learn much because my head was too full of foolishness, but one thing I did learn and that is there's a sight of things I don't know." He hesitated, and then said earnestly, "Brother Page, don't think because I don't feel called to preach that I'm goin back on religion. I reckon that even if I didn't believe in God, I'd kinda have to imagine Him, because the way I am, I have to have something to steer by. I'm just too much for myself without it—I get all mixed up, and things hurt me too much, and I get too full of hankerins and rages. I'm too much of a handful for myself alone. I've got to have help. One help is religion and the other's education. Half of what riles people and drives them crazy out here is just plain dumb ignorance. Well," he ended, his face burning, "I've kinda mixed myself up saying all this. But what I mean is that I know the one right honest thing I can do to serve God just now is to get to know something."

Amused and touched, Page suggested gently that if Peter could find a school in the new region, it would be a good idea to attend it all winter. But in the spring, he could go out for three months to form his circuit and come back to quarterly meeting a year from now with his report. Gently but firmly he refused to take back the paper. "Keep it, lad," he said. "It's your entrance certificate to the best college you'll ever find betwixt heaven and earth." Peter finally put it away in his blouse. His own determination was as great as the presiding elder's. He would not form a circuit. But he was relieved when Page produced two small notes recommending his mother and sister to Methodists in the new country. He'd just sail into the church up there under his mother's colors.

2

While Peter and Eddie were away, the moving to the new home had been managed by Dean, who was moving to Livingston County, too. Dean was one of several Negroes who had made themselves powers by hiring out Negroes for the slave owners, and guaranteeing their satisfactory performance, at the same time organizing them into Methodist classes and improving mind and soul, and helping to buy their freedom. So when Peter reached home, after six weeks of absence, he found all in readiness to move. His father had been in Livingston County all summer. Their house was furnished and waiting. Peter helped with the last minute chores, and then set out with his mother and Sis ahead of the big new four wheeled wagon which held all their goods. Dean and Jassamine and the two handsome little Deans rode behind, and a train of Negro drivers brought up the rear with the horses and cows. They rode westward to the Cumberland and then northward along the river toward its mouth. When they passed the bounds of Logan County, and between him and all that he had known there a low ridge, yellowing in the soft autumn haze, stood like a wall, Peter felt a strange relief. Never again would he meet his brother John on the road to Russellville. And ahead of him in that new land, unrolling in golden amplitude of grassy meadows and long cool stretches of forest and lazy, shallow streams, there waited, with veiled faces, two blessed unknowns—a friend and a sweetheart. For in six weeks of adventure the emptiness in his heart had not been filled.

The new country was the land at the mouth of the Cumberland, bordered on its western and its narrow northern side by the Ohio River. Though it was new, the pioneers here were able to get, by way of the river, the household articles which had been scarce under the rule of Dromgole in Logan County. Mary, Peter, and Sis could not believe their eyes when they saw their new home. Glass windows! A smooth polished plank door with iron hinges and a latch! Separate bedrooms for Peter and Sis and their parents. A polished table and rush-bottomed chairs! A rocking chair! A fireplace with a crane and a Dutch oven! And rows and rows of kettles and skillets!

"All honestly come by," said Jus. "Down the Ohio from Pittsburgh. I ordered them through Daniel Broadhead, at Louisville, an old officer of the Revolution. He gets goods in from thirty-five to forty days, straight through from Philadelphia and Baltimore— everything the Yankees can manufacture, and everything Yankee ships can bring in from foreign ports. There's nothing we need feel the lack of any more."

"And not a stain of blood and thievery on any of it?" asked Mary. She could hardly conceive of the luxuries of life being quite pure from taint.

"None," said Jus, "so long as you get things straight from honest merchants like Broadhead. But he says he takes a heartbreaking loss on whatever he brings in. A fourth of all he orders, Mason's gang gets."

"Mason's gang!" said Peter. "I thought we were getting away from him up here."

"Gettin away from them! Why, Son, we've moved right into the midst of them!"

There was no time for further discussion then because Mary wanted to get unpacked before dark and cook supper in the new pans and skillets. After supper was over, and the new red and white table cloth removed, and Mary and Sis were gingerly washing the new white crockery dishes in the new tin dishpan, fearful of injuring such treasures, Peter and Jus tipped their new rush-bottomed chairs side by side against the wall, ready for a real talk.

Peter began by asking what Jus had meant by calling this Mason's country.

"Just what I said. This country, from up the Ohio River, beyond where the Wabash comes down into the Ohio out of Indiana Territory, past Cave-in-Rock, and down here past Fort Massac, at the mouth of the Cumberland, has been Mason's main field of operation for years."

Peter was startled and appalled. When John Page asked him to make a map of this country and find out who was living here, had he known this? But he only observed, "It was common talk at the Annual Conference that Mason is in Mississippi Territory." Then he told about the preacher they had picked up, after he had been abused by Mason.

Jus was much interested. "I hope your preacher swore to it all. But the fact is we've got enough sworn statements about Mason as a robber to indict him in any court from Vincennes to Natchez. But there ain't a log jail that can be trusted to hold him, and we'll never be safe from him till he's dead. He can't be punished with death unless out-and-out murder is pinned on him, and he takes good care that isn't done. Whoever he robs, he strikes an attitude, and says, 'Thank God, I never shed blood'!"

Peter felt oppressed. A new country but the same bad men. There was silence for a moment. Then Jus changed the subject. "Who do you think I saw at the fort here? Cherokee Bill."

"Cherokee Bill!"

"He's on the staff of General William Harrison, the up-and-coming young governor of Indiana Territory. His headquarters is in the little old French village of Vincennes, a hundred miles up the Wabash River. The Commandant here at the fort tells me Cherokee is a very useful man. For one thing he's got a complete copy of the Mystic Band's constitution. Want to hear some of it? It sure is a fancy piece of writing."

Peter listened absorbed, while Jus read from long legal sheets, "The government shall be by valiant brethren, known as Grand Masters. The Grand Master shall not consent to be introduced. (Peter remembered the strange visiting clergyman at the Mason weddings.) Every faithful member of the Band shall endeavor to make proselytes ... Members shall be taken on probation for three months and tried in every way ... The Grand Master shall be constantly on guard about his brave band ... They shall be sworn as a Christian fraternity to deny Christ ... This is the only true society that lives by Christian principles ... It's against Nature to let any man fare sumptuously day by day while his neighbor, as good or better, goes hungry. (Across the years Peter remembered Alston, in that cabin in the snowy woods, intoning a ritual—"Take from the rich and give to the poor. The poor are understood to be members of the Holy Band") ... Persons of the last named color never to be admitted."

Finally, wiping his eyes, which were smarting with the strain of reading by candle light, Jus said that, having got hold of this, Cherokee was working on the Band's ciphers, which were combinations of numbers to represent letters, which they left as messages in hollow trees, and on the invisible ink the Grand Masters use. "Cherokee says there's a penalty—he doesn't know what—for anybody in the Band but the Masters, using the ink."

Peter was thinking. "So I'm to go into this fancy robbers' den and make a circuit! Can God's mercy save even these?" He quailed before the whole idea.

Observing that Peter looked unhappy, Jus added cheerfully, "And there's one more piece of news. I've been saving it, Son. Jerry's been up here."

Peter brought the front legs of his chair down with a bang. "Jerry. Here? Oh Pappy, where?"

"Nowhere I can tell you right off," answered Jus. "He was clerking up at Broadhead's early in the summer, so Cherokee says. He left Broadhead's before I was there in August, and now Cherokee don't know where he's gone."

"Oh," said Peter. He was bitterly disappointed.

Jus said soothingly, "Don't worry. Now that we know he's been up this way, I'll get word to Cherokee to look out for him through the Indians, and I'll pass along word too through the lawyers that ride circuit, and you can tell your Methodist elders to have the circuit riders look out for him for you. We're bound to pick him up somewhere."

Peter was trying to formulate a question. "Was he—I mean—" Jus looked at him shrewdly, and said in a low voice, with a wary eye on Mary, who was now shining up the new skillet, "He has an honest job, and, so far as Cherokee knew, everything else was all right,"—which, when translated, meant that Jerry had been sober when Cherokee had seen him. Peter felt greatly relieved.

When Peter sank into bed that night, soothed by his evening prayer, he felt better about the new country. He thought of Jerry, and all the things he'd have to tell him, and mentally traced his probable routes of travel, and got to worrying about him so that he had to discipline himself by resolutely turning to his go-to-sleep routine. This consisted in thinking through the events of the day, and matching each to a Bible verse. He thought of the stream they crossed, coming into the borders of his father's land here, the quiet waters creaming around the horse's knees as they rode through. "He leadeth me beside the still waters." He thought of the rich, steaming cup of coffee for supper—a plentiful supply of this supreme luxury of the frontier having been among the things Jus had had sent down from Louisville. "My cup runneth over." He thought of what his father had told him about this land up here, and wondered again if John Page knew what he was doing when he asked him to map out a circuit in the Band's own territory. "Yea, though I walk through the Valley of the Shadow of Death, I will fear no evil." And with that he fell asleep.

3

Jus was so delighted with Peter's wish for a higher education that, before the end of next court day, he had located an institution called Brown's Academy, about a day's ride away, and had sent Peter to look it over for himself. Brown's Academy proved to be a spacious and comfortable log cabin which served both as the teacher's residence and as his classroom. It was handsomely set against a grove, alongside of which ran a stream, which formed a deep gorge. The big main room of the cabin, which was also Mr. Brown's sleeping room, dining room, kitchen, and living room, was furnished with a desk for the teacher, several bookcases full of more books than Peter had ever seen, and several woodcuts of strange scenery and strange doings by people in strange costumes, a big blackboard, and some plank tables with plank benches, where the pupils worked. The students, some twenty boys in all, ranging from fifteen to twenty-five in age, boarded with the widely dispersed families on the newly broken farms, and rode their own horses from four to seven miles to school.

Peter felt a little dubious about Mr. Brown himself, but two prospects charmed him. One was the reading of all those books. The other was the prospect of boarding with "Father Reuben" and "Mother Lou," who had the largest and most comfortable cabin for miles around. These good people were Methodists, and had steadily refused to take boys from the Academy because they did not like liquor and pranks. On this account Peter was told not to go near them. He went, and announced himself as a Methodist, and was heartily welcomed and asked to sit down at the table with them. After giving him the privilege of saying grace, they stuffed him with fried chicken and milk gravy, raised wheat biscuits, coleslaw, and currant jelly—all new and wonderful culinary items which he longed to run right back and tell his mother about. Father Reuben and Mother Lou had been described as "old," and old they seemed to Peter, with a stable and comforting antiquity. But actually there were no old people in the West in those days. The only indications of age in these "old" folks was a little silver in his curling beard, and some extra inches on her waistline, and the possession of two married daughters who lived near by—all of which led this good couple to assume airs of patriarchal and matriarchal dignity. Having been fed and made much of by Father Reuben and Mother Lou, Peter was so eager to enroll as a member of their household that he had, perforce, to go back and enroll with Mr. Brown.

Peter then went home to report to his family and to get his belongings, and Jus came back with him to confirm the arrangements. After a brief talk with Mr. Brown, Jus was satisfied that Peter would not here be subjected to the over-weening influence of preachers. Mary, on the other hand, was satisfied that he would be in a good Methodist home. So everybody was happy.

Mr. Brown had started life as a Methodist preacher, but he had left the church in the great secession of 1792, and was now an advocate—between long sips of the bottle—of natural religion and primitive Christianity, and the open enemy of Baptists, Presbyterians, and all bigots whatsoever—and particularly of "Asbury Methodists." After he had left the church, he had acquired such higher learning as was available west of the mountains under Mr. Rankin in Lexington, and so had fitted himself to open this school, which taught all the branches of an "English education," and of a higher or "Latin" or "classical" education. An English education was primary school education in writing, reading, and arithmetic, with special emphasis on penmanship, spelling, and parsing. The classical education gave, in tabloid form, something like the modern high school and college education. It included Natural Philosophy, Moral Philosophy, Latin and Greek.

Under Natural Philosophy was included as much as was then known of all the natural sciences, including geography. Under Moral Philosophy was included the elements of economics and sociology, a sketchy survey of history, with emphasis on Greece and Rome, and some dogmas concerning the human spirit and its relation to the cosmos. Latin was taught, as English was, with emphasis on grammar. Greek was supposed to be taught, but since Mr. Brown knew little Greek and his pupils wanted to learn less, it never even came up for discussion between Peter and his new teacher.

Peter felt he had already met everybody at Brown's Academy in Russellville. Intellectually Mr. Brown was an own brother to Ol Waterbug and Doctor Allen. His course in Moral Philosophy was slanted against revealed religion and drew heavily on Locke's *Two Treatises Concerning Government*, Rousseau's *Social Contract*, Grotius *On War and Peace*, and Tom Paine's *First Principles of Government* and *The Rights of Man*. Peter was interested to see that what he had heard from Doctor Allen came from books on Mr. Brown's shelves which he could hardly wait to lay hands on.

Just as he had already known Mr. Brown, so he had known all these boys. They were other versions of Skinny Dromgole and Red

Maulding, frank and open, with an easy, good-natured, devil-may-care bearing. Since there were no extra-curricular activities, no athletics, no student government, and not even the required chapel customary in schools under church domination, outside of Mr. Brown's classes, they did as they pleased—skylarking, drinking, looking for girls to seduce, and picking fights with each other.

For a week or two, Peter was popular. Mr. Brown was impressed with the way he pitched into his lessons. Peter loved them all, with the exception of Latin. And he confided to Father Reuben, "When it comes to Latin, there just isn't enough use in it to pay for the time it takes to learn. I'd rather learn Chickasaw. The Romans are dead, but the Chickasaws can still be saved." For their part the boys were impressed by the fact that Peter was well-dressed and well mounted, and had a father who was a lawyer and, apparently, a man of substance. At first they thought he was altogether one of their own breed, because his manners were easy, his come-backs in talk quick, and he had an aplomb based in long acquaintance with their kind. It was only slowly that they noticed that he did not drink, swear, or use tobacco, and was exasperatingly immune to the social appeals and intimidations with which they whipped other boys into conformity with their manners and customs. As Peter confided to Mother Lou, "I've been able to go my own way, without having to fight for it, ever since I got my full growth. Nobody wants to take on a big fellow." So Peter grinned and tossed back at these boys as good as they sent. But Mr. Brown detected in him too much of the taint of orthodox Christianity and devoted most of his lessons in Moral Philosophy to combatting it.

The daily diet of Tom Paine, Locke, and Adam Smith raised questions which could only be settled by the Bible. Finding that Mother Lou had a Bible, Peter borrowed it and settled his latest argument with Mr. Brown in favor of himself. Then, feeling lonesome for Jerry and his infinite companionableness, he remembered that there were friends in the Bible named David and Jonathan, and became absorbed in the mental state of Saul, and the attitudes of his large family of sons and daughters, and the position of David as leader of folks whom Peter defined as "Regulators." To a boy who had never read a novel or seen a play, this tale, whose situations and characters would be good fiction in any age, was utterly engrossing. When he returned the Bible, and told Mother Lou and Father Reuben about it, they were as interested as he, and asked him to read them a piece of the story every evening. This Peter did, explaining and elaborating it, till he built it into something as real as the lives of their family and neighbors. Mother Lou told her daughters about it, and they came in for the reading, bringing their husbands. They told their friends, and the friends came.

Out of these meetings they formed a Methodist class, with Peter as leader. Secure in his license to exhort, but saying nothing to them about it, Peter told them about the big outdoor meetings they had had in the Cumberland country south of here, and they staged such a meeting themselves, on a lovely Indian summer Sunday, the morning service followed by a picnic lunch and that by an afternoon service, ending with the early sunset. In a world in which there was, as yet, no organized social activity, this was a happy and exciting day, and, by the time Peter reached school next morning, stories of it were flying all over the countryside.

Peter knew there was going to be trouble when Mr. Brown sarcastically greeted him as the Methodist parson, and all the boys hooted. All through the class in Moral Philosophy, Mr. Brown baited him, and Peter prayed for patience. After classes were over for the day, and Peter was mounting his horse, two of the boys came to him and, drawing him aside, confessed that they had many problems and wanted guidance. Would Peter talk with them by themselves and pray with them? Peter felt suspicious. But, on the chance that they might be in earnest, he agreed to do what he could. The boys asked Peter to meet them in a secluded spot on the grassy bank between the grove and the creek. From the bank the wall of the creek dropped seven feet to the water, which was ten feet deep.

Approaching the meeting place warily, Peter was seized by two boys. One of them he threw over his shoulder and into the deep pool below. The other grappled with him. Peter threw him to the ground and rolled over and over with him to the edge of the pool and plunged with him into the water. As he swam to shore and shook himself, he reflected that he hadn't done badly with that. They had planned to duck him and had been throughly ducked by him, and were slinking away through the woods without a word or backward glance. And though he was wet himself, under the circumstances it was worth it.

Next day, Mr. Brown, puffing and frowning, told Peter to stay after school. Mr. Brown was seated by his desk. He opened a door above it and took out a bottle of brandy and two glasses. He poured a drink and offered it to Peter. Peter refused politely. "Damn it," said Mr. Brown, "when I do a young man the honor of proposing a drink with him, I don't expect to be refused."

"I mean no discourtesy, Sir," said Peter. "But I do not drink."

"Not even when I tell you to," roared Mr. Brown.

"No, Sir."

"Take that, you puking baby preacher," said Brown, suddenly dashing a glassful of liquor into Peter's face. It stung his eyes. They watered. He quietly wiped his eyes and brushed the wet off the front of his jacket with his hand. Mr. Brown had gulped one glass of brandy. He poured a second glass and gulped that. He belched and started at Peter, his face red and furious. Peter said, "Sir, I feel I should explain what happened yesterday."

"To Hell with your explanations. You fellows can murder each other for all I care. It's your manner to me I won't have. You put on airs. You think you're grown up. You think you know enough to talk to the whole countryside. You think Asbury will hear of you, and make you one of his elect. You are a boy wonder, you are! I'll show you! You're just a boy. And I'm your master." He picked up the birch rod which always lay on his desk but which, to his credit, Peter had never seen him use. "Old as you are, I'll teach you. Unfasten your pants!"

Fury and shame swept over Peter. He prayed. "I must accept all persecution." "But not this," the voice of common sense said. "Why should I?"

"Do you intend to do as you're told?"

"No, Sir."

"God damn you, you mewling baby parson," roared Mr. Brown. "You'll do as I say or I'll know the reason why."

Peter's thoughts were going round and round. He measured the teacher with his eye. Easy enough to floor him. But was it right?

And if it was not right, what was? He thought of the text, "Turn the other cheek." He knew he was not yet Christian enough for that. The preacher had risen. Peter had risen. The teacher lurched toward him. Peter dodged. He thought, "He's drunk. He's blind, stinkin' drunk." The preacher raised the birch. Peter ducked. The birch came whizzing down through empty air. Peter was beginning to enjoy this. As the teacher swung at him, he stepped lightly from side to side as in a dance, beginning to grin irrepressibly. Mr. Brown was growing more and more furious. His face was fiery red. The vein on his forehead was swollen. He looked as if he were about to have a stroke. A voice in Peter, old, quiet, mature, said, "Seems like we've had enough of this." He carefully reached out his foot and tripped the teacher. Mr. Brown fell, shaking the desk. The bottle of brandy rolled off the desk, and to the floor, and the smell of it filled the room. Peter walked quietly out and shut the door.

He intended to go straight home and never come back. But he thought, "I came to get an education. He's got what I want. He's got books. He knows." He could think of no other place where he could learn anything. Little as there was to get here, he found it exhilarating to have something to read in addition to the Bible, to have the world of thought, even though it might be infidel thought, opened to him. He listened to Mr. Brown with almost perpetual curiosity. And he loved the Methodist family and the little class meeting. If he left Brown's Academy, he would have to leave that.

So he presented himself as usual next morning, arguing angrily with himself, "Why should I be afraid? Why should I be ashamed? I'm a free man. There's nothing he can do to me. He can't even whip me."

To his surprise, Mr. Brown greeted him courteously, and the day passed as if nothing had happened. Two boys had not been ducked. Mr. Brown had not been tripped. All was peace. But when classes were dismissed for the day, Mr. Brown said to Peter, in a most gentlemanly manner, "Peter, stay behind a few minutes. I want to talk to you."

"Oh, Oh! Now we're in for it," thought Peter, following the teacher to the seat by his desk, all his frontier boyhood waking in him a kind of animal watchfulness. He knew he had nothing to fear. And yet he was afraid. Afraid of what? he asked himself. Afraid of doing what he might be sorry for. He prayed, "Help me, Lord."

But Mr. Brown said, "Peter, I'm doing something it's very hard for a man of my age to do, and something that is not even wise. I am asking your pardon."

Peter was taken aback. The tears rushed into his eyes. "Oh, Sir, no," he blurted out. "I don't want to give offense, Sir. I only want to learn."

"You do give offense, Peter," said Mr. Brown, sadly and gravely. "You give offense the way the sight of a nice pink baby cherub would offend the damned in Hell."

"But—but what do you advise me to do, Sir?"

Mr. Brown looked at him sourly. "Get that stubborn proud young head of yours ready for the martyr's crown."

CHAPTER 35   Livingston County, Kentucky
Autumn, 1802 to May, 1803

Peter stayed on at Brown's Academy through the winter and into the spring. One spring evening, after he had gone to bed, there was a loud knocking at Father Reuben's door. Peter heard his own name. He thought he recognized the voice. He started up in bed. Cherokee Bill stood over him, his face lit by a candle in the hand of Mother Lou. Her ample form was wrapped in a blanket over her nightgown. Cherokee said, "Get into your clothes. Quick. I'm bringing around your horse. I'll explain later."

"Put the spurs into him," said Cherokee, as Peter leaped on his horse. For dark aeons of time Peter could not think. He could only follow as Cherokee swung under the dark shade of trees that hung so low that he had to lie flat on his horse to keep his head from being sheered off by the branches, through streams which, swollen by the spring rains, splashed and roared around his legs. Over a hill under the pale stars, through a prairie lying silvery and vibrant with choruses of peepers. Down into darkness so thick he could tell where Cherokee was only by the beat of his horse's hooves, and the crashing of branches ahead of him. Once or twice Cherokee shouted back instructions. "Ground's swampy here but solid underneath. Don't stop. Follow." "Low branches. Look out for your neck!" Once or twice he was able to glance up and take his bearing by the stars. He managed to formulate a thought. "It can't be something's happened to Pappy. Or Mammy. We're going south."

In the dark they drew up before a cabin, where he could tell by the neighing and restless tramping of hooves that horses were tied. A man came out with a candle sheltered in an open-fronted tin can. "All ready for you," he said briefly. Cherokee said, "We change horses. Get off, and on to the one he's holding there."

Changing horses, Peter managed a question. Cherokee answered, "It's Jerry. He'll be hanged at noon. He wants to see you. We'll have to break our necks to make it."

"Jerry! Hanged!" Peter was stunned. He did not think or feel. He was like one felled by a mortal blow.

Cherokee said briefly, "Caught red-handed. One of Mason's gang."

Peter came to in a red fury of pain and battling resistance. "I don't believe it!"

"It was proved sure enough. He didn't deny that he'd been with them, nor that he'd killed a man. All he denied was robbery."

This began to make sense to Peter. In his world, killing was more venial than robbery. "There's some mistake. We've got to stop it," he said. "Pappy—"

"I saw your father. He's trying to get a stay of execution, but I know he can't. There's no grounds for it. And nobody's in a mood to wait, once one of the varmints is caught."

"But Jerry isn't a varmint. Oh—oh—it's wrong. Something's gone wrong."

"The boy's no good—never has been much," said Cherokee harshly. "Your father and I do what we can because of his father. Jerry was brought up right. He'd no business to get mixed up with the Band. And the quicker any one who has anything to do with that outfit swings, the better it'll be."

"But Jerry's not one of the Band," said Peter stubbornly. He was thinking so hard and fast that he could not even feel the pain and horror of it. But the horror was there, huge and hideous, waiting to overwhelm him.

Cherokee said, "All I know is he was caught red-handed. Confessed to murdering a man. The man's watch and ring was found on him."

"I don't believe it. I don't believe it." The horses' hooves beat out the words as they rode headlong.

Dawn came up over a scallop of hills. They plunged east through almost unbroken forests. Their horses were played out. They changed horses again and went on, with desperate glances at the sun mounting relentlessly. They topped a slight ridge. "There it is. That's the jail. He's in there," said Cherokee. Peter saw a clearing and some log cabins, and crowds massing around one cabin. They put spurs to the horses again and flew. The sweat was pouring down Peter's face. His horse was running rivers of sweat. Suddenly he realized that the water in which he seemed to be bathed was also the water streaming from his own eyes.

Then he was off the horse and on the ground, feeling the earth reeling under him and pains shooting up his thighs. A short, gentle man, with grizzled hair falling back from a bald front, had him by the hand, and was leading him up a path. He heard a voice somewhere—it must have been Cherokee's—saying, "Peter, this is Father John, the Baptist minister." Cherokee went ahead, pushing the crowds to right and left to make way. Then the door of the cabin opened, and Peter stooped through it. There, in the darkness, chained to a stake driven in the ground, was Jerry. Jerry—the delicate pale face, the foxlike features, the limpid gray eyes! Peter's knees melted. "Oh, Jerry," he blubbered, falling on his knees and clasping the slight form to him as if he would never let it go. Jerry burrowed his face into Peter's chest and wept. Father John stood by, wiping his eyes and clearing his throat.

Then Peter was soothing Jerry as if he were a child. "There. There," he said. He started up and said desperately to the kind-looking man standing by, "Oh, Sir, surely there's a way to stop it. He didn't do it. He didn't. I know he didn't."

But Jerry was wiping his eyes and his face looked suddenly peaceful in that dim light. "There's no use, Pete," he said quietly. "They're too mad to listen, and they've a right to be mad. It's too late. I've got to pay."

"But, Jerry, you couldn't be—" He hesitated, unable to say it.

Jerry spoke with a strange calmness and maturity, his clear sharp-featured face serene, his grey eyes quietly luminous. "Peter, I've got less than an hour to live, and I want to spend it preparing to meet my Maker. I'll tell you what happened, and then we'll forget it. I happened to meet John in Louisville and he got me to go down the river with him and a load of goods to New Orleans. On the way back he said he had to get some horses. Would I come with him? So we came this way, and John May and John Setton joined us."

"But," said Peter, horrified, "you knew who they are. They're Peter Alston and Wiley Harpe. Oh Jerry, how could you?"

"I didn't know. It's never been proved. John had convinced me that the whole talk against them was nothing but tarring them for what their 'kin had done. He said folks were suspicious because country bumpkins don't understand business and business dealings."

Jerry paused and choked and began to tremble. "Up to then I'd done pretty well about—you know—about drink. I hadn't broken down more than two or three times, and I was going to church regular and praying. But being with John I was out of the way of any church, and I got to drinkin' some. Well, the afternoon we met up with May and Setton at a station, where they had some more than usually good liquor, and I guess I must a drunk deep. After that it is mostly a haze. But so far as I can remember, John gave me a bag of money to carry, and he said, 'Guard it with your life.' And I said I would. He said there were robbers on the roads who were after them, 'knowing they had come up from New Orleans with money they were going to buy horses with. He said if any one rode straight on me in the path, shoot to 'kill. I said I would.

"Well, we started off just at dusk, after having dinner and plenty to drink, and we were to ride to another station to sleep, through a deep wood where, he said,the robbers might be. And suddenly out of the brush on one side came three men, and the leading one turned into the path and came on facing me. John was right behind me,

and he said, "He's comin on you. He's after the money. Shoot!"
If I'd had my wits about me, I'd have thought twice. But I was
pretty well loaded, and when he said, 'Shoot,' I shot. I heard the
man fall—at least I think I did—and then I was knocked off my
horse into the bushes and didn't know a thing till I heard yells. And
somebody grabbed me and pulled me up. Lights were flaring and
men were shouting. I was dazed and my head splitting. The ones
that were yelling were Regulators. They picked me up and carried
me to the jail, and they gave me a trial right away—I don't think it
was a proper court. They said they had to make themselves judge
and jury, for once they'd got one of Mason's gang, they couldn't
wait for the law to let him loose—and for that I hardly blame them.
I told my story. The man that passed sentence said whoever put
me up to it, I was with the gang, and I'd killed a man, and that was
enough. The man who was killed and his two friends who weren't
hurt and who swore to everything—these men had driven a drove of
horses east to Virginia to sell and they were coming back with a
heap of money. A watch and ring were found on me that they said
belonged to the murdered man, though how I got them I don't
know. But the money was all gone. John and the other two had
made off with it. And there I was left to take the punishment."

He spoke coolly and clearly, with a kind of detached calm, as if
he were talking about somebody else. But in Peter, a voice from
his unregenerate childhood was saying over and over, like the beat
of a savage drum, "John! Stomp on him! John! Mash him! John—
Hell's too good for him!" He was maddened with anger and pity.

Jerry went on, almost serene, "They wanted to hang me the day
they sentenced me. But I cried and said I was a Baptist and give
me time to prepare to meet my Maker. They sent for the Baptist
preacher. He found where Cherokee was, and Cherokee went for
you. And now"—he sighed like a tired child. "And now you're here—
I—I've got all I want."

Father John had stood by all the while. Now he said, "The minutes are ticking away, and Eternity is at hand. My son, shall I
pray?"

Jerry clutched Peter's hand. "My f—f—friend can pray with me.
He's s—saved." Father John understood. "I will leave you alone,"

he said. "I'm responsible for him, but I can stand just outside the door and watch."

The volcano inside Peter burst in furious tumbling words. "It's no time for prayin. It's time to stop this." He started up. Tied as he was to the stake, Jerry clutched Peter's leg and hung on with the grip of desperation. "No, Pete. I say, No!" Peter was trying to shake him off. Jerry wailed, "Peter, you must listen to me. A minute—only a minute. Listen!" There was such urgency in Jerry's voice that Peter again sank to the ground beside him.

Jerry, speaking clearly and gravely, said, "Pete, I don't want to go free. I want it to be just as it is. I ain't fit for this earth. If you got me out, I'd be in some trouble or other again. It just ain't the world for me."

Peter felt with a sudden and terrible clarity that this was true. He said, "We're all astray and lost on this earth. Heaven is the only home for any of us."

Jerry's face shone. "And I'm lucky, Pete, for to-night I'll be in Heaven." Peter was startled. Jerry was saved? Here, in prison, he had come back to God? "Pete," Jerry was saying, and, in that dim light, Peter could feel rather than see a sudden radiance on him. "Pete, do you know I think this is all God's way of getting me out of it, because He's spoken to me. I know for sure now. I'm elected."

Peter would not have believed that he could be so glad to hear false doctrine as he felt at that moment. Jerry was saying, "Father John has been here steady, and he brought me back to what I knew when I was baptized. And I saw then what God had been at all the time. As one of his elect, I'd no business to put Polly between Him and me. I'd no business to go astray after drink. There was no help for it. He just had to get me into some place like this where I'd have to come face to face with Him, and know the truth. Last night it was just as if God stood here in this room, and He said, 'Son, the world ain't for you. And it's for your good I'm takin you out of it. Don't be afraid. Just hold fast my hand, and tomorrow night you shall sleep in Paradise'."

Father John looked in. "Fifteen minutes to Eternity," he said.

Peter put his arm around Jerry. He had come to a decision. "I'll go up to the gates with you, Jerry." He gulped, and cleared his throat. "Jerry, on the road with Bishop Asbury, I learned some right sweet hymns. Would you like me to sing you one?"

Jerry pressed his hand and nodded. Peter sang

Jesus, the sinner's friend, to Thee,
Lost and undone I turn and flee
Weary of earth, myself, and sin.
Open Thy arms and take me in.

He stopped. Jerry said eagerly, "Go on, Pete. Sing." Peter sang

Talk with me, Lord, Thyself reveal,
While here on earth we rove,
Speak to our hearts and let us feel
The kindling of Thy love.
With Thee conversing, we forget
All time and toil and care.
Labor is rest and pain is sweet,
If Thou, my Lord, art there.

Father John looked in. "The chariot is waiting. Are you ready?"

Peter felt Jerry's spasmodic clutch, as he caught his voice in a kind of sob. "You'll go with me, Pete? All the way?"

"Yes," said Peter. His knees were knocking together.

The guard who had been stationed outside with a gun came in and unfastened Jerry, and, gripping his arm, propelled him toward the open door. But he let Peter walk on the other side, holding Jerry's hand. Father John was standing just outside with a kind of white shroud in his hands. Jerry's eyes shone. "It's like when I was baptized. It's my going-to-God robe." As a matter of fact, it was a baptismal robe. The custom was that a condemned man should wear his shroud to the gallows. Having no shroud, the Regulators had borrowed a baptismal robe.

Peter pressed Jerry's hand. Still bitterly, futilely rebellious, he felt shamed by Jerry's exaltation. He prodded his own imagination. How would it feel to know that, in half an hour, you would be face to face with God? He nerved himself to rise to the glory of that thought, and said, "It won't be long, Jerry. You will soon be home with God." Jerry looked at him gratefully.

Then Peter saw the wagon, drawn by two horses. The guard

said to Jerry, "Get up and sit on the box there." Peter looked at the
box and reeled in horror. It was a coffin! As was the custom, Jerry
was to ride to execution seated on his own coffin. The function of
the seat offered him pierced Jerry's mystical mood, and he clutched
Peter's hand. "Pete! Pete! Ride up there with me! Sit by me, Pete.
Don't leave me alone."

Peter's eyes met Father John's. The minister nodded slightly.
"I will speak to the captain," he said. Then Peter saw that the
Regulators were drawn up in ranks, with the captain in front of
them. While the minister spoke to the captain, Jerry clutched his
robe around him. Peter could see that it was his wall between him
and the horror beyond. He turned his eyes away from the coffin
up to the sky. "Look up, Jerry. There're the eyes of God up there.
And they look down so lovin."

Gratefully Jerry raised his eyes. The two boys stood hand in
hand, looking up to the azure sky of May. Peter was praying intensely but silently, trying to make re-assurance flow from his hand
to Jerry's. Father John returned. "It's all right," he said. Peter
mounted the wagon carrying Jerry in his arms. He was so relieved
that he was to be allowed to ride with him that the idea of sitting
on the coffin had lost its horror. The wagon started. Peter tried to
sing. His voice stuck in his throat. He forced it loose. He sang

Jesus, in whom the weary find
Their late but permanent repose
Physician of the sin-sick mind,
Relieve my want, assuage my woes
And let my soul on Thee be cast,
Till life's fierce tyranny is past.

The wagon jolted. Peter's stomach kept turning over. He was on
the edge of an agony of nausea. But he had to rise above it. He
had to keep Jerry's mind on God only. He noticed fleetingly that
the Regulators were marching in front of and behind the wagon
and that Father John was walking alongside it. He turned his eyes
and his thoughts from them. The spring air was soft and balmy.
The birds were singing. The azaleas bloomed in pink drifts along
the wooded road as they rumbled on. The kind blue sky looked
on the two boys. They raised their eyes and their voices soared.

They came to the place of execution. It was a clearing in the midst of the forest, walled in by huge trees, and filled with spectators, except where the Regulators were keeping an open space for the wagon to go through. They drove between the crowds, the boys sitting side by side on the coffin, hand in hand, their eyes on the kind blue sky, singing. The wagon stopped under an enormous oak whose lowest branch, huge and gnarled, projected about thirty feet above them. A man climbed into the wagon and slipped a hood over Jerry's head. Peter froze with horror. He cast one glance at the limb of the tree, dark over head. That limb was the gallows! The man had a rope in his hand. He said to Jerry gently, "Here, Son. I got to put this collar on."

Jerry turned to Peter impulsively. Peter threw both his arms around him and kissed his cheek through the cloth hood. The hands of Father John were tenderly separating them, and Father John was saying to Peter, "You must get down."

"No! No!" Jerry wailed.

Peter said, "Let me stay."

"You're liable to be thrown."

"I'll manage."

The preacher lifted up his voice in earnest prayer. Peter stood in the wagon with bowed head, one arm lightly embracing Jerry, and felt, with unutterable relief, that peace and exaltation had returned to the doomed boy. Suddenly Peter felt his arm jerked sharply away. The preacher's voice soared in a clarion call, "Father, into Thy hands I commit my spirit;" the driver whipped up the horses, the wagon lurched forward in a headlong run, and Peter was thrown or jumped, and was lying face downward, grovelling in the dirt, unutterably sick, his whole being heaving as if in an earthquake. The wagon, lurching under the black limb, had left Jerry hanging above him.

2

"That's what Jerry said—it was John—" Peter's voice broke. The murky fury boiled up again from the deepest wells of his being. He'd prayed against it for days. Now the black poison choked him.

He was sitting with his father and mother and sister by the fire in the new home. It was past midnight. They'd been sitting like this since dusk. It was a warm night, and the door was open into the fragrant darkness outside. But they huddled close to the fire, as if it were winter, shivering. Jus sat slumped forward, heavily. Sis was leaning against her mother, sobbing. Mary's head was buried in her hands.

Jus shifted his big foot and said, "It all rests on Jerry's word."

"God help me," said Mary. "I believe it's true."

"I believe it," said Peter grimly, "and so I told Aunt Brenda."

Mary looked up. In the firelight her face was old and as if carved in marble—an old face that once was beautiful, moulded by a lifetime of pain, carved in marble. "Brenda—his mother—she was there?" A sharp perception of what it would be—if one were to see one's boy hanged—made her bury her face in her hands again, shuddering.

Peter was silent. He was remembering the instant when he knew Brenda was there. He could not speak. Jus answered for him, "She came on the field just as I did—it was the moment when—when it was all over. I heard her scream."

Scream! Peter's home, his family, melted away. He was back on that field again, where he had fallen, face down. Through the darkness and the sickness and the shaking horror, he'd heard the scream. It filled all space. It was as if a thousand desperate hands were beating against a closed door, and a thousand voices that had become one voice were shrieking out the pain and terror and protest of all the broken, angry hearts of the world. With that sound he had come to the end of endurance, and had lost consciousness in a blessed anaesthesia which had been but a minute, but seemed like a thousand ages, when slowly he came to, and found Father John shaking him and saying, "His mother is here. Come speak to her."

He was so lost in remembering, that it was only when his father said sharply, "Peter, your mother's asked you a question twice," that he realized that he was here now, in his own home, with his parents. "I—I'm sorry," he said, turning to his mother, "Yes, I spoke to Aunt Brenda before Otto and all the Baptists. She was bitter against me." He paused. Again the walls of home seemed to melt away.

Bitter! He could see her dark fanatic eyes—would he ever stop seeing them?—and hear her words cutting like knives. "It should a been you—you and yours. Without you it would never have happened."

Jus prodded him. "Pull yourself together, Son. Repeat what you said."

"It wasn't much," Peter answered, nerving himself to speak clearly. "I said that I believed every word of Jerry's story. And to the extent that the shame could be lifted from him and put where it belongs, it ought to be done. And I said they weren't called on to spare any words to let it be known who was at fault. I said I'd known Jerry since as long as I had known anything, and I knew where he was weak, but I said there was the difference betwixt Heaven and Hell between what he was and what that man was that had put him where he was, and I knew that, too, because I was that man's half-brother, in the flesh, never—please God—in the soul. Never! I said that I, for my part, would back Jerry's story, and that what was ours, in this share of shame, we'd bear and stand up to. And in this I thought I was speaking for every one of my family except one I was ashamed, beyond all speaking, to call kin."

"You did right," said Mary softly. "And Brenda—how did she take what you said?"

Peter found it difficult to answer. Finally he murmured, "She'd been bitter about it, but the hard feeling was eased a little. She—she—kissed me."

"Nobody has a right to be bitter," said Mary. "But if any one did, it would be Brenda. This makes four she's lost to that Band—Dutch, and dear little Heinie, and Obadiah, and now Jerry." Realization again overwhelmed her. "But we've lost enough," she said, her voice strangling in her throat.

Sis began to cry in sympathy. Peter sat dully, looking at the fire and holding out his big hands to it as if they were cold. The hands were trembling. He was not conscious of feeling anything. He was too tired to lay hold of those psychological resources which had come to mean so much to him. He couldn't pray. He couldn't remember a Bible verse. He was completely numb. And God had hidden His face.

For a few minutes there was silence, broken only by Sis's suppressed crying. The blessedness of being young and a girl! thought Jus. She could cry unashamed. Finally Mary said, with resolution, "Jus, I want you to understand how I feel. Whatever is right to do about John, I want that it should be done."

"I know you do," said Jus, "and I glory in it. You are a woman to be proud of, Mary. But the plain fact is that I don't know what to do. I went down there thinking I might get a stay of execution—apart from the fact that I wanted to be company for Peter, because I knew how he'd be broken up." Peter turned to his father. A faint sensation of gratitude pierced his darkness. Jus was saying, "I felt awful bad when I found it had happened—just two minutes before. I thought if I'd been a little faster I might have done something. But Father John thought not. It weren't a regular court that tried him. Those were Regulators. But, even so, Father John said most of them were good men and they tried to keep a show of justice and order. Father John said the general feeling was such that if the Regulators had consented to put off the execution and have another hearing on it, there'd have been a lynching.

Jus paused a minute, and stared into the fire, and then he went on, "But after it was over, there were some that were pretty sorry. And nothing changed their minds so much as what Peter had done—the way he went with Jerry and stood by him to the last, and he the kin of the one Jerry had said had led him into it."

Peter stirred. His father's words were like a needle piercing his numbness waking him in spite of himself, but only to pain. Jus went on, "Because of Peter they were ready to listen to me. I told them that making an end to one poor misguided boy didn't put one thing in the way of the real criminals. And I told them that from here on it would be a sight better if they did what they did by way of the courts. Nobody knew better than me what drives folks to set up as Regulators—I'd been a Regulator myself. But, I said, poor as the courts might be and slow and liable to be turned aside and corrupted, still they could go further and faster than crowds that start circling round and round and barking up the wrong tree."

Again a faint light pierced Peter's unutterable depression. He cast his father a dimly appreciative glance. Jus continued, "Well, the upshot was that we and the Regulators parted friends. Father John had a Christian burial and almost everybody came. And what I hadn't said to them, Father John did."

He paused again and looked into the fire with a set and sombre face. Finally he sighed heavily. "Now as to John, what's to come I don't know. Those two men that were with the murdered man— they can swear out statements as I told them and go ahead against John. I gave them all the facts I thought would help them, and I said if they wanted a lawyer, go to Ninian Edwards, never by any chance to Bill Reading."

There was silence, while each of them carried what Jus had said to its terrible conclusion. Justice would catch up to them all. John must be caught, sooner or later. There would be a trial, and all eyes turned on them as kin to John. The shame—

Mary broke the silence. Her face, where the firelight shone on it, had grown young again, and almost serene with steadying purpose. "God's mercy is still open to them all. Day and night, waking and sleeping, I will pray for my son's soul—that God may bring him to lay hold on the forgiveness that is God's to give, even up to the eleventh hour. But never will I lift my hand against the doing of earthly justice, come what may. What's done has got to be paid for." Here she abandoned circumlocution, and ended grimly, "I'll never try to save him from a hanging, but only from Hell."

"It will be hard for us," said Jus. "We've got to face up to that. But the thing to remember,"—here his glance swept from Peter to Sis and back to Peter, "is that no one's got a right to shame us save for what we ourselves do. The thing is to do right, and hold up your head, and look the world in the eye—whatever comes."

"And so far as family goes," said Mary, more softly, turning and putting her arm around Sis. "We're all one family on this earth, and God is our Father."

Jus looked at Peter. The boy's heavy gloom disturbed him. There had been no praying that he knew of, no reading of the Bible all day. Folks might argue the truth of religion, but the plain fact was that for the burdened soul, it was medicine—if you could take it. He rose, and lit a candle.

"Jus, what are you going to do?" asked Mary in a startled voice.

"I'm gettin' your Bible, so's Peter can read to you and Sis. I thought it would be 'kinda comfortin'."

Amazed, Peter took the Bible from his father's hands. He dimly realized why his father had done this. He felt rebuked not by his father but by God through his father. For a minute he leafed through the pages, wondering what would be best to read. Mary said softly, "Read about who Jesus said was his mother and his brethren." Peter read: "While he yet talked to the people, behold his mother and his brethren stood without, desiring to speak with him. Then one said unto him, 'Behold thy mother and thy brethren stand without desiring to speak with thee.' But he answered and said unto him that told him 'Who is my mother, and who are my brethren?' And he stretched forth his hand toward his disciples and said, 'Behold my mother and my brethren. For whosoever shall do the will of my Father which is in heaven, the same is my brother, and mother and sister'."

3

Peter was riding back to school. Three days at home had reduced the shock and pain to the point of endurance. And he carried with him the heart-warming memory of that morning's conversation with his father.

"I reckon you'd better pull yourself together, Son, and go on back and finish out your schooling."

Peter shook himself out of the murky confusion of thoughts and cross-purposes and answered, "I was thinkin—John Page—he wants me to go through Livingston County, and make a map, and a survey of all that's here—human and things for humans to use, and church members and—and Rogues—everybody and everything. It's so's they can lay out a circuit."

"How long do you figure that would take?"

"Brother Page reckoned on three months at the least. He wants me to meet him at the last quarterly meeting of the Red River Circuit next fall, with all the details."

Jus was silent. He didn't want his son to be a preacher. There was no future in it. On the other hand, as things had turned out, he was profoundly grateful to these preachers for cutting Peter loose from John's outfit before it was too late. Moreover, this mapping of the social, economic, and human resources of Livingston County wasn't a bad proposition. "Wouldn't mind doing a thing like that myself, apart from the exhorting, and all the religious fal de rol. It would give a man a lot he could use later on, if—say—he was to be a judge riding circuit or run for Congress. No use worrying too much about the boy's current attack of religion. Religion is a kind of pap that's really good for you when you're just gettin' your mental growth, and are liable to be pretty much at sixes and sevens amidst the evils and troubles of the world. Sooner or later Peter's religion would kinda simmer down, and take its place in a larger view of livin. And he'd be a wiser man for having gone through it, and a steadier." His mind made a long journey forward into the future. Judge Cartwright, Senator Cartwright, President Cartwright—no heights a smart one like Peter, who had learned to manage himself amidst life's pitfalls, couldn't reach—with a father's good steady shoulders to stand on.

He came out of his meditation and said mildly, "Seems like you could finish your school term and still have time do what John Page asks of you. It's better not to leave things half done. However, you're your own master—under law, or, to put it your way"—here his black eyes twinkled into his son's—"under God."

He drew out a leather bag, and loosened the drawstrings, and counted out twenty-five silver dollars. "Whatever you do, you'll have to eat."

So he had bade Peter a casual good-bye, and ridden off to attend court, and Peter had kissed his mother and sister, and mounted Big Boy and started for school, under a spring sky threatening showers. The trail by which he must travel was a bridle path—there were no roads yet in this new country, not even the rutted double path which in those days was called a "road." And much of the way lay through primeval forests which, at this time of year, had not the overmastering gloom of the full foliage, but were fresh, and open, and all alive, with fresh springing undergrowth and here and there, running between great, mossy trunks, thickets of hawthorn in bloom, like great patches of snow. From time to time he passed a clearing, where crews were busy rearing log houses, or planting in burnt-over ground between stumps of trees.

Peter rode along, too absorbed in his own thoughts to go through those routines of observation which were usually his entertainment on long rides, for once neither noting nor speculating on signs of animal or human presence. All his mental processes were clogged by a mass of undigested thought, and souring, fermenting anger and hate and protest. He had tried to clear it all out by praying and by reading his mother's Bible, in vain. Dimly he was conscious that it came from the pushing of the memory of Jerry out of his mind. He couldn't think of Jerry. That was past all endurance. Mixed in his misery was a still unresolved sense of his own responsibility. He could not forget Brenda's piercing eyes and her words dripping acid, "It should have been you—you and yours." He knew this was not just. And he forgave her the injustice because of what she had suffered. But some obscure element of truth in the accusation continued to torture him. He was responsible for Jerry. He had always been, as far back as he could remember. For under the conditions of frontier living the stronger child had always to be responsible for the weaker.

He tried to push it all aside. His father wanted him to go back to school. That was enough. Better not think. Just do what had to be done. Do it! He put spurs to Big Boy and galloped at a pace too fast for thought.

But he had to let Big Boy rest at last, and his thoughts began again. The circuit. Suppose he was to do as Elder Page said. It would be kinda interesting. But he wouldn't know how to go about it. He'd make a fool of himself. He stopped and let Big Boy nibble at a little patch of fresh spring grass, in an open space where a big tree had died and fallen. He took out the paper Page had given him and read it through. Authority to exhort and to form classes. Collect all facts that might be useful. Plan a circuit—routes to follow, time it would take to get from one place to the next, possible preaching places, population, conditions of the people. "Your certificate to the best college betwixt Heaven and earth." It might be. You could sure learn a lot that way. But no—he couldn't. Sometime may be, when he'd learned more, and he didn't feel so bad—weighed down and all mixed up and not up to anything. He sighed heavily, and put away the paper and spurred Big Boy again.

But he couldn't put the circuit out of his mind. He would find himself thinking, "If I was to do it, I'd—." But after building a daydream, he would demolish it with, "It's a crazy idea. Elder Page sure went off half cocked that time." However, as his mind began to work, the sense of heavy oppression began to diminish a little.

He had to walk Big Boy up a long slow rise of ground. When they got to the top there was an open grassy stretch, and the forests and clearings rolling away on all sides, lit by the sudden bright beam that had struggled out between two clouds, parting them and letting a widening stretch of blue shine through. The sudden sunshine warmed him clean through, piercing even the pain and darkness of his soul. He stopped and let Big Boy taste the grass here, and relaxed in his saddle. "God made the world beautiful," he thought. "If only man didn't stink it up so." He remembered that time when he was going down to Logan County with his father—the second time they went down, in the fall of '93. Cherokee had said, "The Injuns say the pale face dirties the air and dirties the ground, wherever he is."

Peter remembered that he had thought about this, and it seemed to him that it was so. Anxiously he had asked his father, "Is it true that we dirty the air and the ground?"

He remembered his father's answer. "Son, it's true for a while. There's no gainsayin' that life, whether human or animal, is cleaner and decenter before it gets mixed up with us than it is for a long time after we come around. But that's something that will pass, Son. It's something savages have to go through before they're really civilized. If we keep at it, the day comes when everything gets better. The land gets cleaned up. The grain and fruit get bigger. The animals are better fed and not so likely to be killed by each other. It can be done, Son, and that's what we're aimin to do in our new country."

So his father had said. Now Peter thought bitterly, "It can't be done with men the way they are. You've got to get at men first, and change em from the inside out—make em new. A new heaven and a new earth, a new country—you can't have em if you leave men the way they are—foul and festering and stinkin so rank inside themselves."

For the first time in days he thought spontaneously of a Bible verse. "Seek ye first the kingdom of Heaven, and all these things shall be added to you." It was true. He'd seen it. There was the Roberts boy—what a mess he used to be, dirty, head down, mumbling like he was only half human. When he first felt the stirrings of the spirit, what did he do—took the first bath he'd ever had in his life. And when he came the next time to meeting, he'd put on a shirt. And now look at him. Building himself a decent house, even finding an honest living for his sisters—the first they'd ever had in their lives.

Peter looked out over the rolling woods, and the light bright patches of clearings, to the far blue gleam of the Cumberland going down to meet the Ohio. To think of that whole country there crossed with roads where you could go safely and never think of robbers. Goods flowing into it so that you could buy anything and find no stain of thievery and murder on it. Neat houses, towns, schools, courts where justice would really be done, honest members of the legislature—all that life in Russellville had made his folks want so desperately. In his mind he laid out a dream country, and in it he found a friend, a comrade henceforth in all his adventures, and with the friend he fared forth and he found a sweetheart—He pulled himself and pulled Big Boy up sharply. "What's the use? It can't be. Too many Johns and Sam Masons around." John! The poisonous hate and fury which had been down there under the surface of consciousness all this while erupted, like an infernal lake boiling over, all sulphur and brimstone. "He and his kind have got to get off the earth," he thought fiercely. "It ain't big enough for them and the rest of us, too." For one second his mother's words came back to him. Pray for John. Even John could be redeemed.

"Well," he thought, "They've got to be redeemed, or they're going to be kicked down to Hell now." He gave Big Boy such a dig that he went off like a cannon ball over the side of the hill and crashing down into a gully and through a stream, and for a while it was all Peter could do to keep his seat and his neck.

As they were going up the next rise of ground, the shower which had been threatening all morning came down on them. Then the sun came out clear and warm, and when they reached an open place, Peter stopped to dry out in it. All around, the pink azaleas were blooming, and above, the blue sky was fair and kind. Then, like ice breaking, something hard and rigid he'd been holding between himself and the memory of that day—of those last moments with Jerry—gave way. It all came back, irresistible, immediate—the ride with Jerry, the pink azaleas in bloom, the blue sky looking down, and he and Jerry, hand in hand, looking up into the sky, finding the eyes of God there, singing. He began to sing softly what he had sung that day, "Talk with us, Lord, Thyself reveal." He felt strangely eased, as if a great painful boil had burst and the poison were flowing out.

All the rest of the way to the path that turned off to Brown's Academy he was trying to piece together a passage he had heard read many times on that long trip from the east with Asbury. He'd remember a bit of it, and would think a long time, and then he'd remember a little more. Between the scraps he remembered, he made comments to himself.

"The wilderness and the solitary place shall be glad for them. (*For circuit riders*) Strengthen ye the weak hands and confirm the feeble knees. (*That might a meant Polly—and Jerry. They weren't bad. They were weak. The strong will have to lock arms and be a wall around the weak till they are strengthened*) Say to them that are of fearful heart, 'Be strong! . . . Then the eyes of the blind shall be opened and the ears of the deaf unstopped. (*Like mine was. Not a minute too soon.*) Then shall the lame man leap as a hart and the tongue of the dumb shall sing (*Like they do when they're converted. There's lot of foolishness in it. But there's health-giving joy, too. I've seen it*) . . In the habitation of dragons . . shall be grass with reeds and rushes (*And where Mason and his gang hid out, a little*

town and a church and a school, and corn fields all around) And
a highway shall be there . . . the unclean shall not pass over it. (*You
just bet your last dollar they won't, because we're going to change
them or hurry them right off to Hell*) and the wayfaring men,
though fools, shall not err therein (*Poor Jerry—he was considerable
of a fool. The world's got to be made safe for fools*) No lion shall
be there, nor ravenous beast (*That means John!*) And the ransomed
of the Lord shall return (*That means Methodists, the right honest
ones, and—oh yes, I reckon it means Baptists and Presbyterians, too*)
and sorrow and sighing shall flee away."

By the time he had worked it all out, he had come to the path that
led off to Brown's Academy. Peter drew Big Boy up almost automatically so that it seemed as if the big horse had balked of his
own accord. It occurred to Peter that he had been pretty mean
to Big Boy to-day, taking out all his ornery moods on him, with
sudden starts and proddings and reining him up sharp. He leaned
over and patted the strong gray neck. "Ol Hoss, what are you thinking of? That's Brown's Academy. That's not the school we're goin'
to. You and me—we're entered in the best college twixt Heaven
and earth—Saddleback College."

The End